Handbook

of

Transistor Circuit Design

KEATS A. PULLEN

Ballistic Research Labs
Aberdeen Proving Ground

Handbook

of

Transistor Circuit Design

PRENTICE-HALL, INC.

Englewood Cliffs, New Jersey

1961

Preface

The word "handbook" is defined in *Webster's New Collegiate Dictionary* as "a manual; a guidebook." In the engineering and scientific fields, a handbook is understood to be a book containing a relatively brief but thorough and complete exposition of a given subject or group of subjects.

Based on these definitions, I feel that the *Handbook of Transistor Circuit Design* is a handbook in the dictionary sense and, in fact, that it is more than a handbook. It might be called a teaching handbook inasmuch as it is a guidebook to a systematized approach to the design of circuits for transistors and other active devices, and it also contains enough examples and problems to help the user develop a capability in the design of circuits using these devices. It is a handbook in the sense that I have included information on related science which has proven useful in my work with these devices. Several of the techniques, notably the topological method and the orthogonal handling of nonlinearities, have been developed to provide a higher degree of usefulness than previously had been available.

The orientation of this handbook is in one sense practical and in another sense analytic. It is practical in that it gives design procedures which can significantly improve the potential reliability of transistor circuits. These procedures are coordinated and consistent with one another, and they are selected in a way which takes advantage of the more stable properties of the active devices.

This handbook is analytic in the sense that the methods used are subjected to considerable mathematical and scientific scrutiny prior to adoption and also because a considerable body of analytic procedure not previously applied extensively in electronics is utilized for improving the finally resulting circuits. The use of organization procedures for characteristic data of semiconductor devices leads to a better understanding of the devices themselves and it also leads to more efficient design procedures. Likewise, the use of topological methods of analysis of sections of circuits makes possible coordination of relatively complex subnetworks in the synthesis of circuits to specified characteristics.

The first chapter contains a descriptive review of the properties of conductors, semiconductors, and insulators and develops the conductivity and mechanical relations required for generation of diode and transistor action. It is followed by a chapter on the theory of specification of data for devices, the chapter leading to establishment of the parameters and the variables used in this handbook.

The third chapter discusses methods of measurement of the properties established as important in transistors and related devices. Many useful measurement techniques are described. The following chapter includes derivations of the basic operating equations for typical operating configurations and develops many of the significant relations among the standard representations.

The balance of the book is concerned with the development of methods of design and stabilization of circuits, d-c, a-c, RF, oscillator, mixer, and various types of switching circuits.

In addition to the main chapters, the appendices contain a table of symbols and definitions, and a derivation of the small-signal distortion equation, brief reviews of topological analysis and orthogonal analysis. An extensive bibliography is included which should prove useful in finding additional material on many of the subjects discussed. A large number of special curve sets are also included for the use of the reader, and a special nomograph for small-signal calculations. These curves and the nomograph can be a considerable help in the practical design of circuits.

KEATS A. PULLEN

Contents

CHAPTER THREE

Measurement of Variables and Parameters   71

CHAPTER FOUR

Circuit Parameter Relations   102

Handbook

of

Transistor Circuit Design

CHAPTER ONE

Basic Principles

1.0 Purpose of this Handbook

The principal objective of this handbook is to develop and describe a systematic method of design of transistor circuits. This method is capable of providing reasonably accurate results quickly and easily. In accomplishing this purpose, however, it is desirable to include a limited amount of theory of the behavior of the devices in their circuits in order to clarify the reasons for some of the design procedures. Because of the relative confusion in the semiconductor field over the choice of variables and parameters, and because of the sketchiness of the tabular data on the parameters, it also appears desirable to discuss briefly some of the simpler measurement techniques that can be used by the circuit designer for checking the properties of active devices.

The casual reader of the table of contents might think that including material on such subjects as symbology, topology, orthogonal polynomials, appropriate choice of variables and parameters, selection of the common electrode, methods of measurement, and the best form of network configuration represents an unnecessary digression from the major purpose of this volume. Review of the wide variety of approaches to circuits appearing in articles, papers, and textbooks, however, shows that the subject of circuit design for transistors contains many contradictions. It is for this reason that an effort must be made to establish a single consistent system of design that includes the most important individual techniques as limiting cases. Such a system can be useful and helpful to the practical designer because it makes unnecessary the use of a variety of alternative methods that for one reason or another may be of limited applicability.

The system of design described in this book has other important advantages that may not be immediately obvious. For example, the characteristics of operation of a circuit can be analyzed by the described method to the extent that a considerable part of the experimental test time usually required in the laboratory becomes unnecessary. As a consequence, the reliability of operation obtained is such that appreciably less coordination time may be required to obtain unified operation of the complete system. The objective of the first four chapters is to develop the techniques and procedures required with this systematized approach.

After the basic information problems have been evaluated, the subject of the subsequent four chapters is the design and the stabilization of simple circuits. Chapter Five considers the design of four basic configurations:

1. Common-emitter amplifiers
2. Common-base amplifiers
3. Common-collector amplifiers
4. Degenerative-emitter amplifiers

Chapter Six discusses the stabilization problem, the problem of keeping the transistor operating properly over a range of both ambient temperature and power dissipation. Following this chapter on stabilization, attention is next directed to transformer-coupled amplifiers, and the design of a variety of types of these amplifiers is considered. Transformer-coupled transistor amplifiers are much more important than their tube counterpart because the use of a transformer with a transistor may permit reduction of the total circuit power input by a factor of two or three as compared with a few percent change in the sum of heater and plate power input if a transformer-coupled tube circuit is used. The final chapter in this group, Chapter Eight, considers the design of RF and IF amplifiers, including also a discussion of the problem of automatic control of gain.

The next three chapters examine the fundamental principles of operation of different types of oscillators, examining in particular the problem of initiation and build-up of oscillation. The first chapter of the group discusses the mathematics of relatively linear feedback networks. The second applies the theory to L-C oscillators, and the third develops the theory for use with R-C oscillators.

In Chapter Twelve, the theory and design of mixers and converters is considered and the relation of their behavior to the characteristics of oscillators and amplifiers studied. The use of parametric amplifiers and tunnel diodes is also discussed.

In Chapters Thirteen and Fourteen the design of circuits having high degrees of nonlinearity, such as multivibrators and counting circuits, is analyzed. The objective in both these chapters is to provide a systematic approach that gives as complete a picture of the behavior of typical circuits as is possible. Likewise, design procedures are considered in detail.

Such material as is available on tunnel diodes at the time of writing is being included in appropriate sections of this book. In particular, some notes on the measurement of the current-voltage relation and the negative conductance of the device is explained in Chapter Three, some comments on the use of the devices as amplifiers in Chapter Eight, some notes on mixer applications in Chapter Twelve, and bistable applications in Chapter Fourteen.

Because of the breadth of coverage of the material in this book, it of necessity cannot be a textbook but must build to a considerable extent on other documents. For this reason an extensive list of bibliographical references is included. References to particularly important papers include a brief synopsis of the content. Two general references that might be noted separately are *Conductance Design of Active Circuits*, and Chapter Twelve of *Radio Engineering Handbook*, edited by Henney.[1] These references indicate some of the more fundamental procedures in greater detail than they can be recounted here. The first of these gives considerable detail information on the application of similar techniques to tube circuit design, and shows how the additional data can be used to enhance reliability and efficiency.

1.1 Properties of Conductors

Solid materials can be separated into three different classes, namely, conductors, insulators, and semiconductors. The group of conductors includes largely the metals having valences one, two, and three. All of these materials have large numbers of free electrons for conduction of electric currents. In terms of the valence and conduction bands, this means that at normal or room temperature there are available unoccupied energy positions to which the electrons can move with only very small increments of applied energy. In terms of the theory of quantum energy

---

[1] *Conductance Design of Active Circuits*, by K. A. Pullen, Jr., John F. Rider Publisher, Inc., New York, 1959.

Radio Engineering Handbook, K. Henney (editor), fifth edition. McGraw-Hill Book Co., Inc., New York, 1959.

states, at the temperature of absolute zero, there is a group of states all of which are occupied, and there is a higher energy group of states all of which are vacant. As the temperature of the material is gradually increased a few of the states occupied at absolute zero become unoccupied, and the electrons that occupied them move into some of the higher energy states. As a consequence, as is shown in Fig. 1–1, whereas the probability of occupancy of any given energy state at absolute zero temperature is either unity or zero, as the temperature is increased the probability of occupancy of any one given state near the edge of the nominally occupied area may decrease to a value as small as one-half, and the probability of occupancy of a state in the nominally unoccupied area may rise to as much as one-half.

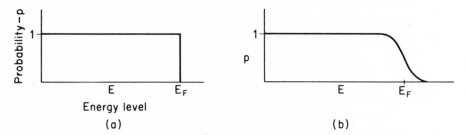

(a)   (b)

Fig. 1-1. Fermi energy distribution
(a) at absolute zero temperature
(b) above absolute zero temperature

Now, the curves in Fig. 1–1 imply that there is a continuous distribution of possible energy states available in the conductor. Actually, although there may be a very great number of possible states available over the range, there actually is a finite number of them, and they are located at finitely spaced increments from one another. In addition, there are actually ranges of energy, or energy bands, for any given material in which there are no occupiable states for the electrons at all. These areas may be difficult to find in a material whose atoms are not arranged in an orderly fashion (such a material may be called an amorphous or a polycrystalline material) because such a disorder introduces distortion into the fields around the individual atoms, and may thereby introduce spurious levels. These additional levels are sometimes called trapping levels.

Materials that have a high electrical conductivity are ones in which the boundary between the occupied and the unoccupied states (commonly called the Fermi potential) falls in one of the bands having closely spaced possible energy levels. In these materials the removal of an electron from an occupied state to a previously unoccupied state requires very little energy, and as a result, the normal variation of energy from atom to atom and from electron to electron, as a consequence of thermal probability distributions, is sufficient to provide for the required transfer energy. Ample quantities of conduction electrons are therefore available in any material in which the Fermi potential falls within one of the bands of permitted energy levels (Fig. 1–2).

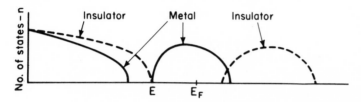

Fig. 1-2. Distribution of occupation states

As the temperature of any material is increased from room temperature, the distribution of probability of occupancy changes as indicated in Fig. 1–3, and the conductivity of conductors changes as a consequence. A relatively reduced slope of the probability contour across the conduction band results, and the lattice vibrations of the molecules increase, increasing the effective area of the lattice atoms and decreasing the mean-free-path of the electrons and also their relaxation time. This effect reduces the conductivity of a conductor but may increase the conductivity of semiconductors.

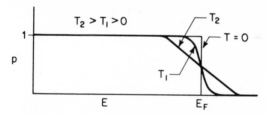

Fig. 1-3. Effect of temperature on energy

The interference of the lattice with the passage of electron waves through a conductor depends to a large extent on the irregularity of the structure, because it has been shown that under ideal conditions an electron can traverse approximately a hundred atomic distances between collisions. Consequently, in a work-hardened crystalline material such as copper wire, the irregularities resulting from movement of crystal groups with respect to one another decreases the mean-free-path, thereby decreasing the conductivity, which is given by the equation[2]

$$\sigma = ne^2\tau_F/m = n_{\text{eff}}e^2\tau_F/m \tag{1}$$

[2] Equations 1 through 4 are from *Solid State Physics*, A. J. Decker. Prentice-Hall, Inc., Englewood Cliffs, N. J., 1957. (See Equations 9-6, 11-8, and 11-32 and Problem 9-3).

where τ_F is the relaxation time of electrons having energy corresponding to the Fermi potential, σ is the conductivity, n (or n_{eff}) is the effective number of electrons per unit volume, e is the electronic charge, and m is the mass of the electron. The relaxation time is related to the mean-free-path, λ_F, and the Fermi drift velocity, v_F, in accordance with the equation

$$\tau_F v_F = \lambda_F \qquad (2)$$

The magnitude of the mean-free-path is inversely proportional to the absolute temperature in degrees Kelvin, with the result that the conductivity is approximately inversely proportional to the absolute temperature.

1.2 Properties of Insulators

With nonconductors, or insulators, however, the situation is quite different. Insulators are materials in which there are no available conduction electrons, because the Fermi potential falls in an energy band in which there are no occupiable electron states. In fact, the insulator has a large energy gap between the energy states possessing electrons and the lowest available unoccupied states. An electron could easily surmount the cliff possessed by the insulator if an energy-state stairway were available. The conductor in effect has such a built-in stairway for conduction electrons between the occupied states and the unoccupied states, and the insulator has not. As a result, in an insulator the electrons are trapped in a manner that makes it very difficult for them to break away from their individual atoms and carry an electric current.

The Fermi distribution function,[3] which gives the probability of any existing energy state being filled, may be stated mathematically in terms of the equation

$$F(E) = 1/[1 + \exp\langle(E - E_F)/kT\rangle] \qquad (3)$$

where E is the electron energy in electron volts, E_F is the Fermi potential, k is Boltzmann's constant, and T is the absolute temperature. For very small values of T, the exponent is either very large in magnitude and positive, or large and negative. As a result, the value of $F(E)$ is either unity or zero. As the value of T becomes larger, a gradually longer transition range develops about the value $E \gtrless E_F$, with the result that the transition becomes more gradual, as is shown in Fig. 1–1. For practical purposes, the number of electrons available for use in conduction is a function of the derivative of the Fermi distribution function in the neigh-

---

[3] *An Introduction to Junction Transistor Theory*, by R. D. Middlebrook. John Wiley & Sons, Inc., New York, 1957.

Solid State Physics, by A. J. Dekker. Prentice-Hall, Inc., Englewood Cliffs, N. J., 1958.

borhood of the Fermi potential, because when the derivative is zero, either at low energy where the value of the function is unity or at high energy where it is zero, there is no possibility of making use of available energy levels. The levels are either all full or there are no electrons available.

If, therefore, a material is available in which the Fermi level occurs in the middle of a range of energy for which no permitted levels exist, and the Fermi derivative function is zero at the edges of the forbidden band, then no conductivity can develop, and the material is an insulator. The edges of the range of energy levels for conduction electrons may be determined from the derivative function

$$dF/dE = (1/kT)/[\exp \langle (E - E_F)/kT \rangle + 2 + \exp \langle (E_F - E)/kT \rangle] \quad (4)$$

Evidently, unless the value of E is nearly equal to that of E_F, or T is very large, the value of the denominator is very, very large, and the derivative is very nearly zero. In fact, if $E - E_F$ is as much as five or six kT s, then the value of the derivative is small to the point of being negligible. Materials that are normally classed as insulators have a forbidden band between fifty and five hundred kT's wide, with the result that if the Fermi level is properly spaced within the band, infinitesimal numbers of electrons are available for conduction purposes at ordinary room temperature. As the temperature is increased, however, the value of kT becomes larger, and the value of the distribution function slopes off more and more gradually because of the increased value. A point is finally reached at which electrons do become available as a result of thermal action, and conduction commences. With glass, for example, the temperature at which conductivity becomes significant is in the neighborhood of 500° F. The cliff is generated by the forbidden band in the insulator, and the ladder is provided by the sloping of the distribution function. Only when the slope is sufficiently gradual to reach across the forbidden band does the insulator begin to conduct, because only then are electrons of sufficient energy available to step across the cliff.

1.3 Properties of Semiconductors

The semiconductor is neither a conductor nor an insulator, but it sometimes behaves like one, and sometimes like the other. At ordinary temperatures, semiconductors have a small but finite conductivity; the value may range from that of a very poor conductor, typically $\sigma = 100$ mho square centimeters per centimeter, to a value as small as 0.001 to 0.0001 mho square centimeters per centimeter, or a rather good insulator. The conductivities of first quality insulators normally are measured in micromhos or small fractions of a micromho. The range of conductivity of a semiconductor is a consequence of the narrow width of the forbidden band within which lies the Fermi potential for the material. Thermal ionization and crystal dislocations can then provide an adequate number of charged carriers to give the conductivity.

The number of conducting charges available in a pure semiconductor depends in large degree on the accuracy and uniformity of the crystallization of the semiconductor material. Every defect in the structure is a focal point for the generation of current carriers. Consequently, to be satisfactory, semiconductors used in many electronic applications are required to have an extraordinarily high order of regularity and perfection. Otherwise, a high inherent conductivity exists in the material, and it is difficult to obtain proper control of the properties of a device constructed from the material.

Certain materials when introduced into the crystal structure alter the behavior of the crystal in a manner which makes available additional carriers, and thereby increases the electrical conductivity. These materials, or impurities, may either make additional carriers available thermally, or they may cause the release of one type of carrier alone. If, for example, a few stray atoms of tin, which crystallizes in the same form as most normal semiconductors like germanium and silicon, are introduced into the crystal, and the atoms introduced have a narrow forbidden band, then the impurity can cause rapid generation of thermal carriers. Other materials that have a different number of valence electrons from the matrix crystal provide polarized carriers when introduced into the lattice.

1.4 Types of Semiconductors

Of the wide variety of semiconductors available to the device designer, the materials of greatest over-all importance are silicon and germanium. Historically, the first semiconductor used in electrons was galena, or lead sulfide; it was used as a rectifier in many early crystal radio sets. Somewhat later, the cuprous oxide rectifier was developed, making it the first extensively used intermetallic semiconductor. At a somewhat later date the selenium rectifier was developed to overcome the deficiencies of the cuprous oxide units. The next few paragraphs discuss briefly some of the semiconductor materials that are finding application in diodes and transistors, and also some of the materials that show potential for being useful when technological problems of utilizing them have been solved.

Germanium. Germanium is a semiconductor of valence four, or one that is inherently neutral in polarity when crystallized in a tetrahedral bond arrangement. The normal crystallizing pattern for this material is the face-centered cube. Germanium has the narrowest width of forbidden band that can be used effectively in diodes and transistors, namely, approximately 0.7 volt.

The rating of the width of the forbidden band in terms of volts (or electron volts) measures the energy difference across the gap or band. Potential times electron charge gives electron energy. For this reason, and because it is common practice in the field of electronics, the energy differences are given in electron volts, or volts for short.

The narrow energy gap of germanium limits the maximum temperature to which it may be used effectively as a semiconductor. As will be shown in the next section, it is necessary that semiconductor materials for use in diodes and transistors be altered or doped with impurities that give them the ability to conduct by means of either positive or negative charges. This being the case, it is important that the conductivity due to thermal effects be kept small compared to the conductivity due to the doping materials over the range of operating temperatures. The number of conducting particles in a neutral semiconductor (single crystal) is given by the equation (12–19 from Dekker, *Solid State Physics*)

$$n_e = n_h = 2(2\pi kT/h^2)^{3/2}(m_e^\gamma m_h^\gamma)^{3/4} \exp\,(-E_g/2kT) \qquad (5)$$

where n_e and n_h are the numbers of electrons and holes, k is Boltzmann's constant, T is the absolute temperature in degrees Kelvin, h is Planck's constant, m_e^γ and m_h^γ are the equivalent masses of the electrons and holes,

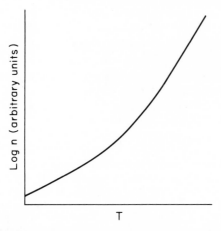

Fig. 1-4. Variation of number of charged particles with temperature

near the edges of the conduction and the valence bands respectively, and E_g is the gap-width energy. This equation shows that the number of charged particles available is a function of the three-halves power of the temperature times an inverse temperature exponential. The value of this product increases rapidly with temperature, as is shown in Fig. 1–4.

Silicon. Silicon is used extensively in both standard and switching diodes and in transistors, and it has replaced germanium almost completely in the power rectifier field. Silicon has some important advantages compared to germanium, and also some important disadvantages. The first and possibly the most important advantage is that it has a gap energy of approximately 1.2 volts, or almost twice that for germanium. The second advantage is shown by the number of thermally-generated carriers in the two materials at room temperature (300° Kelvin)[4]

For silicon: $n_i = 1.5 \times 10^{10}/\text{cc}$

For germanium: $n_i = 2.4 \times 10^{13}/\text{cc}$

(6)

The simplified equations for the values of n_i^2 as a function of temperature for the two materials are[5] '

Germanium: $n_i^2 = 3.1 \times 10^{32}T^3 \exp(-9100/T)$

Silicon: $n_i^2 = 1.5 \times 10^{33}T^3 \exp(-14{,}000/T)$

(7)

The ratio of these two equations gives a measure of the relative change rate with temperature

$$n_{iS}^2/n_{iG}^2 = 5 \exp(-4900/T) \tag{8}$$

Since exp (7) is approximately equal to 10^3 (actually $e^{6.9} = 10^3$), the value of the ratio of n_{iS}^2/n_{iG}^2 at $T = 300°$ Kelvin is approximately 5×10^{-7}. Similarly, at 400 degrees Kelvin, the ratio has a value of 2.5×10^{-5}, showing that the thermal carrier concentration rises about twenty-two times faster in silicon than it does in germanium, but the number of charges still is a factor of 500 smaller than that in germanium at 400 degrees Kelvin. The derivative expression also shows that the rate of increase of n_{iS}^2 is greater than that of n_{iG}^2.

[4] Large energy gaps are useful in semiconductor materials principally for the reasons that a large energy gap in a material gives it an extremely small level of thermal conduction, and that a material with a large energy gap is one which can be used in a high temperature environment. A very low value of thermal base conductance in conjunction with good doping conditions in the emitter and the collector makes possible a relatively higher value of current gain, and a lower input admittance. Normally, a diffused base region, with epitaxial construction, is required to make optimum use of the low base conductivity available, and to give optimum high-frequency performance. Even though the rate of increase of conductivity with temperature may be larger with a wide-gap material than with a narrow-gap one, the larger value of the gap width may more than offset the rate of rise of conductivity. This is the condition of silicon as compared to germanium.

[5] F. J. Marin, J. P. Maita, *Phys. Rev.*, Vol. 96, 1954, p. 1464.

Transistor Electronics, by D. DeWitt, A. L. Rosoff. McGraw-Hill Book Co., Inc., New York, 1957, Appendix I.

Another advantage of silicon compared to germanium is the higher value of avalanche voltage or breakdown voltage that applies with silicon devices. This higher breakdown voltage is to a considerable extent a result of the relatively high inherent resistivity available in silicon. Whereas germanium diodes are limited to applied voltages less than 150 to 200 volts, silicon junctions have been used successfully to over 1,000 volts.

Semiconductor silicon has three limitations that have delayed its application in electronics. The first of these is the difficulty encountered in growing perfect single crystals. The technological problems of producing the required grades of silicon have been solved, however, and large numbers of silicon diodes and transistors are being produced. Other technological problems with respect to making devices are the control of the formation of junctions, and controlling surface phenomena (passivation), to minimize leakage current. Probably the most important limitation of silicon, important because it is an inherent characteristic, is the relatively low value of the diffusion constants for charge carriers in germanium. These constants are less than a third of the corresponding values for germanium, with the result that the frequency limit for a silicon transistor of a given structural design is at most a third of the corresponding high-frequency limit for a corresponding germanium unit.

Diamond. Diamonds have not found any use for either diodes or for transistors because of fabrication and doping problems. It appears reasonable to suppose that the best grade of commercial diamonds available may be sufficiently free of defects to be usable as the raw material for semiconductor devices, and the gap energy certainly is sufficiently wide that the range of operating temperature for a device made from it would be excellent. Because of its hardness and the difficulty in diffusing it with the proper combination of impurities, however, it may find its first application as a crystallizing base for a more routine semiconductor material.

The mobilities of the carriers in a diamond are somewhat higher than those for silicon, but not as high as those for germanium. It is, therefore, one of the best potential materials for use in high temperature devices, devices required to operate to several hundred degrees centigrade. Until single-crystal diamonds can be obtained economically and can be diffused with the necessary conduction zones, the diamond probably will have only textbook interest as a semiconductor material.

Alpha-Tin. The alpha form of tin — at least in theory — is usable as a semiconductor, although its use is limited by its very narrow energy gap to temperatures considerably below normal room temperature. A superficial examination of its properties indicate that it might have some applicability as a material for use in diodes and transistors. How it might behave in its super-conducting region is of considerable interest. For example, transistors or diodes made from alpha-tin would require cooling at least to the temperature of dry ice, but they might make sufficient additional power economy available to be worth the development. A germanium-tin mixture might be useful, because less cooling might then be required. Mobilities appear to be nearly the same as those of germanium.

Intermetallics. Certain compounds that have the electron-doublet type of bonding exhibited by carbon compounds and by crystalline semiconductors can be formed from elements in other than the fourth group of the periodic table. These compounds can be crystallized in the regular face-centered cubic lattice, and they can show the properties possessed by germanium and silicon when they are crystallized in the single-crystal form. The following table, adapted from Jenny,[6] indicates the properties possessed by some of the possible combinations having promise as basic materials for semiconductor devices. It also includes a listing of the gap energy and mobilities.

TABLE I
Semiconductor Properties

Semiconductor	E_g (electron volts)	U_e	U_h
α – Sn	0.08	3,000	?
Ge	0.7	3,900	1,900
Si	1.1	1,500	500
SiC	2.8	>100	>20
C (diamond)	6.0–7.0	1,800	1,200
InSb	0.18	65,000	1,000
InAs	0.33	20,000	200
GaSb	0.68	4,000	700
InP	1.25	>4,000	>100
GaAs	1.35	>5,000	>400
AlSb	1.52	≧400	≧400
GaP	2.25	>100	>20

Most of the intermetallic compounds having potential application belong to the group that may be called the IIIA-VA group, made up of the elements, N, P, As, Sb, Bi, of group VA and the elements B, Al, Ga, In, and Tl of group IIIA. There is at least one additional group of combinations that may be found to have possibilities once problems of chemical formation, purification, and crystallization can be solved; these combinations belong to what may be called the IIIB-VA group, consisting of the elements Sc, Y, La, and the rare earths in addition to the elements of group V.

[6] D. A. Jenny, "The Status of Transistor Research in Compound Semiconductors," *Proc. IRE*, Vol. 46, No. 6, June, 1958, p. 959.

Mixtures of intermetallic compounds can be formed just as mixtures of the various table IVA semiconductors may be formed. In these materials, the band gap energy is intermediate between that for either compound alone. The use of a uniform distribution of the mixtures throughout the bar of semiconductor does not provide optimum operating conditions, however, as the use of a higher concentration of the intermetallic having the higher gap energy in the emitter zone has been shown to increase markedly the injection efficiency of an emitter structure, making a larger number of emitter carriers available for diffusion to the collector.

There are other compounds that could be used as basic semiconductor material, but these materials are so complicated in structure that the probability of getting a good single crystal from which to make semiconductor devices is relatively small. A more complete table of possible intermetallic compounds as listed in Table II. This table is divided into two sections, the first part including the materials on which the most work has been done, and the second those materials with small probability of being useful.

TABLE II

Intermetallic Semiconductors

Those of high probable usefulness (see Table I for properties):

| InSb | GaAs | SiC | GaSb | InP | AlSb | GaP |

Other materials:

| AlP | AlAs | InP | InAs | $AgTlTe_2$ | $CuInSe_2$ |
| $CuAlS_2$ | Cyanthron | Indanthracene | Anthracene |

The doping of the intermetallic semiconductor with impurities to provide polarized semiconductor material is discussed separately in the section on types of semiconductor, inasmuch as some special problems occur in accomplishing the polarization.

The so-called dry-disk rectifiers, using typically copper oxide or selenium make use of combinations of elements that behave as intermetallic compounds. The copper oxide rectifier, for example, uses cuprous oxide as the active material. The behavior of these devices is so irregular that they will not be discussed further here.

1.5 Intrinsic and Doped Semiconductors

A refined semiconductor material may be classified either as an intrinsic material or one that has been altered by the deliberate addition of impurities that alter its electrical properties. The latter type of material is referred to as a "doped" semiconductor. Most of the semiconductor material used in diodes and in transistors is of the doped variety; because, however, any doped or polarized semiconductor must be prepared from a single-crystal specimen of highly purified intrinsic crystal, intrinsic material must be discussed first.

Intrinsic Semiconductor. An intrinsic semiconductor is one containing the smallest possible amount of impurities after refining. Experiment has shown that any irregularities in the crystal structure or any impurities crystallized into it reduce the resistivity of the material by the process of introducing ionization centers. Because the total number of ions that move about in a semiconductor is limited by chemical physics to a quantity called the intrinsic number, or n_i (or p_i, to which it is equal), the presence of a large number of ionization centers makes necessary rapid recombination and, as a result, the period of existence of each ionized element is small. The lifetime of each charge must be large compared to the particle diffusion time across the base for transistor action to occur. The ions available in an intrinsic semiconductor that is not under optical or electrical stimulation always occur in matched pairs, one negative, or electron, and one positive, called a hole or vacancy in solid-state physics.

The manner in which the relatively high conductivity of an impure semiconductor is produced is rather curious, because in general the material must be electrically neutral in the absence of electrical fields. If the impurities are limited to compensating impurities and the crystallization takes place in such a way that the impurities can pair off and form a group of intermetallic compounds in the lattice, then the conductivity of the overall crystal will not be altered by the presence of the impurities. Unfortunately, however, it is difficult if not impossible to bring the stray atoms into such positions that they can form intermetallic compounds in the lattice, with the result that microscopic volumes of the crystal are polarized with one polarity, and adjacent volumes are neutral or of the opposite polarity. As a consequence, in each of these volumes, an excessive number of carriers compared to intrinsic material is available. The large number of conducting charges available causes the conductivity of the material to be relatively high.

A crystal can be extremely pure and have a relatively high conductivity if there are many defects and dislocations in the crystallization, as each and every location at which such a defect causes a grain boundary acts to accelerate the generation of carriers. For this reason, the number of carriers of one type is in excess on one side of the boundary, and the number of the other is in excess on the other side. The large number of carriers again markedly increases the conductivity of the material. Because the variations in the conductivity of different regions of the semiconductor material used in transistors have a strong influence on the behavior of the resulting devices, the crystals used for semiconductor devices must have the highest possible purity, and must be crystallized with as high a degree of regularity as is possible. After crystals of the proper perfection have been produced, they may be altered by the introduction of the proper dilutants to give the required polar characteristics.

Polar Semiconductors.　Semiconductors may be made polar, or they can be made to favor one type of carrier in preference to the other, by introduction of very small amounts of a material possessing a different number of valence electrons. The most logical impurities to choose for semiconductors like germanium and silicon are materials having valences either three or five, materials falling in the groups IIIA or IIIB, or VA or VB in the periodic table. The materials in group III have three valence electrons, yielding a doped semiconductor of the acceptor, or positive type, when introduced into a semiconductor material. Similarly, the introduction of materials from group V makes an extra electron available, producing a donor or negative type semiconductor.

Because the simplest intermetallic semiconductors are made from crystalline compounds of materials in the third and fifth groups of the periodic table, they cannot be readily doped with other materials from the same group. As a consequence, they use materials from either periodic groups II or VI as doping ingredients, giving either acceptor or donor structures as with ordinary semiconductors. The resulting polarized semiconductors behave in a similar manner to either doped germanium or silicon.

Negative, or N-type Semiconductors.　If a group V material is introduced into a semiconductor crystal lattice in low concentration, possibly one atom in 10^6 to 10^9, then very little over-all damage is done to the uniformity of the crystallization of the single-crystal semiconductor. Normally, the N-type semiconductor that results has sufficient donor impurity added to increase the available number of negative carriers by from one to many orders of magnitude with respect to the concentration in intrinsic material. For germanium, this means that greater than 10^{14} impurity atoms are required in each cubic centimeter (4.45×10^{22} atoms), and for silicon, greater than 10^{11} impurity atoms per cubic centimeter (5.03×10^{22} atoms). The minimum impurity ratio for germanium then is $1{:}1.85 \times 10^8$, and for silicon, $1{:}3.35 \times 10^{11}$. The maximum number of polar impurities a crystallized semiconductor can absorb without disturbing the crystallization depends on the doping impurity used and its method of application, and also somewhat on the polarity and the semiconductor itself. High concentrations of impurity atoms are required in the emitters and the high density edge of the graded bases in high-frequency transistors and particularly in tunnel, or "Esaki" diodes.

The presence of electrons from the donor atoms in the semiconductor causes a reduction of the number of holes or positive charges present in the lattice, since the increased number of electrons causes the recombination of holes to occur much more rapidly than can occur in intrinsic material. The number of holes present in an N-type semiconductor can be determined from the equation

$$n_n p_n = n_i^2 \tag{9}$$

where the subscript n refers to N-type material, and the n and p indicate electrons and holes respectively, and n_i is the number of carriers in intrinsic material.

Positive, or P-type Semiconductors.   In a similar manner, a positively polarized type of semiconductor, one in which the current carriers are holes (the absence of electrons) is formed by the introduction of very small amounts of materials from groups IIIA or IIIB of the periodic table. The methods of introduction of these materials into the semiconductor are the same as with donor impurities; experience has shown, however, that, in a reproducible manufacturing process, larger concentrations of some doping materials can be added to a specific intrinsic semiconductor than can others. This is the reason that more NPN silicon transistors have been available than PNP, whereas for several years more PNP transistors were made from germanium than were NPN units.

As a consequence of the ion-product law, the presence of increased numbers of p-type, or hole, carriers in a semiconductor material causes a considerable reduction of the number of electrons available for conduction purposes. Consequently, the conduction of current in acceptor-type materials depends on the hole-carriers. As the total number of one type of carrier is increased in a polar material with respect to intrinsic material, the conductivity is increased proportionately. The ion-product law for p-type materials takes the form

$$n_p p_p = n_i^2 \tag{10}$$

The majority carriers here are the p_p, or hole, carriers, and the minority carriers are the n_p, or electrons.

Ohmic Contacts.   One of the problems in the utilization of doped semiconductor materials is the making of ohmic, or low resistance, contacts on the material. Making such contacts is an art all by itself, because the solders used have to include the right materials to wet the surface, and must also have expansion coefficients that are compatible with the material on which they are placed. Often a doping agent is placed in the solder to improve the characteristics of the contact, and sometimes, as in surface-barrier transistors, the entire junction may be plated on the semiconductor.

The flux used in soldering is often important in assuring adequate wetting of the surface and in distributing the contact area sufficiently in width to keep the contact resistance to a small value.

1.6 Semiconductor Diodes

Diodes are two-terminal devices that pass current with comparatively little difficulty in one direction, but pass only very small amounts of current in the reverse direction. Ideally, a diode should have high conductance, greater than 0.01 mho for any voltage across it in the conduction direction, and should have only a very small conductance, less than ten micromhos, in the reverse direction. In practice, no diodes meet these ideal conditions, vacuum diodes having high conductance when the anode is more positive with respect to the cathode than approximately minus 0.3 volt. For more negative voltages, the conductance is virtually zero. Semiconductor diodes have very small values of conductance for collector-to-cathode potential, less than a few tenths of a volt, and have high conductance for more positive values of potential. The voltage at which transition occurs in a diode depends on both the semiconductor material itself, and also on the doping conditions in the two sections of the diode.

A semiconductor diode is made from a piece of doped semiconductor, the doping consisting either of only one type or of two zones, one being doped P-type and the other N-type. In some applications, the doping in one of the zones has been diffused into the semiconductor, and then the device is said to have a graded junction rather than an abrupt junction. One or more leads is now soldered to the segment of semiconductor, one for a point-contact diode, and two for a junction diode. These soldered leads must make ohmic contacts on the surface.

If the piece of semiconductor used for making the diode is not a single crystal and free of defects, large numbers of carriers will be available, and ready conduction in either direction can result. The result in the diode is a poor forward-to-backward ratio, and in a transistor, very low current gain.

When the diode is polarized in the conduction direction, the majority carriers in the P- and N-type regions are swept toward the junction by the applied field, and they recombine with the majority carriers from the opposite side of the junction, thereby causing current to flow. When a reverse potential is applied, however, the field tends to accelerate only the minority carriers toward the junction, and draws the majority carriers away from it. Diode current flow continues until the majority carriers in the neighborhood of the junction have all combined with minority carriers, at which time the current decays to an extremely small value. Then minority carriers occupy positions in the neighborhood of the boundary to establish electrical equilibrium in the diode.

Historically, the earliest semiconductor diodes used were a form of point-contact diode, the galena crystal detector. Most of the diodes used as detectors still are point-contact diodes, because junction diodes tend to have an excessively large shunt capacitance. Junction diodes find a wider application in the field of power rectification, because shunt capacitance is relatively unimportant, whereas current capacity is very important.

Point-Contact Diodes. Point-contact diodes are really a special form of junction diode in that the junction layer is introduced into the semiconductor through chemical action on the point resulting from current pulsing or other processing techniques. These diodes are made by soldering a small semiconductor wafer to a terminal to give an ohmic contact on one side, and bringing the catwhisker contact, a specially pointed wire, against it. The wire may contain a trace of indium or gallium or other material if a high conductance diode is required. After contact is made, the diode is pulsed with pulses of current from a capacitor to weld the point to the semiconductor and to transfer enough material from the point to establish a junction region in the wafer.

The point-contact diode has a very small internal capacitance across the junction because of the fine wire used in the contact point, but it does include a small amount of series inductance instead. Because the internal series resistance in such a device is comparatively small, the device can be useful to frequencies as high as several hundred megacycles. Point-contact silicon diodes have been used in radar equipment to frequencies as high as thirty thousand megacycles, and possibly higher. Their principal application has been as a nonlinear device for frequency conversion or mixing.

Junction Diodes. Junction diodes have the rectifying junction formed internally within the piece of semiconductor material from which they are made. The junction may be formed by growing it in the semiconductor as it is crystallized from a molten bath, or it may be formed either by an alloying or a diffusing process. The characteristics of each of these types of diodes are discussed separately.

Grown-junction diodes. These diodes are produced by changing the doping of the raw semiconductor alternately for one polarity and then the other as a crystal is being drawn from the molten bath. In this way, a small number of layers of semiconductor of alternating impurity type may be introduced into the bar of single-crystal material. The bar may then be cut into layers and then into dies from which the individual diodes may be fabricated. Only a very small chip of semiconductor is required for each diode, so that a piece of grown semiconductor may be used to make hundreds of diodes.

Alloy diodes. These diodes are made from chips of semiconductor having an arbitrary type of impurity by heating the individual chips and alloy preforms in special furnaces. The preforms are doped with material that will cause the development of a zone on each die which has opposite electrical polarity from the balance of the chip, and it also provides a soldering surface for attaching the electrical connection. The temperature to which the segments must be heated is well below the melting temperature for the base-region material but is high in the preform contact region that semiconductor flow alloying can be accomplished without difficulty.

Diffused-junction diode. This diode is a comparative newcomer to the field of rectifiers, and it shows tremendous promise for many applications. It is comparatively easy to manufacture these devices to a given specification, because the manufacturing process involves the use of gaseous diffusion at constant pressure, velocity, temperature, and time. The amount of impurity deposited on the surface can be precisely controlled in this way, and the penetration characteristics likewise can be controlled by a further temperature-time baking cycle. Extremely good uniformity of modification of the surfaces of the dies is thus obtained. The resulting junctions are what might be called "tapered" junctions, and they have excellent high-frequency properties. The mesa diode is a special diffused-junction diode.

Tunnel Diodes. Tunnel diodes are a special form of P-N diodes in which the semiconductor is doped to a point of saturation with polar elements. Esaki, who developed the first of these devices, showed that as

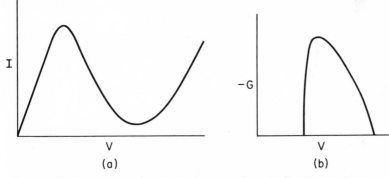

Fig. 1-5A. Voltage-current relation, tunnel diode

Fig. 1-5B. Equivalent negative conductance, tunnel diode

a consequence of the heavy doping, the current in the forward direction has a maximum and a minimum as the forward potential across the device is increased from zero to the barrier potential (Fig. 1–5). This causes the devices to develop a negative conductance that may have a magnitude as large as 0.03 mho or more. The theory of operation of these diodes is not fully understood, but it is believed that the negative-conductance phenomenon is a result of quantum-mechanical tunneling. The negative conductance normally sets in at approximately 0.050 to 0.070 volt, and the positive conductance again develops at a voltage in the neighborhood of 200 millivolts with typical units. The effective source impedance of the biasing voltage in this range must be sufficiently small so that the magnitude of the product of the source resistance by the negative conductance must be less than unity if stable operation of the diode at a point in the negative conductance region is required.

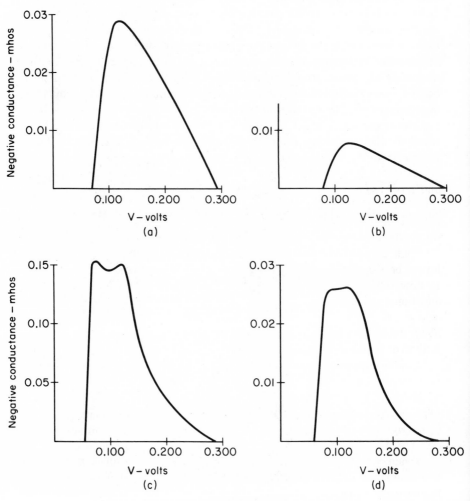

Fig. 1-6. Typical negative conductance contours

The overall operating characteristics of the tunnel diode are dependent on the maximum and the minimum values of current. The minimum value should be as small as possible to maximize the operating efficiency of the device, otherwise the maximum negative conductance is dependent primarily on the maximum current value. The form of the curve of conductance against voltage varies considerably from one device to another, and it may have a multiplicity of maxima or it may have only a single one. For some typical devices tested by the author, the maximum value of the negative conductance in micromhos is approximately five times the maximum current in microamperes. Some typical curves of negative conductance as a function of voltage are shown in Fig. 1–6.

Properties of Diodes. A wide variety of types of characteristics may be obtained in semiconductor diodes, depending on the conductivities of the semiconductor used in the layers of the diode, and also on the method of formation. Some diodes have moderate forward and reverse conductivity, some have high forward and reverse conductivity, and some have high forward and low reverse conductivity.

The frequency response of diodes is determined by the time required, when the diode is switched off, to sweep the active carriers out of action. In practice, this requires the sweeping out of all the minority carriers (these are the majority carriers that have been swept across the boundary and have thereby become minority carriers) that have been left near the junction of the device. The time required for the removal of lingering carriers determines the maximum switching speed of the diode and also its maximum operating frequency.

High forward conductivity in a diode requires that one of the two layers be heavily doped so that it can provide large numbers of carriers to flow through the boundary or junction in the forward direction. The additional doping may be applied to either of the polarized regions. For that reason only the region for which the most effective doping material is available need be doped heavily. For example, with germanium, either indium or indium and gallium may be used to provide the high conductance.

Low reverse conductance requires that at least one of the diode layers be formed from low-conductivity material, one which contains only small numbers of majority carriers to absorb the minority particles. Then a relatively high reverse breakdown voltage results because one of the layers is nearly intrinsic, and the leakage current available is limited to the carriers in intrinsic material.

Diode recovery time can be improved by the introduction of some trapping levels in the neighborhood of the junction in the low-conductivity material. Development of techniques of introducing traps has made possible the production of diodes capable of switching very rapidly. At the same time, they have very high resistivity in the reverse direction and high conductance in the forward direction.

The barrier, or blocking, potential of a diode is the forward potential required to place the diode on the edge of the conducting region. Often it is necessary to apply such a forward potential on a diode to sensitize it and to minimize the magnitude of signal necessary to make it perform the function required of it. This bias is usually applied by the introduction of a small magnitude of current through the use of a high forward potential and a current limiting resistor. It has been used extensively in converter circuits for microwave radar receivers. The forward voltage required to sensitize the diode is dependent on the width of the energy gap of the basic semiconductor and also to some extent on the effective doping levels on the two sides of the junction. The barrier potential is also important in transistors.

1.7 Transistors

A transistor is an amplifying device capable of controlling the flow of power in an auxiliary circuit. It is made of doped semiconductor, and has a minimum of three leads, at least one of which is attached to the semiconductor through an ohmic contact. A minimum of three active regions is required in a transistor; the first is called the emitter, the second, the base, and the third the collector. The first region serves the same function as is served by the cathode of an electron tube — that is, it makes available a cloud of charged particles that may be drawn in greater or smaller number to the collecting electrode. The second region, the base region, is the one that provides the current-control action; in fact it behaves very much like the grid in an electron tube. The third region, the collector, collects the current passed by the emitter through the base region.

Historically, the first transistor capable of providing amplification was the point-contact transistor. Other types that have been found useful include many types of junction transistors, field-effect transistors, and unijunction transistors. Of these principal types, the most important at present are the junction units; the unijunction and the field-effect transistors have found limited usage, whereas the point-contact transistors are almost unused. Each of these types of transistors is discussed briefly in the next few paragraphs, after which the more detailed electrical properties of junction-type transistors will be discussed.

Point-Contact Transistors. These transistors are constructed of a piece of doped semiconductor with a pair of fine pointed wires, very closely spaced, in contact with it. One of these wires has been alloyed with the elements required to cause it to have opposite polarity to that of the block of semiconductor, and the other has been alloyed with elements that make it the same polarity as the block. The wire of opposite polarity is used as an emitter, and the one of same polarity, after suitable forming, behaves as a collector. The forming operation is one of pulsing the collector-base circuit of the transistor from a charged capacitor. This process apparently sets up some carrier traps in the neighborhood of the collector, and causes the device to behave as an NPNP or a PNPN transistor. The presence of the hook-collector or trap-collector makes possible the development of values of alpha in excess of unity. The difficulty in controlling the parameters of hook-collectors in the production process has resulted in point-contact transistors being replaced by junction transistors.

Junction Transistors. The majority of junction transistors consist of three layers of doped semiconductor, the layers being doped alternately N-type and P-type. These layers are arranged in a manner that will permit the die to be formed from a piece of single-crystal semiconductor. A number of methods of fabrication of junction devices have been developed, among the most important of which are alloying, growing, electrolytic erosion followed by plating, and diffusion. The following paragraphs discuss briefly the physical methods of production of transistors made by these processes and indicate the special properties that result from the method of construction.

Alloy-junction transistors. These transistors are made from small slices of doped semiconductor by placing small solder forms containing a doping material on opposite sides of the dies, and heating sufficiently to fuse the forms with the surfaces. The forms fuse with and penetrate the surfaces, thereby forming areas of reversed polarity with respect to the original material. This method of construction has proven effective for use with transistors whose properties are not overly critical, but it has not proven to have the degree of reproducibility required for applications in which both wide frequency response and large power-handling ability are required. The principal difficulty is that the penetration of the doping material is difficult to control and irregular surfaces are often produced by minor imperfections in the crystal. Such irregularities make it difficult

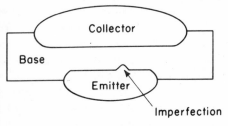

Fig. 1-7. Schematic transistor cross section with imperfection

to get the layers of optimum thickness without developing points in which high stresses can develop and cause failure of the transistor as shown in Fig. 1–7.

In spite of the difficulties involved in obtaining an ideal structure with an alloy transistor, most of the transistors for routine application are made by alloying because an adequate structure can be easily obtained. Units having frequency responses into the low megacycle range are readily constructed, and rather good values of current gain may be obtained.

Grown-junction transistors. The basic semiconductor material for these transistors is formed in the process of growing a bar of single-crystal semiconductor, and altering the polarity and conductivity of the crystal during growth in such a way as to make available two layers of one polarity of semiconductor separated by a very narrow layer of low-conductivity material of opposite polarity. Ideally, the thin layer should have a conductivity approximately ten times that for intrinsic material so that the current gain from emitter to collector can be as near unity as possible. The conductivity of the collector region of the grown transistor normally is somewhat higher than that of the base, but it cannot be made extremely large without introducing difficulties in adjustment of the base conductivity. The emitter region, on the other hand, requires a rather large conductivity to provide the required carriers and to keep the emitter series resistance to a minimum. A particularly critical compromise is required for the emitter region if more than one region in the bar is to be made in a form useful for transistors. Whereas the initial region may be able to develop reasonable current gain, additional regions may provide current gains of ten or less.

The process of growing a good grown-junction transistor is very delicate, in that the impurity control must be extremely precise, and the mixing of the melt must also be excellent. The control of the rate of draw and of the bath temperature must be very accurately controlled to obtain layers with the proper thickness and conductivities, and to be sure that proper segregation of impurities results. The rate of draw is particularly important, because the polarity of the resulting crystal can be reversed by alteration of the rate of draw under some combinations of impurities in the molten semiconductor. Fortunately, however, each junction region may be separated into as many as several hundred individual dies from which transistors can be made, and the control cost can be spread over the group.

The attachment of the leads on a grown-junction transistor is a delicate problem, because the base lead in particular can ruin the over-all characteristics of the device if it is improperly installed. The location of the central, or base, layer may be determined electrically or optically and its boundaries defined, after which a lead may be soldered or welded in position.

The fact that the collector region in a grown-junction transistor may have a rather small conductivity can introduce series resistance between the active junction region and the lead connection that may interfere with the proper operation of the transistor. The resulting collector series (or spreading) resistance, $r_{c'}$, will be discussed further in the sections considering high-frequency operation and oscillation. It will be shown that this resistance can increase the internal amplification of the device and as a result enhance the possibilities of undesired oscillation.

Large numbers of grown-junction transistors have been used and will continue to be used because experience has shown that often a transistor can be built that will function rather adequately using grown structures, even though no other methods have been found that will permit the construction of stable and reliable transistors based on the semiconductor.

Melt-back transistors. The melt-back transistor is closely related to the grown-junction transistor, because regrowing is used to reverse the carrier polarity in the base region, and quenching to cause the second reversal for the emitter region. Because the base regions in these units prove to have variable density of the polar centers, and the distribution can be made to develop a limited accelerating field, these units behave somewhat like drift transistors.

Surface-barrier transistors. These transistors are special types of alloy transistors in which the transistor base wafer has a collector region and an emitter region plated into etched pits. Because the depths of these regions is only a few atoms, the correct thickness of the base region can be established by the erosion process on the basic wafer, even with thicknesses as small as a few ten-thousandths of an inch. Excellent parallelism of the surfaces of the required pits can be obtained, with the result that a high degree of uniformity is obtained with production transistors. Usually electrolytic etching is used to obtain the proper shape of hollow on each side, and when the thickness of the central portion of the wafer is the required value, as determined by infra-red transmission, the polarity of the bias potential is reversed, and the collector and emitter electrodes are deposited by plating. A solution containing an indium salt, possibly containing a trace of gallium, is used for etching germanium, and the plating yields an area of indium with the trace of gallium in it. A gentle heating, similar to an alloying process, but at somewhat reduced temperature and for a reduced time, may then be used to stabilize the emitter and the collector areas.

Drift transistors. The frequency response of most types of transistors considered so far, because they have relatively uniform conductivity in the base region and, as a result, negligible accelerating field across the base, is limited by the diffusion time for the minority carriers across the base. This diffusion time is not the time for an individually charged particle to cross the base, but the time for a change of distribution to cross it. It is considerably shorter than the particle transit time, and in fact its magnitude is determined by a combination of the product of the mean-free-path multiplied by the ratio of the mean-free-path and the base width. Needless to say, the latter ratio is a measure of the uniformity of the current flow through the base, and is an approximation to the "decay function,"

$$[1 - \exp(-W/L)] \doteq W/L$$

If the loss of carriers takes place very slowly in crossing the base, i.e., if $\exp(-W/L)$ has a value very near unity, then the transistor will function effectively to a frequency that may be many times the radian frequency corresponding to the base width.

Any modification of the structure capable of increasing the speed with which the carriers traverse the base region without at the same time causing more recombinations and losses of carriers, is at least potentially capable of increasing the maximum operating frequency of the device. Such an acceleration may be accomplished by providing a field gradient across the base, thereby increasing the velocity by adding a drift velocity to the diffusion velocity. This accelerating field is introduced through the use of a diffused or graded base region, one in which the conductivity has a comparatively high value adjacent to the emitter but which decreases significantly as the collector junction is approached. Such a base region can be developed by the use of diffusion techniques, and also by the melt-back process already discussed. The diffusion technique is the key to the extremely high operating frequencies possible with mesa transistors.

Mesa transistor. This device is a special form of the diffused-junction transistor that takes optimum advantage of the diffusion process. It uses an emitter electrode that is quite long, but only a few mean-free-path-widths wide, and uses base electrodes closely spaced to the emitter and parallel with it. Optimally, there is one on either side of the emitter. This configuration provides a maximum emitter injection efficiency and a minimum base-spreading resistance. The device gets the name "mesa" from the fact that in order to keep the base-to-collector capacitance to a minimum, all of the high-conductivity part of the base layer must be cut away, except for that directly involved in transistor action. The structure then looks like a mesa, as is shown in exaggerated form in Fig. 1–8.

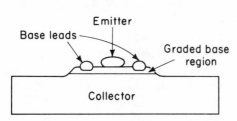

Fig. 1-8. Structure of mesa transistor

Other Devices. A variety of multilayer-type devices, from diodes through triodes and tetrodes, are currently under active development. Many of these devices possess properties having considerable similarity to conventional thyratrons, and they are used extensively as switches. They have higher efficiency, and, except for a lower stand-off voltage, are in most respects the equivalents of their gaseous forerunners. Transistors based on a four-layer construction, with two bases and two emitters, one of which serves as a collector, are said to have a hook-collector, and they have an additional current gain because of the structural properties. They also make excellent switches.

1.8 Mechanical and Conductivity Relations in Junction Transistors

Both the physical properties and the electrical relations of the emitter, the base, and the collector of the junction transistor must satisfy a limited range of conditions with respect to one another for the device to be capable of giving transistor action. Some of these relations have been noted in the discussion of the different common types of junction transistors in the section above, but a further brief discussion is included in this section to clarify the underlying principles prior to beginning the discussion of the variable and parameter relations inferred from the structure. This section is divided into four parts, the first discussing the properties, both physical and electrical, of the emitter region, the second considering the properties of the base region, and the third considering the properties of the collector region. After these discussions, the fourth section considers in more detail important inter-relations of the three regions.

The Emitter. The emitter region of the transistor functions in a similar manner to the cathode structure of an electron tube, in that it serves as a reservoir for the charge carriers, holes or electrons, which constitute the current that flows from the emitter to the collector. In this respect, it behaves much like the space-charge zone in front of the heated cathode in the tube. Mechanically, it is intimately in contact with the base region of the transistor, and it consists of a button or zone of semiconductor somewhat as shown in Fig. 1–9 for several typical transistor constructions.

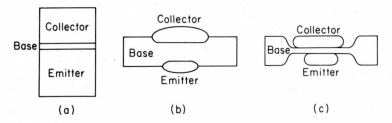

Fig. 1-9. Typical transistor cross sections

The conductivity of the emitter is made as high as possible without introducing structural imperfections into it; it is consequently doped with a combination of impurities that makes it strongly P-type or N-type. This doping makes available large numbers of carriers at the boundary between the emitter and the base, and minimizes the voltage required to permit the flow of carriers across the boundary. The high conductivity of the emitter makes possible an extremely small internal series resistance in the emitter circuit between the boundary of the junction and the external lead, thereby making possible a high operating efficiency in the device. In other words, the value of $r_{e'}$ is very small in a transistor with a properly designed emitter region.

The emitter may be formed in the shape of a button, as is common in many of the low-power transistors for use at low frequency, or it may be in the form of a ring, as in many power transistors. A common form for it in some of the very-high-frequency transistors is a linear stripe. These units combine relatively high power capacity with excellent frequency characteristics. An excellent discussion of design of high-efficiency emitters has been given by Emeis, Herlet, and Spenke.[7] They show that with any appreciable concentration of current in the emitter region, the effective width of the operating area is very, very small, consisting essentially of only a line under either one edge or both edges of the emitter, depending on whether one or two base stripes are provided. For this reason, no advantage is gained in having more than a line emitter on any power transistor. The use of diffusion techniques has made possible the construction of practical transistors based on the linear emitter.

The Base Region. The active base region of a transistor, a very thin layer of semiconductor in contact with the emitter, serves to control the flow of carriers through the device. In this way, it corresponds to the control grid in the electron tube. The base may consist of an extremely small segment of semiconductor adjacent to the emitter, as in the grown-junction device, or it may be part of the building block of semiconductor on which the transistor is constructed, as with surface-barrier and alloy transistors. Or it may be a very thin layer diffused onto the surface of a block of semiconductor as with mesa transistors.

The conductivity of the semiconductor in the base region of a low-frequency transistor ordinarily should be very small to keep the base current small. At the same time, the base conductivity should be sufficiently large so that, over the transistor operating temperature range, it is at least a few times the intrinsic conductivity at the corresponding temperature.

[7] R. Emeis, A. Herlet, and E. Spenke: "The Effective Emitter Area of Power Transistors," *Proc. IRE*, June, 1958, p. 1220.

The conductivity of the base region is important in at least one other respect. Very low values of conductivity result in a considerable value of resistance between the base lead and the active base area. This introduces what is known as base-spreading resistance into the device. This resistance prevents adequate grounding of the base region in a transistor used in the common-base configuration, thereby reducing the stability of the resulting amplifier. In addition, the resistance contributes to the phase shift that develops in the current gain as the frequency is increased and determines the maximum input conductance developed in the base circuit. The complex behavior introduced by the base-spreading resistance and the resulting complex phase shift reduce the usefulness of current gain as a basic parameter for a transistor to the point where the principal value of current gain is in expressing low-frequency characteristics.

The spreading resistance should be as small as possible for a given magnitude of base conductivity, as only in that way can undesired variations in the behavior of the circuit be avoided. An early method of minimizing the difficulty was by the use of comparatively high-conductivity material in the base, thereby reducing the $r_{b'}$ and also reducing the values of the alpha and beta for the transistor. Up to a point, the reduction of the current gain does not introduce as deleterious effects as those resulting from the presence of a large value of base-spreading resistance. The minimum acceptable value of alpha is approximately 0.80. This arrangement has been replaced with the diffused base, because with it both high current gain and small base-spreading resistance are available.

The use of a base contact that completely surrounds the emitter contact is advantageous only with devices in which the high-conductivity skin is used, as the prime resistance introduced between two probes in contact with low-conductivity material can be shown to be localized around the point of contact. The presence of the high-conductivity skin therefore makes available a relatively small contact resistance. Since the region of the emitter that contributes most effectively to transistor action is a stripe along the edge in the neighborhood of the base contact, a narrow linear emitter with a linear base contact on either side is optimum if a skin of high conductivity is available on the base region. The parallel linear contact may be bent into ring

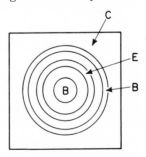

Fig. 1-10. Annular transistor

contacts as shown in Fig. 1–10; or a structure such as is shown in Fig. 1–11, in which the emitter and base are deposited in interconnected stripes over the entire surface, may be used to increase the power handling capability of the device.

The high-conductivity surface skin on the base, if left unaltered, increases the effective area of the base, and acts like a conducting metal plate of a capacitor. As a result, if the base-to-collector capacitance must

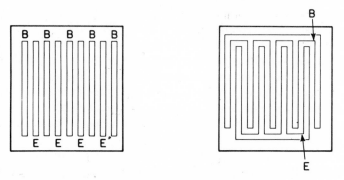

Fig. 1-11. Power mesa configurations

be kept as small as possible (a condition that usually is desirable), all but the minimum necessary part of the high-conductivity base region should be etched away, producing the mesa as shown in Fig. 1–12.

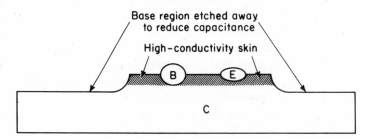

Fig. 1-12. Diffused mesa structure

Effects of Contamination. Surface and volume effects within the base region commonly can cause a serious reduction of the efficiency of the transistor. For example, presence of contamination across the surface from the emitter to the collector can introduce a short-circuit across the transistor, causing it to fail completely. At the same time, any imperfections in the base region, either on the emitter or the collector side or outside of the direct field, can capture, or trap, some of the minority carriers in the base and interfere with normal operation. In addition, if some of the carriers diffuse in the wrong direction, as indicated in Fig. 1–13, they will not be able to reach the collector in time to enable them to contribute to the current gain of the device. They finally recombine with a majority carrier in the base region instead. The presence of an accelerating field, such as results from diffusing the base region into the transistor, minimizes the number of carriers that recombine in this manner.

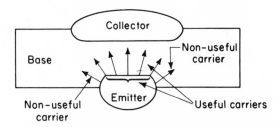

Fig. 1-13. Condition for loss of carriers

The Collector Region. The collector region, as the name implies, acts as a collector for the charges that are passed by the emitter through the base region. It functions in much the same way as does the plate of a tube. It may consist of a substantial block of semiconductor, or it may be only a small button of material, depending on the method of construction of the transistor. The grown-junction and the mesa transistors have blocks of semiconductor in the collector region, whereas most other types use the button form.

The conductivity of the collector region may be relatively high, although it may not be desirable for it to be as high as that of the emitter region unless bilateral operation is required. (In bilateral transistors, it is necessary that the transistor function as a transistor in both directions. In other words the base must be able to control current flow with the collector serving as an emitter as well as with the emitter so serving.) The conductivity should be sufficiently high in the collector region of the normal transistor so that the series resistance between the junction region and the collector terminal will be at most a few ohms. It should be small enough so that the value of the expression $g_{f'}r_{c'}$ is less than unity. Otherwise, an excessive amount of phase shift and loss of output signal can result from the presence of the series collector resistance, $r_{c'}$. Values of the forward conductance, $g_{f'}$, as large as 100,000 micromhos and more can be developed in low-power and medium-power transistors, with the result that values of $r_{c'}$ that are larger than five to twenty-five ohms may introduce design problems of serious nature. The problem is particularly serious in high-frequency amplifiers and oscillators. The transistors most likely to have large values of $r_{c'}$ are grown-junction units and NPIN and PNIP types. In any case, relatively good conductivity at the points of attachment of leads is very desirable, because it simplifies the making of ohmic contacts for the leads.

Relations Between the Emitter and Collector. Efficient operation of a transistor is dependent on a minimum number of the charge carriers from the emitter recombining prior to arrival at the collector, and a minimum number of charges back-diffusing from the collector to the base.

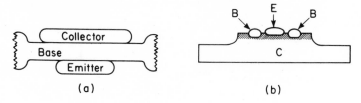

(a)   (b)

Fig. 1-14. Condition for high emitter efficiency
                (a) alloy, surface-barrier
                (b) diffused-base

For a minimum number of dispersed carriers in the absence of a drift field, it is essential that the collector more-or-less "surround" the emitter, and it is also desirable that the distance from the emitter to the collector be small and as constant as possible from all parts of the emitter. Figure 1–14 shows the type of structures that give the best characteristics for alloy, surface-barrier, diffusion, and mesa transistors. These structures provide minimum path-length and efficient collection.

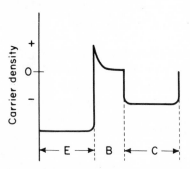

Fig. 1-15. Carrier distribution-diffusion device (NPN)

Figure 1–15 shows the distribution of doping that gives optimum operation in terms of practical devices for the structures shown in Fig. 1–14. Particular note should be taken of the fact that with a graded base region, either a collector of limited area or a base skin of limited area must be used to minimize the base-to-collector capacitance. In practice, the area limitation is applied to the base region to keep the collector efficiency as high as possible.

1.9 Transistor Noise

The noise generated in transistors may be divided among three different types, the $1/f$ type, the uniform type, and the f type (Fig. 1–16). These definitions are based on the variation of the average noise intensity with frequency because the noise amplitude as a function of frequency decreases with increasing frequency in the $1/f$ region, because it is relatively independent of frequency in the frequency-independent region, and because the average amplitude increases with frequency increase in the f region.

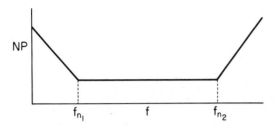

Fig. 1-16. Variation of noise power per cycle with frequency

These three regions are separated by transition frequencies that are defined as f_{n1} and f_{n2}, where f_{n1} is the corner frequency between the $1/f$ and uniform regions, and f_{n2} is the corner frequency between the uniform and the f regions. The values of these two frequencies and the value of the noise figure in the region of uniform noise as a function of frequency are the data on noise, which are important to the designer in that they define the noise characteristics of the transistor throughout its operating range.

Strictly, as is always true of noise signals, the amplitudes indicated by the relations are the averages of their mean-square values, because noise is by nature a completely unpredictable condition on an instant-by-instant basis. At any one instant, the spectrum of the noise energy as a function of frequency may, and in general will, differ widely from the nominal value indicated by the rms average. Over the long term, or on the average, however, the value of the noise power does approximate the distributions indicated.

The noise in the low-frequency, or $1/f$, region, is similar in its general characteristics to flicker noise in vacuum tubes. This type of noise is introduced into a transistor through imperfections resulting from crystal flaws or surface defects in the device. The proper treatment of the surfaces of the transistor, or passivation, normally reduces to rather small values the flicker type of noise. The presence of an excessive amount of this type of noise may indicate the existence of "tunneling" or areas of potentially unstable surface or junction conditions. It may introduce irregularities into either the output conductance or the input conductance of the device. A few commonly used transistors do have high values of f_{n1}, but in general the devices most commonly used have values of f_{n1} that are less than 100 cycles.

The corner frequency, f_{n2}, is of considerable importance in transistor circuit design because it also specifies the maximum switching rate for a conventional R-C multivibrator.[8] The period corresponding to this frequency in radians is approximately equal to the time required for the transport of an individual carrier across the base region of the transistor. These numbers are not numerically equal, but agree within a factor of two. The noise for frequencies above this frequency increases because the non-uniformity of current flow becomes the controlling factor in noise production. The comparatively long drift time in diffusing across the base region is long enough, compared to the period of the wave, to permit phase irregularities to be introduced as a consequence of beam transit time. This noise is similar to drift noise in klystron tubes.

[8] J. J. Suran, F. A. Reibert, "Two-Terminal Analysis and Synthesis of Junction Transistor Multivibrators," *IRE Trans.*, *PGCT*, March, 1956, p. 26.

CHAPTER TWO

Variables and
Parameter Relations

2.0 Introduction

The representation of the junction transistor in terms of static variables like voltages, currents, small-signal parameters, immittances and ratios of immittances, can take a wide variety of forms. The utility of any of these forms of representation of a device depends on the relative magnitudes and the stabilities of the variables and the parameters and their relations to one another. For this reason, it is important to evaluate the various possible arrangements in which the properties of the device can be expressed in terms of basic physics, and to select the form of presentation, that expresses these characteristics in the form that minimizes the precision required of measurement and minimizes the error encountered from changes in temperature and other environmental conditions. The purpose of this chapter is to make a brief examination of the parameter and variable problem to select a system of representation that can be used effectively for a wide variety of applications.

Since the representation of the characteristics of devices like transistors is extremely complex (from seven to ten small-signal parameters alone may be required), it is essential that the data be organized in a manner to provide the required information in the simplest and the most direct manner. As a result, it is important at each stage of the development of a system of symbology, variables and parameters to evaluate the comparative importance of the various types of data, so that the more important factors can be displayed prominently and those of reduced importance be given less emphasis. This organization should be so arranged that maximum ease of measurement and maximum use of the information results and a minimum of difficulty is introduced by thermal and other forms of instability.

The first subject to be discussed in this chapter is the symbology required in order to develop a general system of nomenclature that can be used for the presentation of variables and parameters throughout this book. After this discussion, the possible choices of input and output variables are considered and a preferred combination is selected that provides the required device data in convenient form. This selection must be coordinated with the plotting arrangements used for the data on the variables.

The remaining sections of the chapter are concerned with the selection of a form of relation of small-signal parameters that makes possible direct design with a minimum of difficulty for a comprehensive group of types of circuits, and the selection of the basic configuration to be used in general design problems. The relations selected should be optimum for as wide a variety of important design problems as possible, and should yield other designs as limiting cases. The configuration selected should make possible the measurement of the properties of the device with a minimum interference from associated circuitry. These sections must solve the controversial questions of the small-signal parameters to be used in the book and the question of the appropriate common electrode for the transistor. The chapter is closed with tabulations of the relations among the various systems of parameters.

2.1 Symbology

The set of symbols used in this book, a complete tabulation of which is included in Appendix I, are based on the standard system developed by the Institute of Radio Engineers and the American Institute of Electrical Engineers. Some minor modifications have been made in the system because the use of the small-signal methods to be described makes possible much more complete calculations than have heretofore been possible and also makes necessary some additions and modifications to the system to take full advantage of the improvements made possible by the methods.

The system of identification of the terms in the small-signal equations for operation of a transistor or for any network having an input and an output circuit (two-port network) until recently consisted of identifying the sets of terminals as set one and set two, with the immittances bearing two numbers each (y_{11}, y_{21}, h_{12}, etc.). This method has been replaced in the United States by the use of a subscript "i" for the input current and voltage, and a subscript "o" for the output current and voltage. The designation of the immittances has been changed completely, typical sets in the revised system reading y_i, y_f, y_r, and y_o, or h_i, h_f, h_r, and h_o. This system of symbology has not met with favor abroad inasmuch as the words for input, forward, reverse, and output in other languages are completely different from the English words, with the result that the subscript letters have no significance. Just what the conclusion of the attempts at coordination will be is not currently clear, but because the use of the letters does conform with convenient usage in English it will be used, along with a subscript "c," for the modified output admittance in this book.

The graphic symbols used for representation of transistors and transistor-like devices have been in a state of confusion for many years. Fairly general agreement has been reached, both here and abroad, on the symbol originally introduced by the Bell Laboratories for representation of the point-contact transistor. This symbol, shown in Fig. 2–1, is not particularly satisfactory for junction transistors, but it has had general acceptance.

PNP   NPN

Fig. 2-1. Standard transistor symbols

Ideally, a graphic symbol can be expected to fulfill the following conditions if it is to be of maximum utility:

1. It should represent the device physically in a way that gives some indication of the behavior of the device.

2. It should be easy to draw.

3. It should be consistent with other related symbols.

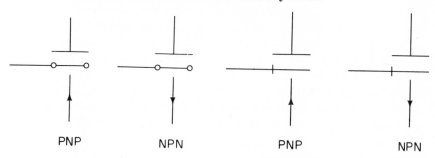

PNP   NPN   PNP   NPN

Fig. 2-2. Symbols of Lo *et al.*   **Fig. 2-3.** Modified Lo symbols

A symbol consisting primarily of horizontal and vertical lines with a minimum of slant lines and circles would be the most satisfactory arrangement to draw, and it might also best fulfill the consistency and physical representation requirements. The symbol shown in Fig. 2–2 was introduced by Lo, Endres, et al[1]. It can be rendered somewhat easier to draw by the use of the format shown in Fig. 2–3, a form that appears to be generally satisfactory. Some of the other symbols that have been used are shown in

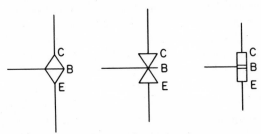

Fig. 2-4. Other symbols

Fig. 2–4. Although the writer tends to prefer either the symbol of Lo, Endres, et al. or the modified form of it, the standard IRE symbols will be used in this volume.

2.2 Input and Output Variables

The current and voltage variables used in the presentation of the static data on junction transistors must be selected to yield information on both the output and input characteristics in a manner that is, as far as possible, free of environmental variations. For example, the output relation, which involves normally the collector voltage and the collector current, is expressed in terms of one of the input variables, because the input controls the exact combination of output values obtained with the device. The fact that the value of the Fermi potential of the semiconductor material is strongly a function of temperature makes desirable the use of input current as the additional variable, in spite of the fact that the output current is controlled by a combination of the Fermi potential and the doping levels. Both the base current and the emitter current have been used quite extensively as this input variable, but the trend has for some time been toward the use of base current.

This choice of base current is actually dictated by requirements on precision of measurement. The base current, the emitter current, and the collector current all must be known, and are related by the equation

$$i_b + i_e + i_c = 0 \qquad (1)$$

[1] *Transistor Electronics,* by A. W. Lo, R. O. Endres, J. Zawals, F. D. Waldhauer, and C. C. Cheng.   Prentice-Hall, Inc., Englewood Cliffs, N. J., 1955.

The collector current, i_c, which is usually taken as the output current in circuits, and the current having the smaller magnitude between the remaining base current, i_b, and emitter current, i_e, are selected as the plotting current variables. The use of the smaller in magnitude of the two possible input currents as the plotting variable relaxes the accuracy and precision requirements on the measurement of the device currents because the mathematically difficult feat of differencing two large numbers with high precision need not be performed. Table I shows the measurement accuracies required for the emitter and collector currents and for the current gain, alpha, to get base current and beta accuracies of ten percent.

The use of collector voltage and current as the coordinates in conjunction with contours of constant base current has received general acceptance for presentation of the output relations for transistors. However, an input relation is also required, presenting the two input variables in terms of one of the output variables. This input relation is normally presented on a separate set of curves, although there is at least one method of combining the two sets of data into one family.

The set of variables selected for the input contour relations may include either the group input voltage and current and output voltage, or the

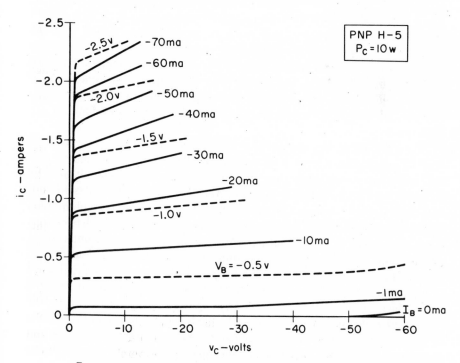

Fig. 2-5. Combined input-output curves. *Curves courtesy Minneapolis Honeywell Regulator Co.*

group input voltage and current and output current. There are a number of combinations of each of these groups, and the ease and convenience of use can be considerably altered by the shift from one form to another. For this reason, a careful examination of the properties of each is required.

The form of data presentation in which both sets are combined on a single chart includes both contours of constant base current and contours of constant base voltage on a single coordinate array of collector current and collector voltage (Fig. 2–5). This arrangement is convenient because the construction of one load contour on the set of curves makes possible direct reading of both the input current and input voltage. The curves are excellent for applications in which no small-signal data are required, but they become somewhat crowded if four sets of small-signal contours are added. Furthermore, they do not present the static data in a form that can be used easily for determination of small-signal data by differencing. For this reason, where small-signal data are required, one of the two-graph presentations is more convenient. The selection of the optimum form of the two-graph presentation is next considered.

2.3 Plotting Arrangements

The configurations used for the input and output families of data should present both the current-voltage relations for the input circuit, and the current-voltage relations for the output circuit in a form that simplifies the direct coordination of the input and the output characteristics. In the following paragraphs, the use of both the contours of input voltage and of input current as a function of output voltage and current is discussed, and then other configurations using separate input families are considered.

The plotting of the input variables in terms of the collector voltage may be accomplished in at least four ways. The contour lines may represent constant values for either the base current, the base voltage, the collector voltage or collector current. And the coordinate scales for use with each possible contour variable in the establishment of a graph may be subject to selection also. Because the output curve family consists of contours of constant value of input current as a function of the output voltage and current, and because corresponding points on the input and output families must be coordinated in the process of design of a circuit, the use of input curves based on contours of constant value of the input current, one of the coordinates then being base voltage and the other either collector voltage or collector current, appears to have significant advantages. One or the other of these two arrangements has been used on data sheets recently published by device manufacturers. For example, Amperex and Valvo GMBH have for some time plotted the input family in much the same way as is done in this book, Fig. 2-6, and Fairchild, RCA, and others have recently published curves with the collector current as the third variable rather than collector voltage. Typical examples of these curves are included in Appendix VI.

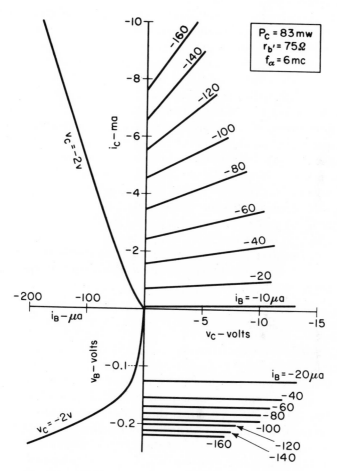

Fig. 2-6. Typical curves — OC45. *Courtesy Ampere Electronics Corp.*

In the amplification region, region II, the collector current varies but little with change of collector voltage and a fixed base current, with the result that considerable crowding can occur. When plotted as a function of collector voltage, however, the curves spread out in a form that facilitates the use of the available data. This form of the curves is particularly helpful in the estimation of admittance parameters.

The input relations as a function of collector current are most useful in region III, the current-saturation region. In this region, the base voltage changes rapidly and the collector current also changes rapidly, and the data on saturation conditions required in switching design are available. With devices intended primarily for use in switching circuits, the combination of the standard collector family of curves having the base current as the contour variable in conjunction with a base family also having the base current as the contour variable and the base voltage and collector current as the coordinates may prove more useful than the corresponding input family with collector voltage as the coordinate. However, the difference is so small that the advantages of using collector voltage in region II make it the preferred coordinate for general use.

One difficulty in plotting the input contours as a function of collector current is that it is more difficult to sweep the collector current than it is the collector voltage. The current can be swept by sweeping the voltage in region III, but the action is unsatisfactory in region II because of the slow variation of I_c with V_c.

Contours of constant value of the collector voltage have frequently been used in the past as a means for presenting the input characteristics. There appears to be a trend away from this format, however, for reasons discussed in the next section on information content. These curves are difficult to plot on automatic curve-tracers, and they are rather difficult to use effectively.

2.4 Information Content

One of the important considerations in the development of a system of data presentation on any device like a tube or a transistor is the organization of the information and the data to make all important factors readily available, and to provide the less important data in a manner which makes them available, but does not stress them or weight them excessively. A typical question, the answer to which might be found by the use of the concept of the value of information, is the selection of the appropriate component of current for use in plotting data sheets for transistors.

When the junction transistor was first introduced many manufacturers provided their characteristic data on the devices in terms of collector voltage and current, and emitter current. Users soon found that design was inconvenient at best using this arrangement, because it was extremely difficult to get a reasonably accurate estimate of the current in the base lead from these data. And, unfortunately, that information was needed quite often. The use of two currents nearly equal in value as plotting variables made necessary the determination of the third current by the process of subtracting two relatively large numbers to get the value of a smaller number. This differencing operation is strongly disapproved of by mathematicians because the precision required of the original data to obtain an accuracy of even fifty percent in the smaller may be extreme. The following table shows the precision required for determining the base current of a transistor to an accuracy of ten percent when the emitter current, the collector current, and either the alpha or beta are given.

TABLE I

Precision Requirements on Current Gain

α	β	Precision:	i_c	i_e
0.5	1.0		10%	5%
0.75	3.0		1.67%	1.25%
0.9	9.0		0.55%	0.50%
0.95	19		0.27%	0.25%
0.98	49		0.10%	0.10%
0.99	99		0.05%	0.05%
0.995	199		0.026%	0.025%

Clearly, the most extreme accuracy may be required of the values of the emitter and collector currents to get any sort of precision in the value of the base current. The base current must be selected as a plotting variable, rather than the emitter, if the precision requirements are to be reasonable.

Voltage Effects.   The potential stress applied from emitter to collector has a strong influence on the behavior of a transistor both at very low values of voltage and at relatively large values. In the region between, the voltage has relatively little influence on the magnitude of current flow. The current-voltage behavior at very low voltages determines the minimum dissipation in the transistor for any given value of collector current, and is for that reason very important. In a similar manner, the variation of collector current with collector voltage at large values of voltage tells a good deal about the characteristics of the individual transistor, since it shows where avalanche current multiplication and severe thermal heating occur. If the value of voltage at which avalanche multiplication occurs is abnormally low, defects of crystallization such as are shown in exaggerated form in Fig. 2–7 are probably present. A bump or point on the boundary between either the emitter and base

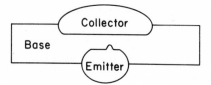

Fig. 2-7. Crystallization defect

or the collector and base causes an area of higher than normal potential stress, and causes the multiplication of the number of carriers at an abnormally low voltage. A transistor can short-through (punch-through) at such points. Unless a device approaches failure from punch-through, this kind of boundary defect has little effect on the behavior of the input circuit, but it alters the output characteristics significantly. The output family of curves appears somewhat as shown in Fig. 2–8.

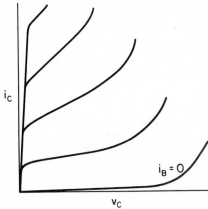

Fig. 2-8. Output curves for a transistor with crystallization defect

Thermal effects in the transistor introduce a hysteresis effect into the output contours as a function of base current, and they also introduce a typical heating effect into the input contours when they are plotted in terms of collector voltage. (The base current contours curve toward minimum magnitude of base voltage as the collector voltage is increased.) This effect is usually only barely noticeable on a sweep-curve analyzer such as the Tektronix Model 575 analyzer. It shows up best when the sweep rate is low enough so that thermal heating has time to occur.

Clearly, the behavior of an input family of curves based on contours of base current in terms of base voltage and collector voltage can be used to provide some idea as to the behavior of the device in its proposed operating circuit and also to detect possible defects. The choice of the collector voltage as the third variable on the input contours is dictated by the fact that under all but saturation conditions the magnitude of the collector voltage per se is more important to device behavior than is the value of the collector current.

The contour set that best expresses the properties of a device presents the data in terms of the variables that are most stable and significant for representing it. Since the output contours are without question more important than the input contours with most devices, the variables for plotting the output curves are the most important to select correctly. The selection of contours of constant magnitude of base current plotted in terms of collector voltage and collector current clearly gives the output characteristics in terms of the most sensitive variables, and gives them in the form showing the highest order of thermal stability.

The coordination of the input and the output families of data can improve the usefulness of both families of curves. Unless the families are so arranged that corresponding points on the two families can be readily located, full information on static behavior is not readily available. To facilitate data transfer, the collector voltage may be chosen as the abscissa on both graphs. If, then, base-current contours are plotted as a function of collector voltage with base voltage as the negative ordinate, the transfer of a point on the output family of curves to the input family requires only the location of a point on one of the base-current contours of the input family vertically below the corresponding point on the output family. If a set of intersections of a load line with the base-current contours on the output family is transferred, one by one, to the input family, then the corresponding input contour may be drawn and static characteristics be tabulated at any desired points by the help of vertical transfer lines (Fig. 2–9).

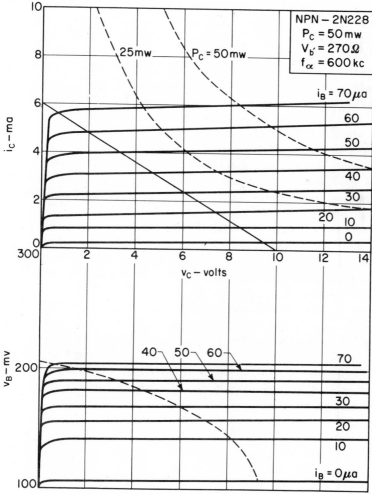

Fig. 2-9. Curve set for 2N228 Transistor

Parameter Data. In addition to information on the static variables, it is necessary to know something of the small-signal behavior of the devices. In the next section the possible small-signal parameters that may be used are considered, and the ones for use in this handbook are selected. In this section the organization of the parameter data for optimizing design effectiveness is examined.

Middlebrook[2] and others have shown that the junction transistor requires between seven and ten small-signal parameters for a full representation. Of these parameters, at least five are either resistances or conductances, a minimum of two are capacitances, another may be an inductance, and one may be a time-delay corresponding to diffusion time. At frequencies so low that the capacitance and inductance may be neglected, either four or five conductances (or resistances) may be used to represent the device. Some of these conductances affect the output behavior primarily, and others the input behavior. Because it can be shown that the static data on active devices like transistors are often less stable than are the corresponding small-signal data such as forward admittance, some method of presenting the small-signal data in a form emphasizing their stability should be used. The form should permit ready coordination with the corresponding static relations. This representation can be made on separate graphs, or it can be coordinated with the graphs of static data by superposing contours of constant-parameter values on them. The present trend is toward provision of more extensive amounts of small-signal data (cf. recent Amperex and Fairchild data sheets), but the means of coordination are still not completely adequate.

In a coordinated plot, the small-signal data that may be associated with the output curve family conveniently consist of parameters affecting the output behavior of the device, namely, the forward transfer function and the output function. Correspondingly, the small-signal data that are of the most importance with respect to the input characteristics are the input function, and possibly the reverse transfer function. The reverse transfer function is rather inconvenient to measure directly, and in fact it is usually measured indirectly. It is usually determined from values of the parameters y_o and $1/z_o$ (or h_o), the first being the output admittance with the input short-circuited to signal currents, and the second the output admittance with the input open-circuited to signal currents. The value of y_r then is given by the equation

$$y_r = y_{i'}(y_o - h_o)/y_{f'}, \quad \text{or} \quad h_r = h_i(h_o - y_o)/h_f \tag{2}$$

The value of y_r or h_r may be calculated directly from this equation on the rare occasions that it is required. The contour of constant value for h_o

[2] R. D. Middlebrook, "A New Junction-Transistor High-Frequency Equivalent Circuit," *IRE Trans. PGCT*, Conv. Rec., 1957.

may be plotted on the input family instead of that for y_r. This substitution will be shown to yield a complete set in the next section. Equation 2 may be modified to yield any of the other reverse transfer parameters as required.

2.5 Basic Small-Signal Relations

A considerable variety of different sets of small-signal parameters has been used in the representation of the active behavior of transistors. A similar situation existed to some extent with tubes in the early days, but standardization of parameters was simplified by the fact that the input function and the reverse transfer function both are of relatively little importance with tubes. Since this is not the case with junction transistors and many related devices, it is necessary with them to consider a more complete representation. The purpose of this section is to evaluate the various groups of parameters that have had a reasonable amount of usage, and to determine from the evaluation which set appears to be potentially the most useful for circuit design. In making this determination consideration must be given to factors such as ease and accuracy of measurement, the optimum measurement configuration, the group that will give the simplest and most direct design procedure consistent with easy extension to high-frequency operation, the relation between the configuration and the physical theory of operation, and the determination of the set that can simplify insofar as possible the problem of design of reliable circuits. As will be evident directly, this analysis leads more toward an admittance (or conductance) type of representation than toward any of the others. The reason the hybrid, or H, parameters have proven satisfactory in many applications is that in many respects they are closely related to the admittance parameters. As noted by Armstrong, their deficiencies as high-frequency parameters are largely a result of deviations from a pure admittance form.[3]

Basically, the easiest approach to the representation of a network device is based on the examination of the various forms of its equivalent network representations to find a configuration that conforms relatively well with the physical behavior of the device and at the same time gives a realizable equivalent network for use with a set of small-signal parameters amenable to direct and reasonably accurate measurement. Once the basic arrangement has been selected, then the modifications required to realize the maximum usefulness of the selected parameters may be made, including the modifications required to correct for such unideal properties as base-spreading resistance.

[3] H. L. Armstrong, "On the Usefulness of Transconductance as a Transistor Parameter," *Proc. IRE*, Vol. 47, No. 1, January, 1959, p. 83.

Network representation of an active device, commonly based on the so-called black box*, is based on one of the following sets of equations (Fig. 2–10)

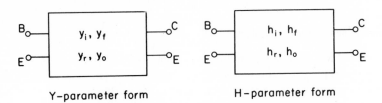

Y–parameter form　　　　　　H–parameter form

Fig. 2-10. Transistor black-box representation

$$i_i = y_i v_i + y_r v_o$$
$$i_o = y_f v_i + y_o v_o \tag{3}$$

$$i_i = g_i v_i + g_r v_o$$
$$i_o = g_f v_i + g_o v_o \tag{4}$$

for the admittance and conductance form of the equations respectively. (The long-standing use of g as the symbol for conductance in electrical engineering dictates the form of Eq. 4. The use of g as the symbol for the inverse H parameters for this reason is not adopted in this book. It has received little acceptance in IRE standards and is used relatively little.) The hybrid form of the equations is

$$v_i = h_i i_i + h_r v_o$$
$$i_o = h_f i_i + h_o v_o \tag{5}$$

Another set sometimes used is the impedance set

$$v_i = z_i i_i + z_r i_o$$
$$v_o = z_f i_i + z_o i_o \tag{6}$$

The remaining two sets, commonly used with cascaded networks, are seldom used with transistors. They are often used with lattice networks.

---

* The name "black box" is used to signify that the type or configuration of components within a specified closed black line or "box" need not be known exactly to specify the external current-voltage relations at each of the ports. This independence of internal configuration may not be valid except at a fixed frequency if the magnitudes of the capacitance and inductance components are to be independent of frequency. A symmetrical set of current and voltage equations is used in conjunction with terminal and transfer immittances. One of the chief assets of the three-terminal, two-port, black-box configuration is the ease with which it can be modified to take account of changes of the external circuit configuration. Such a change is the change of the common terminal.

There are a number of sets of parameters that do not fit closely in the black-box pattern, the most important being those originally introduced with the point-contact transistor, a special set of resistance parameters. These parameters proved quite satisfactory with point-contact transistors, and also are reasonably satisfactory for low-frequency circuits using junction transistors, but their values are difficult to measure directly. The value of the mutual resistance, r_m, is particularly difficult to measure because there is no way of making it directly accessible at the terminals of the device. In addition, the value of r_c is difficult to measure because of its very high value, typically many megohms.

The H Parameters. The H parameters include one impedance parameter, one admittance parameter, and two dimensionless parameters that may be determined in terms of the ratio of two admittances or two impedances as desired. The termination conditions for each of the four H parameters, and also the termination conditions for the other black-box parameters are tabulated in Table II.

TABLE II

| Parameter | Termination | | Parameter | Termination | |
	Input	Output		Input	Output
h_i	Z large	$Z = 0$	y_i	Z large	$Z = 0$
h_o	$Z = \infty$	Z large	y_o	$Z = 0$	Z large
h_f	Z large	$Z = 0$	y_f	Z small	$Z = 0$
h_r	$Z = \infty$	$Z = 0$	y_r	$Z = 0$	Z small
			y_c	$Z = \infty$	Z large
z_i	Z large	$Z = \infty$	z_f	$Z = \infty$	$Z = \infty$
z_o	$Z = \infty$	Z large	z_r	$Z = \infty$	$Z = \infty$

In this table, a notation of infinite impedance indicates that the terminating impedance should be a minimum of ten to 100 times the nominal impedance level at the specified port, and zero that it should be well less than a tenth the nominal impedance at the port, and less than a hundredth if possible. The values marked large and small should be selected to make possible good bridge balance relations. For that reason, they cannot be specified more closely.

An examination of Eq. 5 shows that h_i is a small-signal impedance, h_o is a small-signal admittance, and the ratios, h_f and h_r are current and voltage ratios, respectively. Now, the use of an impedance for h_i is inconsistent with the nature of the transistor because when base-spreading resistance is neglected the input immittance can be shown to be characterized by a parallel resistance-capacitance combination.[4,5] Such a parallel

[4] *Transistor Electronics*, by A. W. Lo, R. O. Endres, F. D. Waldhauer, and C. C. Cheng. Prentice-Hall, Inc., Englewood Cliffs, N. J., 1955.

[5] *An Introduction to Junction Transistor Theory*, by R. D. Middlebrook. John Wiley & Sons, Inc., New York, 1957.

combination is more conveniently represented by an admittance of the form $g_i + jb_i = g_i + j\omega C_i$ than it is in the form

$$(r_i - j\omega C_i r_i^2)/(1 + \omega^2 C_i^2 r_i^2)$$

where $r_i/(1 + \omega^2 C_i^2 r_i^2)$ is the resistive component of h_i in terms of the capacitance of the transistor and its shunt resistance, and the equivalent series capacitance is

$$C_i(1 + 1/\omega^2 C_i^2 r_i^2)$$

Naturally, both of these expressions represent the same immittance, but both components of h_i are strongly dependent on frequency, whereas in the admittance form only the conductance g_i is dependent on frequency. This dependence corresponds in general behavior to the transit time conductance in tubes, rising linearly with frequency, from a frequency in the neighborhood of $\sqrt{f_\alpha f_\beta}$, which in a later paragraph is defined as the noise corner frequency, f_{n2}.[6]

The output admittance term for the set of H parameters is represented by a combination of a parallel capacitance and resistance. Strictly, the capacitance from the collector is divided between the base and the emitter in a transistor, with the larger component normally being to the base. These two capacitances are paralleled in the output admittance function, but they divide, one being part of the feedback immittance with the H parameters. No difficulties are encountered in the use of the h_o parameter with transistors.

The forward transfer ratio for the H parameters measures the current gain of the transistor, and is a useful number in its own right. It has considerable similarity to the mu(μ), or amplification factor for tubes, in that it is relatively constant over the full operating range of the transistor. It does decrease in value slowly as the total current through the transistor increases, because the voltage gradients in the base region reduce the active region of the device quite rapidly as the total current is increased.

The forward transfer ratio is commonly known by a number of different names, including the beta (β) in the common-emitter configuration, and the alpha (α) in the common-base configuration. It is also known by the symbols, h_f or h_{fe} and h_{fb}, for common-emitter and common-base configurations, respectively. The value of h_f or β is usually included in the tabulated data for any transistor.

The reverse transfer ratio, or reverse voltage gain, varies in value as a function of operating conditions, and is rather inconvenient to measure. Its value is small compared to the values of h_i and h_f, but not necessarily

[6] D. Regis, G. T. Lake, "Derivation of an HF Equivalent Circuit for the Drift Transistor Using Y Parameter Measurements," *Defense Research Telecommunications Establishment Report DRTE*, No. 1034, 1960.

with respect to h_o. It is for that reason difficult to handle when transformations of configuration are being made in H parameters. The use of parameters and a configuration that render the reverse transfer immittance negligible compared to the remaining three immittances can significantly simplify transistor circuit design.

The Tee Parameters. The tee parameter configuration may be established in either one of two different forms, the one using a current generator, and one using a mutual resistance, r_m. The former is used with point-contact transistors, the latter with junction transistors. The current-generator form has also found use in the analysis of high-frequency circuits for junction transistors. Because of the difficulties encountered in measuring the magnitudes of the resistance values for the tee parameters, in particular r_m, r_c, and r_d, they are more commonly used as an aid to circuit analysis than in design. A modified form containing both resistance and conductance terms may also be used in this way. Figure 2–11 shows the commonest form of equivalent network. Since this arrangement does

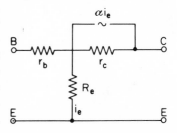

Fig. 2-11. Tee equivalent for a transistor

not have the properties of a black-box representation, the conversion from one common electrode to another offers difficulties in addition to the measurement problems.

The Z Parameters. The impedance equations express the circuit relations for one form of black-box representation in which all the parameters are dimensionally the same. These parameters have been used to some extent in the design of low-frequency circuits, and they do fall within the group that can be measured directly with a comparatively simple bridge. Since the representation of an impedance, $Z = R + jX$ takes the form of a series combination of resistance and reactance, and transistor immittances tend to behave as parallel combinations, this set of parameters is of limited usefulness.

The Pi Parameters. The pi parameters, sometimes called the Giacoletto parameters, have been developed to represent the physical characteristics observed in junction transistors. As a consequence, they provide a good delineation of the characteristics of the devices. They are made up of a set of conductance and susceptance elements in conjunction with a resistance, the base-spreading resistance, and they are in many ways interchangeable with the admittance parameters discussed in the next section. As shown in Fig. 2–12, the transistor is represented by a set of admittances arranged in a typical pi configuration.

The pi parameters are based on admittances for the common-emitter configuration, and are somewhat more complex to convert to other configurations than are black-box arrangements. They can be modified into a current-generator form, or they can be used with the current generator replaced by a forward conductance. They make an excellent basis for representation in the analysis of high-frequency circuits.

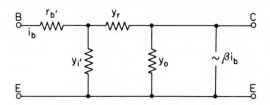

Fig. 2-12. Pi equivalent for a transistor

The individual parameters include, in addition to the base-spreading resistance, the input admittance, the forward admittance, which is the equivalent of the transconductance in a tube, the output admittance, which is equivalent to the plate conductance, and a feedback admittance. The value of the forward admittance is roughly proportional to the emitter current in the device, and consequently is also proportional to collector current to a reasonable approximation. The input admittance has a value that is likely to differ widely from one device to the other, rather than having a value which is nearly the same from device to device as with the forward admittance. Because of this difference in behavior, the separate data given for the two admittances simplifies circuit design.

The output and the feedback admittances also have relatively wide ranges of variation. In addition to the variation from device to device, the value of the output admittance has an apparently rapid variation with frequency. Actually, this latter variation is a result of feedback action. If either $r_{b'}$ or the feedback admittance is zero, then the output admittance is rather well-behaved as a function of frequency.

The Y or G parameters. The Y parameters, which at low frequency reduce to the G parameters, have many points in common with the pi parameters just discussed, and they have points in common with the hybrid parameters as well. Like the impedance parameters, the basic Y parameter set is homogeneous in that all four are admittances. And, like the output parameter of the hybrid group and the input and output parameters of the pi group, both the input and the output parameters of this group are represented by a parallel combination of conductance and susceptance.

The admittance parameters are defined by the equations

$$i_i = y_i v_i + y_r v_o$$
$$i_o = y_f v_i + y_o v_o \tag{3}$$

$$i_i = g_i v_i + g_r v_o$$
$$i_o = g_f v_i + g_o v_o \tag{4}$$

For the present discussion, the susceptance components are neglected, and Eq. 4 used instead of Eq. 3. The basic form of the equations shows that the parameters may be determined by voltage and current measurements at the terminals. Because the currents in any transistor are determined by the relation given in Eq. 1

$$i_b + i_e + i_c = 0 \tag{1}$$

it is evident that if in Equations 3 and 4 i_i is taken to be i_b and i_o as i_c, Eq. (4) may be converted to the form that gives the relations in terms of the emitter current as input and the collector as output by a simple addition

$$i_i + i_o = i_b + i_c = (g_i + g_f)v_i + (g_r + g_o)v_o = -i_e$$
$$i_o \qquad\qquad = g_f v_i \qquad + g_o v_o \qquad = i_c \tag{7}$$

Since $v_i = v_b = -v_{eb}$, and the emitter current has a negative sign in the first of the equations, and since the output voltage must be replaced by $(v_c - v_e)$, the equations take the form

$$i_e = (g_i + g_f)v_e - (g_r + g_o)(v_c - v_e)$$
$$= \sigma(g)v_e - (g_r + g_o)v_c \tag{8}$$
$$i_c = -(g_f + g_o)v_c + g_o v_c$$

where $\sigma(g) = g_i + g_f + g_r + g_o$. In a similar manner, the equations may be rewritten in terms of the base and the emitter currents

$$i_b = g_i v_b \qquad\qquad + g_r v_c$$
$$i_e = (g_i + g_f)v_b + (g_r + g_o)v_c \tag{9}$$

From these equations, making a substitution to get v_c in terms of v_e, the modified form becomes

$$i_b = g_i v_b \qquad\qquad + (g_i + g_r)v_e$$
$$i_e = (g_i + g_f)v_b + \sigma(g)v_e \tag{9a}$$

The following substitution table may be prepared showing the substitutions required to convert the common-emitter equations into the correct form for the common-base or the common-collector configurations.

TABLE III

Parameter Configuration Conversions

Parameter	C-Emitter	C-Base	C-Collector
Input	y_i	$\sigma(y)$	y_i
Forward	y_f	$-(y_f + y_o)$	$-(y_i + y_f)$
Reverse	y_r	$-(y_r + y_o)$	$-(y_i + y_r)$
Output	y_o	y_o	$\sigma(y)$
Mod. output	y_c	$y_i y_c / \sigma(y)$	y_c
Δ factor	$y_i y_o - y_f y_r$	$y_i y_o - y_f y_r$	$y_i y_o - y_f y_r$

For each configuration, the delta factor takes the same form for admittance and for impedance parameters. The sigma factor is the sum of the admittances

$$\sigma(y) = y_i + y_f + y_r + y_o$$

The delta factor is clearly independent of configuration because it has the same value for each arrangement. The modified output parameters, which are components of the delta factor, are included for completeness in this table, and are discussed in detail in the next section.

The parameter conversions for the hybrid parameters are again based on the current node equation, Eq. 1, in terms of the basic equations for the H parameter configuration

$$\begin{aligned} v_i &= h_i i_i + h_r v_o \\ i_o &= h_f i_i + h_o v_o \end{aligned} \tag{5}$$

These equations must first be solved for the appropriate value of i_i, or i_b, and i_o, or i_c before they may be used in conjunction with Eq. 10 in a configuration change. When this is done, the equations take the form

$$\begin{aligned} i_i &= v_i/h_i - (h_r/h_i)v_o \\ i_o &= (h_f/h_i)v_i + (h_o - h_f h_r/h_i)v_o \end{aligned} \tag{5'}$$

In this form, the currents can be combined as desired to provide the correct values of currents for the common-base and the common-collector configurations if the original equations represent the device in the common-emitter arrangement. As is readily evident, the equations for the hybrid parameters do not lend themselves readily to this type of transformation, but give rather complicated coefficients. The corresponding transformation is simple and direct with admittance parameters, and the modified Eq. (5') actually are the basic equations for the admittance relations, but in terms of the hybrid coefficients.

Factors that affect the selection of the parameters for use with an active device include the ease of measurement of the important characteris-

tics, the precision with which they can and must be measured, the reliability with which they can be measured, and the configuration in which
they can best be measured.   In the paper by Follingstad[7] the conclusion is
drawn that the hybrid parameters show somewhat better reliability than
the admittance parameter data, and that they are better than the impedance
parameters. A re-examination based on the optimum circuit configuration
for the determination of the minimum set of device parameters in a form
that is independent of the circuit configuration permits the development
of a somewhat different order for the utility of the hybrid and admittance
parameters. If the optimum set is taken as y_i, y_f, y_o, and either y_c or h_o
(they are the same), it develops that this set in the common-emitter configuration can be measured with a precision well within the required
tolerances.

Ideally, the admittance parameter set that can be shown to be most
convenient to use includes the input, the output, the forward admittance,
and the admittance delta factor. The operating equations derived in the
fourth and later chapters use these four parameters to the almost complete
exclusion of the reverse admittance. Because of the fact it is almost
impossible to measure the delta factor directly, however, the use of a
modified set of admittance parameters, which minimizes the calculation
required to determine the delta factor, is indicated. Such a set is discussed next.

·*The modified Y parameters.*   This set of admittance parameters can
satisfy both the problems of measurement accuracy and also those of
design simplification, giving the advantages of both the hybrid and the
admittance parameters. At the same time they relax the precision required on measurement of parameters considerably compared to either
the *H* or the normal *Y* parameters because of the elimination of the differencing of a product that may be required in the calculation of the value of
the delta factor.

The first three parameters of this set, y_i, y_f, and y_o, are identical with
the corresponding parameters of the regular admittance set, and the
fourth is identical with the output admittance in the hybrid system, h_o.
As a matter of convenience and to keep a consistent pattern of notation,
this parameter is identified by the new symbol y_c. This parameter always
appears in conjunction with the input admittance in the form $(y_i y_c)$, and
this product has already been shown to be the invariant known as the
delta factor. An examination of the corresponding relations for the hybrid
parameters shows (Table VI) that no such convenient interrelations
exist among the hybrid parameters.

[7] H. G. Follingstad, "An Analytical Study of *z*, *y*, and *h* Parameter Accuracies in
Transistor Sweep Measurements," *IRE Trans. PGED*, Convention Record, 1954,
p. 104.

The principal forms of terms in which the parameter y_r appears are the delta factor and the sigma factor

$$\Delta(y) = y_i y_o - y_f y_r \tag{10}$$

$$\sigma(y) = y_i + y_f + y_r + y_o \tag{11}$$

In Eq. 11, the term y_r and usually the term y_o may be neglected compared to the remaining terms because of the relations of their values in the common-emitter configuration

$$y_f > y_i \gg y_o > y_r \tag{12}$$

Consequently, the use of $\Delta(y)$ and $\sigma(y)$ can simplify many calculation problems in design of transistor circuits.

The discussion to this point has neglected the presence of the base-spreading resistance in practical transistors. At low frequencies, appreciably below the beta-cutoff frequency, such a procedure is convenient and useful. Strictly, however, it is necessary to take the admittance parameters as the values for an intrinsic ideal transistor and to extract the base-spreading resistance as a separate entity in higher-frequency applications. The effect of this change is considered in the next few paragraphs.

2.6 Complete Small-Signal Relations

The complete representation of a typical transistor in terms of small-signal parameters requires the inclusion of the base-spreading resistance, and it requires the correction of the internal admittance parameters to compensate for the effect of this resistance, Fig. 2–13. Since the input admittance

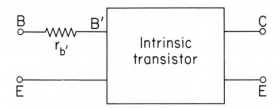

Fig. 2-13. Effect of base-spreading resistance

of the transistor is finite rather than zero, a loss of input voltage occurs across this resistance and the input admittance also is altered by it. The net input admittance for a transistor having base-spreading resistance is given by the equation

$$y_i = 1/(r_{b'} + 1/y_{i'}) = y_{i'}/(1 + y_{i'} r_{b'}) \tag{13}$$

where the primes indicate the internal values of the admittances. This equation may also be solved for the internal admittance in terms of the terminal value

$$y_{i'} = y_i/(1 - y_i r_{b'})$$ (13a)

The differencing in the denominator of this equation shows that difficulties may be anticipated in the determination of accurate values of $y_{i'}$ under high-current conditions.

In a similar manner, the portion of the input voltage that is effective in producing an output current change is that which is applied across $y_{i'}$. Its value may be found to be determined by the equation

$$v_{b'}/v_b = 1/(1 + y_{i'} r_{b'})$$ (14)

Then the effective terminal transconductance or transadmittance is given by the equation

$$y_f = y_{f'}/(1 + y_{i'} r_{b'})$$ (15)

or

$$y_{f'} = y_f/(1 - y_i r_{b'})$$ (15a)

Fortunately, the value of $r_{b'}$ is relatively constant, so that the correction of the measured values of g_i and g_f to the internal values is relatively simple.

2.7 Considerations Affecting Parameter Selections

In the above paragraphs, the parameters that can be used for representation of the small-signal behavior of transistors have been considered, and their properties in design briefly discussed. In this section, the relations of the parameters to the physics of junction transistors and factors affecting their measurement are analyzed in more detail.

Many writers have pointed out that there is no particular need for the set of small-signal parameters used to have any significance to the physics of the device. If, however, a set can be selected that can both represent the device physically and at the same time provide useful data more convenient to use for circuit design, then many advantages in the ease of use result. Ease of measurement is likewise of great importance, because the design data must be readily obtainable.

Reference to the derivations of the characteristics of transistors in terms of junction geometry shows that the input and output relations in a transistor are determined in terms of admittance relationships, with the input circuit being the emitter, and the output the collector.[8,9] The equations for the emitter current and the collector current in particular are expressed in terms of changes of barrier potential with respect to the Fermi

[8,9] See references 4, 5, this chapter.

potential. The general equations for base and collector currents, as given by Lo and Endres, are as follows (Lo, 7–1)

$$I_B = \sigma(G) - [e^{(\Lambda V_B - I_{Br b'})}[(G_{11} + G_{21})/\Lambda]]$$
$$- [e^{(V_C + I_{Br b'})}[(G_{12} + G_{22})/\Lambda]] \tag{16}$$

$$I_C = -[(G_{21} + G_{22})/\Lambda] + e^{I_{Br b'}} \frac{[G_{21} e^{\Lambda V} E + G_{22} e^{\Lambda V} C]}{\Lambda} \tag{17}$$

where the $\sigma(G)$ has the value $\sigma(G) = G_{11} + G_{12} + G_{21} + G_{22}$ and the values of the G's are defined by the equations (Lo, 8–26)

$$G_{11} = b\sigma_i^2 [\coth W/L_p + \sigma_n L_p/\sigma_p L_n]/[(1 + b)^2 \sigma_n L_p] \tag{18}$$

$$G_{21} = -b\sigma_i^2 [\operatorname{cosech} W/L_p]/[(1 + b)^2 \sigma_n L_p] \tag{19}$$

$$G_{12} = -b\sigma_i^2 [\operatorname{cosech} W/L_p]/[(1 + b)^2 \sigma_n L_p] \tag{20}$$

$$G_{22} = b\sigma_i^2 [\coth W/L_p + \sigma_n L_p/\sigma_{p'} L_{n'}]/[(1 + b)^2 \sigma_n L_p] \tag{21}$$

and the symbol definitions are

W = base width
L_p = hole diffusion length
σ_n = n-type conductivity
σ_p = p-type conductivity
σ_i = intrinsic conductivity
L_n = electron diffusion length
$\sigma_{p'}$ = collector p-type conductivity
$L_{n'}$ = collector electron diffusion length
b = ratio of mobilities of electrons and holes $\doteq 2.1$
    for germanium, and
Λ = (q/kT)

These equations as they stand apply to a PNP transistor. To obtain the corresponding equations for an NPN unit, it is necessary to interchange the p and n subscripts throughout, and to invert b to give the ratio of the mobilities of the holes and electrons.

It is important to note that these equations take the form of nonlinear admittances throughout, in that they reduce on expansion of the exponentials to an expansion of either base or collector current in terms of first and higher powers of the applied voltages, V_B and V_C. Consequently, it would appear that the devices behave as nonlinear admittances. Additional corroborating information can be noted in the fact that the irregularities in the diffusion of carriers through the base region introduces an effective capacitance, the diffusion capacitance, in parallel with the input conductance, and a similar capacitance whose magnitude is dependent on voltage is introduced by the boundary charge fields for the device.

The diffusion capacitance is a function of the emitter and base currents because it measures the irregularity or granularity of the current flow through the base region. The ratio of the conductance to the capacitance at the input of a transistor is expressed in terms of the lifetime of the minority carriers in the base region (Lo, Eq. 8–46)

$$g_{Dp}/C_{Dp} = 1/\tau_p \qquad (22)$$

where τ_p is the lifetime. The magnitudes of both the capacitance and the conductance are proportional to the square of the ratio of the base width to the mean-free-path, $(W/L_p)^2$ or $(W/L_n)^2$, depending on whether the transistor is a PNP unit or an NPN unit respectively. If the capacitance depended only on the first power of the ratio, then the diffusion time of the particle across the base would be the prime factor controlling the capacitance. Because it depends on the square of the ratio, however, one can deduce that an additional factor dependent on the uniformity of flow must be considered. The second (W/L) factor, for small values of the ratio, is an approximation to the expansion of the decay exponential, $(1 - \exp(-W/L))$.

The transition capacitances in transistors develop as a result of the stresses across the junctions themselves. The emitter transition capacitance, across the forward-biased base-emitter junction, is large because of the small forward voltage applied to the junction, whereas the collector capacitance is quite small because of the relatively large reverse bias across the collector junction. This capacitance may be represented by the equation (Lo, 7–2)

$$C_T = A V^{-n} \qquad (23)$$

where A is an arbitrary constant dependent on the semiconductor material and its processing, and the exponent n is typically 0.5 or 0.333, depending on the distribution of the impurity atoms in the neighborhood of the emitter or the collector junction.

The conductivity of the base region as determined externally depends on the square of the ratio of the base width to the mean-free-path, just as does the diffusion capacitance. As with the capacitance, if recombination irregularities did not contribute to the current, and to the conductivity, this factor would depend strictly on the volume of the active base region. Because the ratio is squared, however, the recombination irregularities are a prime cause of the base current. The same exponential relation given in terms of its first-term expansion applies

$$(W/L) = [1 - \exp(-W/L)] \qquad (24)$$

In addition to this internal conductance in the base region of a transistor, a finite amount of resistance must of necessity be present between the active region of the base and the base-lead connection. This resistance, known commonly as the base-spreading resistance, would be small except for the fact that the base material must have a very small value of conductivity if the magnitude of the input conductance is to be kept small. If the base conductivity is large, then the recombination of minority carriers takes place more rapidly, and a considerable portion of the emitter current may flow out the base lead instead of flowing on to the collector. The resulting short lifetime of the carriers makes transistor action possible only in devices having extremely thin base layers.

The electrical properties of the transistor, which must be represented by the data and the representing equivalent circuit, can be tabulated in terms of the following parameter relations:

1. A forward admittance, which at low frequencies is approximately proportional to emitter current

$$g_f \doteq 35 \times I_e \text{ (in ma) millimhos} \qquad (25)$$

2. An input admittance roughly proportional to base current for currents, such that $r_{b'} < 1/g_{i'}$.

3. Transition capacitances, which are a function of junction voltages.

4. A diffusion capacitance that is proportional to the emitter current.

5. Output admittances g_o and g_c, which are functions of both collector voltage and collector current.

6. A base-spreading resistance, which is relatively constant but not completely so.

Measurement Considerations: Follingstad has made an extremely thorough analysis of the measurement of transistor parameters, and has determined the accuracy limitations that apply to them.[10] These results show that the best accuracy in measurements can in general be obtained using certain hybrid parameters and using some admittance parameters in the common-emitter configuration. On the basis of this, Follingstad has concluded that the hybrid parameters, because a greater variety of them are amenable to acceptable measurement, are better.

Further examination of Follingstad's data, however, show that in the common-emitter configuration, some of the admittance parameters may be measured with somewhat greater accuracy and reliability than the hybrids, and others with roughly equal accuracy. Because the years of experience in the use of transistor devices since Follingstad's paper have shown that the common-emitter configuration permits the measurement

[10] See reference 7.

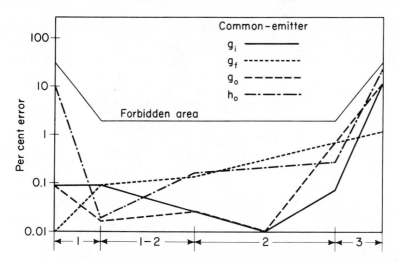

Fig. 2-14. Parameters with satisfactory tolerances

of device parameters with a minimum of dependence on circuit parameters, a re-examination of the conclusions drawn appears desirable.

The desirability of the use of admittance parameters is supported by both practical and theoretical considerations. Among the practical considerations is the availability of high-frequency measuring devices for measuring the values of the given set of parameters. A number of organizations, among them General Radio and Wayne-Kerr, for example, have developed bridges designed for admittance measurements on high-frequency devices, both passive and active. The reason that admittance measure-

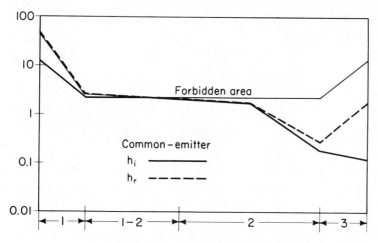

Fig. 2-15. Unsatisfactory parameters

ments were selected is readily discernible from some of Follingstad's curves, because he shows that both h_{11} and h_{12} are marginal for low values of base current, whereas both y_i and y_r can be measured with adequate

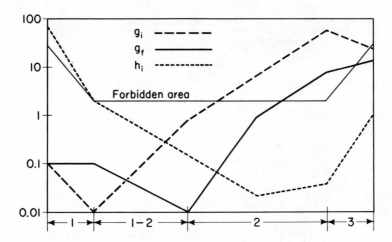

Fig. 2-16. Tolerances with common-base configuration

accuracy. The data in Table IV are condensed from the curves, and a replot from his curves in Figures 2–14, 2–15, and 2–16.

TABLE IV

Expected Accuracies of Parameter Measurements

Parameter	Region	H–CB	H–CE	Y–CB	Y–CE
Input	1	3	3	1	1
	1–2	2	3	1–2	1
	2	1	2–3	2–3	1
	3	1–2	1	3	2–3
Forward	1	3	2–3	1	1
	1–2	1	1	1	1
	2	1	1	1–3	1
	3	2	2–3	3	1–3
Reverse	1	3	3	1	1
	1–2	2	3	2	1
	2	1	3	3	1
	3	1	2	3	1–3
Output	1	1	2–3	1	1
	1–2	1	1	1	1
	2	1	1	1–2	1
	3	2–3	2–3	3	2

In this table, region 1 is the current-cutoff region, 1–2 the weak-conduction region adjacent to region 1, region 2 is the strong conduction region, and 3 the low-beta saturation region, and the classifications of accuracy are:

1. error less than 0.5 percent,
2. error between 0.5 and 2.0 percent,
3. error greater than 2.0 percent.

Clearly, in all regions except region 3, the accuracy of all of the Y data are excellent (common-emitter configuration). The accuracy of the h_o data are generally adequate, particularly grounded base, but the rest of the h parameter data are rather spotty, good here and bad there.

The basic data given by Follingstad have been replotted in Figures 2–14, 2–15, and 2–16 to show in more detail the comparative accuracies available for the common-base and common-emitter configurations. Figure 2–14 shows the data for g_i, g_f, g_o, and h_o, CE, and Figures 2–15 and 2–16 show the accuracy curves for h_i, h_f, and h_r in the common-emitter configuration, and all of the parameters in the common-base configuration. Because the curves are for sweep measurements, bridge methods can give a further improvement of accuracy.

The adequacy of the set of parameters selected for representing transistors must be measured against the tolerance requirements in their use in design, and their stability with time and from device to device. The most important design parameter should if possible be one of great stability so that the design may be oriented for reliability by keeping dissipations conservative and by allowing ample margins for the less-important parameters. The use of y_f and y_i provides just such a separation. The value of y_i is relatively smaller and less stable than the value of y_f, which is the parameter that controls the output current, the two being the most important parameters in design of most transistor circuits.

2.8 Frequency Parameters

The frequency parameters f_α, f_β, f_{n1}, f_{n2}, and f_T, f_{max} are all used on occasion in the description of the response properties of transistor amplifiers. The first two represent corner frequencies at which the amplification of the amplifier changes from one frequency relation to another, and the third and fourth represent corner frequencies at which changes in the noise characteristics occur. The fifth frequency is more convenient to use than the first in calculations involving frequency characteristics of amplifiers because the reduction of the frequency to half increases the gain by six decibels. The f_{max} is important in that it is the maximum frequency at which unity gain can be developed. It is the maximum oscillation frequency.

Three of these frequencies are closely related to one another. The relations are

$$f_\beta = (1 - \alpha)f_\alpha, \qquad f_\alpha = (\beta + 1)f_\beta$$
$$f_{n2} = \sqrt{f_\alpha f_\beta} = f_\alpha\sqrt{(1 - \alpha)} = f_\alpha/\sqrt{(\beta + 1)} \qquad (26)$$
$$f_{n2} = f_\beta\sqrt{(\beta + 1)} = f_\beta/\sqrt{(1 - \alpha)}$$

Since at least one of the three frequencies is normally known for any transistor, and either the alpha or beta also is known, all three frequencies are easily determined.

The importance of f_β originally was considerably overrated in the literature on transistors, because design of the input circuit to allow for input capacitance, a common practice with tube amplifiers, accounts not only for the beta frequency but also for base-spreading resistance and the source impedance of the driver circuit. For this reason it is seldom given, and the value of f_α is given in its stead. Because the corner frequency for the noise spectrum is considerably more difficult to measure directly, it is doubtful if the user can hope to have the value of f_{n2} replace f_α as the principal corner frequency given on data sheets, and as a consequence, the above relations are of considerable importance to designers.

The frequency at which the effective beta is unity is also related to the alpha- and beta-cutoff frequencies and, with transistors having a high value of beta, is almost equal to the alpha-cutoff frequency. This frequency is equal to the gain-bandwidth product for the device. It can be converted into the other frequencies through the equations[11]

$$f_\beta = [f_T]/\beta \qquad\qquad f_T = \beta f_\beta$$
$$f_\alpha = (\beta + 1)f_T/\beta \qquad f_T = \beta f_\alpha/(\beta + 1) \qquad (27)$$
$$f_T = \alpha f_\alpha$$

Because for large values of beta $\beta/(\beta + 1)$ is almost unity, a distinction between f_α and f_T need be drawn only for devices having values of beta less than approximately twenty-five.

The maximum oscillating frequency, $f_{\max}$, is really an over-all figure of merit for the transistor in that it takes into account the value of f_α and also the capacitances and the base-spreading resistance for the device. Its value is given by the equation[12]

$$f_{\max} = \sqrt{\alpha f_\alpha/8\pi r_{b'}C_c} = \sqrt{f_T/8\pi r_{b'}C_c} = \frac{1}{4\pi}\sqrt{\frac{g_{f'}}{r_{b'}C_iC_c}} \qquad (28)$$

The importance of the frequency for unity gain is shown by this equation.

[11] In practice, the value of f_T is considerably less than f_α. The principal cause is transmission delay time, resulting from diffusion through the base region, and another cause may be $r_{c'}$ and C_{cb}. The gain across $r_{c'}$ applies a feedback voltage to C_{cb} and causes the magnitude of h_{fe} to drop to unity at a lower frequency.

[12] P. R. Drouillet, Jr., "Predictions Based on the Maximum Oscillator Frequency of a Transistor," *IRE Trans. PGCT*, June, 1955, p. 178.

Other parameters and variables are important in the design of transistor circuits. However, because practical selections have been made for them that are completely adequate technically, only a brief enumeration is required. One of the most important remaining variables is the breakdown, or avalanche voltage for the collector junction. The minimum value of this voltage permitted in transistors conforming with specifications is needed by the designer to design his circuit to comply with the limitation.

The permissible dissipation limit on a transistor is also important to the user. Device manufacturers normally provide data on this limit, but the value may not always be consistent with good usage, particularly when maximum reliability is important. A method of checking the conservatism of this rating is described in the next chapter.

2.9 Power Relations

The power gain in the transistor amplifier is a function of the operating configuration, and depends on the values of the input and output impedance. The configuration that gives the maximum power gain is the one in which the device shows a minimum dependence on the circuit properties. The equations tabulated below show that this condition is obtained with the common-emitter configuration. This is an additional reason for the use of the small-signal parameter values on the common-emitter basis. The power gain for a transistor amplifier in the common-emitter configuration is given by the equation

$$| K_v K_i | = y_f^2 R_L / [1 + y_i R_s + y_o R_L + y_i y_c R_s R_L][y_i(1 + y_c R_L)]$$
$$= y_f^2 R_L / [1 + y_o R_L + y_i R_s(1 + y_c R_L)][y_i(1 + y_c R_L)] \quad (29)$$

The corresponding equation for the common-base amplifier is

$$| K_v K_i | = (y_f + \ddot{y}_o)^2 R_L / [1 + \sigma(y)R_s + y_o R_L + y_i y_c R_s R_L]$$
$$[\sigma(y) + y_i y_c R_L] \quad (30)$$

In the common-collector configuration, the equation is

$$| K_v K_i | = (y_i + y_f)^2 R_e / [1 + y_i R_s + \sigma(y)R_e + y_i y_c R_s R_e]$$
$$[y_i(1 + y_c R_e)] \quad (31)$$

The numerators for each of these equations are very nearly equal if $R_e = R_L$. For this reason, the controlling factor in power gain is the effect of the $\sigma(y)$ term in the denominators of the common-base and common-collector equations. With the common-base equation, a small value of R_s reduces the denominator term to approximately the same size as the denominator for the common-emitter equation. A similar analysis shows that the common-emitter gain is larger than the maximum gain available with the common-collector configuration.

An important remaining problem of concern to the designer is the determination of the values of the parameters that have been found of importance in design when inadequate small-signal data are available. Even though the data available on transistors are often more effective than those on other active devices, they frequently prove inadequate when serious design work is contemplated. A method of making the required evaluation of the parameters in terms of orthogonal and Legendre polynomials is explained briefly in Appendix IV, and is used extensively in some of the later chapters of this book.

2.10 Relations and Conversions of Parameters

The conversion of small-signal data from one configuration to another is a relatively simple process on the admittance basis, but is somewhat more complicated in other configurations such as the hybrid arrangement. Because of the variety of data published by different manufacturers, it is convenient for the user to have conversion tables for transforming parameters in one system among the three configurations, and also to have substitution tables for converting from one set of parameters to another.

In each of the conversion tables, the reference configuration used in this volume is the grounded-emitter configuration, because the data provided usually are adaptable to it. Occasionally the data on transistors intended for use at very high frequencies are presented in the common-base form. They are almost never given under common-collector conditions. The common-base data may be converted to common-emitter data by equating the value of the parameter in terms of the common-emitter components to the given values and solving.

The exact forms of the conversion equations are given in these tables, the forms as derived from transformation of the basic black-box equations. These equations can be simplified in many cases, and then yield the forms that are normally used. This simplification in particular is required with the common-base hybrid parameters.

It is possible, within the limitations derived by Follingstad, to use combinations of configurations for the measurements if desired. For example, the input conductance or admittance may be measured in the common-emitter configuration, and the forward in terms of the input admittance in the common-base configuration. Similarly, the output admittance may be measured either in the common-base or the common-emitter configuration because the measurements are equivalent.

The following tables of equivalences, which have been adapted from a set published in Electronic Design[13], provide the reader with a fairly

[13] K. A. Pullen, Jr., "Transistor Parameters and Variables," *Electronic Design* July, 1958.

complete listing of the conversions among the more commonly used parameters, and are based on the common-emitter parameters. Table V, which has already been given in this chapter, is repeated here for completeness, since it is extremely useful.

TABLE V

Configuration Conversion for Y Parameters

Parameter	C-Emitter	C-Base	C-Collector
Input	y_i	$\sigma(y)$	y_i
Forward	y_f	$-(y_f + y_o)$	$-(y_i + y_f)$
Reverse	y_r	$-(y_r + y_o)$	$-(y_i + y_r)$
Output	y_o	y_o	$\sigma(y)$
Mod. output	y_c	$\dfrac{y_i y_c}{\sigma(y)}$	y_c
Δ factor	$y_i y_o - y_f y_r$	$y_i y_o - y_f y_r$	$y_i y_o - y_f y_r$

where $\sigma(y) = y_i + y_f + y_r + y_o$; $y_i y_c = \Delta(y) = y_i y_o - y_f y_r$

TABLE VI

Configuration Conversion for H Parameters

Parameter	C-Emitter	C-Base	C-Collector
Input	h_i	$\dfrac{h_i}{\gamma(h)}$	h_i
Forward	h_f	$-\dfrac{[h_f + \Delta(h)]}{\gamma(h)}$	$-(1 + h_f)$
Reverse	h_r	$\dfrac{[\Delta(h) - h_r]}{\gamma(h)}$	$(1 - h_r)$
Output	h_o	$\dfrac{h_o}{\gamma(h)}$	h_o
Δ factor	$\Delta(h)$	$\dfrac{\Delta(h)}{\gamma(h)}$	$\gamma(h)$

where $\gamma(h) = [1 + h_f - h_r + \Delta(h)]$; $\Delta(h) = h_i h_o - h_f h_r$

Note that the delta factor is not invariant in this case.

TABLE VII

Configuration Conversion for Z Parameters

Parameter	C-Emitter	C-Base	C-Collector
Input	z_i	z_i	$\sigma(z)$
Forward	z_f	$z_i - z_f$	$z_o - z_f$
Reverse	z_r	$z_i - z_r$	$z_o - z_r$
Output	z_o	$\sigma(z)$	z_o
Δ factor	$z_i z_o - z_f z_r$	$\Delta(z)$	$\Delta(z)$

where $\Delta(z) = z_i z_o - z_f z_r$; $\sigma(z) = z_i - z_f - z_r + z_o$

Again, the delta factor is invariant.

TABLE VIII

Conversion from Network to IRE Parameters

Hybrid	*Admittance*	*Impedance*	*Conductance*
$h_{11} = h_i$	$y_{11} = y_i$	$z_{11} = z_i$	$g_{11} = g_i$
$h_{21} = h_f$	$y_{21} = y_f$	$z_{21} = z_f$	$g_{21} = g_f$
$h_{12} = h_r$	$y_{12} = y_r$	$z_{12} = z_r$	$g_{12} = g_r$
$h_{22} = h_o$	$y_{22} = y_o$	$z_{22} = z_o$	$g_{22} = g_o$
	$y_c = h_o$		$g_c = h_o$

TABLE IX

Conversion Between Y and Z Parameters

Z to Y	Y to Z
$z_i = \dfrac{y_o}{y_i y_c}$	$y_i = \dfrac{z_o}{\Delta(z)}$
$z_f = \dfrac{-y_f}{y_i y_c}$	$y_f = \dfrac{-z_f}{\Delta(z)}$
$z_r = \dfrac{-y_r}{y_i y_c} = \dfrac{y_c - y_o}{y_f y_c}$	$y_r = \dfrac{-z_r}{\Delta(z)}$
$z_o = \dfrac{1}{y_c}$	$y_o = \dfrac{z_i}{\Delta(z)}$
$\Delta(z) = z_i z_o - z_f z_r$	$y_c = \dfrac{1}{z_o}$
	$\Delta(y) = y_i y_o - y_f y_r = y_i y_c$

TABLE X

Conversion Between H, Y, and Z Parameters

$$h_i = \frac{1}{y_i} = \frac{\Delta(z)}{z_o} \qquad\qquad h_r = \frac{y_c - y_o}{y_f} = \frac{z_r}{z_o}$$

$$h_f = \frac{y_f}{y_i} = -\frac{z_f}{z_o} \qquad\qquad h_o = y_c = \frac{1}{z_o}$$

TABLE XI

Conversion Between H, Y, and Tee Parameters

$$r_d = \frac{1}{y_c} = \frac{1}{h_o} \qquad\qquad r_m = \frac{-y_f}{y_i y_o} = \frac{-h_f}{h_o}$$

$$r_b = \frac{y_o}{y_i y_c} = \frac{\Delta(h)}{h_o} \qquad\qquad r_e = \left(\frac{y_o}{y_c} - 1\right) y_f = \frac{-h_r}{h_o}$$

$$r_c = \frac{y_i + y_f}{y_i y_c} = \frac{1 + h_f}{h_o}$$

TABLE XII

Conversion of *H* Parameters to *R* Parameters

Parameter	C-Emitter	C-Base	C-Collector
r_e	$\dfrac{-h_r}{h_o}$	$\Delta(h)_b - h_{rb}$	$\dfrac{1 - h_{rc}}{h_{oc}}$
r_b	$\Delta(h) - h_r$	$\dfrac{h_{rb}}{h_{ob}}$	$\dfrac{\Delta(h)_c + h_{fc}}{h_{oc}}$
r_c	$\dfrac{1 + h_f}{h_o}$	$\dfrac{1 - h_{rb}}{h_{ob}}$	$\dfrac{-h_{fc}}{h_{oc}}$
r_d	$\dfrac{1 - h_r}{h_o}$	$\dfrac{1 + h_{fb}}{h_{ob}}$	$\dfrac{h_{rc}}{h_{oc}}$
r_m	$\dfrac{h_f + h_r}{h_o}$	$\dfrac{h_{fb} + h_{rb}}{h_{ob}}$	$\dfrac{h_{fc} + h_{rc}}{h_{oc}}$

TABLE XIII

Conversion from *R* Parameters to *Z* Parameters

Parameter	C-Emitter	C-Base	C-Collector
Input	$r_e + r_b$	$r_e + r_b$	$r_b + r_c$
Forward	$r_e + r_m$	$r_b + r_m$	r_c
Reverse	r_e	r_b	r_d
Output	$r_e + r_d$	$r_b + r_c$	$r_e + r_d$

TABLE XIV

Conversion from *Z* Parameters to *R* Parameters

Parameter	C-Emitter	C-Base	C-Collector
r_e	z_r	$z_{ib} - z_{rb}$	$z_{oc} - z_{rc}$
r_b	$z_i - z_r$	z_{ib}	$z_{ic} - z_{fc}$
r_c	$z_o - z_f$	$z_{ob} - z_{fb}$	z_{fc}
r_d	$z_o - z_r$	$z_{ob} - z_{rb}$	z_{rc}
r_m	$z_r - z_f$	$z_{fb} - z_{rb}$	$z_{fc} - z_{rc}$

TABLE XV

Conversion of *Z* Parameters to *H* Parameters

$$z_i = \frac{\Delta(h)}{h_o} \qquad z_f = -\frac{h_f}{h_o} \qquad z_r = \frac{h_r}{h_o} \qquad z_o = \frac{1}{h_o}$$

TABLE XVI

Miscellaneous Relations

$$\alpha \;=\; \frac{y_f}{y_i + y_f} = -h_{fb} \quad \beta \;=\; \frac{y_f}{y_i} = h_f$$

$$g_{i'} = \frac{g_i}{1 - g_i r_{b'}} \qquad\qquad g_{f'} = \frac{g_f}{1 - g_i r_{b'}}$$

$$g_i \;=\; \frac{g_{i'}}{1 + g_{i'} r_{b'}} \qquad\qquad g_f \;=\; \frac{g_{f'}}{1 + g_{i'} r_{b'}}$$

$$y_{i'} = \frac{y_i}{1 - y_i r_{b'}} \qquad\qquad y_{f'} = \frac{y_f}{1 - y_i r_{b'}}$$

$$y_i \;=\; \frac{y_{i'}}{1 + y_{i'} r_{b'}} \qquad\qquad y_f \;=\; \frac{y_{f'}}{1 + y_{i'} r_{b'}}$$

TABLE XVII

RCA (Giacoletto) Parameters

$$g_{b'e} = g_{i'} \qquad\qquad g_m \;=\; g_{f'} - g_r \doteq g_{f'}$$

$$g_{ce} = g_o \qquad\qquad g_{b'c} \doteq \frac{(g_c - g_o) g_i}{g_f}$$

CHAPTER THREE

Measurement of Variables and Parameters

3.0 Introduction

There are two general groups of variables and parameters that must be measured in the evaluation of the characteristics of an active device such as a transistor, the first being the output group, and the second being the input. This chapter discusses first the measurement of the variables in the two groups, the voltages and the currents, in terms of collector current and collector voltage, and also in terms of base current and base voltage. The methods of measurement of the static variables considered include cathode-ray and plotting recorder techniques. The measurement of small-signal parameters is discussed also after a brief consideration of the methods of their measurement and conditions that must be fulfilled in the process.

3.1 Basic Variables

As has already been established, the output variables that may be used most conveniently in design of transistor circuits are the collector current and the collector-to-emitter voltage. (See Appendix I for a full list of symbols.) Since the transistor is a control device, that is, a signal change in its input circuit changes the current and voltage conditions in its output, the presentation of its output characteristics must be in terms of an input variable, normally the base current. Now, both voltages and currents must be measured in a form for recording, so that whatever method of portrayal may be selected, an arrangement must be provided that will permit measurement without disturbing the characteristics of the circuit. As a consequence, some type of electronic voltmeter having an extremely high input impedance must be used for voltage measurements, and a current measuring device capable of being operated at a potential other than ground potential must be available.

The principal problem in the measurement of the collector and the base voltages is the problem of shunt loading by the measuring circuit. Particularly when used in the collector circuit under high-impedance conditions (open-circuit to signal) the voltmeter may introduce an impedance that is small compared to the impedance of the transistor itself, and may seriously alter the measurement. Fortunately, the only parameter whose measurement requires operation of the transistor under relatively high impedance in the collector circuit, in either the hybrid or the admittance configuration, is the output admittance. As has already been noted, it may be measured with either an open or a short circuit for the signal in the input circuit, giving $y_c (= h_o)$, or y_o, respectively. Not only the direct current load but also the signal current in the voltmeter must be kept small compared to the normal signal current in the load, a few microamperes at most.

As long as the small-signal data are not measured simultaneously with the currents and voltages, the determination of the values of current and voltage may be accomplished relatively easily. The reason for this is that the transistor may be operated, for static measurements, with a comparatively low-impedance collector supply, and a relatively low-admittance base-current supply. When it is desirable to make measurements of the small-signal parameters simultaneously or with the same equipment, then it may be necessary to operate the transistor at either high impedance or low impedance for signal frequencies on both the base and the collector circuits.

The question of what constitutes high or low impedance at signal frequencies depends on the characteristics of the individual transistor under test. In the collector circuit, for example, it is important that the loading impedance of the power supply not alter the effective value of the load resistance used with the transistor. With the measurement of either y_i or y_f, the load impedance for the measurement may be as small as a fraction of an ohm, and seldom exceeds 100 ohms, and in the measurement of the output admittances, the power supply admittance should be less than a micromho at signal frequency if the load circuit is connected in shunt, and a small fraction of an ohm if it is connected in series.   As a consequence, the reactance of the filters in the power supply can be of critical importance in a supply designed for low-impedance operation. Figure 3–1 shows the minimum capacitance required in the output of such a supply as a function of frequency in order to maintain the power supply impedance to a tenth of an ohm.

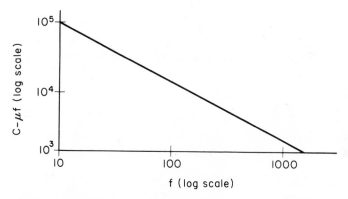

Fig. 3-1. Power supply capacitance as a function of frequency

The minimum permissible impedance level in the input circuit under open-circuit conditions for the signal voltage must be sufficiently large that accurate values of $y_c(h_o)$ can be obtained by the measuring circuits. The minimum impedance level for the device to appear to have an open circuit to signal currents in the base supply must be fifty or more times the value corresponding to the input admittance of the transistor, or the maximum admittance level should be less than 0.02 times y_i. (The product of the supply admittance by h_i should be less than 0.02.) Because with most low-power transistors the value of y_i is greater than 100 micromhos, the admittance of the base-current supply should be less than a micromho.

There are two methods of sweep-testing for measurement of transistor static characteristics, each having some advantages and some disadvantages. The more common method is the use of the cathode-ray tester, and the other is the use of a sweeping system in conjunction with an X-Y graphic recorder. A number of cathode-ray testers are currently available, of which the Tektronix Model 575 tester is typical. The sweep testers using X-Y recorders are specially designed units because most of the static sweep-testing has been based on cathode-ray testers.

3.2 Measurement by Cathode-Ray Testers

Transistor sweep testers using cathode-ray data presentation require two internal power sources, both of which are dependent on the alternating power line for their properties. The collector supply normally provides the independent variable in the form of sinusoidal pulses of voltage of adjustable amplitude. An autotransformer in conjunction with a full-wave rectifier provides the sinusoidal-pulse waveform indicated at the collector

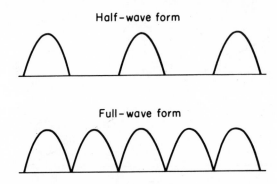

Fig. 3-2. Collector voltage waveform — sweep tester

of the transistor in Fig. 3–2. A staircase generator is required to provide the switching from one contour to the next, and it is normally controlled by a pulse generator that generates switching pulses at either or both the zero-crossings and peak amplitudes for the collector supply voltage. As long as separate supplies are used for the base current and the collector current, the metering of current may be accomplished by the use of a

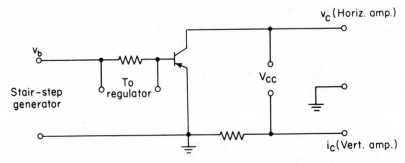

Fig. 3-3. Basic transistor circuit for sweep tester

metering resistor in the ground return of the individual supplies, as shown in Fig. 3–3, adapted from the Tektronix analyzer. A d-c amplifier connected across the resistor then provides the required deflection proportional to current, and a similar amplifier may be used to indicate the voltages developed in the circuits.

The stair-step generator should be adjustable for the correction of the zero level, or it should have a configuration that gives a low source admittance at the nominal zero-current level. A simplified circuit diagram for

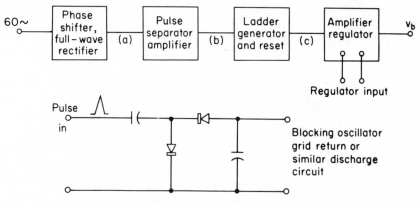

Fig. 3-4. Stair-step generator

a step generator is shown in Fig. 3–4, and the waveforms at specified critical points are shown in Fig. 3–5.

The input characteristics as well as the output may be plotted directly with a cathode-ray sweep analyzer. Typical forms of characteristic curves that may be generated include the form selected for use with transistors in this book, contours of constant base current as a function of base voltage

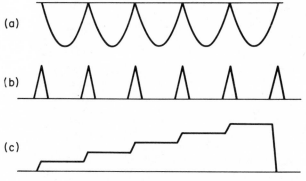

Fig. 3-5. Typical waveforms

and collector voltage, and also the contours as a function of base voltage and collector current. Another form for the input data gives a modified set of output data because it plots contours of constant base voltage in terms of the collector voltage and collector current. Because the base current increases exponentially with base voltage, however, the plotting of constant-voltage contours is difficult to do properly.

The plotting of contours of constant collector voltage as a function of base current and base voltage is difficult with cathode-ray analyzers because they are normally designed to use the collector voltage rather than the base voltage as the independent variable. This form of contour is not convenient as a basis of design either, in spite of the fact it is used quite frequently. If the base and collector leads are interchanged it is possible to plot such contours.

The range of base voltage required for a transistor under active operating conditions may be as small as 100 millivolts or as large as one or two volts. Because the value of the barrier potential for a germanium transistor may be between 0.1 and 0.3 volts (its energy gap width is 0.7 volt) and the barrier value for silicon may be as much as 0.5 volt, the floating base potential (the minimum voltage from base to emitter with a high-impedance termination on the base) may be larger than the total bias range for the base. If the range of base voltage recorded by the analyzer is from zero to the maximum value for the transistor, therefore, the active contours may be concentrated in a very small area on the graph. For this reason, it is often convenient to suppress part of the voltage range so that the active contours may be spread more effectively over the graph. If the contours fall in the range from 100 to 300 millivolts, for example, it is better to suppress the range from zero to 100, and record the curves over the 100 to 300 millivolt range than to use the zero to 500 millivolt range.

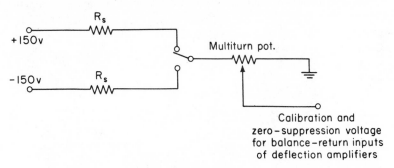

Fig. 3-6. Calibration and suppression circuit

The introduction of a zero-offset voltage to suppress part of the scale may be accomplished with the help of the calibrator circuit in conjunction with the drift and centering control on a cathode-ray system. If the calibration switch is shifted to ten units deflection and the centering control is set to bring the reference line to the center of the screen, the scale range is from 100 to 300 millivolts for a 200 millivolts full-scale. A possible circuit for providing such a calibration is shown in Fig. 3–6, and the results of such a change on the input curve family in Fig. 3–7. (The data were taken on a Tektronix 575 transistor tester.)*

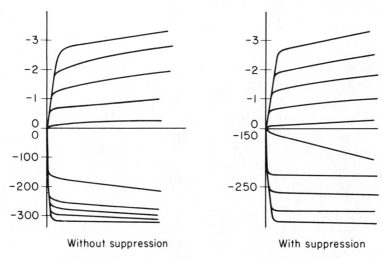

Without suppression   With suppression

Fig. 3-7. Effect of suppression on input curve distribution

The cathode-ray analyzer can be used to measure the properties of a transistor to a higher power level than is normally possible with an analyzer using an X-Y recorder. This is because the average dissipation of the transistor when operated in a cathode-ray analyzer, over its permissible thermal averaging time, is at most a third of its maximum dissipation. The averaging time for power dissipation is an important factor in the use of transistors in that it determines the minimum frequency at which the transistor can be operated at full ratings. At lower frequencies, the maximum instantaneous dissipation must be kept within the rated value instead of keeping the average dissipation within ratings.

The cathode-ray analyzer can be used to determine the dissipation capability of a transistor. This test may be made by setting the curve tracer to present the data on base voltage and collector voltage in terms of base current, and operating the device under repetitive sweep. If after the transistor is cycled through the repetitive sweep for a few seconds, the cycling is interrupted, the drift in base voltage gives an indication of

* The model of Tektronix tester available had only a negative deflection in the calibration circuit. A reversing switch was added to make both positive and negative deflection available. The positive check circuit used a positive regulated voltage that differed in value from that used for the negative circuit, and consequently also required a special voltage divider.

the thermal stability of the device. As the input power is increased, a level is reached at which a considerable increase of drift with increase of power input is noted. The maximum dissipation that can be applied with reasonable probability of reliable operation is then a quarter of the maximum product at the highest base current.

3.3 X-Y Recording

The use of a recording system based on an X-Y recorder for measuring and plotting the data on transistors has the advantage of making instantaneously available a large-scale plot of the characteristics of the transistor. Such a set of curves can also carry the raw data for small-signal contours for use with the conductance-type curve graphs. The time required for plotting the contours on an X-Y recorder and preparing the curves for use is little different from that for the cathode-ray analyzer, yet the accuracy of the resulting data is so much better that a considerable gain in usefulness can result.

If only static data are recorded with an X-Y system, then the characteristics required of the power supplies are the same as those required for the cathode-ray unit. The supplies can be considerably simpler, however, as the staircase generator is not required, and a conventional variable-voltage power supply is normally used for the collector. If small-signal data as well as static are required, however, then the supply problems become somewhat more complex. In any case, the collector supply should have as small an internal series resistance as possible. The impedance at the frequency of the test signal depends on the mode of measurement of the small-signal characteristics. The base-current supply should be a very closely-regulated current source capable of either high or low signal-frequency impedance as required by the small-signal measurement.

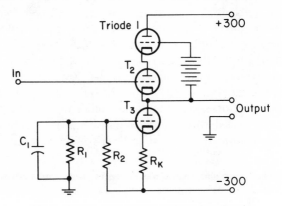

Fig. 3-8. Unity-gain cathode follower

The most convenient independent variable for use with the X-Y recording system is again the collector voltage, and convenient dependent variables are the collector current and the base voltage. The measurements of the collector voltage and the base voltage are both relatively easily made with the help of a balanced-pair circuit using unity-gain cathode followers, Fig. 3–8. With this circuit, the loading will be negligible, even to 100 volts if an external high-impedance voltage divider is used. With many transistors, an isolating repeater may not be required in the measurement of base voltage because the input impedance of a channel of an X-Y recorder is normally at least two megohms. (Because the base voltage is usually less than a half volt, even with silicon transistors, the maximum current drawn by the recorder should be less than a quarter of a microampere. As long as the base-current increments are at least ten microamperes, therefore, the error due to the recorder is negligible.)

The use of a zero-suppression circuit in the measurement of the input characteristics of the transistor is as desirable in a system using an X-Y recorder as it is with the system using cathode-ray display already discussed. This suppression may be accomplished by the help of zeroing controls on some X-Y recorders (such as the Moseley Autograf series) or it may be obtained by the use of a bias cell and a potentiometer to adjust the voltage to the desired value. This voltage is introduced in a manner to remove a part of the base voltage, so that the range seen by the recorder may differ from the actual voltage by a fixed increment.

Basic circuits that are satisfactory for providing the controlled voltages and currents required for testing low-power transistors are shown in Fig. 3–9.[1] Many of these circuits were developed at a time when the capabilities of the devices were only just beginning to be understood. As a consequence, the ranges of voltages and currents that can be developed by these circuits are relatively restricted by present-day standards. Likewise at that time little was known as to the optimum representing parameters, with the result that all possible measuring flexibility was provided to minimize measurement obsolescence. The standardization on admittance and hybrid parameters has reduced the importance of the high-impedance feature built into the collector supply. A more recently built collector supply for use in testing power transistors uses the circuit shown in Fig. 3–10. Both of these types of collector supplies have a current-measuring feature worthy of discussion.

The measurement of the collector current in a transistor is one requiring considerable care, because unless separate supplies are used for both the base circuit and the collector circuit, the measurements must be made at

---

[1] These circuits were developed under Contract DA-36-034-ORD-1419 with the Johns Hopkins University. The principal investigators were Dr. F. Hamburger and R. G. Roush.

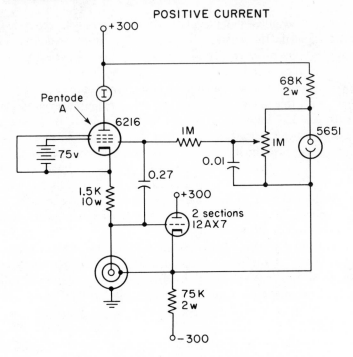

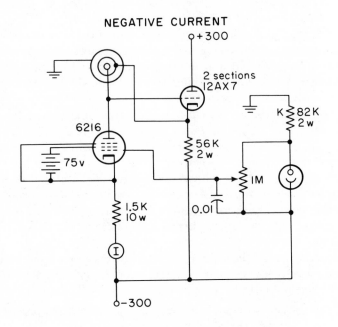

Fig. 3-9A. Constant current supply

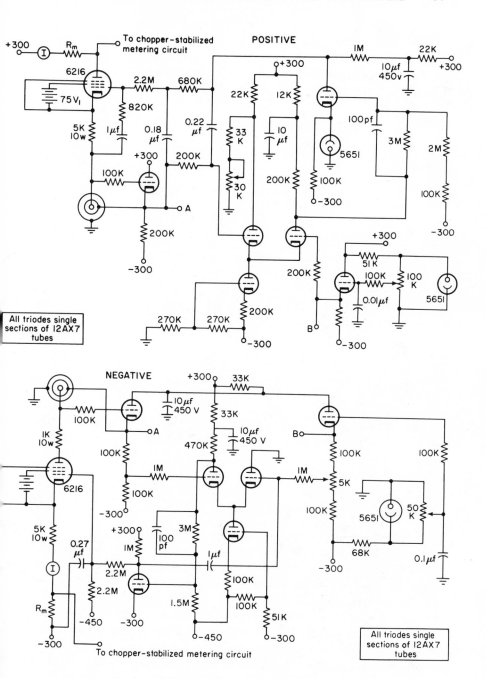

Fig. 3-9B. Constant voltage supplies

voltages that can encourage the development of cross-coupling. In particular, with an X-Y recorder, it is important that the metering leads provided to the recorder have a ground reference for both channels. Circuits for providing metering with chopper-stabilized amplifiers are shown in Figs. 3–9 and 3–10 in two equivalent forms: one for negative output,

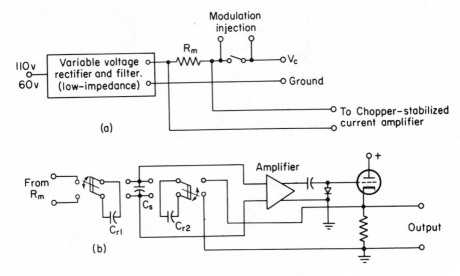

Fig. 3-10. High-power supply

and the other for positive. In Fig. 3–10, a single circuit that can be switched for either positive or negative output is shown. Such a circuit may not be required if adequate supply isolation can be provided, but it is convenient when the isolation is not available.

3.4 Notes on the Relative Advantages

Each of the systems of transistor evaluation, the cathode-ray system, and the X-Y recorder system, has its field of applicability. The former is particularly convenient in routine inspection service, because it gives an approximate over-all view of the characteristics of a device very quickly. The writer normally uses such a tester to get preliminary results such as checking the manufacturer's dissipation ratings and helping to select one or two transistors out of a group for analyzing in the X-Y analyzer. Things such as hysteresis resulting from dynatron regions in the collector characteristics, conditions of excessive drift, abnormally low values of avalanche breakdown voltage in the collector circuit, dissipation capability, excessive values of minimum collector current, the variation in base-to-emitter voltage required to activate the transistor, all may be evaluated and compared both easily and quickly with the cathode-ray analyzer.

It might appear that the cathode-ray tester is almost an ideal transistor tester. For many routine tests in which only static data are required, this is largely true. The use of an analyzer using an X-Y recorder makes available an excellent method of coordinating the static contours with a reasonably wide range of small-signal data. The introduction of an adequate small-signal analysis system in a cathode-ray tester is extremely difficult because of the rapid sweep and phase-balance problems.

The fact that thermal changes can occur in a transistor in the process of sweeping out one of its contours can actually be an advantage in testing devices that have a tendency toward instability. For example, the presence of excessive thermal drift may indicate that the sides of the base layer are not uniform and parallel, and the magnitude of the thermal hysteresis on the collector plot gives an indication of the ability of a given transistor to dissipate power in accordance with the manufacturer's specifications. Thermal overload is indicated by a warping of the base-current contours on the collector family toward higher currents as the collector voltage and current are increased and a corresponding warping of the base-current contours on the input family toward reduced magnitude of base voltage. The presence of avalanche multiplication due to high-field effects will not necessarily cause a warping of the input contours unless local heating of appreciable magnitude occurs.

3.5 Measurement of Small-Signal Parameters

There are two basic methods of measuring small-signal parameters, the incremental method, and the a-c method. The incremental measurement technique is based on the change in the value of one variable resulting from an applied increment in another. For example, a small change in either base current or base voltage may be applied to a transistor, and the resulting collector current change measured to determine either the value of h_f or y_f. This method of measurement is not commonly used because it makes necessary the differencing of two large numbers of nearly equal magnitude. The accuracy problems involved under these conditions have already been discussed. The a-c method makes use of a superposed alternating signal in addition to the static voltages and currents. The resulting signals may be separated from the static currents by the use of a capacitor, with the result that the differencing problem in the sense of the one in the incremental measurement does not exist with the a-c method. The amplitude of the output alternating signal may be compared with the input signal and the value of a self-immittance or a transfer immittance determined.

The measurement of small-signal parameters based on the a-c system may use either a bridge-balance or a deflection-type measuring system. Regardless of the method of measurement used, it appears that phase-selective measuring circuits should be used because many transistors have appreciable reactive components at typical measuring frequencies. The deflection-type measuring systems require precisely controlled sources of

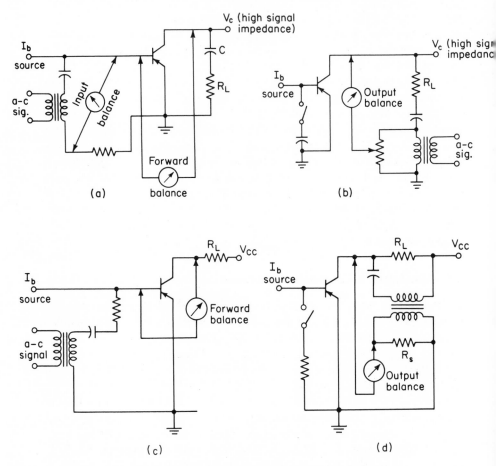

Fig. 3-11. Combination static small-signal circuits

measuring signal in addition to the phase-selective measuring system, whereas the bridge-balance measuring systems depend more on precision resistors and attenuators. Consequently, as pointed out by Follingstad, the bridge measuring system normally gives better accuracy by about an order of magnitude than do the deflection systems.

Deflection systems are used largely in production testing where a simple go no-go gauge using a meter is desirable. Alpha and beta are commonly measured this way, and may be determined as a function of either collector voltage or current as desired. Most of the deflection measuring systems are used under conditions in which comparison with a pre-set standard establishes the adequacy of the device under measurement. Because the deflection method has not proven to be convenient in the preparation of coordinated data sheets, it will not be discussed further here.

Probably the most satisfactory method of measuring the small-signal characteristics of a transistor for plotting on the static curve families is the use of a bridge configuration. A properly organized bridge configuration can be readily coordinated with a static contour-measuring system (Fig. 3–11). Rather good accuracies can be obtained by this method, particularly if Lissajous figures are used for the detection of balance conditions, as is indicated in Fig. 3–12. If the reference voltage used in forming the

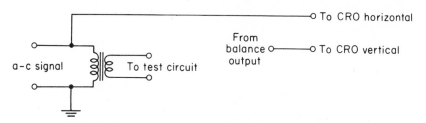

Fig. 3-12. Lissajous balance configuration

Lissajous figure is in phase with the conductance component of the bridge output signal, then the conductance balance condition occurs when the Lissajous figure becomes a horizontal (or vertical) ellipse. The presence of an in-phase or conductance component in the bridge output signal, however, causes the ellipse to slope diagonally. A phase detector could be used for indicating the balance condition, but though it does indicate the balance, it does not indicate the magnitude of noise or harmonic distortion that may be present in the balance signal.

The use of a current, or high impedance, source for the base current makes possible a direct introduction of the test signal, either as a voltage or a current source, into the transistor base. For either input or forward transfer admittances, the use of a low-impedance output circuit is optimum. Such an output circuit may be obtained either by the use of a feedback-regulated voltage supply or one having an extremely large output capacitance or it may be obtained through the use of a low-admittance supply having voltage regulation at d-c and an appropriate shunt low-impedance path at signal frequency. The output admittances are determined with the aid of a series signal source for use with the low-impedance supply, or a shunt signal source with the low-admittance supply. The basic configurations are shown in Fig. 3–13.

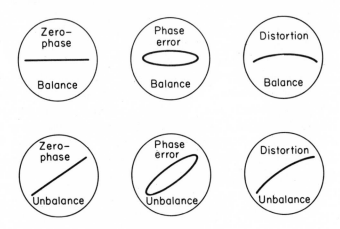

Fig. 3-13. Lissajous figures

3.6 Measurement Techniques

There are two basic types of measurements required for the determination of the small-signal behavior of transistors, and a number of special measurement techniques required for some of the remaining parameters. The basic measurements are for self-immittances and for transfer immittances. Self-immittances are measured by introducing a small magnitude of alternating signal either into the input or the output, and comparing the voltage across the transistor itself with the voltage across a standard resistance. The voltages across the respective immittances, the standard and the unknown, may be repeated by the use of isolation amplifiers, and their magnitudes compared by adjusting the magnitude of one to equal that of the other through the use of a calibrating potentiometer. Typical circuits for making these driving-point immittance measurements are shown in Fig. 3–14. Methods of measuring $r_{b'}$ and C_i will be described in later paragraphs of this chapter.

Part (b) of Fig. 3–14 shows one method of measuring the parameters y_o, and y_c or h_o. Because the shunting capacitance from collector to emitter is normally small compared to the collector conductance, it often can be ignored in low-frequency measurements. The signal voltage from B_1 to ground is repeated by an isolation amplifier, and a portion of it compared against the voltage from B_2 to ground to determine the effective collector admittance. A variable capacitance could be placed in parallel across the standard resistance to give an approximate measurement of the equivalent capacitance from collector to emitter if desired.

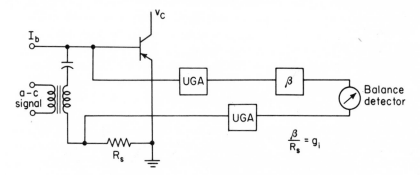

Fig. 3-14A. Basic input and forward immittance circuits

The circuits in parts (b) and (c) may be used either with the base terminal of the transistor bypassed to ground to give a low-impedance input circuit, or they may be used with the base circuit open to signal frequency. In the former case, the measurement gives the value of y_o, and

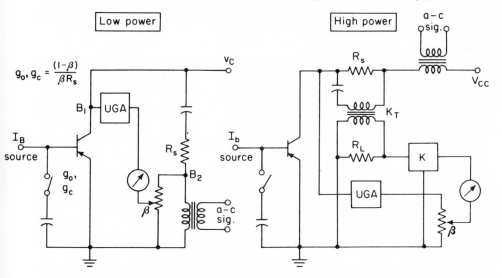

Fig. 3-14B. Output admittance

in the latter, the value of y_c (or h_o). Both these measurements are useful in connection with the design procedures discussed in the remaining chapters of the book.

The method of measuring y_o and y_c shown in part (b) of Fig. 3–14 is excellent for use with low-power transistors, but it is difficult to use with power transistors, primarily because of the difficulty of building a high-current power supply having good voltage regulation and a high internal signal impedance. An arrangement that can be used with power transistors with their relatively high collector admittances is shown in part (c). In this circuit, the signal is introduced in series with the collector supply, and the standard resistance is placed in series with the signal source and the collector. A repeater amplifier with an isolation transformer is used to separate and amplify the voltage developed across the standard resistance. The amplified voltage is then compared with the voltage on the collector to give the approximate value of the conductance. As long as the gain of the amplifier is adequately controlled by feedback, a relatively small value of standard resistance may be used to measure the conductances normally encountered with power transistors.

Although the use of an isolating transformer may appear to be undesirable, actually, if it is properly loaded, it can be calibrated and is somewhat more satisfactory than a differential amplifier for the purpose. A small error in the differential action can be quite serious, whereas no such error can develop with a transformer, only ratio or phase errors, which are much easier to calibrate and maintain than is the differential action. The use of a load resistor whose value is in the neighborhood of 10,000 ohms across the output winding of a unity-ratio transformer having an open-circuit reactance in excess of 50,000 ohms at the measuring frequency gives a circuit capable of accuracies in the neighborhood of a percent after calibration. The coupling coefficient for the transformer should be as nearly unity as possible, greater than 0.999 being desirable. The better the grade and quality of the transformer, the more accurate the results that can be obtained.

The trans-immittance parameters are all basically measured in a similar manner, with the input signal applied at one point, and the output taken from a completely different terminal on the device. These parameters may be called transfer functions, transfer ratios, trans-admittances, or trans-impedances. The ones of particular interest in the balance of this book are the parameters h_f or h_{fe} and y_f or y_{fe}. The reverse trans-immittances can also be measured by the use of the same basic circuit as for the forward.

These transfer immittances can be either transfer admittances or impedances or they can be transfer voltage ratios or current ratios. The transfer voltage and current ratios are really the ratios of a transfer impedance to a self-impedance, or a ratio of a transfer admittance to a self-admittance, with the result that they may be classed as immittances.

The basic circuit for the measurement of either h_f or y_f is shown in Fig. 3–15. The only difference between these two measurements is the point at which the reference signal is extracted. If the reference signal is extracted at the point A, ahead of the current-limiting resistor, R_s, the measurement is that of the current ratios, or β or h_f. If the reference voltage

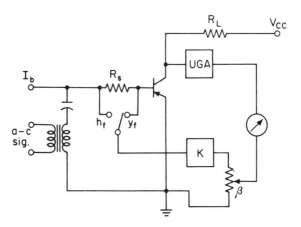

Fig. 3-15. Transfer immittance bridge

is extracted at the point B at the base lead, then the measurement gives the forward admittance, y_f. The value of the load resistor, R_L, used with either of these circuits is normally less than 100 ohms because the measurements of y_f and h_f both are based on a short circuit in the output. The allowable resistance that may be used in the collector circuit is limited by the source impedance of the power supply and by the two output admittances. The value of R_L should lie in the range

$$R_{cc} \ll R_L \ll 1/y_c \quad \text{or} \quad 1/y_o$$

where R_{cc} is the effective source impedance of the collector power supply, including any metering circuits used. This resistance must also be sufficiently small to permit the development of the required value of collector voltage.

If a current metering circuit using a chopper-stabilized amplifier is used, the range of voltage required to get reasonable recording accuracy is one volt full scale. If one of the supply-return metering systems is used, then a smaller voltage may be used, and a smaller metering resistance may be used. The correction factor required to correct for the metering resistance can be appreciable, as can be noted from Table I, which lists the correction assuming that the recorder requires one volt for full-scale current deflection and the value of R_L is ten ohms

TABLE I

Metering Resistance Corrections

Current range, amp	0.1	0.2	0.5	1.0	2.0
Metering resistance, ohms	10.0	5.0	2.0	1.0	0.5
Correction multiplier	0.50	0.67	0.83	0.91	0.96

Either a potentiometer or a voltage divider may be used to correct for this error because it is fixed for any given configuration.

In addition to isolation unity-gain amplifiers, which are used to repeat signal voltages for use with the bridge-balance circuits, stabilized amplifiers having fixed gain, phase-reversing amplifiers, and comparison and unbalance amplifiers are required for the measuring system. Typical circuits that can be used for the purpose are shown in Fig. 3–16.[2]

3.7 High-Frequency Parameters

In addition to the measurements of the low-frequency components of the small-signal parameters, it is necessary to measure at least three additional parameters, for example, $r_{b'}$, C_i, and C_c. These are the minimum components required in the interpretation of the characteristics of any given device. Several methods for the measurement of these parameters are now considered.

First, a brief consideration of the properties to be expected in the device as a result of typical values of these parameters can be helpful because it indicates the type of data required for them. The value of the parameter $r_{b'}$ varies slowly with frequency, and is relatively independent of base current. It may vary somewhat with collector voltage because the collector voltage determines the current distribution in the base region.

Capacitances. The internal base-to-emitter capacitance of a transistor consists of two components, one dependent primarily on the magnitude of the collector voltage, and the other on the magnitude of the emitter current. As a consequence, the input capacitance variation can best be presented in terms of contours of constant value plotted on either the input or the output curve family. Because the collector current is nearly equal to the emitter current for the majority of useful transistor devices, the contours may be introduced on the output family of curves. Figure 3–17 shows how such curves might look on a hypothetical transistor.

The capacitance between the collector and the base of a transistor, or the feedback capacitance, is also a function of its operating conditions.

---

[2] The majority of these circuits were developed under contract DA-36-034-ORD-1419 with the Johns Hopkins University Electrical Engineering Department. The circuit designs were developed by R. G. Roush.

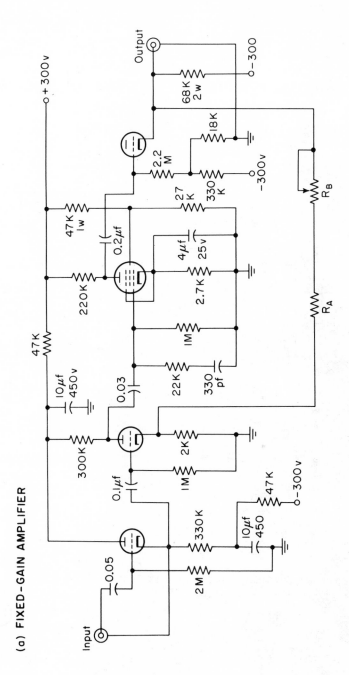

Fig. 3-16. Additional bridge circuits

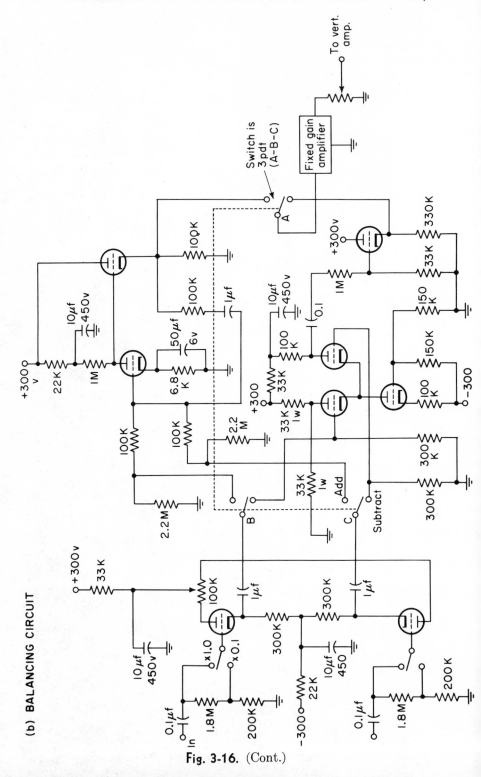

(b) BALANCING CIRCUIT

Fig. 3-16. (Cont.)

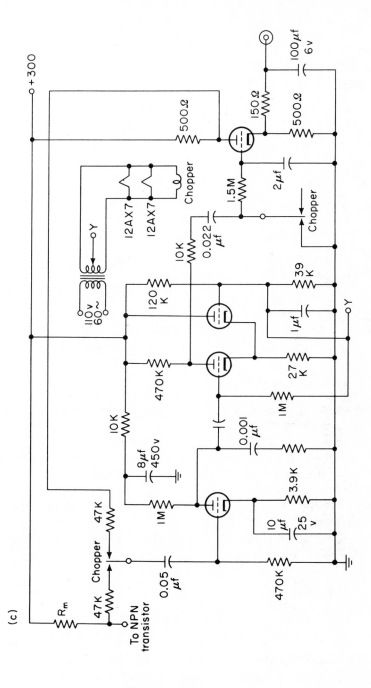

Fig. 3-16. (Cont.)

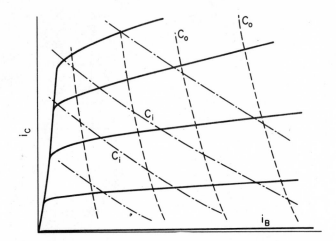

Fig. 3-17. Contours of C_i (— — — —) and C_o (— — —)
as a function of operating conditions

The principal component of capacitance varies with the voltage from
collector to base, having the form

$$C = kV_{cb}^{-n} \tag{1}$$

where the value of n is either 0.5 or 0.33.

Methods of Measurement of Input Parameters. The methods
used for measuring the values of $r_{b'}$, C_i, and $g_{i'}$ all separate the different
components on the basis of measurements at different frequencies. One
quick method of getting a rough value of $r_{b'}$ and C_i is based on the method
described for measurement of g_i. First a measurement of g_i may be made,
only a special potentiometer is used as the standard instead of a simple
standard resistor. Once a sine-wave balance has been obtained at measuring frequency with the full resistance in the potentiometer used as the
standard, a capacitance decade box, C_s, may be introduced, changing the
circuit of R_s in Fig. 14(a) to that shown in Fig. 3–18. First, the approximate
value of C_s required may be calculated from the equation

$$C_s = C_i/g_{i'}R_s$$
$$= (g_{i'} + g_{f'})/2\pi f_\alpha g_{i'}R_s \tag{2}$$

The nominal value of the sum of $(g_{i'} + g_{f'})$ may be obtained (for this
equation) from the emitter current if desired. The capacitor C_s is set to
the value indicated by Eq. 2, and the potentiometer adjusted with a
square-wave input until the Lissajous figure is flattened to a horizontal

line. Once the setting of the potentiometer has been optimized, then the capacitance may be readjusted and R_s trimmed until neither direct nor quadrature components of current remain. When this condition exists, the component values may be determined in terms of γ, the decimal reading on the standard potentiometer, R_s, and βK, the total gain applied to the signal voltage developed across the transistor input. The parameter values are

$$g_{i'} = (\beta K)/\gamma R_s \qquad (3)$$

$$r_{b'} = (1 - \gamma)R_s/(\beta K) \qquad (4)$$

$$C_i = (\beta K)C_s \qquad (5)$$

A possible circuit for the complete standard including R_s and C_s is shown in Fig. 3–18.

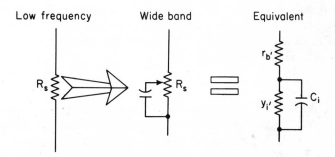

Low frequency   Wide band   Equivalent

Fig. 3-18. Standard admittance representation for transistor input

Two methods of estimating $r_{b'}$ are available which are based on low-frequency data. The first of these is based on the fact that, at least approximately, the input admittance of the transistor, neglecting base-spreading resistance, is linear with emitter or base current. The input resistance of the device is

$$1/g_i = r_{b'} + 1/g_{i'} \quad \text{or} \quad g_i = g_{i'}/(1 + g_{i'}r_{b'}) \qquad (6)$$

Solving for the internal conductance in terms of the external gives the equation

$$g_{i'} = g_i/(1 - g_i r_{b'}) \qquad (7)$$

As long as the operating conditions are such that the value of $(g_i r_{b'})$ is less than 0.5, then $g_{i'}$ may be written in the form

$$g_{i'} = g_{io}i_B \qquad (8)$$

When Eq. 6 is solved for $r_{b'}$ in terms of two different values of base current, i_{b1} and i_{b2}, the resulting equation is

$$r_{b'} = (i_{B1}/g_{i1}\Delta i_b) - (i_{B2}/g_{i2}\Delta i_b) \tag{9}$$

where $\qquad\qquad \Delta i_b = i_{B1} - i_{B2}$

The presence of $r_{b'}$ does not effect the determination of the internal value of current gain, but it does effect the determination of the values of the input and forward admittances. The effect of $r_{b'}$ on circuit behavior is sufficiently important that the sensitivity of g_i and g_f to the value of $r_{b'}$ may help rather than hinder circuit behavior. The corrected values of g_i and g_f, namely, $g_{i'}$ and $g_{f'}$, are given in Eqs. (7) and (10)

$$g_{f'} = g_f/(1 - g_i r_{b'}) \tag{10}$$

The estimate of the value of $r_{b'}$ obtained from Eq. (9) will be correct to within at most a factor of two. The resulting value of $r_{b'}$ may be used in Eq. (10) for the determination of $g_{f'}$. It is usually convenient to take the value of i_{B1} twice that for i_{B2}, in which case the value of $r_{b'}$ is given in terms of the modified form of Eq. (9)

$$r_{b'} = 2/g_{i1} - 1/g_{i2} \tag{9'}$$

The collector voltage should be kept constant for this measurement.

There is an additional method of determining the approximate value of the base-spreading resistance that depends on low-frequency measurements exclusively. This method is based on the fact that the reduction in the value of g_f from $g_{f'}$, 39,000 micromhos per milliampere, is due primarily to base-spreading resistance. As a consequence, the values of g_i and g_f may be measured for a specified value of emitter current, and $g_{f'}$ may be determined by multiplying 39,000 by the emitter current in milliamperes. The value of $r_{b'}$ is

$$r_{b'} = (1 - g_f/g_{f'})/g_i \tag{11}$$

The point at which the evaluation is made may be selected in the region where g_f is approximately half of the nominal value, $g_{f'}$, to minimize the calculating and the measuring errors.

True high-frequency measurements of the base-spreading resistance for a transistor are readily made with most high-frequency admittance bridges. The first step is the selection of a test frequency sufficiently high that the reactance of the input capacitance, C_i, is small compared to $r_{b'}$. Next, a lower frequency may be selected, and both $r_{b'}$ and C_i may be measured in terms of series components, the initial value of $r_{b'}$, being used to guide the measurements. After the value of $r_{b'}$ has been subtracted from $1/g_i$ to give $1/g_{i'}$, the approximate equivalent circuit is complete. The only problems that may be encountered in this procedure are the problems of controlling the static operating point of the active device without influencing the readings. A number of bridges have been developed that include provision for the introduction of the required bias conditions. Among these are the General Radio "Transadmittance" meter, and the Wayne-Kerr bridges. Other bridges that are naturally suited to these measurements are described in the papers by Zawels, Molozzi, Page, and Boothroyd, and by Turner.[3] Zawels' bridge is typical of the special devices created for these measurements, and is discussed in the next paragraph.

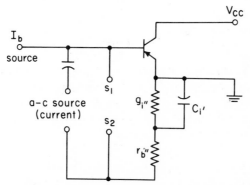

Fig. 3-19. Bridge for wide-band input admittance measurement.   AC source is square-wave current isolated with respect to ground.

$$C_{i'} = C_i$$

$$r_{b''} + \frac{1}{g_{i''}} = R_s$$

Figure 3–19 shows a method of introducing an input test signal into a transistor for measuring $r_{b'}$, $g_{i'}$, and C_i either in one operation with the use of a square wave, or by making separate balances at several frequencies separated by two to three decades from one another. The establishment of balance in a circuit such as this is organized in steps in the order that permits them to be accomplished independently of one another. The most

[3] J. Zawels, "Bridge for Yielding Directly Transistor Parameters," *IRE*, *PG Electron Devices*, January, 1958, p. 21.

A. R. Molozzi, D. F. Page, A. R. Boothroyd, "Measurement of High-Frequency Equivalent Circuit Parameters of Junction and Surface Barrier Transistors," *IRE PG Electron Devices*, April, 1957, p. 120.

R. J. Turner, "Surface-Barrier-Transistor Measurements and Applications," *Tele-Tech*, August, 1954, p. 78.

convenient order to use with this bridge is to make the $r_{b'}$ balance first, adjusting the value of the $R_{b'}$, standard at a very high frequency. Then a low-frequency balance may be made to adjust the $G_{i'}$ standard to the proper value. This adjustment is followed by one C_i at an intermediate frequency. A Lissajous-balance test should now show a relatively good balance as a function of frequency from audio frequencies to a frequency in excess of the upper noise-corner frequency, f_{n2}. If the test signal is large, curvature in the form of a parabolic balance condition will be noted, but it will be symmetrical about the vertical axis if the bridge is properly balanced.

3.8 Tunnel-Diode Measurements

The measurement of the properties of tunnel diodes is a problem of concern to the users of semiconductors, because these devices can be expected to find extensive use in conjunction with transistors and transistor circuits. Several problems are encountered in the development of measuring techniques for any device that displays an internal negative immittance characteristic, because switching and general instability and oscillation can be generated in the process of measurement.

Two types of negative immittances can be generated, the one being single-valued with respect to voltage, and the other single-valued with respect to current. The first possesses the characteristics exhibited by tunnel diodes, and is generally called a negative-admittance device. These devices by nature can be proven to possess a shunting capacitance within

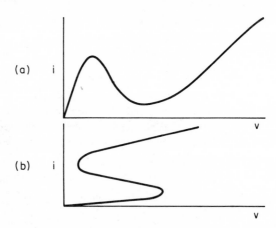

Fig. 3-20. Negative immittance
(a) conductance
(b) impedance

the active region.[4] The second are negative-resistance devices. Four-layer diodes and gas voltage-reference tubes show negative-resistance characteristics, and have internal series-inductance components.

Typical characteristic curves for negative-immittance devices are shown in Fig. 3–20. It should be noted that the tangents to these curves at the inflection-point in the negative-immittance region cross the curves oppositely. On the negative-admittance curve, the tangent must be rotated counter-clockwise to intersect the curve in more than one point, and with the negative resistance, the tangent must be rotated clockwise to intersect at several points. These directions of rotation are toward static instability, thereby showing that an increase of resistance in a load line for a negative-admittance device (NAD) increases the probability of instability, whereas a decrease causes an increase in the probability of instability with a negative-impedance device (NID).

The use of an equivalent, or tuned, resistance with a negative-immittance device can stabilize the circuit and cause an amplification in the process if the resistance characteristics of the active device are used correctly. With a negative-admittance device, a shunt resistance can stabilize the circuit, but a series one cannot. To see why this is so, it is neces-

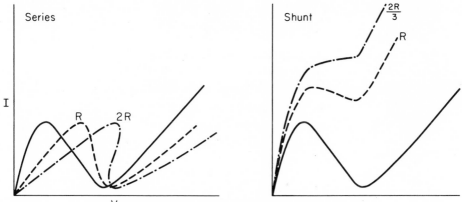

Fig. 3-21. Affect of series and shunt R on negative admittance

sary to introduce first a series resistance into the circuit and determine its effect, and then to do the same with a shunt resistance. Figure 3–21(a) shows the effect of a series resistance on the negative admittance, and 21b a shunt resistance. With the former, although the increase in series

---

[4] Some authors designate negative admittance devices as voltage-stable negative resistances and negative impedance devices as current-stable negative resistances. For a discussion of the capacitance and inductance characteristics, see H. J. Reich, *Functional Circuits and Oscillators*, Princeton, N. J.: D. Van Nostrand Company, Inc., 1961.

resistance shifts the slope of the negative-conductance region to positive, it leaves two knees that still show negative resistance. The result is that stable operation on the central (negative-immittance) section of the characteristic cannot be maintained. If, on the other hand, the resistance is introduced in shunt, then the addition of current proportional to voltage to the diode current can produce a contour that shows positive resistance throughout its length. Such a method of loading can therefore yield a configuration capable of stable operation. Shunt loading is required with NAD devices and series loading with NID devices functioning as amplifiers.

The characteristics of tunnel diodes may be examined either with the help of a special low-impedance test jig, or by the help of a conventional cathode-ray transistor analyzer. Both of these methods are dependent on a cathode-ray presentation. The circuit diagram for use with the low-impedance test set is shown in Fig. 3–22. The voltage divider that supplies

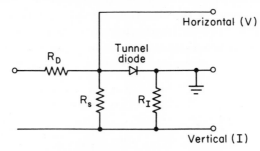

Fig. 3-22. Tunnel diode tester

R_D = Dropping resistance

R_S = Source resistance

R_I = Current metering resistance

$$\left| \frac{1}{g_d} \right| > R_s + R_I$$

where g_d = max negative conductance of tunnel diode

the voltage required for testing the diode must draw a considerable current to keep the source impedance for the diode sufficiently low to prevent switching, and the resistance in series with the diode must be small for the same reason. Irregularities commonly develop in the negative-resistance region for these devices as a result of oscillation conditions. Such irregularities can be located easily, because touching and pressing on the wires and the diode case will cause an alteration of the contour.

When a transistor sweep-tester is used for the evaluation of a diode, it is possible to plot a negative-resistance contour as well as the static. In doing this, however, care must be used to check for oscillation because the measurements can easily be in error if oscillation is present. A large value of load resistance should be placed in series with the diode to assure that the switching occurs at nearly zero conductance instead of at a small negative value. If the series resistance is large, then the trace disappears at the points at which the conductance reaches zero. If, then, a resistance is placed in parallel with the diode, the point at which negative conductance sets in varies with the value of the resistance. The points of disappearance of the trace, in the absence of oscillation, are the points at which the negative conductance is numerically equal to the conductance of the shunting resistance. Consequently, if the tendency to oscillate can be controlled, the static contour and the negative conductance contour can both be plotted using the transistor analyzer.

Practically, it probably is desirable to be able to examine the characteristics of tunnel diodes by both of the methods described above, the low-impedance method, and the high-impedance method, because each method gives useful information that is somewhat more difficult to determine by the alternate method. It is significant to note that, no matter how high the series load resistance is, switching action still occurs with the transistor tester, as is required by the theory explained above. The applications of these devices is described in later chapters.

CHAPTER FOUR

Circuit Parameter Relations

4.0 Introduction

The basic operating equations for transistor amplifiers may be determined in terms of either an equivalent black-box configuration and relation, a modified black-box relation, or on the basis of an arbitrary equivalent circuit, such as the Bell Laboratories tee resistance circuit, or the RCA pi circuit.

The principal advantage in the use of a black-box representation in the derivation of equations for an active circuit is that the equations obtained do not depend on the configuration used for the active device. The conversion of the small-signal parameters among the different configurations may be complicated, but the equations need not be changed because of a change of ground-point. The equations for the three standard forms of amplifiers, the common-emitter, the common-base, and the common-collector, and the equations for the degenerative-emitter amplifier are derived in this chapter, both neglecting the base-spreading resistance as a separate component, and also including it. In all these derivations, the internal properties of the intrinsic transistor are represented by the modified admittance parameters discussed in Chapter Two.

In addition to the routine method of derivation based on Kirchhoff's Laws, topological methods are helpful. The topological method gives the small-signal equations for both the driving-point and the transfer relation with a minimum of waste motion, and also minimizes the possibility of error in the derivation. The procedure for derivation of equations topologically is explained in Appendix III. Topological methods have been used extensively in the establishment of circuit equations in later chapters of this book.

4.1 Basic Equations for Simple Amplifiers

The amplification equation for the common-emitter amplifier, Fig. 4–1, can be derived directly from the basic current equations, Eq. (3) in Chapter Two and the input and the output relations

$$i_b = y_i v_b + y_r v_c \tag{1a}$$

$$i_c = y_f v_b + y_o v_c \tag{1b}$$

$$v_s = i_b R_s + v_b \tag{1c}$$

$$v_c + i_c R_L = 0 \tag{1d}$$

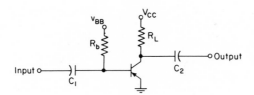

Fig. 4-1. Common-emitter amplifier

Substituting for v_b and v_c gives the equations

$$i_b(1 + y_i R_s) = y_i v_s - y_r R_L i_c \tag{2a}$$

$$i_b y_f R_s + i_c(1 + y_o R_L) = y_f v_s \tag{2b}$$

These equations may be solved for i_b and i_c in terms of v_s to give the driving-point and the transfer admittances. The resulting admittance equations provide the relations between the currents and the input voltage in convenient form. The value of i_b/v_s is

$$Y_{is} = i_b/v_s$$
$$= [y_i + \Delta(y)R_L]/[1 + y_i R_s + y_o R_L + \Delta(y)R_s R_L] \tag{3}$$

or, in terms of the value at the transistor terminals, (for $R_s = 0$), the equation is

$$Y_i = i_b/v_b$$
$$= [y_i + \Delta(y)R_L]/[1 + y_oR_L] \qquad (4)$$

The first of these equations gives the input admittance with the source resistance R_s included as part of the transistor, and the second, with it isolated from the transistor.

The input-output relation may be calculated by solving the Eq. (2) for the collector current in terms of input voltage

$$Y_f = i_c/v_s$$
$$= y_f/[1 + y_iR_s + y_oR_L + \Delta(y)R_sR_L] \qquad (5)$$

This equation gives the forward admittance, or the output current for a given input voltage, for the over-all circuit. In this case there is no reason to determine the gain from the input terminals of the transistor to its output, because the over-all circuit gain is the value desired. This equation may be changed into a voltage-gain equation or a current-gain equation by a simple transformation, multiplying both sides of the equation by $(-R_L)$ for the voltage amplification, and by R_s for the current amplification. For the derivation of the current gain equation from fundamental relations, the input relation, Eq. (1c), is replaced by the equation

$$i_s = i_b + G_sv_b \qquad (1c')$$

where G_s and R_s are reciprocals of one another.

In all the above equations, the only place in which the reverse admittance appears is in the delta factor

$$\Delta(y) = y_iy_o - y_fy_r \qquad (6)$$

Because the evaluations in Chapter Two show the use of the y_r parameter in one other form of term, the $\sigma(y)$ term, and the value of y_r in the common-emitter configuration is negligible compared to the balance of the terms, the use of y_i, y_f, y_o, and $\Delta(y)$ simplifies the design of circuits significantly. At least potentially, the value of $\Delta(y)$ is formed from the difference of two products, and the values of the two products can be approximately equal. For this reason its value should be measured directly. Since there appears to be no method of measuring the factor as a whole directly, it has been determined by the use of the artifice

$$\Delta(y) = y_i(y_o - y_fy_r/y_i) = y_iy_c \qquad (6a)$$

where y_c is the output admittance with the input circuit showing high-impedance to signal currents. It is readily measured, and as a result, the question of subtraction is avoided completely. In the balance of this book, the delta factor is written as $y_i y_c$ instead of $\Delta(y)$. This factor is one of the invariants in an admittance configuration for an active device.

The amplification equation could have been derived without mentioning which variables were voltages and which currents, and what type of immittance parameters were used. This can be verified by comparing the equations for voltage gain in terms of hybrid parameters and admittance parameters

$$K = -y_f R_L / [1 + y_i R_s + y_o R_L + \Delta(y) R_s R_L] \tag{7}$$

$$K = h_f G_s R_L / [1 + h_i G_s + h_o R_L + \Delta(h) G_s R_L] \tag{8}$$

Clearly, in converting (7) into (8), y_f has been replaced by $h_f G_s$, y_i has been replaced by h_i, y_o by h_o, $\Delta(y)$ by $\Delta(h)$, and R_s by G_s. In other words, to get Eq. (8), both the numerator and the denominator of Eq. (7) may be divided by $y_i R_s$, and the balance of the manipulations consist of substitution of the respective H-parameter symbols for the y-symbols. As long as the parameters used are based on the same transistor configuration, this interchange can be used for common-base and common-collector amplifiers as well as the common-emitter circuit. The formulation of the respective terms can be performed dimensionally if desired, because both the numerator and the denominator of a gain equation must be dimensionless.[1]

When the equation for current gain is transformed into the H parameter form, the product of G_s and R_s is unity, leaving only h_f in the numerator and

$$[1 + h_i G_s + h_o R_L + \Delta(h) G_s R_L]$$

in the denominator. If, therefore, the value of G_s is small (current drive), then the amplification, with R_L relatively small, reduces to h_f, the transistor current gain.

Although the derivation of these equations was based on the equations for the base current and the collector current, it could equally well have been based on emitter and collector currents (common-base), or on base and emitter currents (common-collector). In each of these cases, the input signal may either be introduced in series by the use of a voltage and a series impedance, or in parallel with a current and a shunt admittance. Either way, the output is developed in a load impedance. This is the reason for the importance of Table III in Chapter Two. For these two configurations, the amplification equations take the following forms . . .

---

[1] Linvill has also reported the implications of this paragraph in his report *The Theory of Two-Ports*, J. G. Linvill, Stanford University Electronic Research Labs Technical Report TR1505-2 (October 15, 1959).

Common base:

$$K = [y_f + y_o]R_L/[1 + \sigma(y)R_s + y_oR_L + y_iy_cR_sR_L] \tag{9}$$

Common collector:

$$K = [y_i + y_f]R_L/[1 + y_iR_s + \sigma(y)R_L + y_iy_cR_sR_L] \tag{10}$$

The first of these equations (9) may be verified by using the sum of Eqs. (1a) and (1b) with Eq. (1b) and the additional equations

$$v_s = i_eR_s + v_e; \quad v_c + i_cR_L = 0; \quad i_e + i_b + i_c = 0 \tag{11}$$

and Eq. (10) may be verified by the use of Eq. (1a) with the sum of Eqs. (1a) and (1b) along with the additional equations

$$v_s = i_bR_s + v_b + i_eR_L; \quad v_c + i_eR_L = 0$$
$$i_e + i_b + i_c = 0 \tag{12}$$

The input admittances may also be calculated by solving for the input current in terms of either the source or the terminal voltage. For the common-base amplifier, the input admittance in the emitter circuit takes the two forms

$$Y_{ibs} = [\sigma(y) + y_iy_cR_L]/[1 + \sigma(y)R_s + y_oR_L + y_iy_cR_sR_L] \tag{13}$$

$$Y_{ib} = [\sigma(y) + y_iy_cR_L]/[1 + y_oR_L] \tag{14}$$

for the source admittance and the terminal admittance, respectively. Equations (13) and (14) can be formed by substitution of the appropriate conversion values from Table III in Chapter Two in Eqs. (3) and (4) respectively.

The corresponding equations for the common-collector amplifier may be derived either by substitution from Table III in Chapter Two or by solution of the basic equations. The input admittances for this amplifier are

$$Y_{ics} = y_i(1 + y_cR_L)/[1 + y_iR_s + \sigma(y)R_L + y_iy_cR_sR_L] \tag{15}$$

$$Y_{ic} = y_i(1 + y_cR_L)/[1 + \sigma(y)R_L] \tag{16}$$

for the two conditions.

With the common-collector amplifier, the output signal is applied effectively in the input circuit, reducing the net signal voltage applied from base to emitter. This is the reason that the sigma term appears in the denominator of these expressions and the gain expression for this configuration. The effective input admittance is markedly reduced by the effect of the load resistance, and the converse is shown to be true in the next section.

The output admittances may be determined from the basic current relations by transformation of input for output parameters and vice versa, or they may be determined by evaluating the ratio of current to voltage in the output circuit. The equations to be solved are

$$i_b = y_i v_b + y_r v_c \tag{1a}$$

$$i_c = y_f v_b + y_o v_c \tag{1b}$$

$$v_b + i_b R_s = 0 \tag{17}$$

The value of the ratio i_c/v_c, or Y_o, is given by the equation

$$Y_o = [y_o + y_i y_c R_s]/[1 + y_i R_s] \tag{18}$$

Once again, this equation may be transformed from that for the common-emitter configuration to that for the two other standard configurations. The modified admittance equation for common-base operation is

$$Y_o = [y_o + y_i y_c R_s]/[1 + \sigma(y) R_s] \tag{19}$$

Clearly, the output admittance of this amplifier is much smaller than that for the common-emitter configuration. In fact, as the source resistance, R_s, is increased, the output admittance decreases rapidly, but for very small values of R_s, the output admittance is independent of which of these configurations is used.

The output admittance for the common-collector configuration may also be written with the aid of the conversion table. Instead of the $\sigma(y)$ appearing in the denominator, however, in this case it appears in the numerator. Consequently, the output admittance is comparatively large

$$Y_o = [\sigma(y) + y_i y_c R_s]/[1 + y_i R_s] \tag{20}$$

This high output admittance corresponds to the relatively high value of output conductance that may be obtained with the conventional cathode follower. Because the first term of the numerator is very large compared to the second, the value of R_s used can have little if any effect on the magnitude of the numerator. It can, however, have an appreciable effect on the value of the denominator. Consequently, as the source impedance of

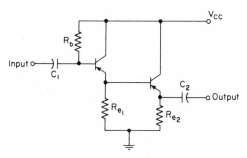

Fig. 4-2. Amplifier coupling using emitter-followers

the signal source is increased for an emitter follower, an appreciable increase of the value of the denominator can cause a significant reduction of the available output admittance, and the circuit may not behave as desired. This phenomenon is also noted with cathode followers, in that the output admittance of a circuit incorporating impedance-boost on the input side often has a relatively low output admittance. The difficulty is commonly avoided by the use of a circuit similar to that shown in Fig. 4–2.

4.2 Modified Black-Box Parameters

It is not possible to simplify the representation of a transistor to an admittance black-box except at low frequencies, since the base-spreading resistance present in the base lead of the transistor prevents the frequency response from conforming with that of the admittance form. It is entirely practical, however, to modify the admittance representation by the intro-

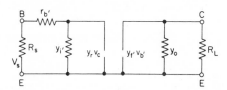

Fig. 4-3. Circuit representation-common-emitter transistor amplifier

duction of a series resistance in the base lead to make allowance for the discrepancy, and the resulting representation is sufficiently accurate for the majority of routine applications. This modification may be made directly in the equations for the common-emitter and the common-collector amplifiers, and the corrected small-signal equations are easily derived, but special consideration is required for the common-base configuration (Figs. 4–3, 4–4, 4–5).*

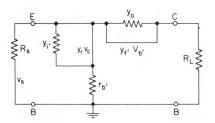

Fig. 4-4. Common base amplifier

* Strictly $r_{c'}$ and $r_{e'}$ also should be included for a complete representation.

The modification of the equations for the common-emitter circuit to take account of base-spreading resistance requires the addition of the equivalent resistance $r_{b'}$ to the source resistance of the voltage source supplying the signal to the transistor. At the same time, the input admit-

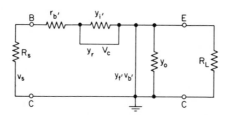

Fig. 4-5. Common-collector amplifier

tance for the transistor amplifier must be determined, including the base-spreading resistance internal to the transistor. The modified amplification for this amplifier may be written

$$K = -y_{f'}R_L/[1 + y_{i'}(R_s + r_{b'}) + y_{o'}R_L + y_{i'}y_c(R_s + r_{b'})R_L] \quad (21)$$

In effect, the original source resistance becomes the sum of two parts, the first being due to the resistance of the voltage source, and the second due to base-spreading resistance. Similarly, the input admittance becomes, for the two cases

$$Y_{is} = i_b/v_s$$

$$= [y_{i'} + y_{i'}y_cR_L]/[1 + y_{i'}(R_s + r_{b'}) + y_{o'}R_L + y_{i'}y_c(R_s + r_{b'})R_L] \quad (22)$$

$$Y_i = y_{i'}(1 + y_cR_L)/[1 + y_{i'}r_{b'} + y_oR_L + y_{i'}y_cr_{b'}R_L] \quad (23)$$

The corresponding equation for the output admittance is

$$Y_o = [y_{o'} + y_iy_c(R_s + r_{b'})]/[1 + y_{i'}(R_s + r_{b'})] \quad (24)$$

If $R_s = 0$, then this equation may be written as

$$Y_o = (y_{o'} + y_{i'}y_cr_{b'})/(1 + y_{i'}r_{b'})$$

A similar set of equations may be derived for the common-base configuration. One significant difference must be taken into account in this configuration, namely, the fact that the base-spreading resistance is introduced into the grounded, or base, lead rather than in either the emitter (input) or the collector (output) circuit. In effect, it lifts the internal common element of the transistor off ground and makes it part of the series circuit. This introduces a $y_{i'}y_c$ term into the numerator of the amplification equation

$$K = (y_{f'} + y_o + y_{i'}y_cr_{b'})R_L/$$
$$[1 + \sigma(y')R_s + y_{i'}r_{b'} + y_{o'}R_L + y_{i'}y_c(r_{b'}R_s + r_{b'}R_L + R_sR_L)] \quad (25)$$

The complete equation for the input admittance is

$$Y_{is} = [\sigma(y') + y_{i'}y_c(r_{b'} + R_L)]/$$
$$[1 + \sigma(y')R_s + y_{i'}r_{b'} + y_{o'}R_L + y_{i'}y_c(r_{b'}R_s + r_{b'}R_L + R_sR_L)] \quad (26)$$

This equation may be reduced to the actual input admittance of the transistor by taking R_s to be zero

$$Y_i = [\sigma(y') + y_{i'}y_c(r_{b'} + R_L)]/[1 + y_{i'}r_{b'} + y_{o'}R_L + y_{i'}y_c r_{b'}R_L] \quad (27)$$

The equation for the output admittance, including $r_{b'}$, is

$$Y_o = [y_{o'} + y_{i'}y_c(R_s + r_{b'})]/[1 + \sigma(y')R_s + y_{i'}r_{b'}(1 + y_c R_s)] \quad (28)$$

Unless topological methods are used for the derivation of this equation, difficulties may arise in the establishment of the correct set of current and voltage relations to use with the basic black-box equations. The following tabulation of the basic relations required in the derivation are included for the convenience of the reader

$$i_b + i_c + i_e = 0, \qquad v_{b'} + v_{e'} = 0$$

$$i_e = (y_{i'} + y_{f'})v_{e'} - (y_r + y_{o'})(v_{c'} - v_{e'})$$

$$i_c = -y_{f'}v_{e'} + y_{o'}(v_{c'} - v_{e'}) \qquad v_{c'} = -i_c R_L + i_b r_{b'} \quad (29)$$

$$v_s = v_{e'} + i_e R_s - i_b r_{b'} = v_e + i_e R_s$$

$$v_{c''} + i_c R_L = 0, \qquad v_{c'} = v_{c''} + i_b r_{b'} = [v_{c''} - i_c r_{b'} - i_e r_{b'}]$$

The equations for determination of amplification and the input admittance take the form

$$i_e[1 + \sigma(y')R_s + (y_{i'} + y_{f'})r_{b'}]$$
$$-i_c[-(y_{i'} + y_{f'})r_{b'} + (y_r + y_{o'})R_L] = \sigma(y')v_s \quad (30)$$

$$-i_e(y_{f'} + y_{o'})(R_s + r_{b'}) + i_c[1 + y_{o'}R_L - y_{f'}r_{b'}] = -(y_{f'} + y_{o'})v_s$$

These equations may be used for the calculation of K_b, Y_{ibs}, and Y_{ib}, but they cannot be used for the determination of Y_{ob}. This must be determined from a pair of equations in which the value of $v_{c'}$ has not been replaced by $-i_c R_L + i_b r_{b'}$. These equations are

$$i_e[1 + \sigma(y)R_s + (y_{i'} + y_{f'})r_{b'}] + i_c(y_{i'} + y_{f'})r_{b'} = (y_r + y_{o'})v_{c''}$$
$$i_e[(y_{f'} + y_{o'})R_s + y_{f'}r_{b'}] + i_c(1 - y_{f'}r_{b'}) = y_{o'}v_c \quad (31)$$

Routine solution of these equations leads to the value of output admittance given above.

Because the input circuit is the base circuit, as it is in the common-emitter amplifier, the equations for the common-collector amplifier can be obtained directly by replacing R_s by the sum of R_s and $r_{b'}$. The resulting equations are

$$K_C = (y_{i'} + y_{f'})R_L/[1 + \sigma(y')R_e + y_{i'}(1 + y_cR_e)(r_{b'} + R_s)] \quad (32)$$

$$Y_{ics} = y_{i'}(1 + y_cR_e)/[1 + \sigma(y')R_e + y_{i'}(1 + y_cR_e)(r_{b'} + R_s)] \quad (33)$$

$$Y_{ic} = y_{i'}(1 + y_cR_e)/[1 + \sigma(y')R_e + y_{i'}r_{b'}(1 + y_cR_e)] \quad (33a)$$

$$Y_{oc} = [\sigma(y') + y_{i'}y_c(r_{b'} + R_s)]/[1 + y_{i'}(r_{b'} + R_s)] \quad (34)$$

4.3 The Degenerative Amplifier

Often in an amplifier some resistance is introduced into the emitter circuit, Fig. 4–6, to provide the kind of degeneration commonly obtained by the use of a cathode resistor in a tube circuit. The modifications this makes

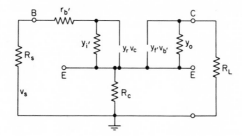

Fig. 4-6. Emitter degenerative amplifier

in the equations are not extensive, but they do introduce significant changes into the circuit behavior. The set of equations required for this derivation are

$$i_b = y_{i'}v_{b'} + y_r v_c$$
$$i_c = y_{f'}v_{b'} + y_o v_c \quad (35)$$

$$v_s = v_b + (i_b + i_c)R_e + i_bR_s = v_{b'} + (i_b + i_c)R_e + i_b(R_s + r_{b'}) \quad (36)$$

$$v_c + i_cR_L + (i_b + i_c)R_e = 0$$

When these equations are solved for the voltage amplification, the resulting equation is

$$K_d = -[(y_{f'} - y_{i'}y_cR_e)R_L]/[1 + \sigma(y')R_e + y_{i'}(R_s + r_{b'})$$
$$+ y_oR_L + y_{i'}y_c \langle R_eR_L + (R_s + r_{b'})(R_e + R_L)\rangle] \quad (37)$$

If the value of R_e is zero, this equation reduces to the standard form for the common-emitter amplifier. With the resistance R_e in the emitter return, the emitter is no longer at ground potential, and a $y_{i'}y_c$ term is present in the numerator of the transfer equation.

These equations may also be solved for the driving-point admittances for the circuit, both with and without a source-resistance component in the input. The input admittance equations are

$$Y_{ids} = y_{i'}[1 + y_c(R_e + R_L)]/[1 + \sigma(y')R_e + y_{i'}(R_s + r_{b'})$$
$$+ y_o R_L + y_{i'}y_c\langle R_e R_L + (R_s + r_{b'})(R_e + R_L)\rangle] \quad (38)$$

$$Y_{id} = y_{i'}[1 + y_c(R_e + R_L)]/[1 + \sigma(y')R_e$$
$$+ y_{i'}r_{b'} + y_o R_L + y_{i'}y_c\langle R_e R_L + r_{b'}(R_e + R_L)\rangle] \quad (39)$$

The presence of the emitter resistance, R_e, increases the complexity of the equations considerably, even more than does the presence of the base-spreading resistance, $r_{b'}$. The usual simplifications do reduce the complexity of the equations, however.

The output admittance is calculated in the same manner as it has been in previous examples. As usual, no substitution is made for v_c, only one for v_b. The equation that results is

$$Y_{od} = [y_o + y_{i'}y_c(R_s + R_e + r_{b'})]/[1 + \sigma(y')R_e + y_{i'}(R_s + R_e + r_{b'})$$
$$+ y_o R_L + y_{i'}y_c \langle R_e R_L + (R_s + r_{b'})(R_e + R_L)\rangle] \quad (40)$$

It is significant to note that both the input and the output admittances of the amplifier can be reduced appreciably by the introduction of the emitter resistance, as the sigma term in the denominators of Y_{ids} and Y_{id} normally is large compared to the balance of the denominator terms, and the $\sigma(y')R_e$ term in the denominator of Y_{od} likewise is large compared to the remaining terms.

The effect of the introduction of emitter resistance on the input and the output admittances of the amplifier are best shown by taking the ratio of the admittances with and without R_e present. This ratio is

$$Y_i/Y_{id} = \{1 + [\sigma(y') + y_{i'}y_c R_L]R_e/[1 + y_{i'}r_{b'} + y_o R_L + y_{i'}y_c r_{b'}R_L]\} \quad (41)$$

Consequently, the value of Y_i may be many times that of Y_{id}. In a similar manner, the ratio of the output admittances may be calculated to determine the effect of the emitter degeneration. This ratio is

$$Y_o/Y_{od} = [1 + \langle(y_{i'} + y_{f'})R_e/[1 + y_{i'}(R_s + r_{b'}])\rangle]$$
$$\times [1/\langle1 + (y_{i'}y_c R_e/[y_o + y_{i'}y_c \langle R_s + r_{b'}\rangle])\rangle] \quad (42)$$

The second bracket of this expression has the value

$$0.5 \leqq [1/\langle1 + (y_{i'}y_c R_e/[y_o + y_{i'}y_c(R_s + r_{b'})])\rangle] \quad (43)$$
$$\leqq 1.0$$

Consequently, the value of the ratio lies in the range

$$0.5\left[1 + \frac{(y_{i'} + y_{f'})R_e}{1 + y_{i'}(R_s + r_{b'})}\right] \leqq Y_o/Y_{od} \leqq \left[1 + \frac{(y_{i'} + y_{f'})R_e}{1 + y_{i'}(R_s + r_{b'})}\right] \quad (44)$$

The term in brackets can have a value that is large compared to unity, so that the output admittance is strongly effected by emitter degeneration, just as is the input admittance.

4.4 Symbol Tables and Definitions

One remaining preliminary of considerable importance to the designer and the user of this book is a listing of the special symbols used for identification of different typical operating conditions. A complete table of definitions used in this book is included in Appendix I, and only the most important symbols and parameters, along with their definitions, are considered in this chapter.

The identification of the different current, voltage, and admittance values for typical operating conditions with transistors should be sufficiently complete to enable the user to identify his different conditions of operation easily and consistently, so that all other users will know the significance of his symbols. For this reason, it has not been possible to delay selection of terminology until the standardizing committees both recognize a need, and also recognize that something must be made available for the user.

The behavior of a nonlinear circuit may be expressed in terms of voltage differences, or it may be expressed in terms of the small-signal characteristics of the circuit as a function of operating conditions. The usual method of doing this has been in terms of voltage differences. This method is satisfactory as long as the accuracy requirements are comparatively small and the design criteria are sufficiently flexible to permit ample dissipation margins. Unfortunately, the development of compact, light-weight, low-power equipment is not readily possible when voltage-difference methods are used, because it is not possible to tell in sufficient detail what the characteristics of the circuit are. For similar reasons, it is desirable that the values of the small-signal data be identified at several different points if the design is to take into account the range of variation to be expected in the active devices. A detailed study of the methods of evaluating distortion in amplifiers is given in condensed form in Radio Engineering Handbook.[2] For that reason, only the results are included here. One derivation that seems to offer difficulties to many is worked out in Appendix II. The amplitudes of other harmonic components may be determined in a similar

[2] *Radio Engineering Handbook*, Fifth Edition, by K. Henny (editor). McGraw-Hill Book Co., Inc., New York, 1959, Chapter 12.

manner. The equations that apply when the second harmonic distortion predominates, and when the third predominates, are

$$D = 25(K_p - K_n)/(K_p + K_n) \text{ percent} \tag{45}$$

$$D = 100(K_p + K_n - 2K_s)/3(K_p + K_n + 6K_s) \text{ percent} . \tag{46}$$

Orthogonal polynomial techniques are the best to use when the variation of amplification with bias is not uniform, because they make possible both the determination of the magnitudes of the harmonic components, and the direct evaluation of the significance of the irregularities that may be noted. The use of this technique is described in Appendix IV.

The standard voltage, current, and immittance symbols used with transistors include instantaneous total values, the d-c value, the instantaneous value, the maximum value of the varying component, and the supply values. In addition, most-positive values, most-negative values, cutoff values, average values, and total changes are included in the tables to follow because these values are of considerable importance to the design procedures that follow. The tables are separated into three groups, one for voltage symbols, one for current symbols, and the third for admittance symbols. The fourth includes the conductance symbols that may be used at low frequency.

In the admittance and conductance tables, the primes have been omitted. If the base-spreading resistance is separated from the transistor, leaving an intrinsic internal device, then y_i symbols and y_f symbols should be primed. It may in some cases be necessary to prime the y_o symbol, because the base-spreading resistance affects the impedance of the base to ground, but the y_c parameter need not be primed under any conditions.

TABLE I

Transistor Voltage Symbols
(Emitter Reference)

Conditions	Base	Collector	Emitter	Input	Output
Instantaneous total	v_B	v_C	v_E	v_S	v_O
d-c (no-signal)	V_B	V_C	V_E	V_S	V_O
Instant. signal component	v_b	v_c	v_e	v_s	v_o
Max. value of varying component	V_{BM}	V_{CM}	V_{EM}	V_{SM}	V_{OM}
Peak positive bias	V_{bp}	V_{cp}	V_{ep}	V_{sp}	V_{op}
Peak negative bias	V_{bn}	V_{cn}	V_{en}	V_{sn}	V_{on}
Cutoff bias	V_{bz}	V_{cz}	V_{ez}	V_{sz}	V_{oz}
Average value	V_{ba}	V_{ca}	V_{ea}	V_{sa}	V_{oa}
Total change	Δv_b	Δv_c	Δv_e	Δv_s	Δv_o
Value for max. collector dissipation	V_{bm}	V_{cm}	V_{em}		
Supply voltage	V_{BB}	V_{CC}	V_{EE}	V_{SS}	V_{OO}

TABLE II

Transistor Current Symbols

Conditions	Emitter	Base	Collector	Input	Output
Instantaneous total	i_E	i_B	i_C	i_S	i_o
d-c value, no-signal	I_E	I_B	I_C	I_S	I_o
Instantaneous signal component	i_e	i_b	i_c	i_s	i_o
Max. value of varying component	I_{EM}	I_{BM}	I_{CM}	I_{SM}	I_{OM}
Peak positive bias	I_{ep}	I_{bp}	I_{cp}	I_{sp}	I_{op}
Peak negative bias	I_{en}	I_{bn}	I_{cn}	I_{sn}	I_{on}
Cutoff bias	I_{ez}	I_{bz}	I_{cz}	I_{sz}	I_{oz}
Average value	I_{ea}	I_{ba}	I_{ca}	I_{sa}	I_{oa}
Total change	Δi_e	Δi_b	Δi_c	Δi_s	Δi_o
Max. collector dissipation	I_{em}	I_{bm}	I_{cm}	I_{sm}	I_{om}

TABLE III

Transistor Admittance Symbols*
(Common Emitter)

Conditions	Input	Forward	Output Admittances Short-Input-Open		Amplification
Instantaneous	y_i	y_f	y_o	y_c	K
Static value	y_{is}	y_{fs}	y_{os}	y_{cs}	K_s
Peak positive bias	y_{ip}	y_{fp}	y_{op}	y_{cp}	K_p
Peak negative bias	y_{in}	y_{fn}	y_{on}	y_{cn}	K_n
Average value	y_{ia}	y_{fa}	y_{oa}	y_{ca}	K_a
Total change	Δy_i	Δy_f	Δy_o	Δy_c	ΔK
Conversion	$0.25\Delta y_i$	$0.25\Delta y_f$	$0.25\Delta y_o$	$0.25\Delta y_c$	$0.25\Delta K$

* *Short-Input-Open* means that the output admittances in the left column are taken with input short-circuited; those in the right column are taken with input open-circuited.

TABLE IV

Transistor Conductance Symbols*
(Common Emitter)

Conditions	Conductance Input	Forward	Output Conductance Short-Input-Open		Amplification
Instantaneous	g_i	g_f	g_o	g_c	K
Static value	g_{is}	g_{fs}	g_{os}	g_{cs}	K_s
Peak positive bias	g_{ip}	g_{fp}	g_{op}	g_{cp}	K_p
Peak negative bias	g_{in}	g_{fn}	g_{on}	g_{cn}	K_n
Average value	y_{ia}	g_{fa}	g_{oa}	g_{ca}	K_a
Total change	Δg_i	Δg_f	Δg_o	Δg_c	ΔK
Conversion value	$0.25\Delta g_i$	$0.25\Delta g_f$	$0.25\Delta g_o$	$0.25\Delta g_c$	$0.25\Delta K$

* *Short-Input-Open* means that the output admittances in the left column are taken with input short-circuited; those in the right column are taken with input open-circuited.

In addition, the following symbol definitions are of considerable importance in the chapters to follow:

TABLE V

Commonly Used Symbols

α_N	Current gain from emitter to collector
α_I	Current gain from collector to emitter
β	Current gain from base to collector
$h_{fe} = h_f$	Current gain from base to collector
f_α	Alpha cutoff frequency, the frequency for which the current gain, common-base, is 70 percent of the low-frequency value.
f_{n1}	Flicker-noise corner frequency
f_{n2}	Upper noise corner frequency
f_{max}	Maximum frequency at which a power gain $\geqq$ unity can be obtained with a transistor
f_T	Frequency for which $\mid h_f \mid = \mid \beta \mid = 1$
$C_D \doteq C_i$	Input capacitance, base to emitter
$r_{b'},\ r_{bb'}$	Base-spreading resistance
C_C	Collector capacitance, base bypassed to ground
C_O	Collector capacitance, base not bypassed to ground
$r_{e'}$	Emitter series resistance (within the semiconductor)
$r_{c'}$	Collector series resistance
t_r	Time for current to rise from minimum to maximum nominal value in switching circuit
t_f	Time for current to fall from maximum magnitude to nominal minimum value in switching circuit
t_d	Ohmic delay time. Interval between the rise of the applied input pulse and the start of the rise of the output pulse generated by minority carriers.
t_s	Storage time. Time interval between the start of fall of the input pulse and the start of the decay of minority carrier flow at the output.

Table VI following tabulates the various important immittance equations derived in this chapter and three important equations from Chapter Five. These equations have been grouped in this form to facilitate their application to design problems.

TABLE VI

Equations containing minor changes from the form given in the text are designated by the addition of the letter "r" to the number in the text.

Equations for Common-Emitter Amplifier

When $r_{b'} = 0$:

$$Y_{is} = y_i(1 + y_c R_L)/[1 + y_o R_L + y_i R_s(1 + y_c R_L)] \tag{4-3r}$$

$$Y_i = y_i(1 + y_c R_L)/(1 + y_o R_L) \tag{4-4r}$$

$$Y_f = y_f/[1 + y_o R_L + y_i R_s(1 + y_c R_L)] \tag{4-5r}$$

$$Y_o = (y_o + y_i y_c R_s)/(1 + y_i R_s) \tag{4-18}$$

When $r_{b'} \neq 0$:

$$Y_{is} = y_{i'}(1 + y_c R_L)/[1 + y_o R_L + y_{i'}(1 + y_c R_L)(r_{b'} + R_s)] \tag{4-22}$$

$$Y_i = y_{i'}(1 + y_c R_L)/[1 + y_o R_L + y_{i'} r_{b'}(1 + y_c R_L)] \tag{4-23}$$

$$Y_f = y_{f'}/[1 + y_o R_L + y_{i'}(1 + y_c R_L)(r_{b'} + R_s)] \tag{4-21r}$$

$$Y_o = [y_o + y_{i'} y_c(r_{b'} + R_s)]/[1 + y_{i'}(r_{b'} + R_s)] \tag{4-24}$$

Equations for Common-base amplifier

When $r_{b'} = 0$:

$$Y_{ibs} = (\sigma(y') + y_i y_c R_L)/[1 + y_o R_L + \sigma(y') R_s + y_i y_c R_s R_L] \tag{4-13}$$

$$Y_{ib} = (\sigma(y') + y_i y_c R_L)/(1 + y_o R_L) \tag{4-14}$$

$$Y_{fb} = (y_f + y_o)/[1 + y_o R_L + \sigma(y) R_s + y_i y_c R_s R_L] \tag{4-9r}$$

$$Y_{ob} = (y_o + y_i y_c R_s)/[1 + \sigma(y) R_s] \tag{4-19}$$

When $r_{b'} \neq 0$:

$$Y_{ibs} = [\sigma(y') + y_{i'} y_c(r_{b'} + R_L)]/$$
$$[1 + y_o R_L + \sigma(y') R_s + y_{i'}\langle r_{b'} + y_c(r_{b'} R_s + r_{b'} R_L + R_s R_L)\rangle] \tag{4-26}$$

$$Y_{ib} = [\sigma(y') + y_{i'} y_c(r_{b'} + R_L)]/[1 + y_o R_L + y_{i'} r_{b'}(1 + y_c R_L)] \tag{4-27}$$

$$Y_{fb} = (y_{f'} + y_o + y_{i'} y_c r_{b'})/$$
$$[1 + y_o R_L + \sigma(y') R_s + y_{i'}\langle r_{b'} + y_c(r_{b'} R_s + r_{b'} R_L + R_s R_L)\rangle] \tag{4-24r}$$

$$Y_{ob} = [y_o + y_{i'} y_c(r_{b'} + R_s)]/[1 + y_{i'} r_{b'}(1 + y_c R_s) + \sigma(y)' R_s] \tag{4-28}$$

Common Collector Configuration (R_L replaced by R_e)

When $r_{b'} = 0$:

$$Y_{ics} = y_i(1 + y_c R_e)/[1 + \sigma(y) R_e + y_i R_s(1 + y_c R_e)] \tag{4-15}$$

$$Y_{ic} = y_i(1 + y_c R_e)/[1 + \sigma(y) R_e] \tag{4-16}$$

$$Y_{fc} = (y_i + y_f)/[1 + \sigma(y) R_e + y_i R_s(1 + y_c R_e)] \tag{4-10r}$$

$$Y_{oc} = [\sigma(y) + y_i y_c R_s]/[(1 + y_i R_s] \tag{4-20}$$

When $r_{b'} \neq 0$:

$$Y_{ics} = y_{i'}(1 + y_c R_e)/[1 + \sigma(y') R_e + y_{i'}(1 + y_c R_e)(r_{b'} + R_s)] \tag{4-33}$$

$$Y_{ic} = y_{i'}(1 + y_c R_e)/[1 + \sigma(y') R_e + y_{i'} r_{b'}(1 + y_c R_e)] \tag{4-33a}$$

$$Y_{fc} = (y_{i'} + y_{f'})/[1 + \sigma(y') R_e + y_{i'}(1 + y_c R_e)(r_{b'} + R_s)] \tag{4-32r}$$

$$Y_{oc} = [\sigma(y') + y_i y_c(r_{b'} + R_s)]/[1 + y_{i'}(r_{b'} + R_s)] \tag{4-34}$$

Complete Emitter-Degenerative Amplifier

$$Y_{ids} = y_{i'}[1 + y_c(R_e + R_L)]/$$
$$[1 + y_o R_L + \sigma(y') R_e + y_{i'}\langle(r_{b'} + R_s) + y_c(R_e R_L + (r_{b'} + R_s)(R_e + R_L))\rangle] \tag{4-38}$$

$$Y_{id} = y_{i'}[1 + y_c(R_e + R_L)]/$$
$$[1 + y_o R_L + \sigma(y') R_e + y_{i'}\langle r_{b'} + y_c(R_e R_L + r_{b'}(R_e + R_L))\rangle] \tag{4-39}$$

$$Y_{fd} = [y_{f'} - y_{i'} y_c R_e]/$$
$$[1 + y_o R_L + \sigma(y') R_e + y_{i'}\langle(r_{b'} + R_s) + y_c(R_e R_L + (r_{b'} + R_s)(R_e + R_L))\rangle] \tag{4-37r}$$

$$Y_{od} = [y_o + y_{i'} y_c(r_{b'} + R_e + R_s)]/[1 + \sigma(y') R_e + y_{i'}(r_{b'} + R_s)(1 + y_c R_e)] \tag{4-40}$$

Feedback Degenerative Amplifier

$$Y_{if} = [y_{i'}(1 + Y r_{b'}) + y_{i'} y_c R_L(1 + Y r_{b'}) + \sigma(y') Y R_L]/$$
$$[1 + y_o R_L + y_{i'} r_{b'}(1 + y_c R_L + Y R_L)] \tag{5-32}$$

$$Y_{ff} = [y_{f'} + Y(1 - y_{i'} r_{b'})]/$$
$$[1 + Y R_s + y_o R_L + y_{i'}(r_{b'} + R_s)(1 + y_c R_L + Y R_L) + \sigma(y') Y R_s R_L] \tag{5-31r}$$

$$Y_{of} = [y_o(1 + Y R_s) + y_{i'} y_c(r_{b'} + R_s) + Y(1 + y_{i'} r_{b'})]/$$
$$[1 + y_{i'}(r_{b'} + R_s) + Y R_s] \tag{5-33}$$

CHAPTER FIVE

Design of Transistor R-C Amplifiers

5.0 Introduction

The steps in the design of transistor amplifiers are, first, the preparation of a static design (or climate), and, second, the development of a small-signal, or dynamic, design. At the same time, the appropriate basic configuration for use with the active device must be selected. Because of the stability problem that develops with transistor circuits, the biasing configuration must be designed with considerable care. For this reason, the biasing problem is considered separately in Chapter Six. The static design procedure for use with transistors is relatively complex because neither of the input variables is negligible in any transistor configuration.

The specification of an appropriate static operating contour for an amplifier is based on the selection of a load line that permits the development of the required power output with conservative values of peak voltage, peak current, and peak power. The projection of this contour on the collector curve family usually is a straight line with a common-emitter amplifier, but it may be slightly curved for either a common-base or a common-collector amplifier.

The discussion to follow considers first the full design procedure for the common-emitter *R-C* amplifier under several typical load-line conditions, and then similar problems for common-base, common-collector, and degenerative configurations.

5.1 Common-Emitter R-C Amplifiers

The construction of the static output load line for an *R-C* amplifier is based on the location of its two end points. One of these points is defined by the coordinates V_{CC}, O, and the second by the coordinates O,

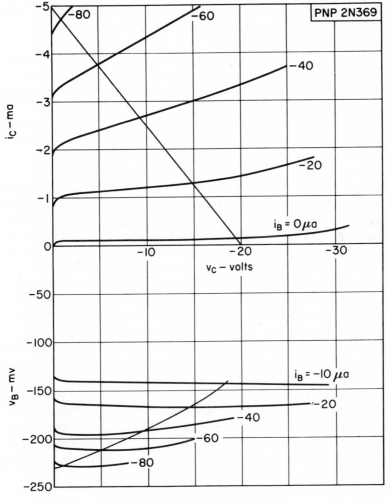

Fig. 5-1. Typical load contours

V_{CC}/R_L. The basic load contour is a straight line drawn through these two points.

Once the load line has been constructed on the output curve family, it must be transcribed to the input family. This process of transcription is easily accomplished if the preferred form of static data described in Chapter Two is used together with the curves in Appendix VII. In Fig. 5–1, the intersection of the load line with any of the base-current contours may be noted, and the intersection point transferred vertically across to the corresponding base-current contour on the input family; this is done with each of the intersection points. Next, the input contour projection of the load contour may be drawn through the various transcribed points, and the data on input voltage and input and output current and output voltage may be tabulated, giving a complete set of static data.

The value of the voltage level in the base circuit is a function of the operating temperature of the transistor, and consequently will fluctuate considerably, but the voltage change from one base-current contour to the next is relatively fixed. As a result, the bias stabilization problem involves primarily the static behavior of the active device.

Once a trial static design has been selected, it is necessary to make a small-signal design to see if the static design provides an environment that makes available the required kind of operating conditions. This phase of design is of particularly critical importance, since it controls the eventual reliability of operation of the circuit. The importance of getting the desired operating conditions with minimum dissipation and minimum potential stresses cannot be overemphasized. Because power dissipation is dependent on the product of voltage and current, and is a function of static behavior, and the adequacy of the signal behavior is dependent on the small-signal characteristics, coordination of the two types of design requires a coordination of the static and small-signal characteristics. This kind of coordination is easily accomplished when conductance-type data sheets are used (Fig. 5–2), and a mean-square approximation to the small-signal data may be obtained by using the polynomial technique of Appendix IV.

After the load contours are properly plotted on the input and output families of curves for a transistor, the values of the small-signal parameters at each of the intersections of the base bias contours with the load contour may be tabulated, and the appropriate values may be used with the equations derived in Chapter Four in the calculation of the amplification and the driving-point admittances. For ordinary low-frequency operation, the black-box equations may be used directly, but for high-frequency operation, the effect of base-spreading resistance must be taken into account in the design.*

---

* The nomograph provided in Appendix VIII may also be used if desired.

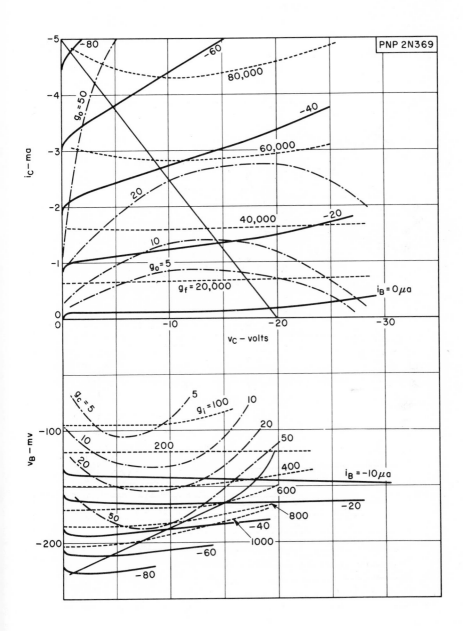

Fig. 5-2. Complete data

It is seldom possible to use a single-load contour for both the static and the small-signal operation of a transistor amplifier because the input admittance of transistors is relatively high compared to the usable output admittance level. Because the single load-line design forms the basis for handling all commonly used standard types of circuits, it is considered first. The following example shows the procedure.

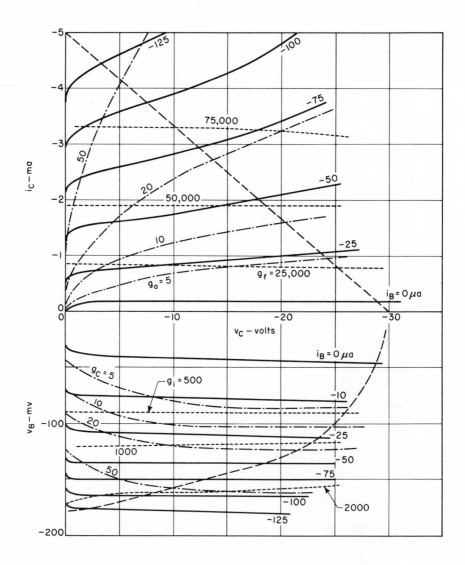

Fig. 5-3. Curves of 2N592 transistor for Example 1

EXAMPLE 1. Design an amplifier utilizing a type 2N592 (34S) transistor, the supply voltage being 30 volts, and the circuit as in Fig. 4–1. Calculate the amplification as a function of base current, and select operating conditions that will limit the distortion to five percent. Determine the values of the intrinsic parameters $g_{i'}$ and $g_{f'}$, using Eqs. (13) and (15) in Chapter Two. The load resistance is 6000 ohms, and the base-spreading resistance is 230 ohms.

The static and small-signal data for the transistor are listed in Table I.

TABLE I

Parameter and Variable Data

I_b μa	V_c volts	g_i $\mu mhos$	g_f $\mu mhos$	g_o $\mu mhos$	g_c $\mu mhos$	$g_{i'}$ $\mu mhos$	$g_{f'}$ $\mu mhos$	I_c ma
25	24	900	30,000	5.2	15	1135	37,830	1.0
50	18	1300	52,000	13	30	1860	74,150	2.0
75	12.3	1700	70,000	26	45	2794	115,000	2.95
100	7.6	2000	80,000	44	80	3700	148,000	3.72
125	3.4	2200	90,000	70	120	4453	182,200	4.42

These data show that if correction for base-spreading resistance is important, the selected values for the contours for g_i and g_f must be more closely spaced for high values of base current if good data on $g_{i'}$ and $g_{f'}$ are to result. The extra values are required in the calculation of the value of the expression $(1 - g_i r_{b'})$ in Eqs. (13) and (15) in Chapter Two because the product $g_i r_{b'}$ may have a value approaching unity. The contours presented in Fig. 5–3 are of limited direct use for design at high frequency for the same reason. Because of the effect of the base-spreading resistance and emitter-current choking effects, the value of g_f can reach a maximum and then decrease slowly as the collector current is gradually increased (Fig. 5–4).

The amplifications and the driving-point admittances may now be determined. For this calculation, it is convenient to take the values of R_s of zero, 500, 2000, and 10,000 ohms to show the effect of the source impedance. Typical results are listed in Table II.

TABLE II

Amplifications and Admittances

Bias	K_o	K_{500}	K_{2000}	$K_{10,000}$	Y_i	$Y_{o\ min}$	$Y_{o\ max}$
25	−175	−118	−60.2	−16.6	950	5.2	14.0 μmho
50	−287	−169	−75	−21.5	1424	13	28.8
75	−370	−183	−73.3	−17.4	1900	26	43.9
100	−380	−175	−66.4	−15.4	2340	44	78.5
125	−381	−173	−64	−13.7	2670	70	118

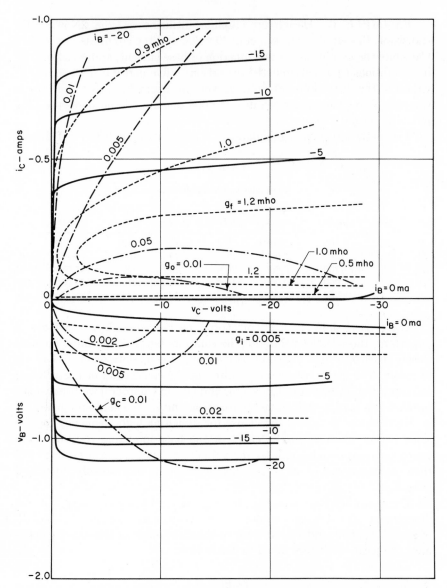

Fig. 5-4. Loop-back in forward conductance contours for Example 1

The values of Y_i may be calculated both on the basis of the straight black-box parameters and also on the basis of the intrinsic parameters, and give approximately the same results. In a similar manner, the values of $Y_{o\,min}$ are the value of output admittance with $R_s = 0$, and $Y_{o\,max}$ the value with $R_s = 10,000$ ohms.

In Eq. 10, Appendix II, the distortion in an amplifier, assuming a linear variation of amplification with bias current, reaches five percent when the maximum amplification is fifty percent greater than the minimum, or, with a minimum amplification of 20, the maximum would be 30. The usable ranges are tabulated in Table III.

TABLE III

Amplification and Distortion

Bias range	Amplification range	Nominal distortion	R_s
50 to 125	−287 to −381	3.5%	0
25 to 125	−118 to −175	4.9%	500
25 to 125	−60.2 to −75 to −64	1.4 (third)	2,000
25 to 125	−16.6 to −21.5 to −13.7	2.7 (third)	10,000

The best operating conditions for minimum distortion are with an input source impedance of about 2000 ohms because the voltage gain is considerable and the distortion also is quite small. For a more accurate calculation of distortion with $R_s > 2000$ ohms, the technique of Appendix IV should be used.

After the bias ranges have been selected for the amplifier as a function of the source resistance, R_s, the required value of base-bias resistance may be selected. Table III shows that the range of bias is from 25 to 125 micro-amperes, giving a Q-point current of about 75 microamperes. Since the supply voltage is 30 volts, the bias resistance required is

$$R_b = 30/75 \times 10^{-6} = 400,000 \text{ ohms}$$

The input coupling capacitance, C_c, is determined in terms of the input admittance calculated in Table II. The capacitance may be determined in terms of the minimum operating frequency f_1 and the equation

$$C_c = Y_i/2\pi f_1$$

A rather large value of capacitance normally is required because the input admittance for the transistor is large.

5.2 Compound Load Lines

A transistor R-C amplifier is seldom used under conditions that a simple load-line configuration applies. Consequently, the problem of handling compound load lines is of considerable importance to the circuit designer. First, a static load line must be plotted as has already been described, and then a suitable static operating point must be selected and the dynamic or active load line determined.

The load resistance selected for use with a transistor must provide the amount of collector current required for proper operation. This selection is one of the most important, yet poorly understood operations to be performed. The maximum available collector current must be sufficiently large so that the peak current required under load can be obtained without

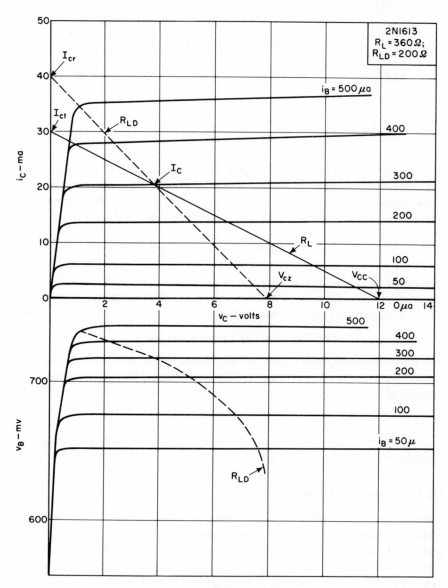

Fig. 5-5. Combination load lines

driving the transistor into saturation. For this reason, the maximum current at saturation along the static load line should be greater than 0.6 of.the peak-loaded collector current (Fig. 5–5).

The positioning of the dynamic load contour for maximum available balanced output signal, given specified values of static load resistance and dynamic resistance, may be established in terms of the ratio of the resistances

$$t = R_{LD}/R_L \quad \text{or} \quad R_{LD} = tR_L \tag{1}$$

The coordinates of the static operating point in terms of the supply voltage and the static resistance are then

$$V_C = tV_{CC}/(t+1) \tag{2}$$

$$I_C = V_{CC}/R_L(t+1) \tag{3}$$

These equations are derived by the simultaneous solution of the basic relations

$$V_C = V_{cz} - tI_CR_L \tag{4}$$

$$I_C = I_{ct} - V_C/R_L \tag{5}$$

$$V_c = V_{CC} - I_CR_L \tag{6}$$

$$I_C = I_{cr} - V_C/tR_L \tag{7}$$

$$V_{cz} = 2V_c \tag{8}$$

$$I_{cr} = 2I_C \tag{9}$$

In these equations, the points specifying I_{cr} and I_{ct} are shown in Fig. 5–5.

The above equations show that the value of I_{cr} need be only somewhat greater than the value of I_{ct}. In no case, with symmetric deviation, can it be as great as twice I_{ct}, since it has to have a value twice I_C. For this reason, a convenient starting point for design of a transistor amplifier is the selection of the collector current under dynamic saturation conditions. The value of the static saturation current selected may be approximately three-quarters of the dynamic saturation current, and its product with the collector supply voltage should be less than twice the rated collector dissipation if the peak transistor dissipation is kept within bounds. Then setting the static saturation current at three-fourths of the dynamic value leads to a dynamic load resistance half the static value, or $t = 0.5$.

Since combination load lines must be used with transformer coupled amplifiers and many transistorized amplifiers, the general technique of handling such designs is described next, and the application to transformer-coupled amplifiers is considered in Chapter Seven.

When an amplifier having different static and dynamic load lines is required, the design procedure followed differs in minor details from that for the simpler form of amplifier. First the static and dynamic load lines are plotted, and the static operating point, the Q-point, is located as described above. It is unnecessary for the static load line to be transcribed to the input family, as the signal behavior is controlled by the dynamic load line. The intersections of the dynamic contour with the various base-current contours are transferred to the input family just as has already been described, and the small-signal calculations are made using the parameter values read at respective intersections along these contours. The complete procedure is required even with cathode followers and emitter followers. ALL SMALL-SIGNAL CALCULATIONS MUST BE BASED ON DATA TAKEN FROM THE ACTIVE OR DYNAMIC LOAD CONTOURS.

EXAMPLE 2.   Design an amplifier using the 2N592 transistor, with a static load resistance for the collector circuit of 10,000 ohms, and a dynamic load resistance of 5000 ohms. The collector supply voltage is 25 volts.

The calculation of $g_{i'}$ and $g_{f'}$ and the remaining corresponding calculations made in Example 1 are left for the reader.

First the load contours are drawn as shown in Fig. 5–5. Then the small-signal data may be tabulated and the various calculations performed. Input conditions for the amplifier are taken the same as in Ex. 1. The nominal value of I_{ct} is 2.5 milliamperes, and using Eq. (2) the collector voltage at the Q-point is 8.3 volts. The static collector current is 1.67 ma. Solving Eqs. (2) and (3) for I_{cr} in terms of V_{CC}, R_L, and t gives

$$I_{cr} = 2V_{CC}/R_L(1 + t) \tag{10}$$

Substituting gives a peak dynamic collector current of 3.33 ma. The dynamic load line passes through the points $(-16.7, 0)$ and $(0, -3.33)$.

The small-signal data as a function of base bias are listed in Table IV.

TABLE IV

I_b	V_c	I_c	g_i	g_f	g_o	g_c
0	15.9	0.16	...	...	...	...
25	12.5	0.84	850	25,000	6	13
50	8.3	1.70	1300	45,000	17	32
75	4.1	2.52	1600	61,000	40	55
100	0.9	3.14	2000	72,000	110	200

Using the value of R_{LD} of 5000 ohms and the trial values of R_s of zero, 500, 2000, and 10,000 ohms, the amplifications and conductances may be tabulated as in Table V.

TABLE V

I_b	K_o	K_{500}	K_{2000}	$K_{10,000}$	Y_i	$Y_{o\ min}$	$Y_{o\ max}$
						micromhos	
25	−121	−84.5	−44.0	−12.4	1080	6	12.2
50	−207	−122	−44.8	−10.8	1390	17	31
75	−254	−137	−57.8	−14.1	1700	40	54
100	−232	−101	−37.7	−8.2	2580	110	196

The data given above shows that the distortion is less than five percent under the following conditions.

TABLE VI

Value of R_s	0	500 ohms	2000	10,000
Bias range	50–100	50–100	25–100	...

The data for $R_s = 10,000$ ohms are irregular, largely because of the $g_i g_c R_s R_L$ term. As a result, a least-squares smoothing of the data by orthogonal polynomials is required for determination of distortion. For values of R_s as large as 10,000 ohms, the transistor behaves as a current amplifier, and its current gain may be expressed by the equation

$$K_I = g_f/g_i \qquad (11)$$

5.3 Frequency Response

The frequency response of transistor amplifiers like those just considered is largely determined by the source impedance of the input circuit in conjunction with the input admittance characteristics of the transistor. The base-spreading resistance of the transistor may be lumped with the impedance of the voltage source in initial calculations, but it must be included separately when the source impedance is small.

The first step in making a calculation of the frequency response of a transistor amplifier is the determination of the alpha-cutoff frequency. Usually this frequency is given on the data sheet for the transistor. If it is not, however, it may be measured approximately in the laboratory. Because the value of this frequency is a wide-tolerance parameter, that is, there is a considerable range within which it may lie, it is necessary that test measurements be made on a number of sample devices. A discussion of the alpha- and beta-cutoff frequencies is included in Chapter Two.

The effective input capacitance of the transistor may be approximated next, since it is determined by the equation

$$\omega_\alpha C_i = (g_i + g_f) \doteq (g_{i'} + g_{f'}) = 2\pi f_\alpha C_i \qquad (12)$$

Because the total input capacitance is a function of both the emitter (or collector, approximately) current and the base-to-emitter voltage, the value of C_i varies from point to point over the operating area. For this reason, it would be convenient if designers had contour plots of the input capacitance as a function of collector current and the input voltage. The user then could easily determine the approximate amount of capacitance with which he must deal.

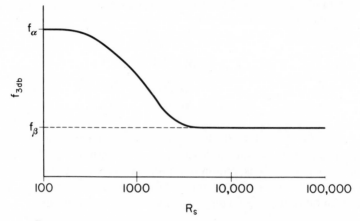

Fig. 5-6. Typical variation of 3 db frequency with R_s

Figure 5–6 shows the effect of variation of the source resistance, R_s, on the frequency response of an ideal transistor having negligible base-spreading resistance. Under such conditions, the limitation on the maximum operating frequency of the transistor is largely determined by the values of the Q-factor for the tuned circuits that may be used with the device. If the impedance of the signal source is zero, the input reactive power into the amplifier rises linearly with frequency, whereas the output power remains relatively constant until output capacitance loading causes it to decrease.

If the power-gain equation in Chapter Two is rewritten, making the substitutions

$$y_{i'} = g_{i'} + j\omega C_i,$$

where $|\,\omega C_i\,| > 1 > y_c R_L \doteq y_o R_L$ and, including $r_{b'}$, it takes the form

$$K_v K_i/(g_{f'}^2 R_L) = 1/(g_{i'} - j\omega C_i)[1 + (g_{i'} + j\omega C_i)(R_s + r_{b'})] \qquad (13)$$

where the remaining terms in the denominator have been neglected because of the above inequality. For frequencies large compared to the beta-cutoff frequency, this reduces to

$$K_v K_i/(g_{f'}^2 R_L) = 1/(-j\omega C_i)[1 + g_{i'}(R_s + r_{b'}) + j\omega C_i(R_s + r_{b'})] \qquad (14)$$

Clearly, below the beta-cutoff frequency, determined by $g_{i'} = \omega C_i$, the power gain is independent of frequency, and above, it decreases at least at a rate of three decibels per octave. Above the frequency for which the second term in brackets has equal real and imaginary parts, the decrease is at the rate of six decibels per octave.

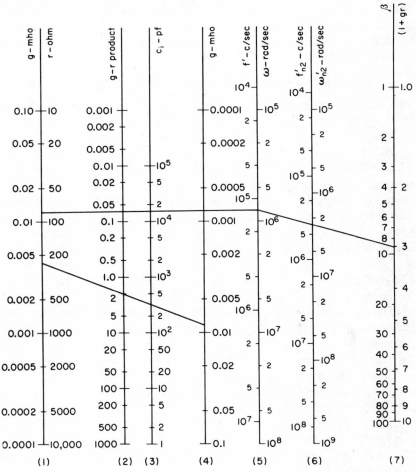

Fig. 5-7. Calculation nomograph

A nomograph may be prepared to solve the elements of this equation. One prepared for the solution of either section is shown in Fig. 5–7. One of the scales of this nomograph is designated by g and r. It may be used with values of

$$(g_{i'} + g_{f'}), \quad g_{i'}, \quad r_{b'}, \quad \text{or} \quad (R_s + r_{b'})$$

in the calculation of either frequency response or input capacitance, depending on which is required.

The first step in calculation requires use of elements 1, 3, and 5 in relating the beta-corner frequency to the input capacitance and input conductance. These lines may also be used to calculate the corner frequency generated by the total source resistance, including base-spreading resistance, and the input capacitance. Lines 1, 2, and 4 may be used to calculate the value of a conductance-resistance product, and may be used in the calculation of such products as

$$g_{i'}R_{s'}, \quad g_{i'}r_{b'}, \quad g_{i'}(R_s + r_{b'})g_{f'}R_L, \quad (g_{f'} + g_o)R_L, \quad \sigma(g')R_L, \quad g_oR_L$$

and similar terms. They may also be used for the calculation of $(g_{i'}R_s)(g_oR_L)$ and similar terms by using the $g_{i'}$ scale on line 4 for (g_oR_L) and the $(R_s + r_{b'})$ scale on line 1 for $(g_{i'}R_s)$.

If the value of $g_{i'}(R_s + r_{b'})$ is less than 25, then it is necessary to use scales 5, 6, and 7 to correct for the $g_{i'}(R_s + r_{b'})$ in the determination of the corner frequency for the voltage-gain expression, but if it is greater, then the corner frequency is approximately the beta-corner frequency determined by $\omega C_i = g_{i'}$. When the correction is required, the value of the product $g_{i'}(R_s + r_{b'})$ found on line 2 is transferred to line 7, and the intersection of the straight line joining the frequency on line 5 with the appropriate product on line 7 with line 6 gives the corrected frequency. As the value of $g_{i'}(R_s + r_{b'})$ becomes large compared to unity, the corrected frequency approaches closer to the beta-cutoff frequency.

The axis line crossing scales 1, 3, and 5 in the drawing shows the calculation for $g_{i'} = 0.013$ mho, $C_i = 16,000$ pfd, and $\omega = 2\pi f = 800,000$ radians per second. Similarly, the axis line crossing scales 1, 2, and 4 shows the calculation for $g_{i'} = 0.009$ mho, $(R_s + r_{b'}) = 230$ ohms, and a product of 2.0 units. This point on scale 2 is transferred to scale 7 to complete the calculation of ω' as 1,600,000 radians per second.

The scales 1, 3, and 5 may be used for calculation of the alpha-cutoff frequency in terms of $(g_{i'} + g_{f'})$ and C_i and the second scale for beta on line 7 may be used to convert the result to the upper noise corner frequency. The reader will find this nomograph useful for many frequency-response calculations of a similar nature.

The collector transition capacitance can introduce a feedback component that will alter the frequency response of an amplifier. In resistance-coupled amplifiers, however, the load impedance in the collector circuit is sufficiently small that its effect usually can be neglected.

EXAMPLE 3.   Determine the variation of the three decibel frequency with input resistance for the 2N592 transistor, assuming its alpha-cutoff frequency is 0.4 mc, and its beta is 40. Take $g_{f'} = 50,000$ micromhos, $g_{i'} = 1250$ micromhos, and $r_{b'} = 230$ ohms.

The beta-cutoff frequency may be read from the nomograph as 9800 cps. To do this, first the value of f_α and the value of $(g_{i'} + g_{f'})$ are used to calculate C_i, and this value of C_i used with the value of $g_{i'}$ to determine beta.

Next, the minimum value of $g_{i'}r_{b'}$ may be determined, and the maximum operating frequency is determined in two steps. First the frequency ω_i corresponding to values of C_i and $r_{b'}$ may be found with scales 1, 3, and 5, and then the value of ω_i on scale 5 converted to the maximum operating frequency on scale 6 by the use of the value $g_{i'}r_{b'}$ on scale 7. The value of ω_i is, because $C_i = 21{,}000$ pfd, approximately 34,800 cps, and a final corrected frequency of 44,900 cps. The highest possible operating frequency of this

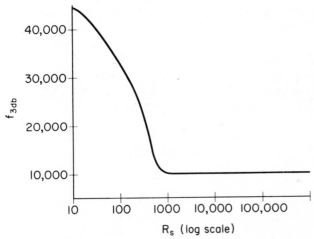

Fig. 5-8. Frequency variation for Example 3

transistor as a voltage amplifier with less than three decibels roll-off therefore is 44,900 cps, and the lowest, 9800 cps. Figure 5–8 shows the variation of the corner frequency with R_s.

5.4 Tolerance Checking

One of the important steps in the process of design of circuits is the checking to determine the consequences of variations of the values for both the fixed components like resistors and also for the values of the small-signal parameters. The most important parameter of the transistor in tolerance checking is the input admittance, inasmuch as it is the most variable important factor. The two output admittances do vary appreciably, but their effect on the design is normally much less significant because of their relatively small magnitude. The forward conductance is a most important parameter, but its value is surprisingly stable with time and from device to device of a given type of transistor. A tolerance range of plus or minus twenty percent is usually more than adequate for the forward conductance, but with many transistors the tolerance required on the input admittance may be as large as minus fifty to plus 100 percent or more.

A narrower range of tolerances is required for the fixed components used with the circuit. The process of checking for the effect of tolerances is not as complex as that which is used with triode tubes.[1] Because a good explanation of the procedure is contained in *Active Circuits*, only a sample problem is included in this book.

EXAMPLE 4.   Assume that transistors for use in the circuit of Example 1 have approximately equal values of internal transconductance (equal $g_{f'}$ values), but that the range of input conductance, for a given collector current, is from 70 percent to 150 percent of rated value. If the base-spreading resistances of all the transistors of the lot are approximately equal, calculate the amplifications and the input and output conductances for the limit transistors. Take the value of $r_{b'}$ as 230 ohms, assume that the values of $g_{f'}$, g_o, and g_c are unchanged from Example 1.

TABLE VII

g_i 50% High

I_b	V_c	g_i	g_f	g_o	g_c	$g_{i'}$	$g_{f'}$	I_c
37.5	24	1223	27,200	5.2	15	1703	37,830	1.0
75	18	1750	46,500	13.0	30	2790	74,150	2.0
112.5	12.3	2130	58,500	26	45	4191	115,000	2.95
150	7.6	2440	65,000	44	80	5550	148,000	3.72
187.5	3.4	2650	72,200	70	120	6680	182,200	4.45

I_b	K_o	K_{500}	K_{2000}	$K_{10,000}$	Y_i	$Y_{o\ min}$	$Y_{o\ max}$
37.5	−158.6	−96.6	−44.2	−11.4	1294	5.2	14.2
75	−254	−135.9	−53.1	−12.7	1914	13	29.1
112.5	−309	−141	−53.6	−12.4	2382	26	44.1
150	−309	−127.0	−46.0	−10.8	2860	44	78.6
187.5	−306	−117.2	−41.1	− 9.2	3220	70	118.2

The values of distortion for these various ranges of bias current should be determined using orthogonal polynomials. Table VIII includes only rough approximations to the actual values.

[1] *Conductance Design of Active Circuits*, by K. A. Pullen, Jr. John F. Rider Publisher, Inc., New York, 1959.

TABLE VIII

Distortion Estimates

R_s	I_b range	K range	Distortion	Component
Zero	75–187.5	254–309–306	3%	Second
500	37.5–187.5	96.6–141–117.2	2.2%	Third
2,000	37.5–187.5	44.2–53.6–41.1	1.8%	Third
10,000	37.5–187.5	11.4–12.7–9.2	1.3%	Third

A similar solution may be prepared for the condition of reduced base current and base conductance as given in Table IX.

TABLE IX

g_i 30% Low

I_b	V_c	g_i	g_f	g_o	g_c	$g_{i'}$	$g_{f'}$	I_c
17.5	24	672	32,000	5.2	15	795	37,830	1.00
35	18	1002	57,000	13	30	1304	74,150	2.00
52.5	12.3	1349	79,400	26	45	1956	115,000	2.95
70	7.6	1622	92,100	44	80	2590	148,000	3.72
87.5	3.4	1816	106,100	70	120	3120	182,200	4.45

I_b	K_o	K_{500}	K_{2000}	$K_{10,000}$	Y_i	$Y_{o\ min}$	$Y_{o\ max}$
17.5	−186.6	−137.4	−77.0	−22.9	711	5.2	13.7
35	−314.6	−138.0	−99.3	−26.5	1097	13	28.4
52.5	−420	−239	−104.4	−26.1	1508	26	43.7
70	−441	−226	−91.8	−22.0	1900	44	77.9
87.5	−450	−213.7	−83.2	−19.5	2200	70	117.4

The values of $g_{f'}$ have been copied directly from the original example, the values of $g_{i'}$ have been scaled up or down from those of the original example, and the appropriate terminal values of g_i and g_f calculated. The range of operation and distortion data may be tabulated as in Table X.

TABLE X

R_s	I_b range	K range	Distortion	Component
Zero	35–87.5	314.6–450	4.5%	Second
500	35–87.5	204.8–239–213.7	1.1%	Third
2,000	17.5–87.5	77–104.4–83.2	2.1%	Third
10,000	17.5–87.5	22.9–26.5–19.5	1.8%	Third

Once again, if reasonably exact data on distortion are desired, orthogonal polynomial techniques should be used.

The range of the effect of the parameter variations is large, and it must be allowed for in the process of design, either by the use of degeneration or by the use of special compensation techniques. Examples of such compensation may be found in the sections on feedback amplifiers, 5.7 and 5.8, in this chapter.

5.5 The Common-Base Amplifier

The common-base amplifier is seldom used as a component of an *R-C* amplifier chain because of the fact that the current gain available is somewhat less than unity. Unless the interstage coupling circuit is capable of generating a current gain, therefore, no net amplification results in a series of cascaded common-base amplifiers.

The first step in the design of this type amplifier is the selection of an appropriate load contour. As with the common-emitter amplifier, it is convenient to plot the static and dynamic load contours on the output curve family, and then transfer them to the input family. However, because the characteristic curves are commonly presented with the emitter as the reference electrode, a correction must be made for the fact that the output circuit now is from collector to base rather than collector to emitter.

This correction is easily made once the input and output contours for the load have been plotted in the common-emitter configuration. At each intersection of a base-current contour with the input load contour, the base voltage may be read and added to the collector voltage on the corresponding base-current contour for the output curve family. A new corresponding point may be plotted on the input family also, and a recorrection made if the base-current contour is not very nearly horizontal. The resulting points specify the common-base load contours for the input and the output curve families. The geometrical construction is shown graphically in Fig. 5–9.

Once the corrected operating contour has been established on both the input and the output curve families, then the balance of the design is routine. The values of the small-signal parameters are read at the selected points along the corrected operating contour and the calculations made using the Eqs. (25) through (28) derived in Chapter Four. The input admittance for the common-base amplifier is at least ten to 100 times larger than that for the corresponding common-emitter configuration, and the over-all power gain is correspondingly less, but for applications in which a wider frequency-response range is required than can be obtained with the common-emitter configuration, the common-base circuit can be helpful. The following example gives an indication of the behavior·that can be expected from a medium-frequency transistor used in the common-base configuration.

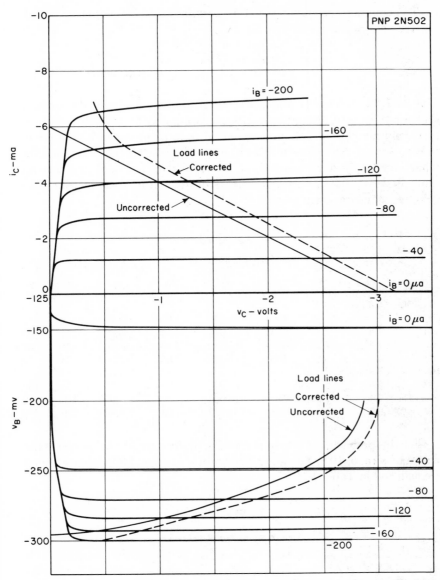

Fig. 5-9. Common-base load lines

EXAMPLE 5. Using an HA-5002 transistor (NPN type), a supply voltage of five volts, a load resistance, R_L, of 500 ohms, and a base-spreading resistance of 70 ohms, design a common-base amplifier and determine its circuit characteristics. Take the alpha-cutoff frequency of the transistor as one megacycle.

The equation for amplification for the common-base amplifier, including base-spreading resistance, is

$$K = (y_{f'} + y_o + y_{i'}y_c r_{b'})R_L/[1 + y_{i'}r_{b'} + \sigma(y')R_s$$
$$+ y_o R_L + y_i y_c(r_{b'}R_s + r_{b'}R_L + R_s R_L)] \tag{15}$$

The load line is plotted and corrected as described, giving the contour shown in Fig. 5–10. Then the small-signal data may be tabulated, and the input and forward admittances converted to intrinsic values by the use of the value for the base-spreading resistance. Then the amplifications and the input and output admittances may be calculated. The data in Table XI show these results, and include some adjustments in areas in which the data are somewhat incomplete.

TABLE XI

Small-Signal Data

I_b	I_c	V_c	g_i	g_f	$g_{i'}$	$g_{f'}$	g_o	g_c
0 μa	0.3 ma	5.0	0	0	0	0	0	0
20	1.1	4.7	1600	30,000	1,800	33,100	8	12
40	1.8	4.4	2700	51,000	3,330	63,000	14	20
60	2.4	4.05	3700	61,000	5,000	82,400	21	38
80	3.1	3.8	4500	70,000	6,560	102,000	33	50
100	3.8	3.5	5000	80,000	7,700	123,000	39	72
150	5.5	2.7	5800	105,000	9,760	177,000	70	120
200	7.4	1.85	6500	125,000	11,900	229,000	120	180
250	8.7	1.5	6700	138,000	13,200	260,000	220	300

For this problem, the source resistance, R_s, may be selected as one of the values of zero, 5, 10 or 20 ohms. The amplification and admittance values are as listed in Table XII.

TABLE XII

Amplifications and Admittances

I_b	K_o	K_5	K_{10}	K_{20}	Y_i	micromhos $Y_{o\ min}$	$Y_{o\ max}$
20	14.6	12.6	11.1	9.0	31,500	8.4	5.4
40	25.5	20.1	16.6	12.3	53,400	15.2	8.0
60	30.3	22.9	18.4	13.3	64,200	25.4	12.7
80	32.4	24.1	19.2	13.6	73,700	38.4	18.0
100	39.5	27.8	21.5	14.8	83,800	50.6	22.2
150	51.7	33.5	24.7	16.2	109,200	90.8	33.6
200	60.6	37.0	26.6	17.1	127,300	147.4	48.9
250	63.6	38.1	27.3	17.3	134,300	258	80.9

The fact that $Y_{o\,min}$ is larger than $Y_{o\,max}$ is a result of the fact that a small source impedance gives a large output admittance, and vice versa.

The range of amplification that can be used for each set of operating conditions and the distortion and available total voltage change in the output circuit may now be tabulated as in the previous examples. The required value of source resistance is almost unbelievably small because of the correspondingly large input admittance values noted in the table above. The approximate value of input resistance varies over the range from seven to thirty ohms.

TABLE XIII

Distortion Range

R_s	Δv_c	I_b range	K range	D
0	1.2	150–250 μa	51.7–63.6	2.6%
5	2.0	100–250	27.8–38.1	3.9%
10	2.55	60–250	18.4–27.3	4.9%
20	2.9	40–250	12.3–17.3	4.2%

Frequency Response: — The frequency response of the common-base amplifier is determined primarily by the susceptance component of the input admittance of the transistor. If the equation for voltage gain is revised to include the capacitance, it takes the form

$$K = (g_{f'} + g_o)R_L/[1 + \sigma(g')R_s + g_{i'}r_{b'} + j\omega C_i(R_s + r_{b'})] \qquad (16)$$

This equation has been simplified by neglecting the terms involving $y_{i'}y_c$ and y_o in both the numerator and the denominator. Two limiting conditions can be established for the maximum frequency for the amplifier, the first when R_s is small compared to $r_{b'}$, and the other when $R_s \geqq r_{b'}$. For the first condition, the following limiting equation holds

$$\omega = (1 + g_{i'}r_{b'})/r_{b'}C_i, \qquad R_s \to 0 \qquad (17)$$

For the second condition, the equation takes the form

$$\omega = (g_{i'} + g_{f'})R_s/(r_{b'} + R_s)C_i = \omega_\alpha \qquad (18)$$

The use of a voltage source gives an amplifier in which the frequency limitation depends on the value of $g_{i'}$, whereas the use of a moderately large value of R_s (a constant-current source) gives a much higher limiting frequency, approximately the alpha-cutoff frequency. This mode of operation is used extensively for high-frequency amplifiers. The further behavior of the circuit is considered in a later chapter.

5.6 The Common-Collector Amplifier

The common-collector amplifier is the transistor equivalent of the cathode follower used extensively as an impedance converter. This amplifier has properties that are useful when a low-impedance signal source is required, but it often can be replaced by a properly designed common-emitter amplifier. The procedure for design of the common-collector amplifier parallels that used with the common-base amplifier, but it differs in several important aspects. The general method of design of this circuit is first discussed in the next few paragraphs, and then an example is worked out to show the detail steps required in determining the characteristics of the circuit.

The construction procedure for the load lines required for the common-collector amplifier may be based on those used with the common-emitter amplifier. As with the common-base amplifier, an adjustment is required to correct for the changed configuration, but the correction with this circuit is for base-current flow in the output resistance. The effect of this current is to increase the voltage developed across the load resistance, and thereby to reduce the effective value of the voltage from collector to emitter (Fig. 5–10). Unless the transistor has a very small value of beta, the change that results is very small, and often may be small enough that it may be neglected.

Both a static and a dynamic load line must be constructed for use with this amplifier, as the normal dynamic value of load impedance may be a small fraction of the static value, and it is impossible to make even moderately reliable calculations of the amplifier characteristics on the basis of the static load contour alone. Under true small-signal conditions, where the excursion is very small with respect to the Q-point, such a construction may not be necessary, but if the emitter current change is appreciable, both lines must be constructed. Even under small-signal conditions, an appreciable change in gain and terminal impedances can result from loading.

Once the operating load contour has been plotted, then the values of the respective small-signal parameters at the different intersections of the load line and the base-current contours may be tabulated as has been done in previous examples. These data may be used with Eqs. (32) through (34) in Chapter Four for the calculation of the operating characteristics of the transistor emitter-follower.

The frequency-response characteristics of the emitter-follower are more complex than for either of the amplifiers previously considered because the capacitive term appears in both the numerator and the denominator of the gain expression. As a result, as the operating frequency is increased, first a knee is reached at which the amplification decreases as a function of frequency (the denominator knee), and at a higher frequency, nominally the

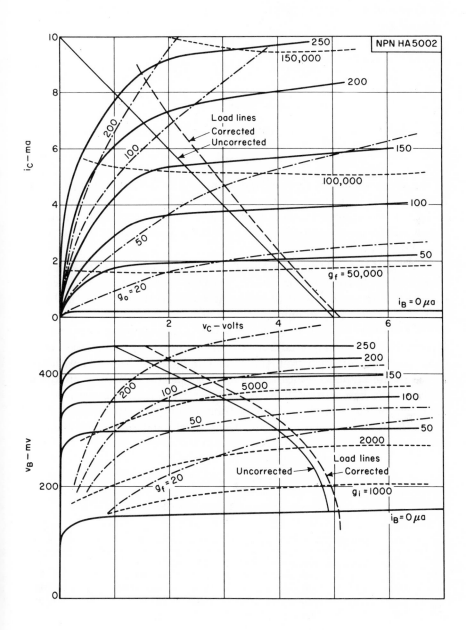

Fig. 5-10. Load lines — common-base amplifier for Example 5

alpha-cutoff frequency, the amplification once again levels off because of the knee in the numerator polynomial. The two equations that govern the behavior are:

roll-off knee

$$\omega_a = [g_{i'} + g_{f'}(R_e/\sigma(R)) + 1/\sigma(R)]/C_i \tag{19}$$

level-off knee

$$\omega_b = (g_{i'} + g_{f'})/C_i \tag{20}$$

In the first of these equations, the value of $\sigma(R)$ is defined by the equation

$$\sigma(R) = r_{b'} + R_s + R_e \tag{21}$$

In the above equations, if R_e is large compared to the balance of $\sigma(R)$, or $R_e > r_{b'} + R_s$, then the two frequencies for the two knees are about equal, and a flat frequency response can be obtained, but otherwise an equalizing circuit will be required to compensate for the roll-off between ω_a and ω_b.

EXAMPLE 6.   Determine the characteristics of an emitter-follower using a type GT 761 PNP transistor. Take the supply voltage as six volts, the value of R_e (or R_L) as 1200 ohms. Assume that the value of the base-spreading resistance is 75 ohms.

The reference load line may first be plotted as shown in Fig. 5–11 and the corrected load contour plotted from it. It is not necessary to read the values of the voltage correction from the input family as was required with the common-base amplifier, since the change in collector voltage is produced solely by the base-current flow. After the corrections are made and the corrected contour is plotted, it may be transcribed to the input curve family in the usual manner. Then the small-signal data and such static data as are required are listed in Table XIV.

TABLE XIV

Data for Common-Collector Amplifier

I_b μa	V_c volts	I_c ma	g_i $\mu mhos$	g_f $\mu mhos$	$g_{i'}$ $\mu mhos$	$g_{f'}$ $\mu mhos$	g_o $\mu mhos$	g_c $\mu mhos$
20	4.98	0.80	370	27,000	380	27,700	17	20
40	4.04	1.59	800	53,000	852	56,400	43	49
60	2.96	2.47	1600	83,000	1818	94,600	80	100
80	1.92	3.30	1940	103,000	2250	119,400	130	130
100	1.00	4.03	2200	119,000	2630	142,500	195	190

The values of g_o and g_c for this transistor are very nearly the same, indicating that the feedback conductance is extremely small. The very

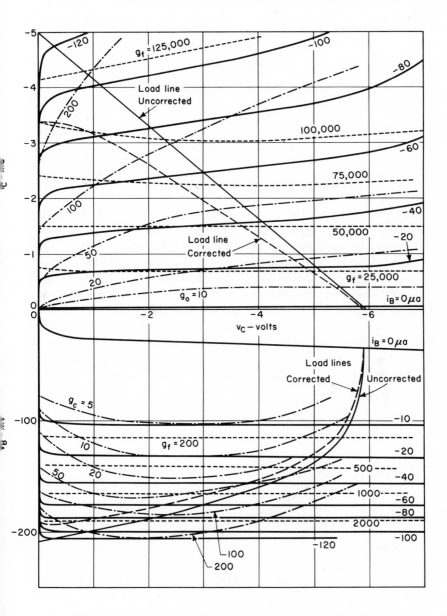

Fig. 5-11. Emitter-follower load line for Example 6.
$R_e = 1200\Omega$

small value of base-spreading resistance also is indicative of an excellent input characteristic.

The amplification and the input and output admittances of the common-collector amplifier are calculated by the use of Eqs. (32), (33), (34) in Chapter Four. The resulting data are given in Table XV.

TABLE XV

Small-Signal Behavior for Common-Collector Amplifier

I_b μa	K_o	$K_{10\ K}$	$K_{20\ K}$	$K_{50\ K}$	$K_{100\ K}$	Y_i μmho	$Y_{o\ min}$ $micromhos$	$Y_{o\ max}$
20	0.972	0.873	0.794	0.622	0.458	10.9	28,080	6010
40	0.985	0.873	0.784	0.598	0.430	12.2	57,250	6460
60	0.992	0.845	0.736	0.530	0.361	15.6	96,420	5970
80	0.994	0.844	0.734	0.527	0.357	15.3	121,600	6420
100	0.994	0.840	0.727	0.518	0.350	15.0	145,100	7150

Several things of interest can be noted from this table. The first is that whereas the amplification with zero source impedance ($R_s = 0$) rises with base current, the amplification decreases for the remaining columns. This indicates that for an intermediate value of R_s it should be possible to obtain a relatively constant value of amplification. In fact, if the value of R_s is set at 4000 ohms, the amplifications are 0.930, 0.938, 0.928, 0.929, and 0.927, values which for all practical purposes are identical.

In addition, the input admittance that is available with the circuit is rather lower than might have been expected, in that it is equivalent to

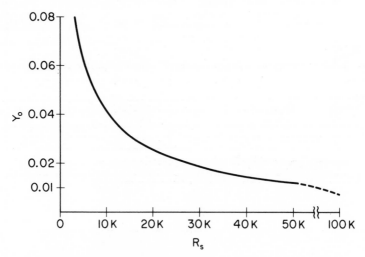

Fig. 5-12. Output admittance as a function of R_s for Example 6

60,000 to 100,000 ohms. Such a circuit has the characteristics that are required with signal repeater circuits. The output admittance, however, which is very high for values of R_s near zero, is relatively small for the higher input resistances. It is actually quite stable, as is the input admittance, corresponding to about 175 ohms compared to the 8 to 30 when the value of R_s is nearly zero.

It is of interest to see just how the output admittance of the amplifier varies with variation of the value of R_s. The data required are given in Table XVI, and the result is plotted in Fig. 5–12.

TABLE XVI

Impedance Variation — Emitter-Follower

R_s ohms	Zero	4,000	10,000	20,000	50,000	100 000
Y_o micromhos	145,100	71,800	41,400	24,800	12,000	7,150

These data are tabulated for a base current of 100 microamperes.

It is clearly evident that if the lowest possible output impedance, or highest admittance, is required with a very low source admittance, it is necessary to cascade emitter-followers. For example, using two of the circuits in cascade yields a source admittance of about 15 micromhos, and, even when used with a source resistance of 100,000 ohms, may be expected to develop an output admittance of several hundredths of a mho. It is important that a separate emitter load resistance be used with the input emitter-follower if full advantage of the transforming action is required.

The distortion developed in emitter-follower amplifiers is extremely small, but because the amplifier requires a drive signal equal to the output, the low-distortion feature is at least somewhat illusory. In addition, the distortion is very strongly dependent on the magnitude of the load admittance because the voltage developed across the admittance is re-introduced into the input circuit to help provide the stabilization. For these reasons, even more than ordinary care must be used in the design of routine emitter-followers.

The frequency response that may be obtained with the amplifier whose design is developed above may be obtained from the equations for response derived above. Because the value of the alpha-cutoff frequency for the GT-761 is listed as 10 mcs, a nominal average value for C_i may be calculated. If the average value for $g_{f'}$ is taken as 80,000 micromhos, then the value of capacitance is 0.0013 microfarad. For a value of R_s negligible compared to that for R_e, and $g_{i'}R_e \geqq 1$, the frequencies ω_b and ω_d are nearly equal, and the response is uniform to a frequency at which the simple representation for the device is inadequate. For a source resistance equal to the load resistance, R_e, then the frequency ω_d is half ω_b, and six decibels loss occurs in the transition range. For values of R_s such that $R_s \gg R_e$, then the frequency ω_d is approximately equal to the beta-cutoff frequency.

5.7 Emitter Degenerative Amplifiers

The use of some emitter degeneration in an amplifier can often improve both its static operating characteristics and its small-signal characteristics, Fig. 5–13. The use of d-c emitter stabilization in fixing the static behavior

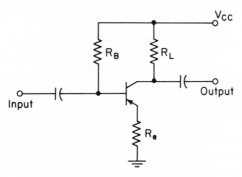

Fig. 5-13. Emitter-degenerative amplifier

is discussed in the next chapter, and the design of amplifiers with emitter stabilization of the small-signal characteristics is discussed in the next few paragraphs.

The load line for the degenerative amplifier is plotted in almost exactly the same way as that for the ordinary common-emitter amplifier. Although strictly there is a small correction required for base current, the position of the load line is usually changed but very little compared to its position for the simpler amplifier. After the load line is drawn, the static and the small-signal data are tabulated and the values of y_i and y_f are converted into the corresponding values for $y_{i'}$ and $y_{f'}$. Once the data are tabulated and converted, then the small-signal characteristics, amplification, and input and output admittance, may be calculated. The amplification of the amplifier is

$$K_d = -(y_{f'} - y_{i'}y_cR_e)R_L/[1 + y_oR_L + \sigma(y')R_e$$
$$+ y_{i'}(r_{b'} + R_s)[1 + y_c(R_e + R_L)] + y_{i'}y_cR_eR_L] \tag{22}$$

The value of $\sigma(y')R_e$ may be small or it may be large, depending on the value of R_e selected for use. Because the value of $\sigma(y')$ is approximately equal to $y_{f'}$, the amplification can be determined almost completely by the ratio of R_L/R_e if the value of R_e selected is such that the denominator may be reduced to approximately $\sigma(y')R_e$. This requires that the remaining terms of the denominator sum to a value just a little greater than unity, and the $\sigma(y')R_e$ term be at least ten. Then the amplification equation takes the form

$$K_d = -y_{f'}R_L/[1 + \sigma(y')R_e] \doteq -R_L/R_e \qquad (23)$$

The input admittance, Y_{id}, of the degenerative amplifier is appreciably smaller than that for the ordinary amplifier as a consequence of the $\sigma(y')R_e$ term in the denominator. The approximate ratio of the input admittance for the conventional amplifier to that for the degenerative amplifier is given by the equation

$$\begin{aligned} Y_{is}/Y_{ids} &\doteq 1 + [\sigma(y')R_e + y_{i'}y_cR_e\sigma R]/[1 + y_oR_L \\ &\quad + y_{i'}(r_{b'} + R_s)(1 + y_cR_L)] \end{aligned} \qquad (24)$$

where σR is defined as $\sigma R = (r_{b'} + R_s + R_L)$ and Y_{ids} is

$$\begin{aligned} Y_{ids} &= y_{i'}[1 + y_c(R_e + R_L)]/[1 + y_oR_L + y_{i'}(r_{b'} + R_s) \\ &\quad + \sigma(y')R_e + y_{i'}y_c(\sigma RR_e + R_L(r_{b'} + R_s))] \end{aligned} \qquad (25)$$

In these equations, the corresponding forms at the transistor terminals, Y_{id}, and Y_i/Y_{id}, may be obtained by letting R_s be zero. Also, the value of R_e may be assumed to be small compared to R_L unless an extremely large amount of degeneration is required. The denominator of the quotient on the right-hand side of Eq. (24) normally has a value of approximately unity, in which case Eq. (24) may be reduced to the simplified form

$$Y_i/Y_{id} \doteq 1 + \sigma(y')R_e \qquad (26)$$

The value obtained from Eq. (26) is within a factor of two of the correct value even with large values of $r_{b'}$.

The output admittance of the degenerative amplifier is also decreased as a result of the emitter degeneration. The ratio of the output admittances for the two conditions is given by the equation

$$\begin{aligned} Y_o/Y_{od} &\doteq [(R_s + r_{b'})/\sigma R][1 + \langle \sigma(y')R_e + y_{i'}y_cR_eR_L\rangle/ \\ &\quad \langle 1 + y_oR_L + y_{i'}(r_{b'} + R_s) + \sigma(y')R_e \\ &\quad + y_{i'}y_c[(r_{b'} + R_s)(R_e + R_L) + R_eR_L]\rangle] \end{aligned} \qquad (27)$$

Neglecting R_L, as is usually done, the equation reduces to

$$Y_o/Y_{od} \doteq [(r_{b'} + R_s)/\sigma R][1 + \langle \sigma(y')R_e\rangle/\langle 1 + y_{i'}(r_{b'} + R_s)\rangle] \qquad (27a)$$

where the reduced value of Y_{od} is given by the equation

$$\begin{aligned} Y_{od} &= [y_o + y_{i'}y_c\sigma R]/[1 + y_{i'}(r_{b'} + R_s) + \sigma(y')R_e \\ &\quad + y_{i'}y_c(r_{b'} + R_s)R_e] \end{aligned} \qquad (28)$$

The value of $(r_{b'} + R_s)/\sigma R$ is normally rather close to unity, with the result that the ratio is largely determined by the value of the $\sigma(y')R_e$ term. The over-all value may be as large as from ten to fifty, depending on the amount of degeneration used.

Because the degenerated value of output admittance is so small, the effective admittance of the stage as a whole is dependent primarily on the value of R_L, which has been selected for use. In all but the common-collector amplifier, among the simple structures, the total admittance is almost completely dependent on the loading of the output circuit itself.

EXAMPLE 7. Design a degenerative amplifier using the HA5003 transistor with a collector supply voltage of 20 volts and a load impedance of 2000 ohms. Take $f_\alpha = 1.5$ megacycles. Select a value of R_e that can limit the over-all amplification of the circuit to 0.2 of its nominal value determined from $y_{f'}R_L$.

The load lines may be plotted as shown in Fig. 5–2. The approximate base-spreading resistance is 360 ohms, as calculated from the values of forward conductance and input conductance. If the base bias current of 40 microamperes is selected for the calculation of the degeneration factor, then $\sigma(y')R_e = 4$, giving a value of R_e of approximately 17 ohms. The error in the collector voltage due to base current may now be calculated; because the base current is a maximum of approximately 60 microamperes, an error of 0.001 volt is introduced, a negligible amount.

Once the suitability of the basic load line has been established, then the data may be tabulated for the calculation of the operating behavior of the transistor. The small-signal data are given in Table XVII.

TABLE XVII

Data for Emitter-Degenerative Amplifier

I_b μa	I_c ma	y_i μmho	y_f μmho	y_o μmho	y_c μmho	$y_{i'}$ μmho	$y_{f'}$ μmho	V_c
0	1.4	0	0	0	0	0	0	17
20	4.36	670	115,000	43	130	881	151,300	11
40	6.8	1050	150,000	85	190	1688	241,100	6.2
60	8.6	1500	148,500	200	380	3260	301,000	2.7

In this problem, the largest value of y_f has been calculated back from $y_{f'}$ which has been estimated from the collector current and the value of the base-spreading resistance. The technique is described in Chapter Four.

The values of the amplification and the input and output admittance may be calculated from the data in Table XVII. For this calculation, the values of R_s of zero, 500, 2000, and 10,000 ohms may be used.

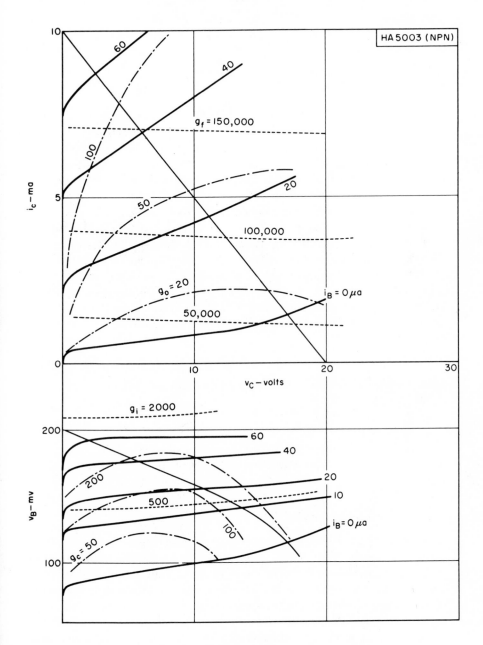

Fig. 5-14. Load lines for degenerative amplifier
HA 5003 (NPN) for Example 7

TABLE XVIII

Equivalent Circuit Parameters

I_b	K_0	K_{500}	K_{2000}	$K_{10,000}$	Y_{id}	Y_{odo}	Y_{od50}
20	-74.0	-65.4	-48.0	-19.9	273	21.2	80.8
40	-78.6	-67.8	-44.7	-16.3	379	33.6	115.8
60	-69.7	-52.3	-29.9	-9.1	664	77.2	198

These data show that the relative input admittance is still rather large, although it has been appreciably decreased by the degeneration. Because the maximum output admittance listed in the table is less than 200 micromhos, the total admittance, combining the 500 micromhos for the 2000-ohm load and the output admittance for the transistor, is less than 700 micromhos or more than 1400 ohms.

The amount of distortion that results in this circuit can be calculated by either the use of the distortion equations or by orthogonal techniques from the amplification data in Table XVIII. Because the procedures are the same as those used in previous examples, they will not be repeated here.

The frequency response may be determined by substituting $g_{i'} + j\omega C_i$ for $y_{i'}$ and evaluating the relative magnitudes of the frequency-independent and the frequency-dependent terms. If the $y_{i'}y_c$ terms in the numerator are neglected, and the denominator is solved for frequency, the resulting equation is

$$\omega = [1 + g_o R_L + (g_{i'} + g_{f'})R_e + g_{i'}(r_{b'} + R_s)]/[C_i \sigma R] \qquad (29)$$

If the value of R_s is small, then this equation may be simplified to the form

$$\omega = [1 + g_o R_L + (g_{i'} + g_{f'})R_e]/[C_i(r_{b'} + R_e)] \qquad (30)$$

This frequency is nearly equal to the alpha-cutoff frequency if $R_e > (r_{b'} + R_s)$, and otherwise is between the alpha- and beta-cutoff frequencies. The value of ω may be calculated with the help of the nomograph in Fig. 5–7.

5.8 Another Feedback Amplifier

Another form of feedback amplifier may be constructed using collector-to-base feedback (Fig. 5–15). This arrangement stabilizes the amplification of the circuit, and also increases its input admittance. There is one special problem to solve with this amplifier, namely, taking proper account of the feedback resistor, Y, in the static design.

This feedback element introduces a shunt load resistance from collector to base, a voltage usually somewhat above ground potential, and as a result it introduces a small alteration in the effective supply voltage for the amplifier. The current drawn by the feedback resistor normally is negligible in comparison to the load current drawn by the transistor. Otherwise, the correction process becomes rather complex, as both voltage and current corrections are required.

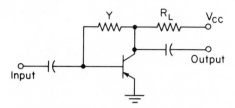

Fig. 5-15. Feedback amplifier — type II

The feedback current introduced into the base lead of the transistor is in phase-opposition to the input current introduced into the transistor, thereby decreasing the over-all current gain. This current flow does not effect the position of the load contour significantly, however, but it reduces the signal current available for the base of the transistor. The amplification equations automatically take this division into account. The equations are

$$K = -[y_{f'} - Y(1 - y_{i'}r_{b'})]R_L/[1 + YR_s + y_{i'}(r_{b'} + R_s)$$
$$\times (1 + y_cR_L + YR_L) + y_oR_L + \sigma(y')R_sYR_L] \qquad (31)$$

The input and output admittances are defined by the equations

$$Y_i = [y_{i'}(1 + Yr_{b'}) + y_{i'}y_cR_L(1 + Yr_{b'}) + \sigma(y')YR_L]/$$
$$[1 + y_oR_L + y_{i'}r_{b'}(1 + y_cR_L + YR_L)] \qquad (32)$$

$$Y_o = [y_o(1 + YR_s) + y_{i'}y_c(r_{b'} + R_s) + Y(1 + y_{i'}r_{b'})]/$$
$$[1 + y_{i'}(r_{b'} + R_s) + YR_s] \qquad (33)$$

EXAMPLE 8.   Design an amplifier using a collector-to-base feedback circuit. Select a value of Y such that the gain is reduced to 0.2 of the undegenerated value. Use an HA-5003 transistor with a collector supply voltage of 20 volts, a load impedance of 2000 ohms, and f_α of 1.5 mcs.

As in Ex. 7, the first step is to determine the value of Y required by the use of the equation

$$\sigma(y')R_sYR_L = 4$$

with $R_s = 500$, 2000, and 10,000 ohms. Then the correction voltage required to compensate for the feedback network may be determined and the correction introduced into the circuit. Finally, the amplification and driving-point admittances may be calculated in the usual way. Because a typical value of $\sigma(y')$ is 0.1, the value of Y, with $R_s = 500$, is approximately 25,000 ohms (40 micromhos).

5.9 Summary

Comparison of the various amplifier designs described in this chapter shows the differences in operating characteristics and indicates the areas of application for each. Factors which affect the selection of configuration include power gain, current gain, frequency characteristics, and distortion.

The common-emitter configuration is normally used because it has a relatively high input impedance and large current, voltage, and power gains. The high value of gain can be obtained for low-frequency signals, but the bandwidth available is considerably less than for the other configurations. Distortion is large but can be controlled by degeneration.

The common-base amplifier has a very low input impedance, and a current gain slightly less than unity. This configuration has a bandwidth approximately equal to that of the common-emitter amplifier with a low-impedance source and a maximum bandwidth equal to the alpha-cutoff frequency with a high-impedance source. It must be used with some form of transformer as an interstage device if an over-all power gain is to result in cascaded common-base amplifiers. The use of the common-base configuration minimizes feedback from output to input and, as a result, simplifies the design of high-frequency amplifier cascades.

The common-collector amplifier has a high input impedance, possibly many times that for the common-emitter configuration, and a comparatively high output admittance also. Because the output signal developed is re-introduced into the input, the distortion in this amplifier is extremely small. The current gain is large compared to unity, but the voltage gain is slightly less than unity.

The emitter-degenerated amplifier combines some of the properties of the common-emitter and the common-collector amplifiers, using the emitter resistance to improve the input characteristics and to reduce the over-all distortion. This circuit trades gain for reduced distortion and increased input impedance.

The common-collector amplifier can be used to provide input signal to a common-base or a common-emitter amplifier, giving in the former the transistor equivalent of the cathode-coupled amplifier and in the latter a follower-isolation amplifier. In these arrangements, the common-collector amplifier functions as a coupling transformer.

The shunt-feedback amplifier, with an impedance connected from its collector to its base, has a very low input impedance and uses current feedback instead of voltage as is the case with the emitter-degenerated form. This arrangement is used with very low impedance-signal sources or applications in which current-source operation is required with very small values of input impedance.

CHAPTER SIX

Circuit Stabilization

6.0 Introduction

One of the major problems in the use of transistor circuits is the stabilization of operating conditions so that the circuit can give the required performance over an adequate range of environmental conditions.

6.1 Thermal Factors

There are two principal thermal factors that affect the stability of transistor circuits, and others of lesser importance. The first of these thermal factors is the reverse-leakage current of the collector-base junction, so-called I_{co}, and the second the variation of $V_b(V_{be})$ with temperature. The leakage current increases rapidly as the temperature of the transistor is increased, and limits the conditions under which the transistor can provide effective operation (Fig. 6–1). This current, in conjunction with the current gain of the transistor, limits the minimum usable current through the common-emitter amplifier, thereby restricting the available range of operation.

Strictly, it is possible to use the transistor in the

common-emitter circuit with very small values of currents, but the non-linearity of the behavior of the device when the base current has a reverse polarity is so pronounced that it is not practical to attempt to do so. The currents in a transistor may be expressed in terms of the leakage current by the equation

$$I_B = [(1 - \alpha)I_E - I_{co}] = [y_{i'}I_E/(y_{i'} + y_{f'}) - I_{co}] \tag{1}$$

$$I_C = \alpha I_E + I_{co} = [y_{f'}I_E/(y_{i'} + y_{f'}) + I_{co}] \tag{2}$$

Solving Eq. 2 for I_E gives

$$I_E = (I_C - I_{co})/\alpha = (y_{i'} + y_{f'})(I_C - I_{co})/y_{f'} \tag{3}$$

These equations may be converted into any alternate form that might prove useful.

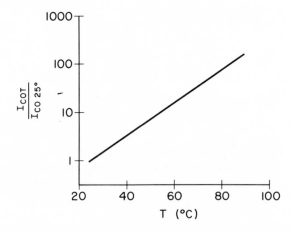

Fig. 6-1. Ratio of I_{co} at temperature T to value at $T = 25°C$

The variation of the base-to-emitter voltage with temperature for fixed magnitudes of base and emitter current is the second important thermal property of a transistor requiring compensation. The voltage between base and emitter affects the static operation of the transistor, and it also affects the small-signal operation. Because the static, or Q-point for the transistor varies rapidly with temperature if the base voltage is fixed, it is necessary to fix the Q-point in a way to assure that a full range of operating conditions are available over the required range of operating temperature. The static stability must be determined in terms of the practical circuit in use, and the circuit must be designed to provide the required stability.

The factors controlling the stability of a transistor circuit may be readily derived in terms of the circuit shown in Fig. 6–2. This circuit is the general bias circuit, and it can be readily converted into any of the three basic bias circuits.[1] By taking R_{c2} and R_e both equal to zero, and R_b infinite,

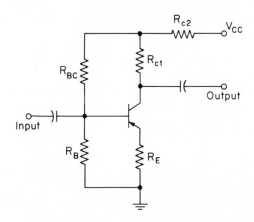

Fig. 6-2. Basic stabilizing circuit

the circuit reduces to the unstabilized form, and by taking $R_{c1} = 0$, it gives the simple feedback stabilizer.

The analysis of the bias circuit may be performed topologically, or it may be performed in terms of the equations

$$V_{CC} = (i_f + i_c)R_{c2} + i_f R_{bc} + i_b r_{b'} + i_e R_e + v_{b'e} \qquad (4)$$

$$V_{BB} = -(i_f - i_b)R_b + i_b r_{b'} + i_e R_e \qquad (5)$$

$$i_b = (1 - \alpha)i_e - I_{co} = y_{i'}i_e/(y_{i'} + y_{f'}) - I_{co} \qquad (6)$$

$$i_c = \alpha i_e + I_{co} = y_{f'}i_e/(y_{i'} + y_{f'}) + I_{co} \qquad (7)$$

Equations (6) and (7) are given in two forms. The first of the forms may be used with static calculations, and the second with small-signal calculations. In the latter form, they may be used extensively in basic small-signal derivations, but the value of I_{co}, being essentially constant, is neglected.

These Eqs. (4) through (7) may be solved for the emitter current in terms of the base voltage and the leakage current to give

$$i_e = \langle [R_b R_{bc} + r_{b'}(R_b + R_{bc} + R_{c2})]I_{co} + (R_b + R_{bc} + R_{c2})v_{b'} \rangle / \langle (1 - \alpha)$$
$$[R_b R_{bc} + r_{b'}(R_b + R_{bc} + R_{c2})] + R_b R_{c2} + R_b R_e + R_{bc}R_e + R_{c2}R_e \rangle \qquad (8)$$

[1] H. Hellerman, "A Generalized Theory of Transistor Bias Circuits," *Paper 57-1023*, American Institute of Electrical Engineers, New York.

Taking the partial derivatives first with respect to I_{co} and then with respect to $V_{b'}$ gives the following slopes

$$S_e = \partial i_e / \partial I_{co} = [R_b R_{bc} + r_{b'}(R_b + R_{bc} + R_{c2})]/[D] \tag{9}$$

where

$$[D] = \langle (1 - \alpha)[R_b R_{bc} + r_{b'}(R_b + R_{bc} + R_{c2})] + R_b R_{c2} \\ + R_b R_e + R_{bc} R_e + R_{c2} R_e \rangle$$

$$S_{e'} = \partial i_e / \partial v_{b'} = (R_b + R_{bc} + R_{c2})/[D] \tag{10}$$

Substituting $\alpha = y_{f'}/(y_{i'} + y_{f'})$ in these expressions gives the small-signal form

$$\partial i_e / \partial I_{co} = (y_{i'} + y_{f'})[R_b R_{bc} + r_{b'}(R_b + R_{bc} + R_{c2})]/[D'] \tag{9a}$$

$$[D'] = \langle y_{i'}[R_b R_{bc} + r_{b'}(R_b + R_{bc} + R_{c2})] \\ + [R_b R_{c2} + R_b R_e + R_{bc} R_e + R_{c2} R_e](y_{i'} + y_{f'}) \rangle$$

$$S_{e'} = \partial i_e / \partial v_{b'} = (y_{i'} + y_{f'})(R_b + R_{bc} + R_{c2})/[D'] \tag{10a}$$

These equations may be modified to give the change in the signal or active collector current by replacing the numerator $(y_{i'} + y_{f'})$ by $(y_{f'})$

$$S_{c1} = \partial i_c / \partial I_{co}$$
$$= y_{f'}[R_b R_{bc} + r_{b'}(R_b + R_{bc} + R_{c2})]/[D'] \tag{11}$$

$$S_{c1'} = i_c / \partial v_{b'}$$
$$= y_{f'}(R_b + R_{bc} + R_{c2})/[D'] = \beta S_{e'} \tag{12}$$

Because the information often required of the partial derivative with respect to I_{co} is the effective current gain, Eq. (11) may be converted into the form*

$$S_{c1} = \beta/[1 + (1 + \beta)(R_b R_e + R_b R_{c2} + R_e R_{c2} + R_{bc} R_e)/ \\ (R_b R_{bc} + r_{b'}(R_b + R_{bc} + R_{c2}))] \tag{13}$$

For $R_e = 0$ and R_b infinite, this equation reduces to

$$S_{c1} = \beta/[1 + (1 + \beta)R_{c2}/(R_{bc} + r_{b'})] \tag{14}$$

Evidently, R_{c1} does not enter into the stabilization of the emitter or the collector current, although it will enter into the stabilization of the collector voltage through the product $i_c R_{c1}$.

Similarly, with $R_{c2} = 0$, Eq. (13) reduces to

$$S_{c1} = \beta/[1 + (1 + \beta)(R_b R_e + R_{bc} R_e)/(R_b R_{bc} + r_{b'}(R_b + R_{bc}))] \tag{15}$$

---

* Since this is a static analysis, α and β may be used.

Clearly, the emitter resistance is an important factor in this configuration, as the partial derivative decreases rapidly for increasing values of R_e. Because the change in collector current in these equations is the change in the active component, to obtain the total current change it is necessary to add unity (to add I_{co}) to S_{c1} to get S_c.[2] The remaining stability factors that on occasion may be used are all directly derivable from S_e, $S_{e'}$, S_{c1}, and $S_{c'}$. These four are normally the only ones required in circuit design.

The problem in stabilizing a transistor circuit is one of reducing the numerical value of the stability factor to the point where variations introduced by either $v_{b'}$ or I_{co} are small enough to permit adequate operation of the stage. In fact, the two stability factors are related by the equations

$$S_{c'} = S_{c1}/[r_{b'} + R_b R_{bc}/(R_b + R_{bc} + R_{c2})] \qquad (16)$$

or

$$S_{e'} = S_e/[r_{b'} + R_b R_{bc}/(R_b + R_{bc} + R_{c2})] \qquad (17)$$

These equations indicate that operating stability in terms of the base voltage (internal) is improved by an increase in the value of $r_{b'}$. This is readily provided by inserting an external resistance in the base lead in series with $r_{b'}$. Such a circuit modification does not affect the current gain of the amplifier, but it may reduce the voltage gain.

EXAMPLE 1.   Determine the stability factors to the collector current for a transistor having a current gain, β, of 100, a value of $r_{b'}$ of 500 ohms, $R_{c2} = 5000$ ohms, $I_{cq} (= I_C) = 1.0$ ma, R_{bc} suitable for the required collector current with $V_{cc} = 10$ volts. Then introduce three volts of emitter degeneration, and redetermine the stability factors.

For the first condition, the voltage across R_{bc} is five volts, and R_{bc} has a value of 500,000 ohms. An open circuit exists in the R_b position. In this configuration the maximum value of S_{c1} (minimum stability) is obtained when not R_{c2} but R_{c1}, is 5000 ohms. The corresponding value of S_{c1} is exactly equal to the beta of the transistor, or 100. If, however, R_{c2} is 5000 ohms and R_{bc} 500,000 ohms, the value of S_{c1} then is 49.7, giving a substantial improvement in stability.

The value of R_e must be 3000 ohms for three volts of degeneration to be developed in the emitter circuit. Since approximately 10 microamperes of current must flow in the base lead itself, the current flow in the divider chain, R_b—R_{bc}—R_{c2}, designated i_f, should be greater than twice the base current, or between 30 and 50 microamperes. Taking i_f as 50 microamperes, then the values of R_b and R_{bc} are approximately 75,000 and 40,000 ohms

---

[2] These derivations parallel those in *Junction Transistor Electronics*, by R. B. Hurley. John Wiley & Sons, Inc., New York, 1959.

respectively. The over-all stability factor, S_{c1}, with this arrangement is $S_{c1} = 4.93$. This means that a change in the leakage current in the base of the transistor is accompanied by a total collector-current change of only $(1 + S_{c1})I_{co}$ or 59.3 microamperes instead of the one milliampere change in the uncompensated arrangement.

In the process of introduction of the stabilization, the voltage and current gains for the transistor have been degraded. The input conductance of the transistor, correcting for degeneration, may be as small as 3.3 micromhos, and it has a conductance of approximately fifty micromhos in parallel with it, giving a net current gain of possibly five. If, however, the resistor R_e is bypassed for signal-frequency currents, then only the feedback from the collector to the base degrades the current gain, and then only if the load resistance is placed at R_{c2} rather than R_{c1}. The input conductance of the transistor itself is 400 micromhos (2500 ohms), and the voltage gain, assuming a low-impedance signal source, is 200. (For the source impedance to be low, the loading effects of R_{bc} and R_b on the source voltage must be negligible.) This means that the apparent value of the resistance of R_{bc} will be decreased by a factor of 201, to approximately 225 ohms. The current gain of the amplifier is also reduced by this feedback, the final value being approximately 8.25. The over-all voltage gain will also deteriorate if the signal source has appreciable impedance.

Returning the feedback resistor to R_{c2} instead of to the collector supply has severely deteriorated the characteristics of the amplifier, and has not introduced any noteworthy compensating advantages. If R_{c2} is reduced to zero, and the value of R_{c1} made 5000 ohms, and the value of R_{bc} readjusted accordingly, this loading does not occur, and the stability is reduced very slightly. The new value of S_{c1} is 5.05, or negligibly poorer than the previous best value of 4.93. The new value for R_{bc} is 140,000 ohms, and the equivalent parallel resistance for R_b and R_{bc} is 49,000 ohms, or almost an open circuit in comparison with the input conductance of the transistor.

With the modified configuration having $R_{c2} = 0$ and $R_{c1} = 5000$ ohms, the emitter resistor may be unbypassed, or a portion of it may be unbypassed, if an increase of input resistance (decrease of input conductance) is desired. The final circuit, using a combination of voltage and current stabilization on the base and emitter, is shown in Fig. 6–3.

The value of the rate of change of collector current with base voltage may also be calculated. For the simple circuit, with R_b infinite, and with collector feedback, the value of $S_{c'}$ is 0.0002. Using the fully compensated design gives a new value of $S_{c'}$ of 0.00014, or only a small improvement. The simplest form for use of the equation for $S_{c'}$ is

$$S_{c'} = \beta/[R_{eq} + r_{b'} + (\beta + 1)(R_e + R_{eq}R_{c2}/R_{bc})] \qquad (18)$$

where $R_{eq} = R_b R_{bc}/(R_b + R_{bc})$. The objective is to reduce the value of $S_{c'}$, an operation that can be accomplished either by reduction of the numerator or by increase in the value of the denominator. Evidently, little can be done with the numerator. In the denominator, the first term may be small compared to the second. The last two terms may be simplified to read

$$\langle R_{c2}R_b/(R_b + R_{bc})\rangle + R_e \tag{19}$$

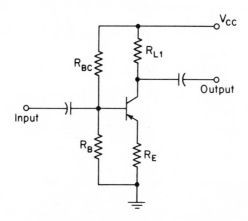

Fig. 6-3. Reduced stabilizing circuit

where the value of R_{c2} should be small if a low input admittance is desired. The value of $R_b/(R_b + R_{bc})$ is less than unity, and R_b is roughly proportional to R_e. The final approximating equation then reduces to

$$S_{c'} \doteq A/R_e \tag{20}$$

where A is an arbitrary constant. Its value will be between 0.1 and 10.

6.2 Dynamic Stability

The variation of the base-to-emitter voltage also influences the values of some of the small-signal parameters for a transistor. In particular, the magnitudes of $r_{b'}$, $y_{i'}$, and $y_{f'}$ are strong functions of the operating temperature of the device. The forward conductance of a transistor has a dependence on temperature expressed by the equation

$$y_{f'} = y_{fo'}(T/T_o)^{-1} \tag{21}$$

It is accompanied by changes in the base-spreading resistance, $r_{b'}$, and input admittance, $y_{i'}$, in terms of the equations

$$r_{b'} = r_{bo'}(T/T_o)^{2.3} \qquad y_{i'} = y_{io'}(T/T_o)^{-3.2} \tag{22}$$

where the subscript o refers to the reference temperature, and its absence to the altered temperature.[3]

The effective forward admittance (transconductance) for the common-emitter amplifier is defined by the equation

$$Y_f = y_{f'}/[1 + y_{i'}(R_s + R_e + r_{b'}) + y_{f'}R_e + y_oR_L$$
$$+ y_{i'}y_c\langle(R_s + r_{b'})(R_e + R_L) + R_eR_L\rangle] \qquad (23)$$

Assuming that the terms involving y_o and y_c may be neglected, this equation reduces to

$$Y_f = y_{f'}/[1 + y_{i'}(R_s + R_e + r_{b'}) + y_{f'}R_e] \qquad (24)$$

and the admittances may be replaced with conductances if desired. Taking the logarithmic derivative, and equating to zero gives the required value of R_s for stabilization of the effective forward admittance

$$R_s = -R_e + 1/2.2y_{i'} \qquad (25)$$

These equations assume that the d-c operating point for the transistor is stabilized in accordance with the method described above. If then the total input admittance for an amplifier is calculated based on these relations, its value as a function of temperature, neglecting the effect of the output circuit, is given by

$$Y_i = y_{io'}(T/T_o)^{-3.2}/[1 + r_{bo'}y_{io'}(T/T_o)^{-0.9}] \qquad (26)$$

Evidently, the input admittance varies rapidly with the absolute temperature, T.

6.3 Control of Thermal Runaway

Thermal runaway may develop in a transistor if an increase in transistor temperature is accompanied by a significant increase in its power dissipation. Because the temperature rise of the transistor is a function of the power dissipated and of the thermal resistance in degrees per watt, the increase in dissipation per unit temperature change must be greater than the dissipation required to cause the unit temperature change if thermal runaway is to result.

The first question in the determination of conditions for thermal runaway is to determine the conditions under which maximum dissipation occurs, and also the conditions under which dissipation rises and decreases with change of collector current. Writing the equation for the collector

---

[3] R. A. Schmeltzer, "Stabilization of Transistor Gain Over Wide Temperature Ranges," *RCA Review*, June, 1959.

dissipation in terms of the collector current, and differentiating, gives the relation

$$P_c = v_c i_c = i_c(V_{cc} - i_c R_L) \tag{27}$$

$$dP_c/di_c = V_{cc} - 2i_c R_L \tag{28}$$

The condition for maximum dissipation is

$$i_c = V_{cc}/2R_L \quad \text{or} \quad v_c = V_{cc}/2 \tag{29}$$

Now, taking the temperature rise as defined by the equation

$$\Delta T = C_t \Delta P_c = (V_{cc} - 2i_c R_L)\Delta i_c C_t \tag{30}$$

where C_t is the specific temperature change in degrees per watt, the change in collector current in Eq. (30) is caused by changes in the value of I_{co} as a function of temperature. The substitution

$$\Delta i_c = \beta S_c \Delta I_{co} = \beta S_c \gamma_c \Delta T \tag{31}$$

may be made, where γ_c is the rate of change of I_{co} with temperature. Substitution in Eq. (32) gives

$$k\Delta T = \beta C_t S_c \gamma_c (V_{cc} - 2i_c R_L)\Delta T \tag{32}$$

where k is a constant of proportionality inserted into Eq. (30) for convenience. When k has a value greater than or equal to unity, the circuit is thermally unstable, and when it is less than unity, it is stable. Under unstable conditions the temperature continues to rise, and unless the term $(V_{cc} - 2i_c R_L)$ decreases sufficiently to restore stability before thermal damage occurs, the transistor will destroy itself. The importance of the factor S_c, the only adjustable element in the equation other than $i_c R_L$, is clearly apparent. The data on γ_c are often given with the data on a transistor and the value of S_c can be evaluated as described earlier. The static values of i_c and S_c must be selected to assure that stable operation will result throughout the expected temperature range.

Equation 32 shows that the temperature increment will be either zero or negative, and k zero or negative, whenever the value of i_c obeys the relation

$$i_c \geqq V_{cc}/2R_L \tag{33}$$

This condition can be used for the stabilization of R-C amplifiers, since the output signal voltage must be developed across a load resistance, and such a resistance can be introduced into low-power amplifiers using transformers, but not into a high-power amplifier without causing excessive circuit losses.

Power amplifiers have a particularly serious stability problem in that the bias should be provided from a constant-voltage source, one which gives a voltage bias that is a function of junction temperature, because the source must permit the peaks of current to flow without altering the static operating point. At the same time, the static resistance in the collector and the emitter circuits must be small because of the high efficiency requirement on the amplifier.

The only way in which the collector current of a power amplifier can be regulated is to set up a metering control circuit that measures the minimum total emitter current flowing in the transistor amplifier when the signal polarity reverses. A circuit that can provide control by reducing the static base voltage for the output transistors is shown in Fig. 6–4. The

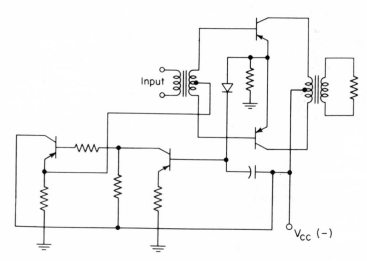

Fig. 6-4. Power amplifier protection circuit

diode D_1 is used to charge the capacitor C_s to a voltage corresponding to the static current level as determined by the emitter-degeneration resistor for the power amplifier, R_e. This voltage is amplified and inverted in phase to provide the base current for the amplifier by way of the emitter-follower. The value of the degeneration resistance, R_e, must be sufficiently small that the minimum voltage across it is less than 0.5 volt to minimize power loss and to limit the degeneration introduced by it. The emitter-follower may be used as a driver amplifier for the drive signal, as well as a dissipation-limiting amplifier.

CHAPTER SEVEN

Transformer-Coupled Amplifiers

7.0 Introduction

Transformer-coupled circuits, including transistors, are used extensively because of the high current efficiency that can be obtained from them. The efficiency is much higher than with tube circuits because of the absence of heater power requirements for the transistor.

The use of coupling transformers is more important with transistor amplifiers than with tubes because of the high input admittance of the transistor. The converse admittance relation is true with tubes, so much so that in the early days of radio, matching transformers were used to compensate for low tube gains. The operating properties of the transformer-coupled tube amplifier have proved to be sufficiently inferior to the properties of resistance coupled amplifiers that the reduced power dissipation available proved to be unimportant except for power output circuits. The relatively high input admittance of the transistor and its consequent transformer loading, and the absence of heater power loss, makes the power dissipation situation entirely different for the transistor amplifier. In addition, the resistive loading on the transformer reduces markedly the transformer distortion otherwise encountered.

The impedance ratio used for an interstage or an output coupling transformer must be selected in terms of the supply voltage and the available power that can be developed by the amplifier, and also in terms of the input load admittance of the load circuit. The open-circuit inductance of the output winding must be selected to give a reactance at least equal to the impedance of the load at the minimum operating frequency, and it should be several times the load impedance for best operating conditions. The turns-ratio is selected to give the correct input impedance.

Transformer-coupled amplifiers are used extensively as low-power and compact communication amplifiers, and with power output amplifiers. Transformers of the kind used in hearing aids may be able to pass a frequency band only approximately a decade wide, whereas an amplifier using larger transformers may pass as much as two or three decades. Before the design of transformer-coupled amplifiers is considered in later sections of this chapter, it is convenient and useful to examine the properties of transformers that are important in this circuit application.

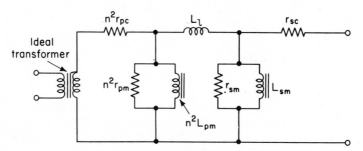

Fig. 7-1 A. Transformer equivalent π circuit

The discussion of transformers can be separated into a discussion of the two basic types, namely, tightly coupled transformers, and loosely coupled. At least superficially, the behavior of both types is similar in that

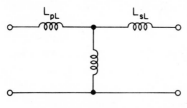

both have at least one resonant frequency per winding (the frequencies may coincide under certain conditions), and they may be represented in terms of either pi or tee equivalent circuits. The tee equivalent circuit has been used most commonly in representation of transformers, particularly tightly coupled units, but the pi representation has many advantages.[1]

Fig. 7-1 B. Equivalent tee circuit

[1] H. W. Lord, "An Equivalent Circuit for Transformers in Which Nonlinear Effects Are Present," *Communication and Electronics*, American Institute of Electrical Engineers, November, 1959.

Figure 7–1 shows that both leakage inductance values are required in each configuration. However, the significance of the leakage and mutual inductance elements is somewhat different in the two configurations. With the pi configuration, it is possible to calculate the leakage inductance from the physical configuration of the transformer, and the mutuals are related to the open-circuit inductances of the individual windings. The paper by Lord gives an excellent discussion of this configuration.

In addition to their leakage inductance, transformers also display input and output capacitance across the windings and also from winding to winding. These capacitances influence the behavior of the amplifier circuit quite markedly. The combination of the capacitances and the load resistance with the leakage inductance determines the high-frequency limitation, and the combination of the magnetizing inductances with the load resistance determines the low-frequency limitation of the circuit (Fig. 7–2). In

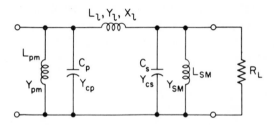

Fig. 7-2. Circuit with capacitances (unity ratio)

transistor amplifiers, the interstage or output transformer is activated from a current source, and the current distributes among all of the paths as well as through the desired path, namely, R_L. The current efficiency, in terms of the network of Fig. 7–2, is given by the equation

$$i_L/i_i = 1/\langle[1 + (Y_{pm} + Y_{cp})X_L][1 + (Y_{cs} + Y_{sm})R_L] \\ + (Y_{pm} + Y_{cp})R_L\rangle \qquad (1)$$

The equation assumes a unity turns-ratio for the transformer. If the ratio is other than unity, the values may be scaled for the ratio. In this way, the step-up or step-down ratio in the transformer may be introduced through the use of an ideal transformer in conjunction with the associated equivalent network of Fig. 7–2.

In practical transformer-coupled amplifiers it is desirable to use a transformer whose magnetizing reactance is large compared to both the leakage reactance X_L and also with respect to $R_L (Y_{pm}X_L < 1; Y_{pm}R_L < 1,$ etc.). Then the operation of the amplifier is dependent primarily on the load termination and the capacitances. The minimum operating frequency is given by the equation

$$f_1 = R_L(L_{pm} + L_{sm})/2\pi L_{pm}L_{sm} \qquad (2)$$

This equation is applied directly when the absolute minimum of size is essential. Introducing a turns-ratio $n_s/n_p = z$, this equation may be revised to read

$$f_1 = R_L(L_{pm'}z^2 + L_{sm})/2\pi L_{pm'}L_{sm}z^2 \qquad (3)$$

where $L_{pm'}$ is the actual magnetizing inductance prior to transformation to the secondary side of the transformer. In a well-designed transformer the values of $L_{pm'}z^2$ and L_{sm} are approximately equal.

For applications in which space and weight are somewhat less important, it is common practice to select a transformer that has a minimum total shunt reactance two to five times the load resistance. In this way, the low-frequency behavior of the amplifier may be considerably improved. A larger transformer having more iron and more wire of a larger diameter is required, giving improved magnetic and electrical characteristics. The leakage inductance, L_L, is much smaller in value, and the magnetizing inductances are larger, making the value of the current ratio given in Eq. (1) both closer to unity in magnitude and also unity over a much wider range of frequencies (a unity turns-ratio is assumed in this consideration).

The maximum operating frequency is dependent on the leakage inductance, the magnetizing inductances, and the input and output capacitances. The inductive reactance of the magnetizing inductances, L_{pm} and L_{sm}, is sufficiently high in all but very marginal transformers that these factors often can be neglected as components of the high-frequency circuit. The maximum frequency is given in terms of the roots of the equation

$$
\begin{aligned}
s^4 L_{pm}L_{sm}L_L C_p C_s R_L &+ s^3 L_{pm}L_{sm}L_L C_p + s^2[L_{pm}L_{sm}C_p R_L \\
&+ L_{pm}L_{sm}C_s R_L + L_{pm}L_L C_p R_L + L_{sm}L_L C_s R_L] \\
&+ s^1 L_{sm}(L_{pm} + L_L) + L_{sm}R_L + L_{pm}R_L \\
&+ L_L R_L = 0 \qquad (4)
\end{aligned}
$$

Depending on the negligible terms, several resonant frequencies may be established

$$f_{2a} = 1/2\pi R_L(C_p + C_s) \qquad (5)$$

where

$$L_L \ll L_{pm},\ L_{sm}, \quad 4R_L^2(C_p + C_s) \ll [L_{pm}L_{sm}/(L_{pm} + L_{sm})]$$

$$f_{2a'} = [(1/L_{sm}C_s) - (1/C_s R_L)^2]^{0.5}/2\pi \qquad (5a)$$

where

$$L_L \ll L_{pm},\ L_{sm}, \quad 4R_L^2(C_p + C_s) \gg [L_{pm}L_{sm}/(L_{pm} + L_{sm})]$$

If L_L is large compared to the magnetizing inductances, then the frequencies are given by the equations

$$f_{2b} = 1/2\pi\sqrt{(L_{pm}C_p)} \quad \text{and} \quad f_{2c} = \sqrt{[(1/L_{sm}C_s) - (1/2C_sR_L)^2]}/2\pi \quad (6)$$

Relatively large values of L_L compared to the values of L_{pm} and L_{sm} are inevitable with micro-miniature transformers, with the result that with them, the frequency limitation is likely to be caused by Eq. (6) rather than Eq. (5). With larger transformers, the limitation on frequency may be caused by either the leakage inductance and the capacitance, or it may be caused by the capacitance and the load resistance.

All terms in Eq. (4) that do not involve $L_{pm}L_{sm}$ may be neglected when L_{pm} and L_{sm} are very large, giving

$$s^2(C_p + C_s)R_L + s^3L_LC_p + s^4L_LC_pC_sR_L = 0 \quad (4a)$$

The approximate resonant frequency under these conditions is given by the equation

$$f_{2d} = \sqrt{[(C_p + C_s)/C_pC_sL_L - (1/2C_sR_L)^2]}/2\pi \quad (7)$$

This equation is the one applying to a high-quality transformer. Critical damping clearly is only obtained when the first term in the bracket is less than or equal to the second term, or when the load resistance is determined by the inequality

$$R_L^2 \leqq [C_pL_L/4C_s(C_p + C_s)] \quad (8)$$

This loading condition may be comparatively easy to obtain with transistor amplifiers, but it has been almost completely overlooked with corresponding amplifiers using tubes.

The importance of the leakage inductance on the frequency response of a transformer circuit is dependent on the relative magnitudes of the inductive reactances X_{pm} and X_{sm} and the capacitive reactances of the distributed capacitances, C_p and C_s. As long as the input signal is provided from a current source such as the collector circuit of a transistor, the effect of the inductance L_L may be neglected if the shunt reactances are large compared to R_L. If, however, the signal source behaves as a voltage generator, the leakage inductance can and does limit the frequency response. Then the limiting frequency may be determined in terms of one of the following equations

$$f_2 = R_L/2\pi L_L$$

or $\hspace{12cm}$ (9)

$$f_2 = \langle\sqrt{[1/L_LC_s - (1/2R_LC_s)^2]}\rangle/2\pi$$

where in the first equation C_s is negligible, and in the second it is not.

These equations should be used for the determination of the frequency response limit when the transformer is activated by a low-impedance, or voltage source.

7.1 Design of Transformer-Coupled Amplifiers

With the exception of the frequency-response calculations, the design of the transformer-coupled amplifier closely parallels that for the R-C amplifier having a load line combination to consider. The static load line for the transformer-coupled amplifier has a slope corresponding to a very small value of resistance, the resistance of the primary winding. The slope of the dynamic load line is dependent on the load on the transformer. Since the load on the transformer may be a function of the operating point if it is determined by the input admittance of an additional transistor amplifier, the plotting of the load contour may introduce difficulties. The position of the contour may be a function of the signal amplitude as a result of current-averaging occurring in the input circuit.

The polarity with which the secondary winding of a coupling transformer is coupled from input to output can be important inasmuch as in one polarity the heavy-current direction for the load circuit may correspond to the direction of relatively small input current, and vice versa. Typical contours corresponding to these conditions are shown in Fig. 7–3. Because of the importance of these loading effects, it is necessary to design transformer-coupled amplifiers from the output back to the input.

The design of a simple output stage is relatively conventional, since the load impedance is nearly constant, varying principally as a function of frequency, and not as a function of the operating point. The techniques used for the design of the simple stage are extended for use with push-pull power amplifiers in a later section.

The supply voltage selected for use with the collector circuit for a transformer-coupled transistor amplifier should be less than approximately 35 to 40 percent of the maximum rated voltage for the device (sufficiently low that the load line will not cross the bias curves in an avalanche region) to ensure that a breakdown failure will not occur during ordinary usage. The static load line may be drawn at the corresponding supply voltage with a slope corresponding to the d-c resistance of the transformer winding. Dissipation contours, one corresponding to half of rated collector dissipation, and the other to full rated dissipation, should be plotted, and the Q-point for the power amplifier so selected that the static dissipation does not exceed half the rated value, and the dynamic load line should be so oriented that it does not cross the contour for full rated dissipation.

If the transistor amplifier is one which only handles a small amount of power, the dissipation criterion is secondary, and the collector leakage

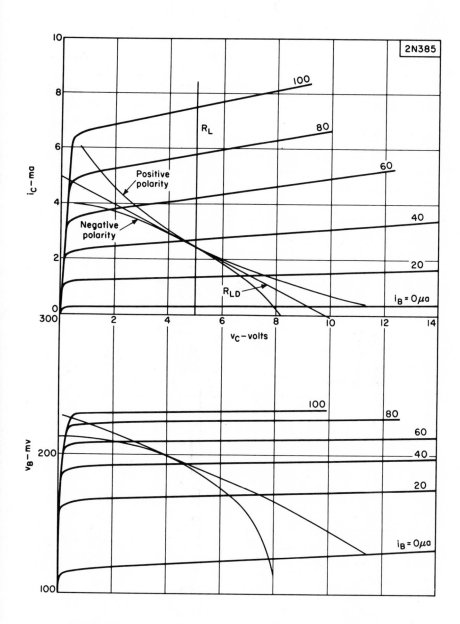

Fig. 7-3. Effect of transformer polarization in interstage load line

current may be the principal factor controlling the design. Because of the extreme nonlinearity of the behavior of the transistor in the neighborhood of the contour for zero base current, it is necessary to select a static operating point that will ensure that a small-signal amplifier will have a minimum instantaneous collector current at least several times the open-base collector current when the operating temperature for the device has been elevated to the maximum operating temperature for the assembly. Although the transistor can be operated with reverse current flowing in the base lead (this is essentially what is done when the value of I_{co} is determined), the behavior is so nonlinear that operation under these conditions is not normally satisfactory. For this reason, data on either $I_{c'}$ or on I_{co} and β are helpful to the designer, particularly if they are given as a function of temperature. A convenient method for providing such data is shown in

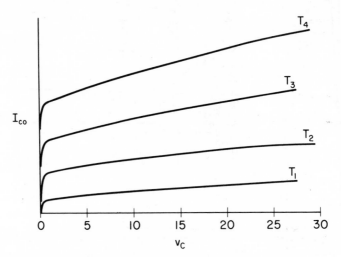

Fig. 7-4. Typical contours of I_{co} vs V_c at different temperatures

Fig. 7–4. The two graphs present contours showing the variation of collector current with collector voltage for fixed temperatures and either zero base current or zero emitter current. In this way, any irregularities in the behavior of the transistors in the low-current area may readily be recognized. (Valvo GmbH uses a correction curve set for this purpose on many of their transistors, Fig. 6–1)[2]

The use of either of these methods can lead to the use of the minimum acceptable value of static collector current, because the value of the current at any required temperature may be added to the peak signal current to

[2] *Valvo-Handbuch*, Halbleiter, 1959, Valvo GmbH, Hamburg 1, Germany.

give the.minimum static current. The nominal value of the current gain, β, may be used to determine the peak output current change available in the collector circuit for the given input current change, and an impedance level may be selected that makes as full use of the current gain as possible. (The output admittance reduces the available current gain, particularly for large values of load impedance.)

The base-current contours corresponding to the minimum and the maximum instantaneous input current may be selected on the output curve family, as shown in Fig. 7–5. These two contours specify the mini-

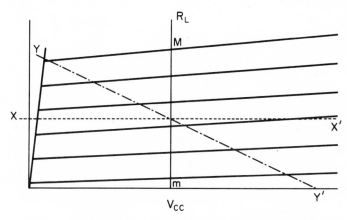

Fig. 7-5. Maximum power conditions — idealized curves

mum and maximum values of collector current, and their intersection with the line of static collector current, X–X', shows the limiting condition for maximum (infinite) load impedance. If the contours for constant base current can be approximated adequately by straight lines, the maximum output power is obtained with the collector current change between the limit contours reduced to half the change available along the static load line. This condition is indicated by line Y–Y'. There is no advantage to using a load impedance greater than that required to produce the line Y–Y', since the available collector-current change is reduced sufficiently that the available output power also is reduced at higher impedance levels. The voltage gain is increased, however.

The value of the dynamic load impedance selected should be smaller than the value given by the maximum power condition if the base-current contours cannot be approximated by straight lines. Such a curvature condition can occur if the dynamic load line crosses the contour of maximum base signal current in the neighborhood of its knee. The load impedance should be selected to yield a minimum collector voltage that is 0.5 to 1.0 volt greater in magnitude than the value at the knee.

EXAMPLE 1. A transformer-coupled amplifier is required using the GT 761 transistor, the supply voltage being $V_{cc} = -3$ volts, and the minimum collector current, $I_{cp} = 0.8$ ma at $v_c = 5$ volts. What is the maximum load resistance permitted if the base-current change is 40 microamperes?

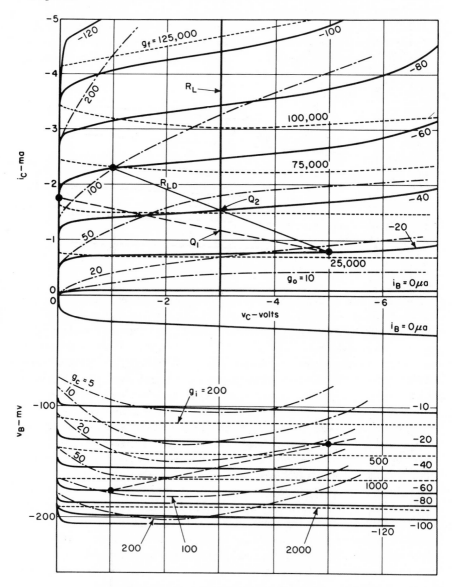

Fig. 7-6. Active load-line selection for Example 1

The total collector-current change from a base current of 20 micro-amperes to 60 microamperes is 1.9 ma, giving a minimum change along the dynamic load line of 0.95 ma. The corresponding point along the 60 μa base contour is marked on Fig. 7–6, and the load contour drawn. The impedance for maximum power is nominally 5260 ohms. Since the contour curvature is high, however, the value that would be chosen would be less than this.

$$R_L = (5.0 - 0.5)/(2.2 - 0.8) = 3200 \text{ ohms}$$

The calculation of the amplification and distortion is similar to that described for the simple R-C amplifier.

7.2 Curved Load Contours

Curved load contours can be generated through the loading action of a nonlinear resistance, such as the input admittance of a transistor, or through the introduction of modifying voltages, either due to the current drawn in active devices, or through reactive components of voltage. The contours resulting from nonlinear resistance and from external current-injection conditions are single-valued, whereas the contour resulting from reactive components of voltage are normally oval in shape. The plotting of each of these types of curved contours is now considered, and the applications to transistor circuits are analyzed in the next few paragraphs.

The load contour reflected onto the output of one transistor from the succeeding transistor is readily transcribed by transplotting the input admittance with the aid of the transformer impedance-ratio. The input contour for the output amplifier may be determined in conventional manner by transferring each intersection of the load line with a bias contour from the output to the input curve family. The approximate input power required is given by the equation

$$P_i = 0.125\Delta v_b\Delta i_b = 0.125(V_{bp} - V_{bn})(I_{bp} - I_{bn}) \tag{10}$$

The approximate admittance level is given by the equation

$$Y_i = \Delta i_b/\Delta v_b \tag{11}$$

The value of this admittance, and data on its variation with bias may be estimated using orthogonal polynomials if detailed data are not available on the small-signal parameters. The driving transistor is selected on the basis of its ability to dissipate at least three to four times the power given by Eq. (10), because the static dissipation must be at least twice the input power for Class A operation for an amplifier.

Once the driver transistor has been selected, a trial supply voltage is chosen, and a minimum load line is plotted. This line is so located that it represents the minimum one capable of developing the required drive power. The impedance corresponding to the load-line slope may be determined, and the ratio of this impedance to the static input impedance of the transistor (or the product of the load-line impedance and the transistor input admittance) gives again the square of the turns-ratio for the coupling transformer.

After the turns-ratio for the transformer has been determined, the next step is the transfer of the load contour from the base circuit of the output transistor to the collector circuit of the driver transistor. The voltage and current changes in the base circuit are transformed by multiplying the voltage changes by the turns-ratio and dividing the current changes by the turns-ratio also. These changes may then be plotted on the collector family for the driver transistor. Both possible orientations for the load contour are shown on the sample curves.

EXAMPLE 2. Determine a suitable transistor to use as a driver for the 2N268 transistor whose curves are shown in Fig. 7–7. Also plot the load contours for the driver transistor for both polarities for transformer coupling. Take the static collector voltage to be ten volts, the base current 6.5 ma, and the static collector current as 500 ma. The transistor beta is approximately 120.

The first thing to notice is that the static point chosen places the transistor under a heavy overload, because its rating in free air is two watts, and the static dissipation level is five watts. Consequently, the static collector current should be reduced to at most 100 ma.

Because the data spread using a static point of 100 ma is inadequate for demonstration of the procedure, and the use of an adequate heat sink can increase the dissipation capacity of the device sufficiently to make possible the use of the load line through a combination of decreasing the static current and increasing the supply voltage, the design process will be completed. Reading from the input curves, the base-voltage change for a base-current change from zero to ten ma is 0.56 volts, for an average input resistance of 56 ohms. The input power required to shift the collector current from $I_{c'}$ to saturation is 0.014 × 0.72, or 12 milliwatts.

Based on this power requirement, the driver transistor should have at least 50 milliwatts collector dissipation rating. A suitable transistor for this purpose is the type 2N369 (302) transistor. Choosing initial conditions for this device of $V_{CC} = -10$ volts, and a static collector current of one ma, the trial load impedance is given by the equation

$$Z_L = V_{CC}/I_c$$

For the conditions stated above, the value of Z_L is 10,000 ohms, giving a turns-ratio of 13.4 : 1. The basic data and the load-line data are given in Table I.

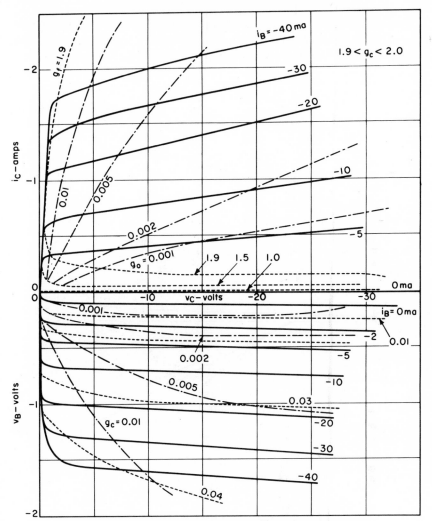

Fig. 7-7. Curves of 2N268 transistor for Example 2

TABLE I

Load Contour Data

i_B	Δi_b	Δv_b	$-n\Delta v_b$	$\Delta i_b/n$
0	−6	−0.42	5.61 v	−0.45 ma
2	−4	−0.21	2.81	−0.22
5	−1	−0.04	0.53	−0.07
6	0	0.00	0.00	0.00
10	4	0.15	−2.00	0.30
14	8	0.23	−3.07	0.60

The load contour and a magnified version of it are both plotted in Fig. 7–8. This contour is plotted in two different orientations, which can be obtained by reversal of the transformer polarity.

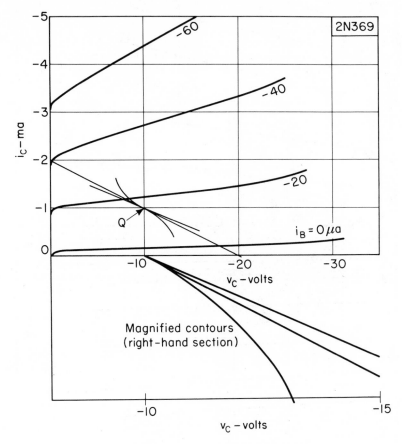

Fig. 7-8. Load contours for Example 2

The major effect of the curvature of the load line is to cause a difference in the total voltage change from the neutral point for the two signal polarities. Because one contour represents a higher average power dissipation than the other for a given average position, the contour that is convex toward the origin should be selected.

This load contour may be transferred back from stage to stage, from output family to input, then from input to the output family of the previous amplifier, until corresponding points for the stages have been localized. Then the small-signal data at all these corresponding points may be tabulated and the over-all gain of the amplifier calculated.

7.3 Amplification Calculations

The calculation of the amplification for a transformer-coupled amplifier parallels the similar calculations for R-C amplifiers, but differs principally in the way the load resistance can be a function of the operating condition. It is therefore necessary to tabulate not only the small-signal data for the transistor as a function of operating conditions but also the value of the effective load impedance. Because many of the stages of the amplifier may be functioning as current amplifiers, the load impedance data may not be important. When they are, however, they can be determined as described.

EXAMPLE 3.   Calculate the load impedances at typical points along the load line for the 2N369 (302) transistor.

Because the turns-ratio was shown in Example 2 to be 13.4 : 1, the square of the ratio is 179. If, then, corresponding points are found on the curve families, the corresponding values of R_L and Y_i may be tabulated.

i_B	0	2	5	6	10	14
Y_i	0.0069	0.0149	0.0221	0.0233	0.026	0.030
R_L	26,000	12,000	8100	7700	6900	6000

The small-signal data may be tabulated from the curves, and the balance of the calculation performed.

7.4 Push - Pull Amplifiers

The amplifiers discussed so far have been relatively linear, or class A amplifiers, and have used only a single active device. The use of a pair of transistors in push-pull, however, makes possible operation under low-power static conditions yet a considerable amount of power under normal operating conditions. Amplifiers having these characteristics are variously known as class B, class AB_1, and class AB_2 operation.

For two transistors, or two active devices, to operate efficiently in push-pull, it is desirable for each device to provide the amplification over approximately one-half of the cycle, with first one device in the active condition and then the other (Fig. 7–8). The switching from one device to the other cannot be instantaneous, because the transition from the off-state to the on-state is gradual with devices like transistors and electron tubes. In addition, the effect of tolerances on the device are such that if an instantaneous transition did exist, it would be impossible to select devices that would switch simultaneously as required.

The characteristics that are well-suited to devices used in push-pull amplifiers are shown in Fig. 7–9. In the transfer region, the amplification should increase from zero at one edge to the specified amplification at the

other edge in a linear manner. Throughout the active region the amplification should have the specified value. If then two devices are connected
so that their static operating points, the Q-points, are at the center of the
transfer region, an amplification that is independent of the operating point
results, and essentially distortionless operation is obtained.

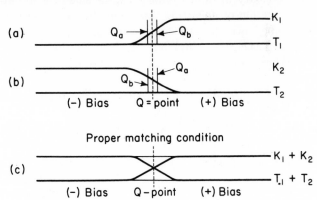

Fig. 7-9. Ideal amplification curves for transistors in
push-pull amplifier

Although it is usually considered to be unnecessary to have small-
signal data on devices used under large-signal conditions, the small-signal
data are not only useful, but rather necessary. This is a result of the
importance of proper matching of the amplification characteristics in the
achievement of a low-distortion design. If, for example, the Q-point is
selected at the point Q_a, then a dip in the amplification is produced in the
neighborhood of the static operating point, and the distortion introduced
into low-amplitude signals is excessive. Similarly, if the Q-point is selected
at the point Q_b, then the amplification in the neighborhood of the static
point will be larger than it should be, and once again, the small-signal
distortion will be excessive. As is evident from the plots of Fig. 7–10, only
a very small error in the value of the static amplification can introduce
severe distortion conditions for small-amplitude signals.

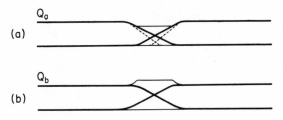

Fig. 7-10. Effect of use of different Q-points

In addition to the bias points, the designer has two other important methods of control of distortion in push-pull amplifiers. One of these methods is the adjustment of the effective source resistance for the input signal supplied to the amplifier, and the second is the return resistance in the emitter circuits for the transistors. The values of these resistances may be used in the adjustment of the amplification to relative uniformity.

The type of matching characteristics obtained as a function of base current differs significantly from that obtained as a function of base voltage. Consequently, it is important that the matching be selected to conform with the type of drive available for the transistor. If, for example, a feedback-stabilized amplifier is transformer-coupled to its driver, and the output impedance of the transformer has been selected to provide essentially constant-voltage drive (this condition exists only rarely), then the matching should be on a voltage basis, whereas ordinarily with a driver transformer driven from a transistor amplifier, current matching should be used. If the output amplifier is excited from a push-pull common-collector amplifier (emitter-follower), then the drive conditions usually are constant-voltage, and voltage matching should be used. The examples show the differences that exist between the two conditions.

The establishment of a fixed Q-point with respect to transistor characteristics under variations of both ambient temperature and input signal level is a difficult problem with transistor amplifiers. The use of emitter degeneration is not satisfactory because the transistors draw more average current with signal input than without it. The use of a base-current limiting circuit is unsatisfactory for that reason. The base-to-emitter voltage is a function of circuit temperature, and the base current is a function of the signal amplitude, a rather incompatible combination.

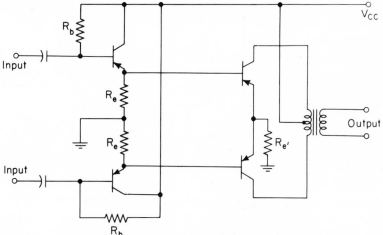

Fig. 7-11. Emitter-coupled power amplifier

The use of an emitter-follower to provide the signal to each transistor of the amplifier is one of the methods of making available a varying average base current under load (Fig. 7–11). The emitter of the driver transistor should be connected directly to the base of the power transistor for such an application. Another possible method is the use of a silicon diode in the forward direction, or a Zener diode to provide a reference voltage varying in a manner which matches the transistor variation (Fig. 7–12). In this

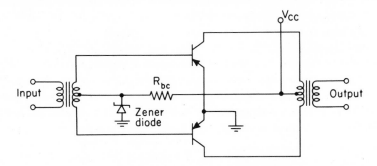

Fig. 7-12. Zener diode stabilizing circuit

method, the current through the diode network should be at least twice the peak base current, and the center-tap of the driver transformer is returned to the potential end of the diode.

The diode selected for use as a biasing element should have a voltage loss that is approximately equal to the base-to-emitter voltage for the transistors at their static operating point, and the voltage should vary as a function of temperature in step with the base voltage variation. The diode should be mounted in close contact with the transistor, or only partial compensation will result, and the possibility of thermal runaway is increased thereby.

Other devices may be used for compensation to protect amplifiers from thermal runaway. Among the more commonly used devices are thermistors and lamp bulbs. The essential characteristic required is either a resistance variation with temperature, or a voltage variation with temperature.

The danger of thermal runaway can be minimized by providing operating conditions that make certain that the dissipation in the active devices decreases as the temperature rises. To do this, it is essential that the static value of current not increase under any conditions, or that the collector voltage decrease more rapidly than the collector current rises. Unfortunately, however, it is not possible to control dissipation by voltage reduction with class B amplifiers, and the control of the static current is rather difficult also. The fine adjustment required to set the static level of current when a thermistor or a diode regulator is used can be accomplished either by the use of a small value of resistance in the emitter circuit, since only a very small range of control is required, or it can be introduced by the use of a low-resistance potentiometer in series with the diode or the thermistor. Because the principal part of the voltage is controlled by the thermal-sensitive device, the adjustment has become rather noncritical.

EXAMPLE 4.   Calculate the amplification as a function of bias for an amplifier using a pair of 2N174 transistors. Select an appropriate Q-point for the amplifier that will prove suitable in a push-pull amplifier. Discuss how a diode may be used for providing the static bias.

On the basis of the characteristic curves for this transistor, a supply voltage of 15 volts appears reasonable, and a trial Q-point of 15 volts, 150 ma may prove satisfactory. With the maximum collector current of two amperes, a dynamic load impedance of eight ohms is required (Fig. 7–13).

The value of R_{LD} of eight ohms is sufficiently small that the simple form for the equations for amplification may be used.

$$K = -g_f R_L/(1 + g_i R_s)$$

or   (12)

$$K_i = g_f R_s/(1 + g_i R_s)$$

The value of R_s, which is used with these equations, depends on the characteristics of the input circuit. For convenience of calculation, values used for the calculation are $R_s = 0$, 10, 20, 50, and 100 ohms. Based on these values, the amplification data may be listed as in Table II.

TABLE II

Amplification Data

i_B	v_C	i_C	g_i	g_f	$K_{v\ min}$	$K_{v\ max}$	$K_{i\ max}$
2 ma	15 v	150 ma	0.024	2.4	5.7	19.2	70.6
5	14.2	240	0.031	3.0	5.9	24.0	73.0
10	12.5	460	0.040	3.6	5.8	28.8	72.0
20	8.0	1.01 amp	0.043	4.4	6.6	35.2	83.0
30	4.2	1.48	0.045	4.7	6.8	37.6	85.0
40	1.1	1.87	0.046	5.0	7.1	40.0	89.3

The input resistance R_s is connected in shunt for the current gain equation, and in series for the voltage gain. The current gain values for smaller input resistance could be calculated, but the shunt loading is sufficient to reduce the gain excessively. The values of current gain for R_s (shunt) infinite are 100 at 2 ma, 97, 90, 102, 104, and 109 respectively for the remaining values of current.

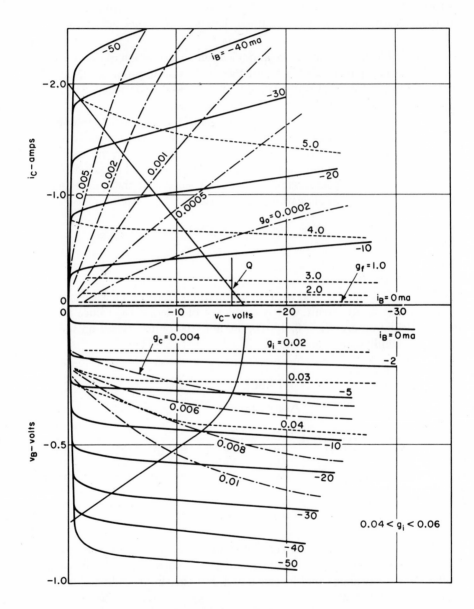

Fig. 7-13. Operating characteristics of power transistor 2N174 for Example 4

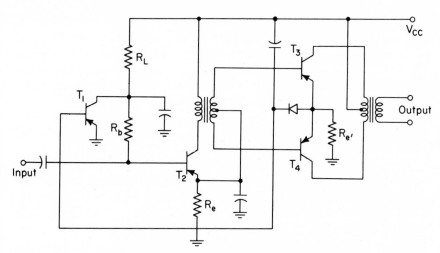

Fig. 7-14A. Type 1 Protective circuit

Possibly one of the most reliable ways of getting thermal compensation for a class B amplifier using transistors is shown in two forms in Fig. 7–14. In this arrangement, an ordinary diode, germanium or silicon as required, is used to control the base voltage of an emitter-follower amplifier that operates in class A. The follower can exactly set the static potential on the base circuit for the power stage and at the same time provide a sufficiently low source impedance to assure adequate current capacity for the input

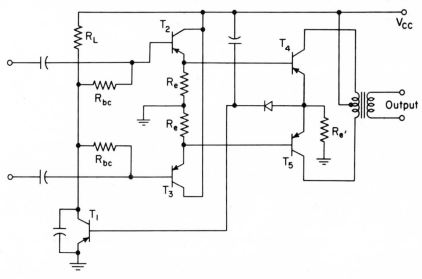

Fig. 7-14B. Type 2 Protective circuit

circuit. For applications in which a suitable interstage transformer is available, the emitter follower may be used to provide the d-c level for the base circuit of the final, and the signal itself may be amplified and introduced into the base circuit of the final through the transformer. This latter circuit configuration is shown in Fig. 7–14(B). Either of these configurations may be used to make available the adjustment required on the static voltage on the input circuit, because a potentiometer connected in series with the charging diode gives the adjustment required to make possible the proper balance in amplification.

Because the current gain is relatively fixed at the ratio of g_f/g_i for the transistor amplifier when a series input circuit is used, and the ratio of g_f/g_i is relatively constant over the entire operating range, the power gain of the amplifier is approximately proportional to the voltage gain. The values of voltage gain as a function of base bias given in Table II are plotted as a function of the source resistance in Fig. 7–15. These curves

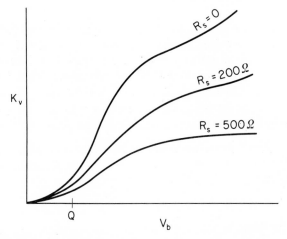

Fig. 7-15. Typical variation of K_v with R_s and V_b

show that the variation of the input impedance affects markedly the operating point, which should be used for best linearity, and they also show that small changes in the selected static point can seriously affect the linearity of the resulting push-pull amplifier. Fig. 7–16 shows the effect of variation of the static base current in half-milliampere steps for a source resistance of 20 ohms. Similar plots may be made for other values of R_s. The best static operating point with $R_s = 20$ ohms calls for a current appreciably less than two milliamperes.

The composite plots of the amplification sum for a push-pull amplifier (Fig. 7–16), show how critical the selection of the appropriate value for the static bias is. The static current increment of a half milliampere between successive contours is almost negligible compared to the 40 ma full-scale current. Because class B amplifiers normally have significant irregularity in the value of amplification near the Q-point, it is important that the static point be chosen to minimize the variation. The irregularity is a

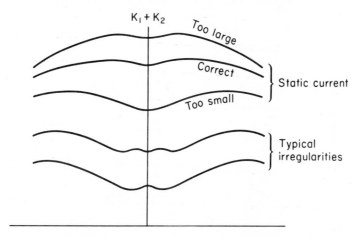

Fig. 7-16. Effect of changes of static bias and contour irregularity

minimum with a static bias current of 0.5 ma, and the distortion characteristics and the balance of the data should be tabulated under this condition. Approximately three percent third-harmonic is introduced into small-amplitude signals.

The design of the thermal compensation circuit based on Fig. 7–14 requires data on both the thermal characteristics of the base voltage for the output transistors and also the thermal characteristics for the emitter-follower and the diodes. First the base voltage required on the output amplifier is noted, and then the base voltage required for the follower to provide the base-current margin for the final is noted. A transistor suitable for use as the emitter-follower is the 2N270, static data for which are shown in Fig. 7–17. At room temperature a base voltage of approximately −120 millivolts is required with the 2N174 power transistor at its static point. The corresponding total base voltage for the 2N270, as can be seen in Fig. 7–17, is −200 mv if the transistor is used as a direct signal driver with a static collector current of ten ma, and 250 mv for 30 ma collector current if the transistor is used to provide the bias by way of a driver transformer.

Brief consideration shows why the two different operating conditions are required for the two methods of using the driver amplifier. When the

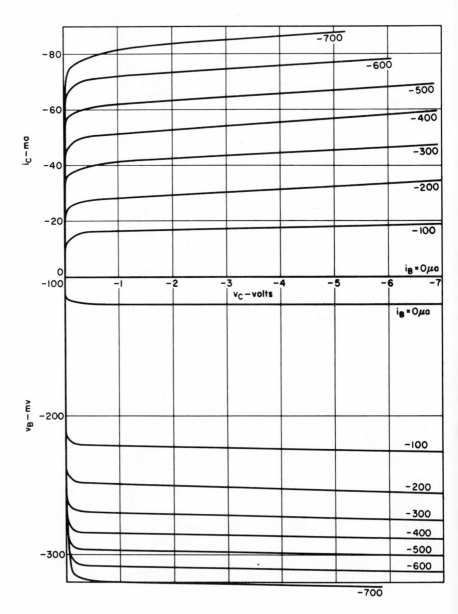

Fig. 7-17. 2N270 curves

driver transistor couples the signal into the base circuit of the amplifier directly, then the signal applied to the base terminal of the driver increases the current available for the base of the output amplifier. When, however, the emitter-follower is used to provide the static bias, and a transformer is used to provide the signal, then signal current from the transformer flows through the driver emitter and it is not accompanied by a change in the base-to-emitter voltage. The only way the voltage can increase is through discharge of the emitter storage capacitor. For this reason, the static current level in the driver must be large enough to maintain the required emitter output voltage. The static emitter current in the driver must be equal to or greater than the peak base current of the final amplifier.

Typical operating conditions for the two forms of output amplifier are enumerated in Table III.

TABLE III

Comparative Data for Power Amplifiers

	(a)	(b)
R_{eo}	1 ohm	1 ohm
R_{e1}	120 ohms	120 ohms
R_{e2}	100 ohm potent.	100 ohm potent.
R_{e3}	3,000 ohms	3,000 ohms
R_{L1}	800 ohms	200 ohms
R_{L2}	7,500 ohms	7,500 ohms
R_b	80,000 ohms	10,000 ohms
V_e	+1 v	+5 v

7.5 Reactive Load Lines

Although many amplifiers use load elements requiring representation in terms of oval load contours, they usually can be represented and analyzed in terms of the equivalent resistive load contour. Occasionally, however, it is important to be able to analyze a circuit in terms of an elliptical load contour, including both the harmonic components and also the in-phase and the out-of-phase components.

The determination of the form of the load contour and the calculation of the amplification along it are discussed in the next few paragraphs. The analysis of the phase and frequency components is somewhat more intricate, particularly for the analysis of the oval load line. The process is described in part C of Appendix IV.

If a reactive load must be used for an amplifier, the shape of the load contour used is a function of frequency, with the result that a separate analysis is required for each frequency of interest. In performing such an analysis, the phasor form for the load impedance is substituted for the resistance in the appropriate form of the amplification equation.

The consideration of the effect of reactance in a circuit is usually most important in output or power amplifiers. Although the terms involving y_o and y_c can usually be neglected in the calculation of the characteristics of these amplifiers, they are included here. For the general case, the amplification equation, common emitter, may be written

$$K = -y_f(R_L + jX_L)/[1 + y_iR_s + (y_o + y_iy_cR_s)(R_L + jX_L)] \quad (13)$$

This equation may be rationalized to eliminate the j terms in the denominator, giving

$$
\begin{aligned}
K &= -y_f(R_L + jX_L)\langle[1 + y_iR_s + R_L(y_o + y_iy_cR_s)] \\
&\quad - jX_L(y_o + y_iy_cR_s)\rangle/[\langle1 + y_iR_s + R_L(y_o + y_iy_cR_s)\rangle^2 \\
&\quad + X_L^2(y_o + y_iy_cR_s)^2] \\[6pt]
&= -y_f[(1 + y_iR_s + R_L(y_o + y_iy_cR_s))R_L + X_L^2(y_o + y_iy_cR_s) \\
&\quad + jX_L\langle1 + y_iR_s\rangle]/[\langle1 + y_iR_s + R_L(y_o + y_iy_cR_s)\rangle^2 \\
&\quad + X_L^2(y_o + y_iy_cR_s)^2] \quad\quad (14) \\[6pt]
&= -y_f[(1 + y_iR_s)R_L + (R_L^2 + X_L^2)(y_o + y_iy_cR_s) \\
&\quad + jX_L(1 + y_iR_s)]/[(1 + y_iR_s + R_L(y_o + y_iy_cR_s))^2 \\
&\quad + X_L^2(y_o + y_iy_cR_s)^2] \\[6pt]
&= -y_f[(R_L + jX_L)(1 + y_iR_s) + (R_L^2 + X_L^2)(y_o + y_iy_cR_s)]/ \\
&\quad [(1 + y_iR_s + R_L(y_o + y_iy_cR_s))^2 + X_L^2(y_o + y_iy_cR_s)^2] \quad (15)
\end{aligned}
$$

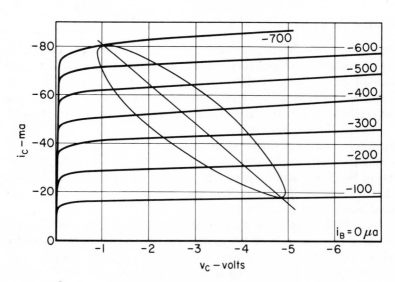

Fig. 7-18. Elliptical load line

With power amplifiers, this equation may often be simplified to the form

$$K = -y_f(R_L + jX_L)/(1 + y_iR_s) \qquad (16)$$

In using either of these equations, the first step is the plotting of the resistive load line, that is, the line for $X_L = 0$. The second step is the plotting of the reactive component. This component does not depend on the magnitude of the collector current, but on either the integral or the derivative of the current. For this reason, the reactive voltage must be introduced at relatively constant output current. This voltage change is stepped off along the base-current contours, since the reactive voltage does not effect the input currency appreciably. The amplification is therefore divided into two components

$$K = K_R + jK_L \qquad (17)$$

The j operator must be kept with the inductive component, not because the phasors are plotted at right angles, but because the rate-of-change has a maximum value when the magnitude of the net current change from the static value is zero. For a sinusoidal input signal, $I_s \sin \omega t$ (or $V_s \sin \omega t$), the magnitude of the reactive voltage, in terms of the maximum change of collector voltage, V_{cm}, may be given by the equation

$$v_{cL} = V_{cm} | K_L/K_R | \cos \omega t \qquad (18)$$

This voltage is measured along a constant-base-current contour on both sides of the resistive contour, as is sketched in Fig. 7–18. In this figure, the

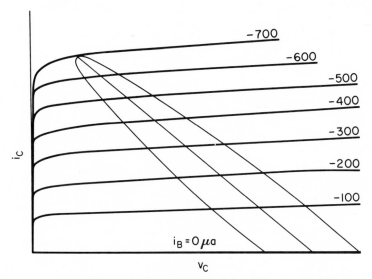

Fig. 7-19. Semi-elliptical load line

ratio of $|K_L/K_R|$ has been assigned the value 0.20 for convenience of plotting, and the simplified form of the equation has been used.

The type of stage in which a reactive load line normally is required is a push-pull class B amplifier. If a 2N301 transistor is used in such an amplifier, and the load contour is plotted for one of the transistors, the result is shown in Fig. 7–19. After the contour has been plotted, the amplification and the other required design data may be compiled as has already been indicated.

CHAPTER EIGHT

RF and IF Amplifiers

8.0 Basic Design

The design of an RF or an IF amplifier using transistors
parallels rather closely the design of transformer-coupled
amplifiers. Because of the input and output tuned circuits
that must be used with them, these amplifiers are sensitive
to feedback through the collector-base capacitance in
addition to the parameters already considered. This capacitance tends to introduce instability and regeneration into
the circuit, and makes necessary the use of relatively small
load impedances in the collector circuits.

Transistors used for RF amplifiers differ from tubes in
several important respects. First, the input and the forward transfer admittances for a given collector current are
both large compared to the values for tubes. The forward
admittance, for example, at about 39,000 micromhos per
milliampere of collector current, is from fifteen to forty
times as large as the corresponding tube transconductances.
Also, the input capacitance is correspondingly larger. By
comparison, the base-to-collector capacitance may be less
than or equal to the grid-to-plate capacitance in a triode
tube, and as a result of the relatively lower impedance

level used with the associated circuitry, it is of considerably reduced importance. The remaining important difference is in the nature of the series impedances between the terminals of the device and the active junctions, the emitter and collector series impedances, $r_{e'}$, $r_{c'}$, and the base-spreading resistance, $r_{b'}$. These resistances affect the operation of a transistor in several ways. The emitter series resistance increases the required drive power for the circuit, and, as a consequence of circuit degeneration, also limits the amplification that can be obtained. The base-spreading resistance increases the drive power required, and increases the tendency for instability in an amplifier. The collector series resistance increases the total impedance in the output circuit, increasing the total internal gain and, as a consequence, increases the probability of regeneration and reduces circuit stability. It also introduces phase-shift into the output circuit.

With transistor and triode tube amplifiers, it is necessary either to unilateralize the circuit (neutralize it usually) or to operate the device in the separation mode (grid or base grounded). These methods of operation limit the feedback coupling from the output to the input, and maximize the usable amplification. The presence of the base-spreading resistance tends to reduce the isolation between the output and the input in the transistor separation amplifier, and can increase its instability.

In either the base-separation or base-input mode of operation, the presence of the base-spreading resistance is a detriment to unilateralization or neutralization, as it makes both the circuit configuration and the component sizes more critical. The configuration for unilateralizing the base-separation circuit is considerably simpler because of the low value of input impedance for the common-base amplifier.

The general equation for the amplification for the common-base amplifier is given in Eq. (25) in Chapter Four. Modifying this equation to the proper form for use with tuned amplifiers gives

$$K = [(y_{f'} + y_o) + y_{i'}y_c r_{b'}]Z_L/[1 + y_o Z_L + \sigma(y')Z_s$$
$$+ y_{i'}r_{b'} + y_{i'}y_c(r_{b'}Z_L + r_{b'}Z_s + Z_s Z_L)] \tag{1}$$

The regeneration is developed in this equation in terms of the expansion of the product $y_{i'}y_c r_{b'}Z_L$

$$y_{i'}y_c r_{b'}Z_L = (g_{i'} + jb_i)(g_c + jb_c)r_{b'}(R_L + jX_L)/[(R_L + jX_L)jB_C + 1] \tag{2}$$

The value of the denominator of (2), for a frequency near the resonance frequency, ω_o, may be written in the form, where $\omega = \omega_o + \Delta\omega$ and $\omega_o^2 L_L C_L = 1$,

$$jB_C R_L + 1 - X_L B_C = j\omega C_L R_L - 2\Delta\omega L_L C_L \doteq j\omega_o C_L R_L - 2\Delta\omega L_L C_L \tag{3}$$

Substituting this into Eq. (2) gives

$$(g_{i'} + jb_i)(g_c + jb_c)r_{b'}j\omega L_L/(j\omega_o C_L R_L - 2\Delta\omega L_L C_L) = y_{i'}y_c r_{b'}Z_L \qquad (4)$$

Rationalizing gives

$$
\begin{aligned}
y_{i'}y_c r_{b'}Z_L &= (g_{i'} + jb_i)(g_c + jb_c)r_{b'}j\omega_o L_L(-2\Delta\omega L_L C_L - j\omega_o C_L R_L)/ \\
&\quad (4\Delta\omega^2 L_L^2 C_L^2 + \omega_o^2 C_L^2 R_L^2) \\
&= [g_{i'}(r_{b'}\omega_o^2 L_L C_L R_L g_c + b_c r_{b'}\omega_o \times 2\Delta\omega L_L^2 C_L) \\
&\quad - b_i(b_c r_{b'}\omega_o^2 L_L C_L R_L - 2g_c r_{b'}\omega_o \Delta\omega L_L^2 C_L) \\
&\quad + j\langle g_{i'}(g_c r_{b'}(-2\omega_o \Delta\omega L_L^2 C_L) + b_c r_{b'}\omega_o^2 L_L C_L R_L) \\
&\quad + b_i(g_c r_{b'}\omega_o^2 L_L C_L R_L + b_c r_{b'}\omega_o L_L \times 2\Delta\omega L_L C_L)\rangle]/ \\
&\quad (4\Delta\omega^2 L_L^2 C_L^2 + \omega_o^2 C_L^2 R_L^2) \qquad (5)
\end{aligned}
$$

Near the resonant frequency, where $\omega_o\sqrt{L_L C_L} = 1$, the negative real term of the numerator of Eq. (5) is the predominant one, with the result that it may be approximated by

$$
\begin{aligned}
y_{i'}y_c r_{b'}Z_L &= -(b_i b_c r_{b'}R_L)/\omega_o^2 C_L^2 R_L^2 \\
&= -(b_i b_c r_{b'}R_{\text{eff}})
\end{aligned} \qquad (6)
$$

where R_{eff} is the effective tuned resistance of Z_L, and the reactive, or j, terms have been neglected because they can be tuned to zero as desired by adjusting C_L or L_L. This term appears in both the numerator and the denominator of Eq. (1), but the total value of the numerator is large compared to unity, whereas the value of the denominator lies in the neighborhood of unity, normally less than three or four at most for the total. For large values of Z_L and $r_{b'}$, it is therefore possible for this negative term to cancel the positive terms in the denominator and to permit oscillation to develop. Since both b_i and b_c are proportional to the capacitances, and these capacitances are functions of V_c and I_c, the amount of negative conductance is proportional to the capacitance. The negative conductance and the capacitances are inverse functions of the collector voltage. Other than for unilateralization, there are two ways of minimizing the possibility of oscillation developing with an amplifier using a given transistor; first, by raising the collector voltage and thereby decreasing b_c, and second decreasing R_{eff} either by using a higher C-tuned circuit, or by tapping the collector to a relatively lower impedance level on the tuned circuit.

The reactance level of the circuit that provides the input signal to the emitter of the transistor should be so selected that the signal reaches the emitter without excessive reduction of the circuit Q-factor, and at the same time it is essential that the coupling be sufficiently tight to obtain efficient energy transfer. The problem of interstage coupling with transistors is complicated by the fact that the input admittance of the transistor is extremely large and its output admittance is extremely small. Consequently, a matching network is required that can readily match a low-impedance load to a high-impedance source. The input impedance may be as small as from one to fifty ohms, and the output impedance in general is larger than 1000 ohms, making the impedance transformation ratio required greater than fifty.

8.1 Coupling Methods

The transformers used at audio frequency for adjusting coupling impedances are replaced at higher frequencies by some form of tuned circuit or transformer. The simplest arrangement, one which has found widespread use, is shown in Fig. 8–1. In this circuit, the inductor is placed in

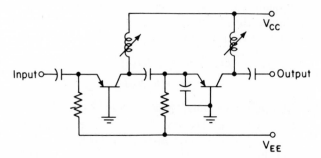

Fig. 8-1. Common-base tuned amplifier coupling circuit

series with the collector, and a capacitive divider couples the collector to the emitter and to ground. If the Q-factor of the tuned circuit is sufficiently high for a resonant build-up to occur, even with resistive loading of the emitter across the capacitance from emitter to ground, then satisfactory operation will result. The condition required for such a circuit to function effectively is that the circulating current representing the stored energy must be large compared to the resistive current withdrawn by the emitter. If this condition exists, then the impedance step-down in the capacitive divider is determined approximately by the square of the capacitance ratio, and efficient energy transfer may be obtained. If there is any question as to the adequacy of the value of the Q-factor, then a tapped coil should be used, because the magnetic field of the coil then assures a square-law reduction of impedance. Such a coupling circuit is shown in Fig. 8–2. With the tapped-coil arrangement, a single capacitor may be used for tuning, rather than a series combination, and a large decoupling capacitor may be used to introduce the signal into the emitter of the succeeding amplifier.

The capacitive divider arrangement often makes use of the input capacitance of the transistor as part of the capacitor C_2, since C_i is relatively large, and often may be an appreciable part of the total required capacitance. A minimum stage-to-stage voltage or current gain of approximately ten is desirable, and because the ratio of the collector impedance

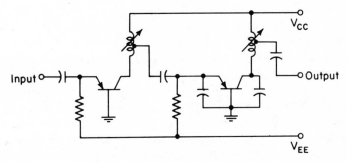

Fig. 8-2. Tapped coupling circuit

to emitter impedance is in the neighborhood of 100, an over-all emitter-to-collector voltage gain of approximately 100 is required. Because the design of this coupling circuit is possibly the most critical stage in the design of an RF or an IF amplifier, it is examined in detail in the next few paragraphs.

EXAMPLE 1. Design an RF coupling circuit for use with a ten megacycle amplifier. For the purpose, assume that $(y_{i'} + y_{f'})$ is 30 ohms, and C_1 is 200 pfd.

Because the emitter of the driven transistor absorbs power from its driver amplifier, it is reasonable to assume that the loading from the emitter will reduce the Q-factor of the tuned circuit for the previous stage at most to half its unloaded value. Assume that the impedance is 3000 ohms when loaded and 6000 ohms unloaded. The emitter impedance of 30 ohms then is transformed to 6000 ohms by the circuit. The capacitance ratio then is

$$(C_1/C_2)^2 = 30/6000 = 0.005$$

and the value of C_2/C_1 is 14 : 1. If then the unloaded Q-factor for the tuned circuit is 200 and loaded, 100, the inductance and capacitance for the tuned circuit are

$$\omega L = 1/\omega C = 6000/200 = 30; \qquad \omega = 6.3 \times 10^7$$

$$L = 0.47 \text{ microhenry}, \qquad C_1 = 529 \text{ pfd}$$

Then, C_2 should have a value of about 7500 pfd.

The extremely low impedance levels are clearly evident in terms of these capacitances. Because 30 ohms corresponds to approximately 33,000 micromhos forward conductance, the amplification obtained from an amplifier using this transistor is

$$K_v = g_{f'} Z_L = 0.033 \times 3000 = 100$$

Since the step-down ratio in the coupling circuit is 14 : 1, however, the net gain is seven, not ten. To achieve a gain of ten, therefore, it is necessary to load the tuned circuit more heavily. This is most easily done by raising the collector impedance level (unloaded). If, for example, it is increased to 15,000 ohms, then the load impedance reflected from the emitter can be 3750 ohms instead of 6000 ohms, and the capacitance ratio is reduced to 11 : 1. The over-all stage gain then is nine and the loaded Q-factor is 40.

The use of the higher unloaded tuned impedance does not introduce difficulties due to degeneration because the emitter of the succeeding amplifier loads the tuned circuit regardless of its frequency setting. Consequently, the modified values for the components, again assuming an unloaded Q-factor of 200, are

$$L = 1.20 \ \mu h, \qquad C_1 = 210 \text{ pfd}, \qquad C_2 = 2300 \text{ pfd}$$

These values are appreciably more practical than those for the design with 6000 ohms unloaded impedance.

The Use of Tapped Coils. Tapped coils may be used with amplifiers, and they are commonly used with oscillators for the reduction of the impedance level from collector to emitter. In this application, the unloaded impedance level is selected, and the tap is adjusted to reduce the impedance to the desired level. Tapped coils have the advantage that the change of current level is obtained magnetically rather than by way of the circulating current. Consequently, relatively lower Q-factor coils may be used effectively with large values of impedance step-down. The step-down in a tapped coil functioning as an auto-transformer is approximately proportional to the square of the turns-ratio

$$z_o/z_i = (n_o/n_i)^2 \tag{7}$$

Strictly, this equation applies only if the coefficient of coupling among the various turns of the coil is high, and as a consequence, the leakage flux is small.

If a tapped inductor is used for the tuned circuit considered in Example 1, the tap should be placed at approximately 0.09 of the way along the coil from its supply end. (For an eleven-turn coil, the tap should be placed one turn from the collector supply.) Because the coupling is relatively loose from one turn to another, the exact position for the tap must be found by trial and error.

Other Coupling Methods. Two remaining forms of coupling circuits are commonly used with transistor circuits, the first of which is the single-tuned transformer (Fig. 8–3), and the second, the double-tuned transformer (Fig. 8–4). With each of these transformers, the secondary, low-impedance winding is installed adjacent to the main tuned coil to provide magnetic coupling and signal transfer. Tuned lines may also be used for coupling elements.

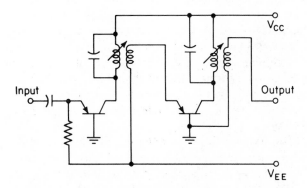

Fig. 8-3. Single-tuned coupling transformer circuit

The double-tuned transformer used with transistor RF amplifiers con-sists of one tuned high-impedance winding, and one low-impedance winding. The high-impedance winding is designed to have a relatively high loaded Q-factor, possibly twenty percent of the unloaded value, whereas the low-impedance winding is commonly designed to have a low value of loaded Q-factor, possibly as small as two to five. Such an arrangement makes the tuning of only one of the circuits critical; the remaining circuit can be used over at least a ten to twenty percent bandwidth.

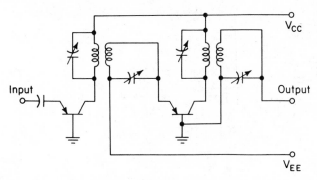

Fig. 8-4. Double-tuned coupling transformer circuit

The advantages of the transformer-coupled circuit over the simple tuned coupling circuit include ease of adjusting the bandwidth by variation of the tightness of coupling between the two windings, ease of signal injection compared to the tapped coil because of the absence of a high-capacity coupling capacitor, and ease of getting the appropriate turns-ratio compared to the tapped coil. Frequently, for example, it may be necessary to place a tap at a fraction of a turn on a tapped coil, whereas a tuned or an untuned coupling coil may have from several to many turns.

The design of the high-impedance winding follows the same procedure for both the single-tuned and the double-tuned transformers. The final value of the loaded Q-factor and the loaded impedance desired are selected, and the required inductance and capacitance are calculated. The unloaded value of Q to be designed into the coil should be from a minimum of four to a maximum of ten to twenty times the loaded value. Once the values of the inductances are known, the inductors may be designed by any of the standard methods.

The coupling inductor may be untuned, in which case its Q-factor is assumed to be unity, or it may be resonated with a capacitor, in which case its Q-factor lies in the range from two to five. If the circuit is tuned, it may use either the series or parallel configuration as desired. For the series-tuned arrangement, the reactance of the inductor and its associated capacitor may be calculated from the equations

$$\omega L_C = 1/\omega C_C = Q_C/(g_{i'} + g_{f'}) \tag{8}$$

where the subscript C refers to the coupling components. Similarly, if the circuit is parallel-tuned, then the susceptances of the associated elements are given by the equations

$$\omega C_C = 1/\omega L_C = Q_C(g_{i'} + g_{f'}) \tag{9}$$

The respective circuits, with the transistor input represented by Y_i, are shown in Fig. 8–5.

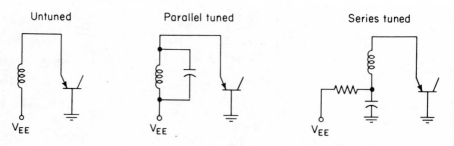

Fig. 8-5. Types of inductive coupling

Each of these circuits has certain advantages. The series circuit, for example, is excellent with regard to economy of parts, but at very high frequencies, a voltage step-down action from the effect of C_i and C_C must be taken into account. This is easily done, but it does increase the complexity of design somewhat. The parallel-tuned circuit, on the other hand, makes direct use of the input capacitance of the transistor as part of C_C, and as a result is easier to design at high-frequencies. It may use more parts than the series-tuned circuit because of the d-c path through the coupling circuit. In addition, because the reactance of the coil and capacitor are appreciably smaller in the parallel-tuned coupling circuit than in the equivalent series-tuned circuit, the problem of constructing an acceptable coupling inductor for use at very high frequencies may make the use of series-tuned circuits more convenient.

The untuned coupling circuit is normally designed for an approximate loaded Q of unity so that the coupling may be made as loose as possible. The coupling efficiency factor has an extremely broad maximum in the neighborhood of a reactance of the coupling coil equal to the terminating load impedance, with the result that relatively large changes of reactance can be tolerated without serious difficulties. When, however, an untuned coupling coil has an appreciable capacitive load component, then the value of inductance selected should be adjusted in accordance with the equation

$$L_C = L_{C1}/(1 + \omega^2 L_{C1} C_C) \tag{10}$$

where L_{C1} is the inductance determined from the equation $\omega L_{C1} = R_L$, and R_L is the load resistance and C_C the loading capacitance. The presence of the capacitance increases the effective value of the inductance, with the result that a smaller value of physical inductance is required.

After the designs of the tuning coil and the coupling coil, either tuned or untuned, are completed, the next step is the adjustment of the coupling to the correct value. This adjustment is easily made with the aid of a Q-meter, because adjusting the coupling circuit consists of moving the coil sufficiently close to the tuned coil to reduce its effective Q to the required value. The tuning capacitor C_L may be replaced by the tuning capacitor of the Q-meter for this adjustment, and any supplementary capacitance required for resonance may be placed in parallel with the capacitor in the measuring circuit. The combination is tuned to resonance and the Q measured. The coupling is adjusted to give the required value of Q at resonance.

The nominal value of coupling required for critical coupling is found in terms of the effective values of Q for the two tuned circuits. If the unloaded Q of the collector circuit is called Q_t, and the Q of the coupling circuit is called Q_c, then the critical value for the coupling, k_c, is given by the equation

$$k_c = 1/\sqrt{Q_t Q_c} \tag{11}$$

If the coupling circuit is untuned except for the internal circuit and transistor capacitance, then Q_c may be taken as unity; otherwise it will be the loaded Q of the coupling link, normally between two and ten. The coupling for the tuned link can be as small as a half to a third the coupling required with an untuned link.

The form and the type of coupling circuit often must be selected on the basis of the physical configuration of the tuned circuit. For example, if it proves impossible to get sufficient coupling to use an untuned link, the design should be changed to use either a tuned link or a capacity divider. The capacity divider usually will prove satisfactory only if the total capacitance from emitter to ground is less than approximately 5000 pfd and larger than the input capacitance of the transistor.

8.2 Transistor Load Lines

After the dynamic load impedance has been determined for the transistor amplifier, the design of the amplifier itself may be undertaken. The collector supply voltage for the amplifier may be selected in terms of the maximum permitted for the transistor, and if maximum operating characteristics at high frequency are required, it should be relatively near to the rated maximum value. The voltage applied to a drift, or diffused-base, type of transistor in particular should be as large as possible, consistent with the noise properties of the device. The selection of optimum operating conditions for an input amplifier stage is a critical operation, inasmuch as minimum noise conditions occur with a comparatively small collector supply voltage, yet a relatively high voltage is required for maximum operating frequency.

The static load line is drawn at approximately constant voltage corresponding to the supply voltage and static resistance of the winding. Then the dynamic load line is plotted across it, intersecting it at the point corresponding to the desired forward conductance in the transistor. The slope of the load line should correspond to an impedance defined by the equation

$$Z_{LD} \geq (K_s)^2/(g_{i'} + g_{f'}) \tag{12}$$

where K_s is the over-all stage amplification from emitter to emitter or collector to collector, and $(g_{i'} + g_{f'})$ is the input admittance of the emitter of the common-base amplifier. The unloaded tuned impedance should be large compared to this value of Z_{LD}.

8.3 Relations of Frequency Limitations

The various limiting frequencies used with high-frequency amplifiers are all related to one another through the basic transistor parameters, the current gain, the input and forward conductances, the base-to-emitter and base-to-collector capacitances, and the base-spreading resistance. Their relations are defined in Section 2.8.

It is desirable in connection with the design of high-frequency circuits to be able to determine to within a factor of at most twenty percent what the values of f_{max} and f_{n2} are, inasmuch as they determine the points at which deterioration of the circuit behavior starts becoming serious, and where it becomes crucial. As long as the operating frequency is less than f_{n2}, the design procedure may be based on normal admittance techniques. At frequencies between f_{n2} and f_{max}, the procedure is critical because of the low gain and the high noise levels.

If adequate data are known on a transistor, either of these frequencies may be determined directly, or they may be determined in terms of the value of f_α by the use of Eqs. (29) and (28) in Chapter Two. It is of interest to note that the two capacitances C_i and C_c play an extremely important part in the limitation of the maximum operating frequency, f_{max}, whose value is

$$f_{max} = (1/4\pi) \sqrt{(g_{f'}/r_{b'}C_iC_c)} \tag{13}$$

This frequency f_{max} is in reality a figure of considerable importance for a transistor. A similar equation for f_{n2} may be derived

$$f_{n2} = (1/2\pi C_i) \sqrt{g_{i'}(g_{i'} + g_{f'})} \tag{14}$$

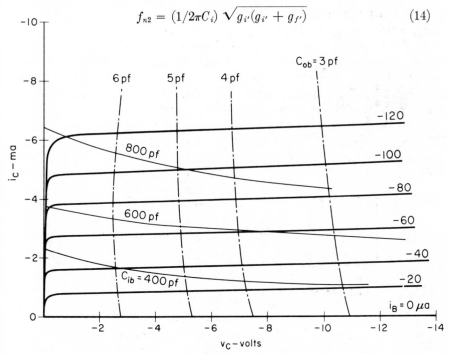

Fig. 8-6. Hypothetical capacitance contours

Either this equation or the equation in terms of f_α is satisfactory for the determination of the noise-corner frequency.

It would appear reasonable to plot contours of constant value for the capacitances C_i and C_c on a family of characteristic curves as a means of presenting the data on the limiting frequencies. A sample of the form such a set of curves might take on a drift transistor is sketched in Fig. 8–6. It should be noted, however, that these curves are hypothetical and do not represent any specific transistor. These data in conjunction with the normal data provided on conductance data sheets should prove ample for design purposes.

8.4 Neutralization and Unilateralization

The neutralization of an amplifier is the process of introduction of compensating voltages or currents from output to input in such á manner as to prevent the direct exchange of energy between the input and the output. Unilateralization not only introduces compensating reactive components, but also compensating resistive components, so that the input and the output are completely isolated except for the amplification action in the active device.

The neutralization of the common-base amplifier is comparatively simple because the feedback elements of the device in this configuration are introduced solely by the base-collector capacitance, which is fairly stable in value, and the base-spreading resistance, which also is rather stable in value. In addition, the extremely small input impedance (large input admittance), coupled with the relatively low impedance isolating area in the base region reduces the effective coupling to a very small value.

The unilateralization of a common-emitter amplifier requires a more complex compensating network than is required for neutralization. At the same time, if properly adjusted, it provides better isolation. The common-base neutralizing circuit is a unilateralizing circuit as well, so that the common-base amplifier when properly neutralized shows complete isolation between its input and its output. The neutralization equation for the common-base amplifier is

$$C_n R_n = r_{b'} C_c \qquad (15)$$

where C_n is the neutralizing capacitor, connected from collector to emitter, and R_n is the neutralizing resistance, connected from the emitter to ground, the base-return terminal.

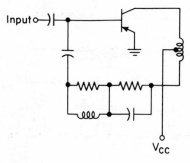

Fig. 8-7. Common-emitter unilateralizing circuit

Unilateralization of the common-emitter amplifier requires in addition to a set of R, L, and C components, an ideal transformer for the inversion of the phase of the feedback signal.[1] The circuit and the sizes of the components are defined in Fig. 8–7. If the equation for the input admittance is separated into input components and transfer components, and the transfer components are balanced out by their negatives, the stage is then unilateralized. Based on the equation

$$Y_i = y_{i'}(1 + y_c R_L)/[1 + y_o R_L + y_{i'}y_c(1 + y_c R_L)] \tag{16}$$

The denominator may be simplified by taking advantage of the relations

$$y_o R_L < 1 \qquad y_c R_L < 1$$

The equation then takes the form

$$Y_i = y_{i'}(1 + y_c R_L)/(1 + y_{i'}r_{b'}) \tag{17}$$

The numerator term involving y_c may be replaced by the complete delta factor, and only the transfer term retained, because from above, $y_o R_L < 1$

$$\begin{aligned} Y_i &= [y_{i'}(1 + y_o R_L) - y_{f'}y_r R_L]/(1 + y_{i'}r_{b'}) \\ &= [y_{i'} - y_{f'}y_r R_L]/(1 + y_{i'}r_{b'}) \end{aligned} \tag{18}$$

This is one of the few applications in which the use of the modified output admittance is less convenient than the basic form. This equation may be further simplified by separating the two numerator terms, and then examining the significance of the result

$$Y_i = y_{i'}/(1 + y_{i'}r_{b'}) - y_r(y_{f'}R_L)/(1 + y_{i'}r_{b'}) \tag{19}$$

Evidently, if an immittance term is added that will identically cancel the second term on the right, the y_r term, then all that will be left is the input admittance resulting from the input circuit and the interaction of the input and the output, will be zero. The $y_{f'}R_L$ term gives the internal gain in the transistor, and indicates that, as is already known, the voltage applied to the unilateralizing circuit must equal the output voltage of the amplifier. This makes necessary the use of an ideal, or unity-ratio, correction transformer. Then the balance of the equation gives the admittance that must be placed in the return path

$$\begin{aligned} y_u &= y_r/(1 + y_{i'}r_{b'}) = 1/(1 + y_{i'}r_{b'})/y_r \\ &= 1/[(1 + g_{i'}r_{b'} + j\omega C_i r_{b'})/y_r] \end{aligned} \tag{20}$$

$$= \cfrac{1}{\cfrac{1}{\cfrac{g_r + j\omega C_c}{1 + g_{i'}r_{b'}}} + \cfrac{1}{\cfrac{g_r + j\omega C_c}{j\omega C_i r_{b'}}}} \tag{21}$$

---

[1] C. C. Cheng, "Neutralization and Unilateralization," *IRE Transactions PGCT* June, 1955, p. 138.

The fact that y_r would represent the feedback admittance can easily be recognized because the amplification of the transistor causes the application of a relatively large signal voltage compared to the base voltage across the voltage side of y_r, and the comparatively high admittance from base to ground would cause an admittance that was connected between collector and base to act as a current source. As a result, the collector-to-base admittance and y_r may be taken as equivalent to one another with ordinary transistors.

The admittance elements that must be used in the feedback path in addition to the unity-ratio transformer have the values

$$g_r/(1 + g_{i'}r_{b'}); \quad C_c/(1 + g_{i'}r_{b'})$$
$$C_c/C_i r_{b'}; \quad g_r/C_i r_{b'} \tag{22}$$

where the first and third are conductances, the second a capacitance, and the fourth an inductance. The first pair are connected in parallel, and the second pair are likewise connected in parallel. With the exception of $r_{b'}$, which is relatively constant, all of the basic elements, g_r, $g_{i'}$, C_i, and C_c are a function of the operating conditions for the transistor. As a result, the conditions for unilateralization of the common-emitter amplifier are rather critical.

Since the value of g_r is extremely small, the first and fourth terms often may be negligible, and the circuit reduces to a series R-C circuit consisting of

$$C_c/C_i r_{b'} \quad \text{and} \quad C_c/(1 + g_{i'}r_{b'})$$

respectively.

8.5 Control of Amplification

The automatic control of amplification in a transistorized amplifier, particularly one which is tuned, is a complicated process because of the variation of the input admittance of the transistor with its operating conditions. If the design can be made in a way that reduces the effect of the variations to a point that they may be neglected, then control is comparatively simple. When, however, the variations of input admittance have important effect on the behavior of the tuned circuits, then the process of design is of increased complexity.

The first question that must be considered in the establishment of transistorized amplifiers having automatic control of amplification is the determination of operating conditions required for varying the amplification. Superficially, the control of power amplification may be obtained either through the control of current amplification or voltage amplification or both. The current amplification for a transistor is relatively independent of the operating conditions from low current to high current. Consequently, the variation of amplification cannot be obtained through variation of current gain, but must be obtained by variation of voltage gain. Because the forward conductance of a transistor is approximately proportional to the current passed, it is necessary to have a current change of ten to one to develop an amplification change of ten to one, and it is also necessary that the load impedance presented by the input terminals of the transistor not vary appreciably.

The input admittance of the transistor normally varies considerably with current, making necessary the loading of the input circuit with a fixed resistance if the input impedance is to be kept reasonably constant. This loading also keeps the bandwidth of the driving amplifier relatively constant as the operating conditions for the transistor change with signal level. This does not correct for the variation of input capacitance, however.

The design of the transistor circuitry to accommodate a varying control current as a function of signal level requires an amplitude detection circuit which can determine the approximate magnitude of the output signal level, and a control circuit that reduces the current in the various transistors as the detection circuit indicates increasing signal amplitude. Such a circuit may include a special isolation amplifier followed by a detector circuit and a d-c control amplifier. The d-c control amplifier may be required to have considerable amplification and appreciable power output because control of transistor amplifiers requires significant amounts of power.

An isolation amplifier operating at the normal operating frequency of the main amplifier is used to prevent the control detector from introducing a nonlinear loading onto the signal circuits. Normally this amplifier may be of the common-emitter type, particularly if its input is paralleled with the input to a common-base amplifier in the signal circuit. Detector loading should further improve the stability.

Either a diode detector, or a transistor functioning as a detector-amplifier, may be used for the detection function. Both of the circuits function in a similar manner, in that the base-emitter junction for the transistor provides the rectification when the transistor performs both

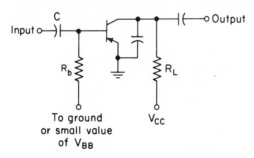

Fig. 8-8. Transistor detector

functions. The rectification efficiency is reduced when both functions are combined in a transistor, however, because with separate elements the diode polarity may be such as to shift the static or d-c level toward the active voltage level, whereas the base-diode rectification in the transistor is not really satisfactory because of its tendency to bias the transistor in the off direction instead of the on (Fig. 8–8).

The type of control amplifier required for regulating the characteristics of the variable-gain amplifier depends on the method selected for introducing the control. Because power is required for this function, the selection of the configuration requiring the minimum input power to the regulation circuit provides the maximum operating efficiency for the over-all circuit. For this reason, the control signal is usually introduced into the base terminals. The only other possible selection, emitter control, requires up to 100 or more times as much current, and therefore would make the control power required excessively large.

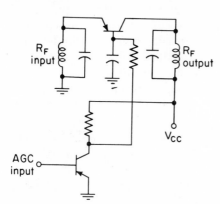

Fig. 8-9. Amplifier with AGC

The control of the amplifier current through the limitation of the base current may readily be accomplished by having the control circuit limit the total voltage applied to the respective bias resistors. A simple circuit for accomplishing this is shown in Fig. 8–9. In this circuit, the control voltage increases or decreases the total current flowing through the regulating transistor, thereby altering the voltage developed across its load resistance and changing the amount of base current available for the amplifier connected to it.

The control amplifier may be converted to a practical circuit by modifying it as shown in Fig. 8–10. In this modification, the output voltage obtained from the control amplifier is repeated by an emitter-follower, and the emitter-follower then controls the individual amplifier stages. This modification is advantageous in several ways. First, it permits the control amplifier itself to operate at comparatively small currents, and limits the loading that must be reflected on the detection circuit. Second, it makes the output admittance of the actual control circuit high because of the emitter-follower configuration that is used. The power amplifier then is self-stabilizing because of the degeneration. Third, the high output admittance of the follower helps the shunt capacitance to isolate the controlled stages from one another and helps to minimize the possibilities of regeneration.

Either polarity of transistor may be used for the control emitter-follower, because either of the configurations (A) or (B) will provide the required control. The use of a transistor of similar polarity to that of the amplifier transistors causes the follower to pass maximum current

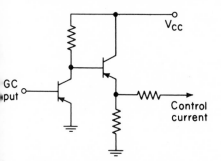

Fig. 8-10A. AGC voltage repeater circuit

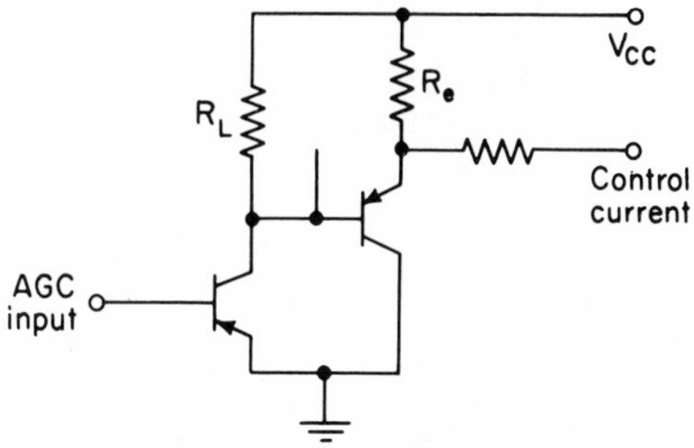

Fig. 8-10B. Alternate AGC voltage repeater circuit

when the amplification of the amplifier is a maximum, providing high filtering action at the control point. At the same time, all of the base current for the amplifier transistors must flow through the control transistor using this configuration.

When the emitter-follower transistor and the amplifier transistors are of opposite polarity types, the control current is diverted through the emitter load rather than through the amplifier transistors, the output admittance of the emitter-follower is lower than can be obtained when both transistor types are the same. The current efficiency as a result is reduced, but the total power required for adjustment of amplification is increased because the control transistor draws current to divert it from the amplifier circuit.

EXAMPLE. 2 Design a common-base amplifier using a 2N247 transistor, and provide a design having a range of amplification between three and ten.

The first step in design of this amplifier is to select the range of current that is to flow in the emitter circuit, and to select the corresponding range of base current. The effective input admittance of the amplifier at its emitter is approximately 35 i_e mhos, for an input resistance of ten ohms with an emitter current of 0.003 amp. If a shunt emitter load of ten ohms is used, then the emitter current must be reduced in accordance with the equation

$$x/(1 + x) = K_{\min}/2K_{\max} \tag{23}$$

This equation assumes that half of the available signal power is dissipated in the emitter loading resistance at minimum input signal. If the maximum amplification is taken as ten, the minimum three, then the minimum value of x required is $3/17$, and the minimum emitter current is 0.53 ma.

The approximate ratio of base current required, minimum amplification to maximum, is $3/17$, or 0.176. The maximum value of the base current required to produce a collector current of three ma is fifty microamperes. The control amplifier to use with the RF amplifier stage should develop a collector voltage change from approximately the supply voltage to a value approximately fifteen percent of the supply voltage.

In applications in which the best possible signal-to-noise ratio is required, it is necessary that the input transistor itself absorb the majority of the available signal power with weak signals, and the parallel input load absorbs increasing amounts of power as the signal strength increases. In such an instance, the supplementary input load resistance should be two to five times the minimum input resistance of the transistor itself. Instead of a shunt resistance of ten ohms as has been selected above, therefore, the shunt resistance should be between thirty and fifty ohms. The range of change of amplification is reduced in exchange for a higher sensitivity for weak signals.

The Emitter-Follower. The design of the emitter-follower providing the base current to the series of amplifiers is relatively conventional, the only critical feature being the selection of operating conditions capable of supplying an adequate magnitude of current at the required voltage. If the circuit of Fig. 8–10(a) is used, all of the emitter current flows into the base circuits of the transistors being controlled, and the power dissipated in the transistor is kept to a minimum consistent with reliable operation. With the circuit of Fig. 8–10(b), however, the current drawn by the transistor must be large compared to the control current, or the voltage cannot be reduced to an adequately small value. The power economy of (a) is considerably superior to that of (b).

Other RF Configurations. There are two important difficulties encountered with RF circuits of the type described thus far. The first and probably the more important, is the variation of the input capacitance with operating current in the transistor. This makes the tuning of the amplifier vary with the operating conditions, and consequently can have serious consequences. The second factor is the variation of the input conductance with the operating point. This condition can be corrected for by the use of the loading resistance as described above, but the total load conductance will vary with operating conditions, and the circuit Q-factor and tuning both will vary with voltage.

A differential-type amplifier (Fig. 8–11), can be used to correct for this situation, because the input circuit of a second transistor may be paralleled with the signal transistor and so connected that the conductive load and the shunt capacitance will remain relatively constant, but at the same time the collector current in the signal transistor can vary as required to provide the necessary variation of amplification. This amplifier can develop full sensitivity with weak signals, yet be readily controlled without the use of a shunt-static load. Such an arrangement can yield a high sensitivity and a relatively low distortion level.

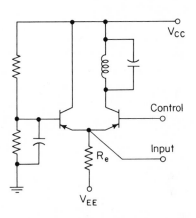

Fig. 8-11. Balanced RF amplifier

The base voltage change that must be developed to shift the collector current from about 0.3 ma to 3.0 ma, or a base current from 5 to 50 microamperes is about 65 millivolts. Because signal is not introduced on the base lead with this circuit, voltage control can be used, particularly with a differential amplifier. The voltage applied on the AVC lead in Fig. 8–11 should have a polarity to cause the loading transistor to draw increased current as the input signal increases.

8.6 Tunnel Diode Amplifiers

Tunnel diodes can be used as amplifiers because their negative conductance can be introduced to neutralize a portion of the positive resistance in an associated tuned circuit, thereby increasing the effective Q of the circuit.

The utilization of a negative-immittance device as an amplifier is possible only under very restricted conditions, because it is necessary for the device to provide most but not all of the energy required by the circuit losses. This means that the maximum value of the negative immittance, as a function of the control parameter, must be slightly less than the value of the circuit positive immittance. With NA devices like tunnel diodes, the diode *must* be inserted in *shunt* with the tuned circuit for this criterion to be fulfilled. The impedance level of the circuit must be adjusted to a value such that the net conductance is slightly positive. This is the reason a knowledge of the maximum value of the negative conductance of the active device is important.

The tunnel diode is the only wide-band negative conductance device at present available. Because of its wide-band properties, a circuit that is designed to be stable at a desired frequency can easily be oscillatory at another frequency in the spectrum (usually a higher frequency). Control of these spurious oscillations is one of the major problems in the utilization of tunnel diodes.

The maximum oscillation frequency for the tunnel diode when used as an amplifier of necessity must be considerably higher than its amplifying frequency. Consequently, the problem in circuit stabilization is one of preventing a net negative conductance at a higher frequency when the required amount of positive conductance is available at operating frequency.

Because of this situation, the tunnel diode is best used as a shunt loading element on a coaxial line. If the output end of the line is terminated resistively with a wide-band resistance, or one which decreases to a small value off resonance, then the likelihood of oscillation developing is minimized. Other than for the use of a parallel-tuned circuit as a load, a possible arrangement for assuring adequately small impedance at high frequency is the use of an additional loading resistance, as shown in Fig. 8–12. In this figure, the potentiometer arrangement is used to adjust the bias to the critical level, and the RF choke is used for the introduction of the bias. The total resistance in this circuit must be kept small, or the adjustment of the bias voltage to the negative-resistance region (between 0.07 and 0.30 volt for germanium) cannot be made.

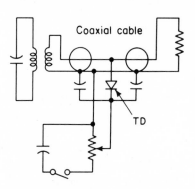

Fig. 8-12. Tunnel diode amplifier circuit

The damping circuit for suppression of high-frequency gain may be placed across the diode terminals. With such an arrangement, the damping resistance should be a fraction of the nominal load impedance, and it should be isolated by a coupling capacitance of such size that the loading of the damping resistance can be neglected at the operating frequency.

Suppression of oscillation in tunnel-diode amplifiers is sufficiently difficult that it is desirable to make use of the oscillation if possible. Some techniques are under development for doing this, and it may also be done with converter circuits. Until many of these problems are solved, the main application of tunnel diodes will be in the field of switching circuits. Experiments made by the author have shown that amplification can be obtained using the circuit of Fig. 8–12, but the amplification compared to direct output with the diode removed from the circuit has been only about three times. Compared to the value with the diode loading the coaxial cable, however, the over-all amplification is approximately ten to twenty times.

8.7 Summary

Although the emphasis has been placed on individual stages in this chapter, conventional techniques may be used to develop stagger-tuned amplifiers, Butterworth amplifiers, and similar configurations. For small-signal stages in which the small-signal parameters show essentially negligible change with the input signal conventional design techniques, described in this chapter, apply. The frequencies and the Q-factors of the individually tuned circuits may be determined, and the transistor loading may be varied to help in the adjustment of the circuit to optimum band-pass characteristics. The amplifier must be of the fixed-gain variety in order that the equalization will not vary over the passband with changing signal levels.

For larger values of signal, when the parameters do vary appreciably with the instantaneous signal voltage, the method of design for variable-source-load impedances described in Chapter Seven may be used. In this instance the loading is averaged and the curved load lines, starting at the output are plotted back from stage to stage. Eventually a stage is reached at which linear techniques apply. The reader should not experience any difficulty extending the techniques described to such amplifiers.

CHAPTER NINE

Nonlinear Theory of Oscillators

9.0 Introduction

The development of effective procedures for design of
oscillators must of necessity be based on a nonlinear or a
piece-wise-linear approach, and should relate the limit-
cycle characteristics in the phase plane to the over-all
behavior of the circuit. The discussion in this and the next
two chapters is an expansion and an extension of the discussion of the principles of oscillator design recently published in *Conductance Design of Active Circuits*.[1] Because
the procedure for design of oscillators must be developed
from the basic nonlinear properties of the amplifying device
in conjunction with the linear or nonlinear properties of
the remainder of the circuit, the first chapter of the group
discusses the nonlinear analytic procedures on which
practical design work is based. This chapter is followed
by one in which designs for *L-C* and crystal oscillators are
developed and one in which practical designs for *R-C* and
time-delay oscillators are developed. The discussion in
Chapters Nine and Ten is concerned with four-terminal

[1] *Conductance Design of Active Circuits*, by K. A. Pullen, Jr. John
F. Rider Publisher, Inc., New York, 1959.

oscillators exclusively. Negative immittance operation is considered in connection with time-delay oscillators in Chapter Eleven.

9.1 Conditions for Four-Terminal Oscillation

The development of an oscillating condition in an electronic circuit requires first that the output power at the frequency of oscillation be greater than the amount of power required to produce it, or there must be power gain in the active device. When this condition can be met, the following additional conditions must be fulfilled:

1. Operating conditions must be such as to minimize noise modulation.
2. The frequency-selection circuit must be properly designed.
3. The over-all phase-shift in the circuit must be an integral multiple of 360 degrees.

In addition to the frequency-amplitude restrictions, there are amplitude-time relations that must be satisfied, the exact relations depending on the type of operation desired. For sinusoidal or continuous-wave oscillators, the following additional conditions apply.

4. The amplification averaged over a single sinusoidal cycle, for stable operation, must be unity.
5. The instantaneous variation from unity must be as small as possible.
6. Sufficient amplification margin must be available at initiation to assure oscillator starting.

These conditions define the required properties for the final circuit and also indicate the design procedures that must be used.

Maximum Oscillating Frequency. The maximum oscillation frequency is that frequency for which a power gain of only unity, and no more, may be obtained from the active device. Mason has shown that this frequency, $f_{\max}$, is determined by the equation[2]

$$U = |\, y_{21} - y_{12}\,|^2/4 \ \mathrm{Re} \ (y_{11}y_{22} - y_{12}y_{21}) \tag{1}$$

Drouillet[3] has taken this basic relation to derive the maximum frequency of oscillation in terms of the normal parameters of the transistor.[3] In the equation for U, the various y and g parameters are the over-all values for the transistor as a whole, including base-spreading resistance and emitter and collector series resistances and their associated reactances. The maxi-

[2] S. Mason, "Power Gain in Feedback Amplifiers," *IRE Transactions*, CT-1, No. 2, 1954, pp. 20-25.

[3] P. R. Drouillet, Jr., Predictions Based on the Maximum Oscillator Frequency of a Transistor, *IRE Trans. PGCT*, June, 1955, p. 178.

mum frequency is given by the condition for which Eq. (1) has a value of U of unity. The value of the numerator is

$$| y_{21} - y_{12} | = [g_f^2/\langle(1 + g_{i'}r_{b'})^2 + (b_{i'}r_{b'})^2 - \omega C_c\rangle^2]^{0.5} \tag{2}$$

Near the limiting frequency, $b_{i'}r_{b'} \gg 1$ and $b_{i'}r_{b'} \gg g_{i'}r_{b'}$. In addition, the value of y_{12} is small in magnitude compared to that for y_{21}, and Eq. (2) reduces to

$$| y_{21} - y_{12} |^2 \doteq [(g_{f'}/b_{i'}r_{b'}) - \omega C_c]^2 \doteq (g_{f'}/b_{i'}r_{b'})^2 \tag{3}$$

Equation (1) may be simplified by the help of this relation to read

$$(g_{f'}/b_{i'}r_{b'})^2 = 4(g_{f'}/b_{i'}r_{b'}) \times \omega C_c U \tag{4}$$

Setting $U = 1$ and $\omega = \omega_{max} = 2\pi f_{max}$ gives

$$\omega_{max}^2 = g_{f'}/4C_iC_cr_{b'} = \alpha_o f_\alpha/4C_cr_{b'} \tag{5}$$

The resulting value of f_{max} is

$$f_{max} = [g_{f'}/C_iC_cr_{b'}]^{0.5}/4\pi \tag{6}$$

The Effect of Noise. The initiation of oscillation in an oscillator is a result of the effect of thermal noise (and other forms of noise) shock-exciting the oscillator circuit, changing the over-all amplification and affecting the phase stability at the same time. Consequently, in oscillators that must meet extreme requirements on frequency stability, it is essential that the transistor used have as small a noise signal voltage as possible, one having an upper noise-corner frequency, f_{n2}, appreciably above the operating frequency for the circuit. In addition, the operating conditions selected for use with it should introduce a minimum of noise.

Loop-Amplification Conditions. The forward conductance of the active device in the oscillator must be sufficiently large that, at the time of initiation, the over-all amplification of the circuit is greater than unity. Also, as the oscillation develops, this amplification must gradually decrease until it stabilizes at an average value of unity as the output stabilizes itself. This average amplification of unity around the feedback loop through the active device and back through the return path can only be obtained by allowing the instantaneous amplification to vary somewhat, rising on one polarity of output, and decreasing on the other. For example, if a parallel L-C tuned circuit is used as the output (or collector) load for the active device, and K_s is the feedback gain (strictly a loss), the equation for the loop gain may be written as

$$Y_f K_s(R + sL)/(s^2LC + SCR + 1) = 1 \tag{7}$$

where Y_f is the forward admittance of the active device, L, R, and C are the component values for the tuned circuit, and s is the familiar Laplacian complex frequency (Fig. 9–1). In this equation, a considerable simplification may be obtained by making the substitutions

$$Y_f Z_L K_s = K \qquad (8)$$

$$Z_L = L/CR \qquad (9)$$

Eq. (7) then reads

$$K(1 + R/sL)/[1 + (sL/R) + 1/sCR] = 1 \qquad (10)$$

Now, the Laplacian operator may be replaced by the real-frequency operator that applies under oscillatory conditions. Then the following substitutions apply

$$s = j\omega = j(\omega_o + \Delta\omega) \qquad (11)$$

$$\omega_o = [(1/LC) - R^2/L^2]^{0.5} \qquad (12)$$

$$\omega = [(1/LC) - (1 + K)^2 R^2/4L^2]^{0.5} \qquad (13)$$

where Eq. (12) applies if $K = 1$, and Eq. (13) when $K \neq 1$. If, now, the change of frequency, $\Delta\omega$, is determined in magnitude as a function of ΔK, keeping only the real-frequency term, the partial difference with respect to K is

$$\Delta\omega/\Delta K = (R^2/L^2 + j\omega R/L)/(-2\omega + j(1 - K)R/L)$$
$$\doteq -\omega_o/2Q^{2*} \qquad (14)$$

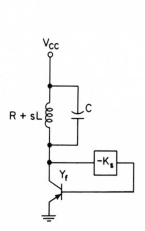

Fig. 9-1. Basic oscillator circuit

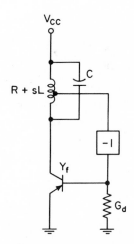

Fig. 9-2. Oscillator with conductive load on feedback network

* Only the real terms have a significant effect on real frequency. The damping is a function of ω/Q.

where Q is the loaded quality-factor of the tuned circuit including *any and all* circuit loading effects, both linear and nonlinear. Consequently, the shift of frequency is proportional to the change in amplification experienced over the oscillating cycle.

The variation of the frequency of oscillation with the operating conditions for an oscillator is a function of the amplification, and through the amplification, of the collector voltage and the emitter or the base current. It is a function of the effective resistance of the tuned circuit, and that resistance is a function of the coupled loads reflected on the tuned circuit from the input and the output circuits of the active device. These components are usually taken into account through the use of a shunt conductance such as G_d in Fig. 9–2. This equivalent loading conductance is introduced across a portion of the inductance of the tuned circuit with the aid of an ideal transformer having a turns-ratio K_s. (The ratio K_s may have the value of unity.) The total value of G_d is a function of $g_{i'}$, $g_{f'}$, g_r, g_o, $r_{b'}$, and also any external loads required in the extraction of signal from the oscillator. Assuming that G_d has been calculated from the transistor data by the equations in Chapter Four, the equation for oscillation for the circuit is*

$$s^2LC + s(G_dLK_s^2 + RC - Y_fK_sL) + 1 + G_dRK_s^2 = 0 \qquad (15)$$

If this is changed into the frequency-and-damping form, the result is

$$-\omega^2LC + j\omega(G_dLK_s^2 + RC - Y_fK_sL) + 1 + G_dRK_s^2 = 0 \qquad (16)$$

The required value of Y_f is directly proportional to the loading introduced by the conductance, G_d, which is determined largely by the input conductance. With a transistor, the values of G_d and Y_f are nearly proportional over a moderate range of base and collector currents, with the result that if the K_s^2L term is large compared to RC, the circuit cannot be stabilized easily by variation of the operating point. Stabilization from action of the transistor itself requires that $K_s^2G_dL$ have a magnitude approximately equal to the value of RC, and Y_fK_sL must equal the sum of $K_s^2G_dL$ and RC.

The frequency of operation for the oscillator of Fig. 9–2 is given by the equation

$$\omega = [(1/LC) + (G_dRK_s^2/LC) - \langle K_s(G_dK_s - Y_f)/C + R/L\rangle^2/4]^{0.5} \qquad (17)$$

Once again, the rate of change of ω with variation of either Y_f or G_d

---

* The transfer impedance, Z_t, may be derived topologically to be

$$Z_t = sK_sL/[1 + sC(R + sL) + K_s^2G_d(R + sL) - sCG_d(L_1L_2 - M^2)]$$

where the primary inductance, $L_1 = L$, and the secondary inductance, $L_2 = K_s^2L$, and the mutual inductance is K_sL, giving the conditions for unity coupling in the transformer.

may be determined by taking the appropriate partial derivative. These partials are

$$d\omega/dY_f = -K_s[K_sY_fL - G_dK_s^2L - RC]/4\omega_oC^2L$$

$$d\omega/dG_d = [(RK_s^2/LC) - \langle K_s(G_dK_s - Y_f)/C + (R/L)\rangle K_s^2/2C] \tag{18}$$

Proper use of these equations can permit at least a minimization of the frequency error due to the variation of transistor parameters. Clearly, the smaller the value of K_s (the higher the step-down ratio), the smaller will be both of these errors. This condition is consistent with the use of the transistor in the conductance mode, with a voltage, or low-impedance source, and a current, or high-impedance output on the active device.

The amplification requirements may be summarized as follows. First, on initiation, the loop amplification must be appreciably greater than unity to assure reliable starting, and it must adjust itself to unity smoothly as the amplitude increases. The variation of amplification from cycle to cycle must be less than the variation over a given cycle of sinusoidal signal to assure a constant amplitude output. Secondly, the amplification over the operating cycle should vary as little as possible from the average value of unity if frequency stability is of prime importance. The mean-square variation of frequency should be minimized as a function of variations in the operating point, amplification, and input and transfer admittances.

Characteristics of the Frequency Selection Circuit.   The function of the frequency-selection circuit is to limit the range of frequencies over which the loop gain may approach unity to the range over which the oscillator is to operate. The frequency-selection circuit may consist of a tuned circuit with appropriate impedance-matching circuits, or it may consist of an R-C-type delay circuit with appropriate matching circuits. It could also consist of an appropriately designed delay line to generate a repetitive signal through time-delay action.

Because of the nature of resonant circuits, the fact that the region of maximum response has appreciable frequency width, the oscillating frequency is controlled by the time delay required to match the input and the output phase. This matching is required to provide energy reinforcement, just as the escapement in a watch or a clock must introduce a pulse of energy into the pendulum or the balance wheel at precisely the correct instant to maintain oscillation. The rapidity of the shift of phase across the resonant peak determines the rate-of-change of feedback phase with frequency, thereby limiting the maximum frequency deviation. Consequently, as shown in Eqs. (14) and (18), the percentage range of frequency error is an inverse function of the Q-factor of the tuned circuit, it being defined for Fig. 9–2 by Eq. (14).

In some types of oscillators, the inductance that has the components R, $j\omega L$, is replaced by the series combination of an inductance and a capacitance, L' and C', the total series impedance being

$$Z_s = R' + j\omega L' + 1/j\omega C' \tag{19}$$

If this combination is substituted for $R + j\omega L$ in the oscillator equations, and the new equation is solved for the Q-factor, the result, if $L' = 10L$; $R' = 10R$; $C' = C/9$ is *

$$Q = (\omega_o L' - 1/\omega_o C')/R' = [L'/C]^{0.5}/10R \tag{20}$$

If, therefore, the Q-factor of the higher-inductance coil is the same as that of the smaller, then the over-all effective Q of the circuit is severely limited.

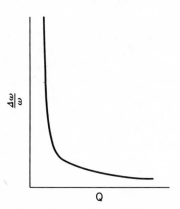

Fig. 9-3. Relation of $\dfrac{\Delta\omega}{\omega}$ to Q

Unless the effective Q of the higher-inductance coil is much larger than for the smaller, no benefit can be obtained. Normally, the losses in the active circuit are much larger than the losses in the tuned circuit, with the result that the most beneficial change is a reduction of the over-all impedance level of the coupling circuit.

It is impossible to separate the consideration of frequency and phase in any oscillator, because frequency is a measure of the rate of change of phase. The variation of frequency generated by circuit noise in an oscillator carries with it a corresponding shift of phase, and the net instantaneous phase at any moment is the phase sum of the noise phase and the signal phase returned through the feedback path. As a result, the higher the rate of phase progression across the peak of the response curve of the tuned feedback circuit, the smaller the total effect of random phase, and the more stable the frequency from the oscillator. Nonuniformity of amplification over the period of the sinusoidal wave also introduces a phase error into the returned voltage that, by reducing the voltage reinforcement in the tuned circuit, makes the phase progression less stable and consequently the frequency less stable.

Effect of Variation of Amplification. The calculation of the effect of variation of amplification can be made by the use of statistical techniques supplemented by the inclusion of a term that gives the equivalent effect

* Clearly, although the net reactance is unchanged, the circuit damping has increased, for the same coil Q-factor, by the ratio L'/L. The rate of change of reactance with frequency has increased from L to $L'/ + L/\omega^2 C' = 2L'$. The net effect is a negligible change in the rate-of-change of phase compared to the simpler circuit.

of the periodic variation. Because the amplification varies about a mean of unity, the first moments of the signal must have an average of zero when measured about a loop amplification of unity. For this reason, only moments of second or higher order need be considered. The most important of these is the mean-square deviation, which is defined in terms of the equation

$$\overline{\Delta K_\sigma}^2 = \overline{(K_L - 1)}^2 \tag{21}$$

where the averaging may be carried out over some integral number of cycles of the output frequency.

The process of achieving both the condition of unity average loop amplification and a minimum value of $\overline{\Delta K_\sigma}$ is of considerable importance, since both conditions must be satisfied simultaneously for maximum frequency stability. If the variation of amplification with input signal voltage is exactly linear, it is impossible to adjust the average amplification directly to unity unless there is a sharp discontinuity from the linear relation at one limit, or unless some device sensitive to signal voltage or power is incorporated to introduce a variation. Such an action may be accomplished by an automatic gain-control circuit or through the use of a power-sensitive device such as a thermistor to control the sensitivity of a bridge in terms of the signal power applied to one of its elements. If there is some curvature in the relation between amplification and signal voltage, then the development of a self-limiting condition can occur if the decrease in amplification for one signal polarity has a greater effect on the average amplification than the increase with the other polarity. If the effects exactly offset one another, or an increase of net amplification results, then unstable operation results, and the oscillator will tend to pulse or squegg.

With most of the conventional tube oscillators, a linear variation of amplification in conjunction with a sharp break introduced by grid rectification is used to provide linear operation and amplitude limiting. With transistor circuits, however, this arrangement may not be available to the

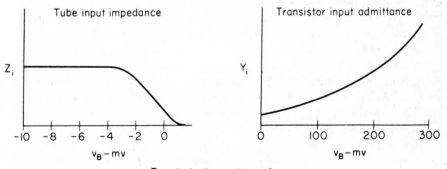

Fig. 9-4. Input impedance

designer because a low-impedance signal source is required for the control element, and no condition of a sharp break of the sort shown in Fig. 9–4 can readily be provided. Consequently, with transistor oscillators, it is necessary to take advantage of a second-order nonlinearity that reduces the average amplification, and a design procedure of substantially increased complexity is required as a result. For this reason, although the basic techniques explained in Chapters 7 and 11 of *Conductance Design of Active Circuits* apply to transistor oscillators, considerable extension is required to clarify fully the procedure.[1]

The mean frequency deviation of the oscillator from its nominal operating frequency may be expressed in terms of the equation

$$\overline{\Delta\omega_\sigma/\omega_o} = \overline{\Delta K_\sigma}/2Q^2 \tag{22}$$

where $\Delta\omega_\sigma$ is the rms deviation of the instantaneous frequency from its nominal value, and $\overline{\Delta K_\sigma}$ is the rms deviation of the amplification. Strictly, these values include not only the nonlinearity of the amplifier itself as a result of the signal voltage, but also that due to noise as amplified in the circuit. The latter produces a random deviation of phase with time. Consequently, the $\overline{\Delta K_\sigma}^2$ term should be divided into at least two parts

$$\overline{\Delta K_\sigma}^2 = \overline{\Delta K_{\omega\sigma}}^2 + \overline{\Delta K_{N\sigma}}^2 \tag{23}$$

where the sum of the squares relation is necessary since the correlation between the sinusoidal signal and noise is zero.

In practical applications, a non-zero derivative of frequency with time makes necessary a broadening of the bandwidth required for transmitting a signal. Because in the final analysis, the bandwidths of precision circuits can only be determined in terms of the equivalent noise-widening as observed in a narrow-band filter, knowledge of the most efficient methods of minimizing the ratio $\Delta\omega/\omega_o$ is of extreme importance. It is necessary for the stability of a calibrating source to be at least ten times that of the device under test for a measurement of the effective noise bandwidth to give an indication of the absolute noise stability of the poorer signal. Otherwise, it is necessary that a series of oscillators be compared with each other, and each compared one-by-one with all the others to get a practical measure of the value of $\Delta\omega_\sigma$.

The statement is frequently made that the stability of the output frequency of an oscillator is independent of the configuration in which the active device is used. Subject to certain limitations, this is correct, but it is important that the degradation of the circuit Q-factor by the active device be identical for the respective circuits, and also that the variation of the amplification with signal have the same characteristics and magnitude. Unless these conditions are fulfilled, however, the frequency stabilities will not be comparable.

The effect of variation of the Q-factor for a crystal on the possible frequency deviation for a crystal oscillator having a ΔK factor of 0.5 is indicated in the following table, the assumed frequency being 10^8 cps.

Q	10^4	2×10^4	5×10^4	10^5	2×10^5	5×10^5
$\Delta\omega_o$	1.5 rad	0.38	0.06	0.015	0.004	0.0006
Δf_o	0.25 cps	0.06	0.01	0.0025	0.0006	0.0001

Consequently, if a crystal having a Q of 10^4 is used at 100 mcs, it is necessary that the variation of amplification over the signal voltage range be limited to an rms value of 0.2 for 0.1 cps bandwidth. Evidently, a thermal regulator may be desirable if rapid and convenient starting is to be achieved. The very minimum excess gain that will assure starting is at least ten percent for a degenerative amplifier and 50 to 100 percent for ordinary circuits.

The Clapp and the Q-multiplier oscillators both can be designed to take advantage of the high order of constancy of gain of the emitter-follower circuit when it is arranged to have minimum loading. (This loading problem is often ignored when oscillators are designed around electron tubes as the active device.) It is of extreme importance that the loading be kept to a minimum, because the value of the Q-factor that must be used with the equation is the value *under operating conditions*.

9.2 Averaging of Amplification

The process of finding the conditions for which the average amplification is unity can be very complex if the variation of amplification with signal is irregular, and it can be quite simple if the variation is linear with signal. Normally it is convenient to calculate the amplifications at three points on the cycle of oscillation, namely, the positive limit of input signal, the negative limit, and the static value. From these three values the approximate linearity of variation may be determined in terms of the equation

$$\Delta K = 0.25(K_p + K_n - 2K_s) \tag{24}$$

where ΔK, the deviation from linearity, ideally should be very small compared with the positive, negative, and the static values of the amplification, K_p, K_n, and K_s. If it is as large as from ten to twenty-five percent of one of the typical amplification values, then a more complex method of averaging may be desirable; for example, the orthogonal polynomial method described in Appendix IV. If it is less than ten percent, a suitable averaging equation for the amplification is

$$K_a = 0.25(K_p + 2K_s + K_n) \tag{25}$$

Modified forms of this equation may also be used for averaging other circuit values when the behavior is relatively linear.

In addition to the use of orthogonal polynomials, the Fourier method may be used for averaging when the amplification is either relatively or significantly nonlinear. Both of these methods can be used to handle the determination of the average amplification in oscillators in which the nonlinearity is considerable. Examples of the use of each of these methods are included at the end of this section, and a more complete explanation of the use of orthogonal and Legendre polynomials is included in Appendix IV.

The polynomial method may be applied to either continuous data, in which case the input-output or the input-amplification relation is known in terms of a closed function, or it may be applied to discrete data for either of the functional relations. For the convenience of the reader, a table of Legendre coefficients for use with power-series expansions is included in the appendix, along with a discussion of the application procedures in simple problems. One of these tables assumes that the power-series term is uniquely defined and not continuously zero over any part of the range $-1 < x < +1$, and the second table gives the values for the conditions that the term is zero for all negative values of x, but is non-zero for values over the range $0 < x < +1$. It may be used for representation of diodes and class B circuits.

With the polynomial method, a series of polynomials that are mutually orthogonal when integrated (or summed) over the range from minus unity to plus unity are either fitted analytically (continuously) over the range of the variables to give the best least-squares fit between the approximating curve and the original function, or they are fitted to give a least-squares fit at a series of uniformly spaced data points over the range. The continuous-fitting method uses Legendre polynomials, and with discrete data, a discrete series known as orthogonal polynomials are used. The orthogonal polynomials have a close relationship to the Legendre polynomials in that they approach the latter when the increment approaches zero. The polynomial coefficients are first determined, corrected if necessary, and then each of the polynomials is replaced by its equivalent in the form of trigonometric (Chebycheff) polynomials, the angular functions being expressed in terms of multiple angles rather than in powers of the simple angle. After this substitution is made, then the coefficients for the corresponding multiple angles may be collected, and the result is a series of terms in the various harmonics of the applied frequency. These harmonics and their coefficients express the response of the network to a sinusoidal input signal.

The Fourier technique for calculation of the amplification is based on the analysis of the amplitudes of the harmonics generated in a circuit through the introduction of a sinusoidal input signal of given magnitude.

The ratio of the fundamental output amplitude to the input magnitude gives the average amplification, and the ratios of the amplitudes of the higher harmonics to the output amplitude of the fundamental gives the distortion components for the over-all circuit. This technique is applicable to oscillators because the input signal can be assumed to be a sine wave, and the distortion resulting from oscillator limiting can be assumed to be generated in a separate nonlinear circuit. The spectrum can be determined in terms of a sine-wave input, and the component amplitudes determined by the Fourier analysis. The process is easily applied when the detector characteristic is known in closed form, but it becomes more difficult with discrete data such as are normally encountered with active circuits.

Since the use of Fourier analysis for both discrete and for continuous data is well known and is described in most elementary electrical engineering textbooks, it will not be described in detail here. Fourier analysis, like the use of Legendre and orthogonal polynomials gives the required answers easily and directly because of the orthogonality of harmonic trigonometric components. As with Legendre analysis, the ratio of the amplitudes of the output and input sinusoidal components gives the average amplification.

EXAMPLE 1.   Determine the average amplification of an amplifier having a response defined by the equation

$$y = ax^2 \quad \text{over the range} \quad 0 \leq x \leq 1$$

Both the gain function and the voltage function may be determined using the Legendre technique. For this problem, assume that the peak amplification in the conduction direction is twenty. With a square-law response starting at the static, or Q-point, this means that the peak output signal is ten volts.

The amplitude of the sinusoidal component may be found directly by reference to Table II in Appendix IV. The value of the coefficient for the voltage-output function may be determined by the use of the column for exponent $j = 2$, and for the gain function, for $j = 1$. The corresponding values for the order coefficients are

$$E_{e1} = 0.375, \quad C_{e3} = 7/48, \quad C_{ko} = 0.25, \quad C_{k2} = 5/16$$

Substituting in Eqs. (7) and (8) of Appendix IV gives

$$K_o = 0.2109, \quad E_1 = 0.429$$

Multiplying the first by 20, and the second by 10, gives the effective voltage output, 4.22 for the first case, and 4.29 for the second.

This result may also be obtained by the use of Fourier techniques, because if the input is $\cos \omega t$, the output is $10 \cos^2 \omega t$ over half the cycle, and zero over the other half. Using the Fourier integration equation for the fundamental component gives

$$E_1 = (10/\pi) \int_{-\pi/2\omega}^{\pi/2\omega} 0.5 \, (1 + \cos 2\omega t) \sin \omega t \, dt \qquad (26)$$

the integration being from $-\pi/2\omega$ to $+\pi/2\omega$. Integrating Eq. (26) gives the required answer

$$E_1 = 4.244$$

Three terms are obtained in the integration, two at fundamental frequency, and one at the third harmonic. All three contribute because of the half-period integration time.

This result can also be obtained in terms of orthogonal polynomial expansions just as it can in terms of Legendre and Fourier expansions. The details of the method of calculation are explained in Appendix IV, and the process of making trapezoidal corrections is also explained. Assuming that a square-law relation is known in terms of either of the two following combinations of data, with $e_i = 0$ the static, or Q-point, the average amplification and output voltage are

e_i	0	0.1	0.2	0.3	0.4	0.5	0.6
e_o	0	0.1	0.4	0.9	1.6	2.5	3.6
K	0	2	4	6	8	10	12
e_i	0.7	0.8	0.9	1.0			
e_o	4.9	6.4	8.1	10.0			
K	14	16	18	20			

The data for e_o may be multiplied by the data in the $j = 1$ and $j = 3$ rows of the table for $2n + 1 = 21$, and each of them may be divided by the sum term S_j to give the required components, approximately 3.9 and 0.42. In a similar manner, the values of the amplifications may be obtained by the use of the K data with rows 0 and 2. Normally, the value based on the amplification will tend to converge more slowly than will the value based on voltages because of the integration implied in the voltage determination.

The accuracy with which results can be obtained by these methods depends on the number of data points that are used for representing the behavior of the circuit. For example, if $n = 4$, the smoothing is poorer and a poorer set of data is likely to result. The accuracy of the results is significantly poorer with "one-sided" data than with complete data because of the difficulty of producing an identically zero value over an extended range.

The selection between the use of the approximate equations for the determination of the second and third harmonics and the use of polynomial methods is based on the number of data points available and the uniformity of the variation they possess. The presence of a sharp break in the contour, with data available for more than six points makes the use of orthogonal techniques desirable. As long as no sharp break is noted in the data, calculation of the values at three points usually is sufficient. If the presence of a sharp break is suspected, however, as many data points as possible should be used.

9.3 Static Circuit Behavior

The development of the static operating conditions for an oscillator is as complex as is the determination of the conditions for unity loop amplification. In fact, it is not possible to separate the two determinations because the manner of variation of amplification depends on the way in which the static biasing operation takes place.

The simplest method of regulating static behavior, rectification limiting, is difficult to achieve and use with transistor oscillators because of the relatively high conductance of the input circuit under amplifying conditions, and because of the relatively uniform variation of the input conductance. Consequently, the nonlinearity of the variation of the control current, as well as the nonlinearity of the variation of amplification, must be used in the stabilization of simple transistor oscillators.

The requirement that the input power for the feedback path be provided at an impedance level that is small compared to the input impedance of the device means that the input voltage will be approximately sinusoidal, whereas the input current will not be. It is, therefore, important to determine how the current variation affects the determination of the appropriate method of introducing control. An examination of the behavior of a typical transistor under equal increments of base voltage shows that the average base current, for a fixed operating point, will increase as the sinusoidal signal is increased in amplitude. This means that one possible method of amplitude control for the transistor oscillator is through limiting its average base current, as the average forward conductance will then decrease as the magnitude of the signal current increases. A typical calculation of such a current averaging procedure is shown in the Ex. 1 in Appendix IV.

Some limiting of average amplification may be obtained with a fixed operating point for an oscillator, because the effect of base-spreading resistance is greatest at high current. However, the range of variation usually is insufficient to assure reliable starting, with the result that some method of shifting the operating conditions to an area of reduced average amplification is desirable.

If the average base current is limited to a fixed value through the use of a series resistor, the increase of amplitude of the signal voltage is accompanied by the shift of the effective position of the output load contour as is shown in Fig. 9–5. The amplitude of the signal voltage corresponding to each load line is just that which will give the required average base current (or emitter current for a common-base circuit). If the amplitude of the oscillation still builds up, it is accompanied by a further shift of the position of the load line.

Through the points on this set of load lines a pair of limit contours may be drawn that represent the excursion for which the average base current exactly equals that for which the circuit has been designed. These contours are often convenient to use, so they may be sketched in, and the positive limit identified by the symbol C_{Lp}, and the negative by the symbol C_{Ln}. The positions of these contours can be determined by calculation of the average current at sets of data on base current on several load lines, and then the amplification calculations may be made as required along these contours and the static contour.

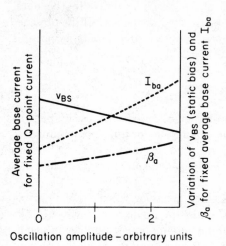

Fig. 9-5. Effect of variation of oscillator amplitude

The only difference in determining the limit contours for the common-base oscillator as compared to the common-emitter is that the calculations are based on the sum of the collector and base currents rather than the base current alone. The correction for the load-contour curvature, which has already been discussed, may be required, but this correction may be made after the final steady-state load line is located.

9.4 Current Averaging

The averaging of the base or the emitter current in the oscillator to find the limit points on any given load line is performed by either of two methods, the three-term averaging formula for applications in which the variation is relatively linear, or the orthogonal-polynomial method.

The averaging formula convenient for use with current variations which might be called square-law, is related to the formula used for the averaging of the loop amplification. It is

$$I_a = 0.25[I_p + 2I_s + I_n] \qquad (27)$$

where I_a is the average electrode current, I_p the electrode current for the most positive value of signal voltage on the electrode, I_s the current at the intersection of the static and dynamic load contours (the Q-point current), and I_n the current at the most negative value of signal voltage. As long as only the first two derivatives of the electrode current are significant over the operating range of the transistor this equation gives adequate accuracy.

In oscillators in which higher orders of nonlinearity are present, the base or emitter current averaging cannot be accomplished by the simple formula, and it is necessary to turn to a more sophisticated method, such as orthogonal polynomials. The sample problem solved next shows the directness of the polynomial method and shows how it compares with the averaging equation.

EXAMPLE 2.   An oscillator has been constructed with a circuit that limits the average base current to 90 microamperes. If the following table gives the values of the base current for equal increments of base voltage and the current at the Q-point is 80 microamperes, find the range of signal voltage and base current.

The averaging equation, Eq. (27), gives the result very quickly based on the table

V_b	100	110	120	130	140	150	160	170	180
I_b	10	20	35	55	80	110	145	185	230

The average currents for peak base-voltage amplitudes of $\Delta V_0 = 20$, 30, and 40 millivolts are 85.0, 91.25, and 100 microamperes, respectively. Evidently, in the limiting condition a base-voltage change of approximately 56 millivolts is developed.

Using the polynomial method, the tables for $2n + 1 = 5$, 7, and 9 may be used, and the first two components, namely C_0 and C_2, may be used in the evaluation of the average current. Trapezoidal corrections may also be included if desired, because the exponent-two condition correction applies. (It is necessary for only the lowest coefficients to be non-zero for the correction process to be effective.) The typical calculation for $2n + 1 = 5$ to give the values of C_0 and C_2 follows.

The matrix equations for C_0 and C_2, leaving blank rows for the odd coefficients, are

$$
\begin{bmatrix} C_0 \\ \cdots \\ C_2 \\ \cdots \\ C_4 \end{bmatrix} = \begin{bmatrix} \frac{1}{5} \\ \cdots \\ \frac{1}{7} \\ \cdots \\ \frac{1}{70} \end{bmatrix} \begin{bmatrix} 1 & 1 & 1 & 1 & 1 \\ \cdots \\ 2 & -1 & -2 & -1 & 2 \\ \cdots \\ 1 & -4 & 6 & -4 & 1 \end{bmatrix} \begin{bmatrix} 35 \\ 55 \\ 80 \\ 110 \\ 145 \end{bmatrix}
$$

From this equation, the values of C_0, C_2, and C_4 are:

$$C_0 = (\tfrac{1}{5}) [1 \times 35 + 1 \times 55 + 1 \times 80 + 1 \times 110 + 1 \times 145]$$
$$= \tfrac{425}{5} = 85 \text{ microamperes}$$
$$C_{0c} = [80 + 2 \times 85]/(3) = 83.3$$
$$C_2 = (\tfrac{1}{7}) [2 \times 35 - 1 \times 55 - 2 \times 80 - 1 \times 110 + 2 \times 145]$$
$$= \tfrac{35}{7} = 5$$
$$C_{2c} = \tfrac{4 \times 5}{3} = 6.67$$
$$C_4 = (\tfrac{1}{70}) [1 \times 35 - 4 \times 55 + 6 \times 80 - 4 \times 110 + 1 \times 145]$$
$$= 0$$

Substituting to find I_o gives

$$I_o = 86.25 \text{ microamperes, uncorrected}$$
$$= 83.3 + 1.67 = 85 \text{ microamperes, corrected}$$

The uncorrected average current is 86.25 microamperes. Similar calculations may be made using $n = 3$ and $n = 4$, giving corresponding average values of current. The correct operating conditions are with a signal magnitude of approximately 28 millivolts either side of the quiescent point, 140 millivolts.

Application Notes. The above discussion is directed to the evaluation of the mathematical tools required for effective design of oscillators, whether they are based on the use of tubes, transistors, or other active devices as the amplifier elements. It is necessary to be able to locate the operating cycle in two respects, first with respect to the limits of current or voltage for the circuit, and second with respect to the over-all, or loop, amplification of the oscillator if effective nonlinear design is to be achieved. The balance of this chapter is devoted to the development of the techniques of application of piece-wise linearization to oscillators using transistors, and the following two chapters are devoted to a detailed discussion of specific circuit applications, the first application chapter considering L-C oscillators and crystal oscillators, and the second considering R-C-type tuned oscillators.

9.5 Basic Design Procedures

A general design procedure can be established based on the discussion above. The first step, as always, is the location of the static and the dynamic load lines on the characteristic curves. A static value of collector voltage is first selected at a value less than one-third of the maximum rated collector voltage, and a static value of the operating current for the control electrode, either base or emitter, is selected. Then a series of trial load lines may be plotted, and transferred to the input family in the usual way (Fig. 9–6). The impedances for these load lines are given by the Z_i for the feedback network. Since the value of Z_i may vary as a result of conductance loading, the representing contour need not be a straight line. In case correction for curvature is required, an initial value of impedance at the static- or Q-point may be calculated based on the small-signal data at the rest-point. The appropriate slope may be determined, and the load contour plotted from the static-point in both directions to the adjacent bias contours. New values of slope may be calculated at each of the adjacent bias lines, and the load line curved just enough to give the correct slope at the bias contours. This process is continued until the full operating contour has been plotted. The corresponding input contour is plotted step-by-step as the output contour is constructed.

After a set of input and output load contours have been plotted, the next step is to mark points of equal base-voltage increment on the input family and transfer the points to the output family. Once these points have been located, the values for the current and voltage variables and the final values of the small-signal parameters may be tabulated from the curves. Then both the input admittance and forward amplification values and the average values for the control current may be calculated for use in the design procedure. The balance of the problem is concerned with the linear components such as inductors, capacitors, crystals, and similar energy-storage elements.

The derived-gain form of the orthogonal equations may be used to determine both the approximate input admittance and the forward transfer admittance for the transistor if adequate small-signal data are not available. This technique of determining the small-signal characteristics of a circuit from the static data is not as good as is using small-signal data in the form provided on some transistors in Appendices VI and VII, but because of the least-squares averaging obtained with the polynomial technique, it is appreciably better than evaluation at individual points. The mean value and the maximum change of the admittances are given in terms of the K factors of Eq. (8), Appendix IV, Section A, through the equation

$$Y_0 = K_0 I/V, \qquad Y_1 = K_1 I/V$$
$$Y_{\min} = Y_0 - Y_1, \qquad Y_{\max} = Y_0 + Y_1 \tag{28}$$

where I is the current scaling factor, that factor by which each of the current entries must be multiplied to give the current in amperes, and V is the voltage scaling factor, equal to half of the total change. The following example shows how this can be done based on the data for Example 2.

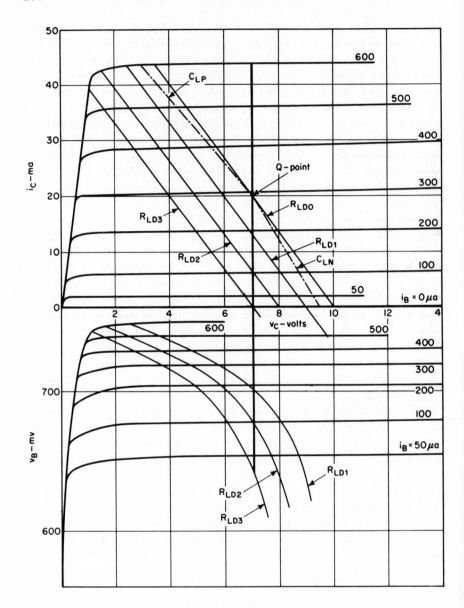

Fig. 9-6. Contour development of 2N1613

EXAMPLE 3. Using the derived gain equations and the trapezoidal correction factors from Appendix IV, calculate the average input admittance and the maximum and minimum admittances for the current-averaging problem, Example 2.

The values of C_{e1} and C_{e3} must now be calculated as they appear in the equation for K_0. The equation for K_1 gives either the uncorrected or the corrected values of the second-harmonic component of amplification, depending on whether the coefficients are corrected or not. The values of Y_0 and Y_1 obtained for $V = 20$ mv are $Y_0 = 2750$ micromhos, and $Y_1 = 750$ or 1000 micromhos, depending on whether the data are uncorrected or corrected, respectively. Similar values may be obtained for other typical operating conditions.

The value of K_0 or Y_0 is important in that it measures the linear behavior of the device, whether it is an input or a transfer coefficient. Similarly, the value of Y_1 or K_1 measures the distortion or nonlinearity in the circuit. The value of Y_0 or K_0 may be independent of the operating amplitude, in which case limiting in the amplification must be generated by variation of the static operating point. The value of Y_1 or K_1 must of necessity increase as the amplitude is increased, because the variations from linearity normally increase with increasing signal amplitude. The smaller the ratio of K_1/K_0 or Y_1/Y_0, the smaller the distortion and the higher the frequency stability of the oscillator.

CHAPTER TEN

Practical L-C Oscillators

10.0 Introduction

The development of practical designs of L-C oscillators based on the techniques described in Chapter Nine requires the coordination of network properties with the properties of active devices. It also requires the selection of transistors capable of functioning as required. With some minor limitations, any transistor that can be used below its upper noise-corner frequency, f_{n2}, may be used effectively in an oscillator circuit. However, because some of the parameters of transistors introduce significant effects into the behavior of an oscillator circuit, a discussion of the factors that can deteriorate the performance of the circuit is important.

One of the parameter groups important in the design of oscillators is the group including the series element resistances, $r_{e'}$, $r_{b'}$, and $r_{c'}$. Each of these should be as small as possible because each has its own degrading effect on transistor behavior. The effect of the presence of $r_{e'}$ is to reduce the effective values of forward admittance available, limiting the effectiveness of a transistor as an active element. Similarly, the presence or $r_{b'}$ either makes signal injection into the base junction difficult or it introduces a regenerative effect into the over-all circuit. The presence of $r_{c'}$ in the circuit tends to introduce instability inasmuch as it makes necessary the introduction of a phase-shift and more than the design amount of gain into the amplifier. A signal voltage proportional to the internal impedance $r_{c'}$ must be developed in addition to that required by the amplifier load circuit when this series impedance is present.

One type of transistor normally has comparatively large values for all three of these internal impedances, and at least one, $r_{b'}$, has both resistive and reactive components. This type of transistor, the grown-junction transistor, is for that reason relatively less satisfactory for oscillator use than many of the other common forms. Transistors having a base whose conductivity increases toward the emitter junction can be made with the smallest values of $r_{b'}$, and they also can be made with rather small values of $r_{e'}$. The value of $r_{c'}$ present in a given transistor, particularly one of the alloy variety, depends primarily on the processing details rather than on the physical design of the collector region. The epitaxial design of the mesa transistor is particularly effective because of its small value of $r_{c'}$.[1]

Alloy and surface barrier transistors, meltback, graded-base, and mesa transistors all are likely to have the properties required for use in an oscillator. Other types may also have the required properties, but their characteristics should be given close scrutiny prior to selection for use in a circuit.

10.1 The Basic L-C Oscillator

The basic equations for direct-coupled *L-C* oscillators may all be derived in terms of a single basic configuration, because the active device enters into the action primarily in the process of cancelling out the positive resistance of the frequency-selection circuit. This relation is a result of the fact that no matter how the configuration is arranged, the amplifier is required to provide a unity loop-amplification, and it is adjusted to do so. The method of adjusting the amplification to unity does not appear directly in this derivation, nor does the amount of energy required of the frequency-selection circuit by the active device appear in the equation.

The fact that all of the basic oscillator forms, common-emitter, common-base, and common-collector, can be studied on the basis of a single circuit has led to some confusion on the relative frequency stability of the three forms. As was shown in Chapter Nine, the frequency stability of an oscillator depends primarily on the magnitude of loading reflected by the active device on the tuned circuit, and the magnitude variation of the amplification

---

[1] H. C. Theuerer, J. J. Kleimack, et al., "Epitaxial Diffused Transistors" (a letter), *Proc. IRE*, September, 1960, p. 1642.

with signal level. This being the case, the best stability can be expected for the arrangement giving the smallest loading and the smallest variation of amplification. Evidently, the common-base oscillator circuit has reduced stability because of the input signal power required by the emitter of the transistor, and by the fact that it has a reduced power gain compared to the common-emitter configuration.

The selection of a configuration between the common-emitter and the common-collector form is somewhat more difficult. The power gain in the common-collector amplifier is much smaller than for the common-emitter, but the uniformity of loading and the uniformity of gain are both much better. Consequently, the selection between the two can be rather difficult. If the common-emitter circuit is properly designed, it can be used in excellent high-stability oscillators, but otherwise, the common-collector circuit often gives the most stable arrangement. That this is true can be recognized from the large amount of use made of Clapp and Q-multiplier type cathode-follower oscillators. The stability improvement in both examples is a result of the reduced and more uniform loading of the active device on the tuned circuit and on the more uniform amplification.

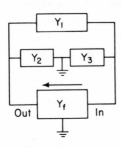

Fig.10-1. General oscillator

The basic oscillator configuration, which is important with energy-storage oscillators (oscillators in which frequency control is a result of exchange of energy between devices capable of possessing kinetic and potential energy), is shown in Fig. 10–1. This circuit utilizes an active amplifier and three reactive elements, two of which possess the same kind of energy-storage and the third which stores the alternate form of energy. If two of the elements are capacitors, the third is an inductor, and the oscillator is a Colpitts oscillator; if two are inductors, one is a capacitor, a Hartley oscillator. Normally the two inductors are both parts of a single tapped inductor, and a relatively high coefficient of magnetic coupling exists between the sections. The coupling simplifies the transformation of impedance required in oscillator circuits.

The basic equations for the general oscillator shown in Fig. 10–1 are rather similar to those derived in Chapter Nine, in that they relate the amplification of the active device to the frequency-selection and transforming action of the storage circuit. They differ only in that the adjustment of the voltage amplification is obtained through the action of the two like-reactive elements directly, instead of including a separate factor for the adjustment. The common or ground point is taken at one end, or at the junction of unlike elements, if either the common-base or the common-collector circuit is used, and it is taken at the junction of like elements if a common-emitter circuit is used.

The input, output, and transfer characteristics of the circuit of Fig. 10–1 may be readily analyzed either by standard methods or topologically, giving the basic input, output, and transfer impedances as

$$Z_I = [(1 + Y_3/Y_1)/(Y_2 + Y_3)]/[1 + (Y_2Y_3/\langle Y_2 + Y_3\rangle)Y_1] \tag{1}$$

$$Z_O = [(1 + Y_2/Y_1)/(Y_2 + Y_3)]/[1 + (Y_2Y_3/\langle Y_2 + Y_3\rangle)Y_1] \tag{2}$$

$$Z_T = [1/(Y_2 + Y_3)]/[1 + (Y_2Y_3/\langle Y_2 + Y_3\rangle)Y_1] \tag{3}$$

If the substitutions required for a Colpitts oscillator are made, namely

$$1/Y_1 = R_1 + j\omega L_1, \qquad Y_2 = j\omega C_2, \qquad Y_3 = j\omega C_3 \tag{4}$$

then these equations take the form

$$Z_I = (R_1 - 1/j\omega C_2)/j\omega R_1 C_2 = L_1 C_3/R_1 C_2(C_2 + C_3) \tag{5}$$

$$Z_O = (R_1 - 1/j\omega C_3)/j\omega C_3 R_1 = L_1 C_2/R_1 C_3(C_2 + C_3) \tag{6}$$

$$Z_T = -1/\omega^2 R_1 C_2 C_3 = -L_1/R_1(C_2 + C_3) \tag{7}$$

when the frequency is

$$\omega^2 L_1 C_2 C_3 = (C_2 + C_3)$$

These relations are subject to the restrictions $R_1 \ll 1/\omega C_2$ and $R_1 \ll 1/\omega C_3$.

Taking the ratio of Z_I/Z_O shows that the impedance ratio, input to output, is

$$Z_I/Z_O = C_3^2/C_2^2 \tag{8}$$

This square relation only holds when the restrictions given on R_1 are valid; otherwise the loading current may be large compared to the charging current, which measures the circulating energy in the network.

In actual practice, the tuned network is loaded not only by its internal impedance but also by an output conductance that represents the loss component of the feedback circuit. This loss is primarily present on the output, but a small amount also is present on the input side of the network in typical applications. The circuit of Fig. 10–1 may be re-analyzed to include this shunt loading, and essentially the same results as those just derived will be obtained. Each of the shunt conductances may be converted into an equivalent series resistance by the typical conversion equation

$$R_s = gL/C \tag{9}$$

where g is the conductance, L is the associated inductance, and C is the capacitance in parallel with g. If the sum of R_s and the resistance R of L is small compared to the reactance of the individual capacitances in the circuit, or

$$1/\omega C_2 \gg R_1 + gL_1/C_3$$

then the transformation (9) may be made, and the input impedance equation may be written

$$Z_I = L_1 C_3 / [R_1 C_2 \langle C_2 + C_3 + C_2 R_1 g \rangle + g L_1 \langle 1 + g R_1 \rangle C_2^2 / C_3] \qquad (10)$$

where g now is the load conductance in parallel with C_3. Normally, the term $g R_1$ under these conditions has a value small compared to unity, and can consequently be neglected. The equation for the input impedance may now be reduced to

$$Z_I = L_1 C_3 / [R_1 C_2 (C_2 + C_3) + g L_1 C_2^2 / C_3] \qquad (11)$$

Dividing numerator and denominator by C_2^2 / C_3 gives the modified result

$$Z_I = L_1 (C_3 / C_2)^2 / [R_1 C_3 (C_2 + C_3) / C_2 + g L_1] \qquad (11a)$$

The last terms in the denominators of Eqs. (11) and (11a) convert the shunt conductance into the equivalent series resistance and scale them in accordance with the transformation ratio for the circuit. When $g = 0$, this equation reduces to Eq. (5).

The transfer term for this circuit may be evaluated similarly

$$Z_T = -L_1 C_3 / [R_1 C_3 (C_2 + C_3) + g L_1 C_2] \qquad (12)$$

Clearly, the larger the internal resistance in the coil or the larger the shunt conductance on the output, the lower the transfer impedance. For optimum operation of a transistor oscillator, the second term in the denominator should be comparatively small, because only if the loading from the transistor is kept small are the required voltage-drive conditions available. This term may be kept small if the value of C_2 is kept small, and the value of C_3 and L_1 adjusted to re-establish resonance. Larger values of both are required. The ratio of C_3 to C_2 should be kept as large as possible within the other circuit limitations.

The limiting conditions for the tuned circuit of the general oscillator may consequently be summarized in terms of the following inequalities

$$\operatorname{Re}(y_o) \times \operatorname{Re}(Z_I) < 1$$
$$\operatorname{Re}(y_i) \times \operatorname{Re}(Z_O) < 1 \qquad (13)$$

where the y_i and the y_o are the input and the output admittances of the transistor in the configuration used, and the Z_I and the Z_O are the tuned impedances of the frequency-selection circuit.

The shunt capacitances of the active device do not enter into consideration in this portion of the design problem because for practical purposes they may be lumped with the capacitances of the circuit itself. If the base-spreading resistance for the transistor were zero, the capacitances would enter only into the selection of the total values of capacitance, but since it is not zero, the decoupling effect in the input must be considered.

The Hartley oscillator differs from the Colpitts only in that the capacitors in the Colpitts are replaced by two magnetic-coupled inductors in the Hartley configuration, and the inductor is replaced by a capacitor. This arrangement does not require capacitors of as large a value as are required with the Colpitts, with the result that it is used for relatively low-frequency applications, whereas the Colpitts is more suitable for high-frequency applications.

The behavior of the Hartley circuit differs in one other significant way from that of the Colpitts, in that if the magnetic coupling between the two sections of the inductor is relatively high (it usually is), then transformer action can be utilized to obtain the required current gain to the output of the circuit. Consequently, smaller values of Q-factor can be used for the tuned circuit without loss of circuit efficiency. The input and the transfer impedance equations take the form

$$
\begin{aligned}
Z_I = [&Y_1Y_2Y_3 + Y_2Y_3Y_4 - Y_1y_{23}y_{32} - Y_4y_{23}y_{32} \\
&- Y_3y_{23}y_{32}]/[Y_1Y_2Y_3Y_4 - Y_1Y_4y_{23}y_{23} + Y_1Y_2Y_3y_{23} \\
&+ Y_1Y_2Y_3y_{32} - Y_2Y_3y_{23}y_{32} - Y_2Y_4y_{23}y_{32} \\
&- Y_1Y_2y_{23}y_{32} - Y_1Y_3y_{23}y_{32}]
\end{aligned}
\tag{14}
$$

$$
\begin{aligned}
Z_T = [&Y_1Y_2Y_3 - Y_1y_{23}y_{32} - Y_2Y_3y_{32}]/[Y_1Y_2Y_3Y_4 - Y_1Y_4y_{23}y_{32} \\
&+ Y_1Y_2Y_3y_{23} + Y_1Y_2Y_3y_{32} - Y_2Y_4y_{23}y_{32} - Y_2Y_3y_{23}y_{32} \\
&- Y_1Y_2y_{23}y_{32} - Y_1Y_3y_{23}y_{32}]
\end{aligned}
\tag{15}
$$

If these equations are multiplied, numerator and denominator, by the product $Z_2Z_3z_{23}z_{32}$, and the substitutions of the various admittances and impedances made in accordance with the following equivalents

$$
\begin{aligned}
Y_1 = j\omega C_1, \quad Z_2 = R_2 + j\omega L_2, \quad Z_3 = R_3 + j\omega L_3, \\
Y_4 = g_4, \quad z_{23} = j\omega M, \quad z_{32} = j\omega M
\end{aligned}
\tag{16}
$$

and the additional substitutions made

$$
\begin{aligned}
g_4R_2 \ll 1, \qquad g_4R_3 \ll 1 \\
\omega^2 = 1/C_1(L_2 + L_3 + 2M + g_4R_2L_3 + g_4L_2R_3)
\end{aligned}
\tag{17}
$$

Eqs. (14) and (15) simplify to the form

$$
\begin{aligned}
Z_I \doteq [&L_2 + C_1R_2R_3 - (L_2L_3 - M^2)/(L_2 + L_3 + 2M)]/ \\
&[C_1\langle R_2 + R_3 - g_4(L_2L_3 - M^2)/C_1(L_2 + L_3 + 2M)\rangle]
\end{aligned}
\tag{18}
$$

$$
\begin{aligned}
\doteq [&L_2 - (L_2L_3 - M^2)/(L_2 + L_3 + 2M)]/ \\
&[C_1(R_2 + R_3) - g_4(L_2L_3 - M^2)/(L_2 + L_3 + 2M)]
\end{aligned}
\tag{18a}
$$

$$
\doteq (L_2 + M)^2/C_1(R_2 + R_3)(L_2 + L_3 + 2M)
\tag{18b}
$$

when the coupling coefficient is large. The transfer impedance is

$$Z_T \doteq -(L_2 + M)(L_3 + M)/C_1(R_2 + R_3)(L_2 + L_3 + 2M) \qquad (19)$$

These equations assume that the input conductance of the active device, g_4, is small to comparable to the loss in the resistance components of the tuned circuit. This condition is required for effective amplitude control in the oscillator and also for a minimum magnitude of distortion and a maximum over-all frequency stability.

In the transfer impedance equation, Eq. (19), the parallel combination of $(L_2 + M)$ and $(L_3 + M)$ determines the value of the numerator, and the total series dissipation resistance and the capacitance, C_1, the denominator. For the Colpitts circuit, the capacitances are summed. The shunt conductance is relatively unimportant with the Hartley oscillator as long as the coupling coefficient is high, or $L_2L_3 - M^2$ is small compared to $(L_2 + L_3 - 2M)^2$. If the coupling is small, then the circulating current must be large compared to the load current in g_4, as is the case with the Colpitts oscillator.

The product of the transfer impedance of the coupling network by the transfer admittance of the transistor gives the loop amplification of the oscillator circuit as a whole. This product is used with the small-signal data from the transistor curves to determine the limiting conditions. The transfer impedance is the product of the circuit Q by the combined parallel admittance of the elements Y_2 and Y_3 and as such can be evaluated in terms of the frequency, the Q, and the equivalent L or C. Because many low-power transistors have forward conductances in the range from 10,000 to 200,000 micromhos, the desired value of the transfer impedance for the coupling circuit lies between five and 200 ohms. Because the Q (loaded) for the circuit should be made as large as possible, in excess of 100 as a minimum, the effective RF resistance of the circuit must be much less than an ohm, often less than hundredths of an ohm. The nominal value of R_s is given by the equation

$$R_s = Z_I/Q^2$$

Consequently the design of the feedback circuits for use with transistor oscillators is a particularly critical process.

10.2 Tuned Circuit Design

The range of values for the trans-impedance for the coupling circuit of a transistor oscillator is at least an order of magnitude smaller than the corresponding values for tube oscillators. As a result, extremely small values of inductance and large values of capacitance are required for use in the tuned feedback circuits. In particular, the difficulty encountered in finding capacitors having the required stability of capacitance along with low internal inductance and leakage can make the practical design of the coupling circuit the most critical part of the entire design procedure.

Normally, the tuning capacitors for an oscillator are either mica or air capacitors, and they may be either fixed or variable, depending on the application. Air capacitors are not readily available with capacitances in excess of 1000 pfd, and mica capacitors suitable for use in electronic equipment seldom have capacitances greater than 10,000 to 20,000 pfd. As a consequence, a simple Hartley oscillator cannot be expected to function adequately at frequencies below about 15 mc, as the capacitive reactance of a 0.01 mfd capacitor such as is required with the transistor version is one ohm at 15 mc. In a similar manner, a Colpitts oscillator using a transistor cannot be expected to function properly at frequencies under 50 mc, as an adequate network for providing the ratio of C_3/C_2 cannot be assembled using available capacitors.

The low-frequency limitation on transistor oscillators may be surmounted by the use of a Hartley configuration with collector connected to a tap. In this way, a relatively smaller capacitance capacitor can provide a large value of apparent capacitance at the collector terminal. Such an arrangement is shown schematically in Fig. 10–2. Then, the impedance level for the frequency-selection circuit can be as much as ten or more times the levels used for the transistor connections, and the general stability of the circuit can be greatly enhanced. The transistor is almost too good an amplifier! When the operating frequency is sufficiently high that the total series capacitance required is less

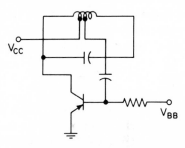

Fig. 10-2. Hartley oscillator

than or in the neighborhood of 1000 pfd, then the circuit configuration used may be the Colpitts circuit, and for lower frequencies, the standard Hartley or the tapped version of it may be used.

The self-resonant frequency, under excitation, of the inductors and capacitors of a coupling network should be at least ten times the operating frequency of the oscillator, and, where possible, it should be even larger. Otherwise, the internal parasitic parameters of the components can seriously degrade the general performance to a point that the general oscillator stability may be unsatisfactory.

Testing for the self-resonant frequencies is accomplished with the help of a grid-dip meter. With an inductor, the operating frequency of the grid-dip oscillator is varied until a frequency is found at which power is absorbed from the oscillator. This test is made with the inductor disconnected from all associated components, tubes, transistors, resistors, or capacitors, but it should be made with the inductor left in its normal operating environment. The absorption frequencies are ones at which the internal inductance resonates with the internal stray capacitances. The lowest frequency at which this phenomenon is noted is called the self-resonant frequency; above this frequency additional absorption frequencies may be found.

With a capacitor, the resonant frequency is found in a similar manner. First, however, the leads for the capacitor are shorted together in a manner that makes the amount of lead inductance a minimum. The grid-dip oscillator is coupled magnetically to the shorted leads, and its frequency is varied until an absorption condition is found. This frequency also is a self-resonant frequency. With a mica capacitor this frequency is much higher than with ordinary paper or film capacitors, and typically is about 37 mc for a 1000 pfd capacitor. Since such a capacitor has four ohms capacitive reactance at its resonant frequency, it is evident that a considerable problem can be expected because of the low impedance levels at which the circuit must function.

The fact that the input capacitance of a transistor may be as much as 100 or more times as large as its output capacitance makes the use of unbalanced pi circuits, with C_3 much larger than C_2, a necessity with Colpitts circuits, and it also makes essential an impedance step-down to the input with the Hartley circuit. Otherwise, it would be possible to use a balanced circuit as an impedance transformer. The high value of conductance reflected from the transistor input makes the use of a balanced network inadvisable, because it adversely affects the frequency stability.

Two examples of the design procedure for oscillators are now considered to show the detail procedure and the problems that may be encountered. For the first of these examples, the 2N247 transistor has been selected as the active device.

EXAMPLE 1.   Design a Hartley oscillator for operation at 10 mc, the oscillator to use the 2N247 transistor. Make a design assuming a standard Hartley configuration, and then redesign using a tapped configuration. Take the value of the effective forward admittance as 25,000 micromhos.

The transfer impedance associated with the transistor is 40 ohms for unity loop gain. For a circuit Q-factor of approximately 100, the reactance level for the transfer impedance is 0.4 ohm. The coefficient of coupling for the windings may initially be selected as unity, and a simultaneous solution made for L_2 and L_3 in terms of the frequency equation and the equation for Z_T.

For a given total inductance, L_T, where $L_T = L_2 + L_3 + 2M$, the maximum possible value for the mutual inductance, M, under conditions of unity coupling occurs when the two inductors L_2 and L_3 have equal value. Then the mutual inductance is equal in magnitude to both L_2 and

L_3, and is one-quarter of the total inductance if a series-aiding connection is used. A table may be prepared showing the relative magnitude of the mutual inductance as a function of the ratio $a = L_3/L_2$.

TABLE I

a	$\sqrt{a}$	L_2/L_T	$(L_2 + M)/L_T$	M/L_T
0.005	0.071	0.873	0.935	0.0617
0.01	0.10	0.826	0.909	0.0826
0.02	0.141	0.768	0.877	0.1086
0.05	0.224	0.668	0.817	0.1492
0.10	0.316	0.577	0.759	0.182
0.15	0.387	0.520	0.721	0.201
0.20	0.447	0.499	0.691	0.213
0.30	0.547	0.419	0.647	0.229
0.40	0.632	0.376	0.613	0.237
0.50	0.707	0.344	0.587	0.243
0.60	0.774	0.317	0.564	0.246
0.70	0.836	0.297	0.545	0.248
0.80	0.894	0.279	0.528	0.249
0.90	0.950	0.263	0.513	0.250
1.00	1.00	0.250	0.500	0.250
1.10	1.048	0.238	0.488	0.250
1.50	1.224	0.202	0.451	0.247
2.00	1.414	0.172	0.414	0.243
3.00	1.732	0.134	0.366	0.232
4.00	2.00	0.111	0.333	0.222
5.00	2.236	0.096	0.309	0.213
6.00	2.446	0.084	0.292	0.208
7.00	2.642	0.075	0.274	0.199
8.00	2.828	0.068	0.263	0.193
9.00	3.00	0.062	0.250	0.187
10.00	3.162	0.058	0.240	0.182
20.00	4.462	0.033	0.182	0.149
50.00	7.071	0.015	0.114	0.109
100	10	0.008	0.091	0.083
200	14.14	0.004	0.066	0.062

The value of a gives the voltage ratio across the inductors for unity coupling between the coils. These data are also plotted in Fig. 10–3. If the coupling is less than unity, the ratio is the product of the value of a and the value of the coupling factor, k. The equation for Z_T may be rewritten in the form

$$Z_T = -k\sqrt{a}L_2[1 - (k - 1/k)\sqrt{a} + 2(k^2 - 1)a]/$$
$$[R_2 + R_3 - g_4 \times (L_2L_3 - M^2)/C_1(L_2 + L_3 + 2M)]C_1 \qquad (20)$$

$$\doteq -M[1 - (k - 1/k)\sqrt{a} + 2(k^2 - 1)a]/$$
$$C_1[R_2 + R_3 - g_4(L_2L_3 - M^2)/C_1(L_2 + L_3 + 2M)] \qquad (20a)$$

$$\doteq -\omega M/Q \qquad (20b)$$

This last form applies either if the value of k is approximately unity or if the value of a is very small compared to unity so that the numerator of Eq. (20a) has a value approximately equal to M. The value of M required

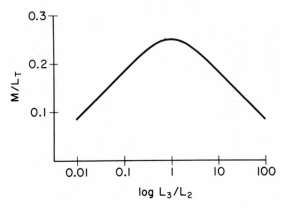

Fig. 10-3. Ratio of M/L_T to L_3/L_2
$$L_T = L_2 + L_3 + 2M$$

may be determined using this equation, and the value of L_T corresponding to it may be determined. Finally the value of C_1 may be calculated.

If a trial value of M of one-fifth of the total inductance is selected, the total impedance level is 200 ohms. For a Q of 100, the value of capacitance, C_1, required is 0.01 mfd, and the inductance required is 0.03 microhenry. Evidently the inductance size is excessively small and the capacitance size excessively large for an effective design.

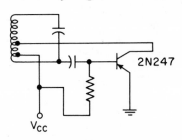

Fig. 10-4. Oscillator circuit

Either the use of a tapped coil having a higher impedance level or the use of a smaller value of a is desirable for this oscillator. If the value of a is 0.15, and the capacitance required is 1000 pfd, and the corresponding inductance is 0.3 microhenry. This inductor requires approximately three times the number of turns as the inductor for the straight design. The collector is tapped down on the coil so that the higher impedance level does not increase the transfer gain in the circuit, Fig. 10–4.

The approximate output impedance level of the tuned circuit is 0.06 × 200 = 12 ohms, because

$$(L_3 + M)/L_T = 1 - (L_2 + M)/L_T$$

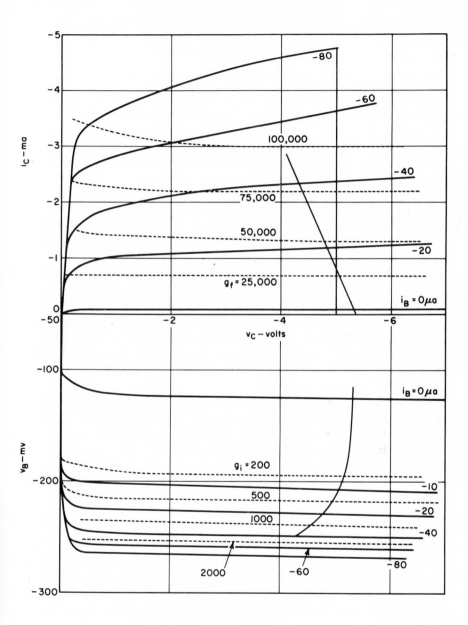

Fig. 10-5. 2N247 oscillator

and the output impedance is approximately

$$Z_O = (L_3 + M)^2 / L_T C_1 (R_2 + R_3) \tag{21}$$

This impedance is certainly negligible compared to the input resistive component of the transistor. Consequently, all of the circuit conditions comply with design requirements, and the final small-signal design may be completed. The input impedance corresponding to the transfer impedance of 42 ohms may be determined by the use of Eq. (18b), and the values used for establishment of the dynamic load conditions. The resulting impedance is 144 ohms.

If a new design is made with $a = 0.01$ for a turns-ratio of ten, the total inductance is twelve times the mutual inductance, and the total is $0.72 \mu h$. This increases the available collector impedance to approximately 436 ohms. A still higher value would be helpful. Because the value of M is the mean of the values of L_2 and L_3 (assuming a coupling coefficient, k, of approximately unity), L_3 is considerably less than either M or L_2 in magnitude.

A static supply voltage of five volts may be selected because the curves in Fig. 10–5 do not permit design at a higher voltage level. The initiating point should be selected to give a forward conductance somewhat greater than 25,000 μmhos; a suitable selection is a collector current of 0.8 ma. Through this point, the reference load line should be drawn and then transcribed to the input family.

At this stage of design, it is evident that the voltage scale is too compact to permit an efficient design calculation to be made; consequently, a replot of the curves has been made on Fig. 10–6 that spreads the range from 4.5 to 5.5 volts out over the full chart. Then the design process may be continued. A series of trial load lines parallel to the reference line may be drawn, and the static operating limits on each determined. Then the set of conditions yielding unity loop amplification may be found.

Evidently, effective design of useful oscillators at reasonable impedance levels requires that the transistors be used at relatively small values of forward conductance and at relatively small collector current. For this reason, curve data for transistors for oscillator service should be based on a maximum collector current value of one or two milliamperes. Operation under these conditions also minimizes the effect of base-spreading resistance because the input admittance of the internal junction then is conveniently small.

The averaging of the forward conductance can be achieved directly by use of orthogonal polynomials as described in Appendix IV, or by the use of the formula

$$Y_{fa} = 0.25(Y_{fp} + 2Y_{fs} + Y_{fn}) \tag{22}$$

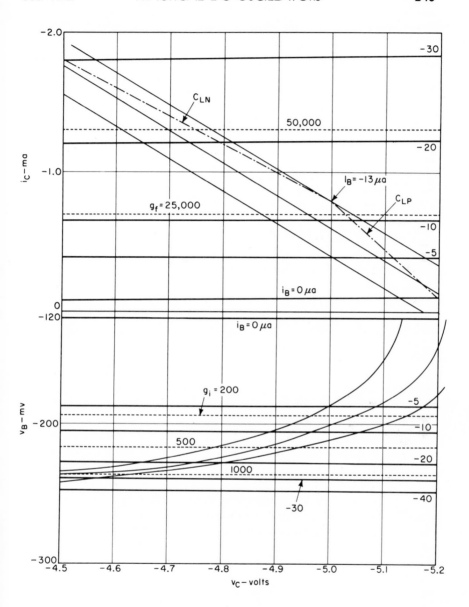

Fig. 10-6. Expanded curves

As described in the previous chapter, a series of points are marked on the input load contour, these points being spaced at equal voltage increments from the static value. These points are transferred to the output load line and either of the averaging techniques is applied to the data obtained from them. The series of points that gives the correct average value of current represents the full range of operation of the transistor along any given load contour. The forward admittances are averaged over the full operating range, and the one providing unity loop amplification represents the correct limit cycle.

EXAMPLE 2. Design a Colpitts oscillator using an SBDT-10X transistor, the oscillator to operate at 100 mc. The base-to-emitter capacitance is 60 pfd.

The output capacitance of a transistor such as the SBDT-10X unit is about 2 pfd. The reactance of this capacitance is 833 ohms, and including the circuit Q-factor, the resonant impedance may be up to 100 times this value, possibly more if the output admittance of the transistor has a sufficiently small real component. A static operating point may be selected at minus three volts and 0.8 ma. The optimum load impedance for use with this static condition is the one giving the maximum potential power output

$$Z_I = V_{CC}/I_{cs} = 3.0/0.0008 = 3750 \text{ ohms}$$

Assuming a Q of 100 for the circuit, the value of X_I is 37.5 ohms, and the required value of capacitance is 44.4 pfd.

The forward conductance of the transistor may be determined by an orthogonal expansion of the gain function in terms of the output currents and input voltages. In Fig. 10–7, the output load line has been transferred to the input family and five equal increments of base voltage have been marked at spacings of 10 mv, giving a total excursion of 20 mv either side of the static-point. If the fundamental component of amplification is calculated and divided by 0.020, the forward conductance results. It has an average value of 23,700 μmhos at a static current of 0.8 ma. The tabulated data follow.

Datum Point	V_b	V_c	I_c	I_b
0	125 mv	4.4 v	0.43 ma	103 μa
1	135	3.64	0.62	148
2	145	3.00	0.80	192
3	155	1.91	1.10	260
4	165	0.90	1.36	322

If the table for $2n + 1 = 5$ in Appendix IV is used to calculate uncorrected and corrected values for the C_j's, the corrections being applied up to the third order only as a consequence of the small number of defining data, the results are

$$C_{0u} = 0.862 \qquad C_{0c} = 0.841$$
$$C_1 = 0.468,$$
$$C_{2u} = 0.037, \qquad C_{2c} = 0.049,$$
$$C_{3u} = 0.003, \qquad C_{3c} = 0.008, \qquad C_4 = 0.0041$$

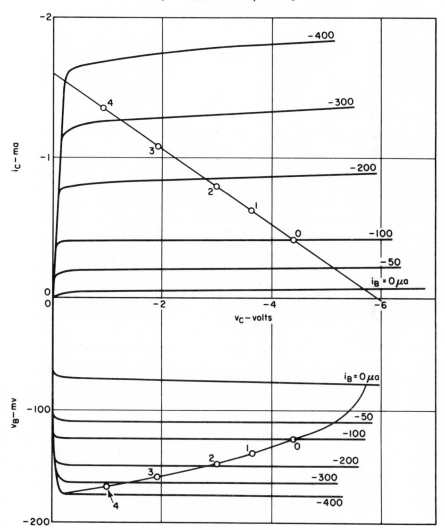

Fig. 10-7. Design of Colpitts oscillator $SBDT$-$10X$ for Example 2

The average value of collector current is 0.853 ma, and the average value of forward conductance is the 23,700 μmhos listed above.* The average value of the input admittance may also be determined from the same data. The corresponding coefficients are $C_{0b} = 213$, $C_{1b} = 110$, $C_{2b} = 34$, $C_{3b} = 0.5$, and $C_{4b} = -0.2$. The corresponding input conductance is

$$G_i = 0.000112/0.020 = 5600 \ \mu\text{mhos}$$

This corresponds to an input resistance of 180 ohms.

Consequently, if base-spreading resistance can be neglected (its value is approximately 51 ohms for the SBDT-10X), the transfer impedance for the feedback network is somewhat greater than 42.2 ohms, and its output impedance must be appreciably less than 90 ohms. The approximate step-down is given by the ratio C_2/C_3. The ratio of the input to the transfer to the output impedances for the general circuit may be written in a combined form to cover both the Colpitts and Hartley oscillators

$$Z_I/Z_T/Z_O = L_2/M/L_3 = (C_3/C_2)/1/(C_2/C_3) \tag{23}$$

With Z_I having a value of approximately 3750 ohms, and Z_T of 42 ohms, the ratio of C_2/C_3 is approximately 1/80, and the ratio of Z_I/Z_O is approximately 6400. The effect of base-spreading resistance and the loss of forward conductance at high-frequency may reduce the available amplification, however, and make the use of a smaller ratio of capacitances necessary.[2] The effective reactance of the input capacitance for the transistor is less than 30 ohms at 100 mc, and the magnitude of the forward conductance may be less than half the nominal value, its phase delay as much as sixty degrees. An additional loss of half is required to correct the phase-shift. As a result, the value of transfer impedance used must be increased at least to 170 ohms, and the capacitance ratio C_2/C_3 must be larger than 0.05.

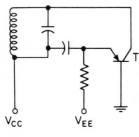

Fig. 10-8. Common-base oscillator

10.3 Circuits for Common-Base Oscillators

The tuned coupling circuit, which is required for use with a common-base oscillator, differs in two ways from that for the common-emitter oscillator, first in that phase-inversion is not required, and second in that the impedance ratio required is considerably larger because of the extremely low input impedance of the active device. Instead of having an RF ground in the middle of the coil or at the tap between the two

V_{CC} V_{EE}

---

* There are insufficient data for accurate determination of a value of C_4 or for correcting it.

[2] R. D. Middlebrook, "A New Junction-Transistor High-Frequency Equivalent Circuit," *IRE Transactions PGCT*, Convention Record, 1957, p. 120.

capacitors, the ground for the common-base circuit is at one end of the coil (Fig. 10–8). The equations for the Hartley oscillator in its common-base configuration need no other change than noting that L_2 in the numerator of Z_2 now is the total inductance, and L_3 is only a part of it. A similar change is required for the Colpitts oscillator in its common-base configuration, the input capacitance in the numerator of the input impedance expression now being

$$C_{2'} = C_2 C_3 / (C_2 + C_3)$$

The tapped coil arrangement is the better one to use where possible with the common-base circuit, because the impedance ratio required is too large to handle through the action of the circuit Q-factor. Typically, the ratio may be as large as 2000 : 1, and the corresponding capacitance ratio would be 45 : 1. An operating Q-factor for the circuit as large as 200 or more is required for efficient and stable operation.

Because of the magnitude of input current required by the active device in the common-base circuit and its resultant low input impedance, a magnetic-coupled circuit (Fig. 10–9) often is desirable as the frequency-selection and feedback network. The tuned circuit should be placed at the point in the circuit in which the loading due to the transistor is a minimum. In both the common-emitter and the common-base circuits, this location is in the collector circuit because the shunt capacitance and the shunt conductance both are smallest there. The selection of the collector return for the tuned circuit is much more important with the common-base oscillator because of the much higher input conductance in the emitter return than in the base.

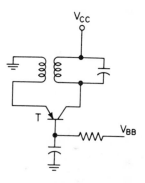

Fig. 10-9. Common-base inductively-coupled oscillator

Inductive coupling is convenient in another way, in that the capacitance values required for construction of the feedback circuit are considerably smaller than the values required in the Colpitts and the Hartley circuits. An untuned link is used to couple energy into the input, either the base or the emitter, and it is partially resonated by the input capacitance of the device. In the common-base circuit, the effect of base-spreading resistance is minimized and the energy can be introduced comparatively effectively.

The value of the reactance of the output link should at most be equal to the equivalent input resistance of the circuit, or

$$X_O G_i \leqq 1 \qquad (24)$$

where X_O is the reactance of the output link. Then the coupling between the link and the tuned circuit should be adjusted until sufficient power for the development of unity loop amplification is provided to the input. The ease of adjustment of feedback through the variation of the magnitude of the coupling coefficient makes this type of design particularly convenient to use.

The procedure for the design of common-base oscillators closely resembles that for the common-emitter oscillator. For an exact design, it is desirable to make the configuration correction already described which transfers the common-emitter load contours into common-base contours, and then to adjust for constant emitter current, because the emitter current is stabilized in this type of circuit. The limit contours are established in the same manner as before, except for the fact that the emitter current is averaged rather than the base current, and the small-signal equations used are for the common-base configuration.

The small-signal equations for the impedances of the feedback circuit using magnetic coupling are

$$Z_I = L_1/R_1 C \tag{25}$$

$$Z_T = -k\sqrt{L_2 L_2}/R_1 C = -M/R_1 C \tag{26}$$

$$Z_O \doteq j\omega L_2 + [j\omega^3 M^2 C/(1 - \omega^2 L_1 C + j\omega R_1 C)] \tag{27}$$

$$\doteq j\omega L_2 + M^2/R_1 L_1 C \tag{27a}$$

where the resonant frequency is defined as $\omega^2 L_1 C = 1$. Evidently, the first two are resonant in nature, that is, they depend on the resonance of L_1 and C, whereas, because of the relatively small coupling, Z_O does not depend on the resonance to any great extent. When the last equation is simplified at resonance to give the form (27a), further simplification by substitution for M gives the form

$$Z_O = j\omega L_2 + k^2 L_2/R_1 C \tag{28}$$

For large values of k, the value of Z_O will depend on the resonant circuit; for small values, on the coupling link. For this reason, a small value of coupling that will give the required transfer impedance with a reasonable value of L_2 should be selected.

The effective value of the secondary inductance, L_2, may actually be increased through the action of the load capacitance from the input of the active device, the modified value of the inductance being given by the equation

$$L_{\text{eff}} = L_2/[1 - L_2 C_i/L_1 C] \tag{29}$$

If the magnitude of the ratio in the denominator is greater than 0.1, then the value of L_2 should be chosen to allow for the effect of the difference. Otherwise, the tuned impedance of the output circuit may be excessive.

10.4 A Series-Mode Oscillator

A series-mode circuit like that shown in Fig. 10–10 is commonly used in the construction of crystal oscillators, and it may also be used with L-C circuits if adequate step-down is incorporated. An extremely large value of Q-factor is desirable in the series element, Y_s, to give maximum frequency stability and minimum series impedance at resonance. Since the circuit must be used in the common-base configuration, current gain is required at the input point to provide for the less-than-unity gain from the emitter to the collector. This is the reason the inductor is shown tapped. The auto-transformer action gives the current gain required.

The equations for use with this coupling circuit, where G_i is the input admittance of the associated transistor, are

$$Z_I \doteq L_T(1 + G_iZ_s)/[R_TC(1 + G_iZ_s)$$
$$+ G_i\langle L_1 + C(R_1R_2 - \omega^2(L_1L_2 - M^2))\rangle] \tag{30}$$

$$Z_T \doteq (L_1 + M)/[R_TC(1 + G_iZ_s)$$
$$+ G_i\langle L_1 + C(R_1R_2 - \omega^2(L_1L_2 - M^2))\rangle] \tag{31}$$

$$Z_O \doteq \langle Z_s(1 - \omega^2L_2C) + j\omega[L_1 - \omega^2C(L_1L_2 - M^2)]\rangle/j\omega[R_TC(1 + G_iZ_s)$$
$$+ G_i\langle L_1 + C(R_1R_2 - \omega^2(L_1L_2 - M^2))\rangle] \tag{32}$$

For small values of Z_s, Eq. (32) reduces to

$$Z_O \doteq L_1/[CR_T + G_iL_1 + CR_1G_iZ_s] \tag{33}$$

For Eqs. (30) through (33), the following conditions apply

$$\omega^2[C(L_1 + L_2 + 2M) + G_iC(R_1L_2 + R_2L_1)/(1 + G_iZ_s)] = 1$$
$$Z_t = Z_1 + Z_2 + 2Z_{12} = R_1 + R_2 + j\omega(L_1 + L_2 + 2M) = R_T + j\omega L_T$$
$$Y_c = j\omega C, \qquad Z_s = R_s + j(\omega L_s - 1/\omega C_s) \tag{34}$$
$$R_T \ll \omega L_T, \qquad L_1L_2 - M^2 \ll (L_1 + L_2 + 2M)^2$$

When G_iZ_s is approximately unity, Eqs. (30) through (33) may be simplified to

$$Z_I \doteq L_T/R_TC \tag{35}$$
$$Z_T \doteq (L_1 + M)/R_TC(1 + G_iZ_s) \tag{36}$$
$$Z_O \doteq L_1/[G_iL_1 + C(R_T + R_1G_iZ_s)] \tag{37}$$

The crystal impedance, Z_s, affects principally the characteristics of the transfer and output impedances, decreasing the transfer impedance sharply and increasing the output impedance off the resonant frequency, $\omega^2 = 1/L_sC_s$. In this application, the value of G_i, the input admittance for the active device, must be sufficiently large to make $G_iR_s \geqq 1$. Otherwise, the frequency-selection action will be inadequate. When a transistor capable of meeting other limitations such as the noise-corner limitation is selected, the effect of the input capacitance of the device normally may be neglected in the design process.

EXAMPLE 3.   Design a crystal oscillator based on the circuit of Fig. 10–10 using the SBDT-10X used in Ex. 2. Determine if load-line corrections are required, and determine suitable values for the impedances in Eqs. (35) through (37). Take the initial operating point as $V_{cc} = -3$ volts and $I_{cs} = -0.8$ ma.

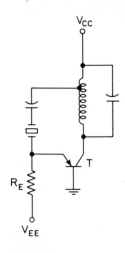

Since less than 0.2 volt correction is required on the load-line position for conversion from common-emitter to common-base operation, the correction need not be made. However, the corrected line is plotted as a matter of interest in Fig. 10–11. Next, orthogonal polynomials may be used to evaluate both $g_{f'}$ and $(g_{i'} + g_{f'})$, taking the value of $r_{b'}$ and correcting the values read from the curves. The tuned circuit may be designed to provide the proper value of Z_I and the turns-ratio selected through the relation

$$Z_I/Z_T = (n_1 + n_2)(1 + G_iZ_s)/n_2 \qquad (38)$$

Fig. 10-10. Crystal oscillator

where n_1 is the number of turns in L_1, and n_2 is the number in L_2. This relation implies that the coils L_1 and L_2 are both parts of a single complete coil and the coefficients by which the numbers of turns are multiplied are thereby identical. The tap is obtained by way of a soldered contact on one of the turns at the appropriate position. Solving Eq. (38) for the transfer impedance gives

$$Z_T = n_2Z_I/(n_1 + n_2)(1 + G_iZ_s) \qquad (39)$$

Evidently, the higher the crystal impedance, the lower the transfer impedance for any given value of turns-ratio, $n_2/(n_1 + n_2)$. In practice, a value of G_iR_s in the neighborhood of unity probably is optimum. Consequently, a crystal having a very small value of series resistance at resonance is of paramount importance in this application.

The use of the load line drawn on the curves for a Z_I of 3750 ohms, gives a forward gain of approximately 86 in the common-emitter configuration. Including $G_iR_s = 1$ in the common-base configuration decreases the common-base amplification to a value of 43. Solving Eq. (39) for n_1/n_2 gives a value of 43.4 ($Z_T = 42.2$; $Z_I = 3750$). For stability reasons, a lower load impedance for the collector circuit may be chosen, since regenerative instability may develop with such a high value of Z_I. The input admittance is approximately 31,000 μmhos, and the forward admittance 23,000 μmhos, neglecting the base-spreading resistance. The calculation of the corrected values is left as an exercise for the reader. A crystal having a series impedance less than 30 ohms at resonance is required.

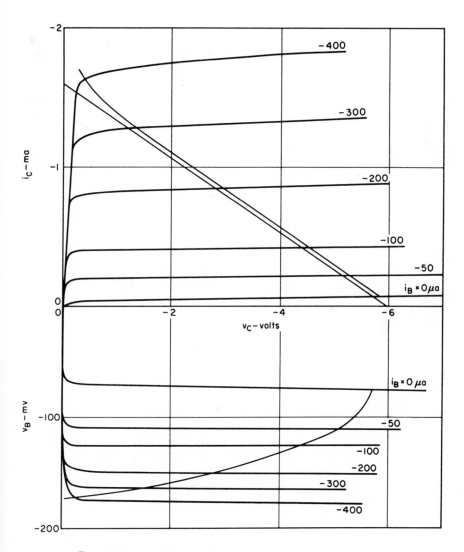

Fig. 10-11. Correction for common-base configuration of a crystal oscillator

10.5 Other Circuits

The variety of circuits that can be analyzed and designed through the combination of conductance techniques and topological procedures is only limited by the user's ingenuity. The determination of the input and output impedances and the transfer impedance for a given network provides all the data on the feedback network required for the coordination of the device with its circuit. As long as a set of input and output curves are available on a given transistor, the curves being in a form that permits convenient replotting of the load lines and the reading of the required coordinates, orthogonal polynomials can be used to convert the coordinate data into estimated operating conditions, and an approximate set of operating specifications can be obtained. If full data on small-signal parameters are available, a better design that delineates the operating limits closely can be developed.

CHAPTER ELEVEN

R-C Oscillators
and Time-Delay Oscillators

11.0 Introduction

The underlying theory of operation of phase-shift oscillators and time-delay oscillators is similar to that of the L-C oscillators just considered. It differs primarily in some differences in boundary conditions that are a result of the type of elements used in the feedback circuits. There are some specific differences between the R-C and the T-D oscillators, which also will be discussed in the section on time-delay circuits.

11.1 Types of R-C Circuits

There are two basic types of R-C feedback circuits, namely, the phase-inverting, and the non-phase-inverting. The inverting types are used with active configurations that generate a phase-reversal of their own, whereas the non-inverting type are normally used with more complex circuits in which both current and voltage gain are available and the output voltage is in phase with the input.

The inverting feedback circuits typically make use of some form of ladder network as shown in Fig. 11–1. The

Z components in this network, Z_j, usually are all of one type, for example, all resistors or all capacitors, and the Y components, Y_k, are all of the alternate type. With R-C ladder networks, one type of element provides energy storage, whereas the other introduces dissipation of energy. Although any number of sections may in theory be used in a ladder network, the use of less than three sections introduces practically impossible operating conditions for the development of oscillations in an inverting circuit, and the use of more than four makes possible the development of more than one mode of oscillation. Ordinarily the ladder used is a three-section ladder with either an input or an output resistive termination.

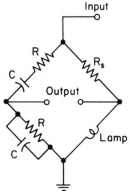

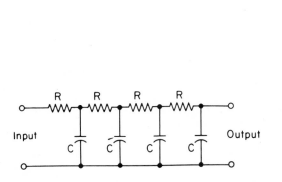

Fig. 11-1. Typical ladder network

Fig. 11-2. Wien-bridge circuit

The non-inverting circuits normally are based on some form of Wien-bridge arrangement such as is shown in Fig. 11–2. The amplifier used with this circuit must have both current and voltage gain, and must have an output voltage in phase with its input. For these reasons, a minimum of two active devices is required for the associated amplifiers. Either of the amplifier configurations shown in Fig. 11–3 may be used for the active path with these oscillators, the more complex one having built-in gain stabilization.

The use of R-C circuits presents difficulties with transistors as the active devices because of the problem of their low, but not zero, input impedance. The design of a transfer network to couple a current source to a low, but not zero, impedance load is appreciably more difficult than coupling from a current source to a voltage load, as is possible with oscillators using electron tubes. As with L-C oscillators, the limitation of amplification in an R-C oscillator can only occur effectively if the source impedance from which the transistor is excited is small compared with the input impedance of the transistor itself. Because even in a common-emitter configuration the base input admittance may be as large as 0.001 mho, the relatively high output impedance associated with many *R-C* networks makes the design of an oscillator around the circuit difficult unless an emitter-follower is used to match impedances. This situation applies equally to the inverting and to the non-inverting circuits.

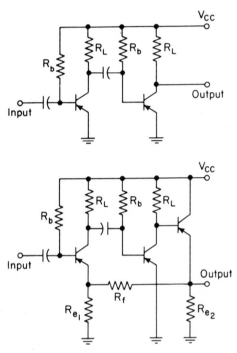

Fig. 11-3. Typical amplifiers

The zero-phase-shift or bridge circuit is designed in a manner that gives it a maximum amplification over a narrow range of frequencies, in the middle of which is the frequency of zero-phase-shift. Typically, the bridge consists of a combination of dissipation and storage elements used in conjunction with similar elements arranged in the dual network configuration as shown in Fig. 11–4. (The network dual arrangement for a series *R-C* network is a parallel *R-C* network, for example.) More complex configurations may be used if desired, and a greater frequency stability may be obtained if the rate-of-change of phase with frequency is increased. Normally, however, a simple *R-C* dual configuration such as is shown in Fig. 11–4 is used with zero-phase *R-C* oscillators.

The amplitude-stabilization of the *R-C* oscillator introduces a special set of problems to the designer. Because of the relatively low equivalent Q of the frequency-selection circuit, bias limiting is not practical with these circuits because of the associated distortion, and some form of thermal bridge limiting is normally chosen. Both the forward and the feedback gain must be kept quite uniform over the operating range of the oscillator, which may be as much as four decades of frequency.

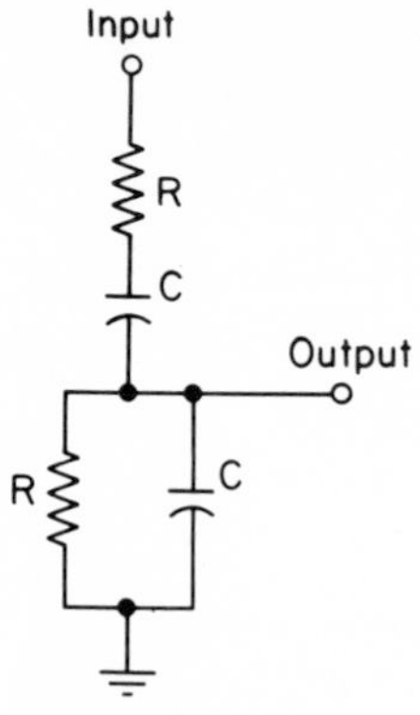

The operation of the Wien-bridge oscillator closely parallels that of the Meacham crystal oscillator as far as phase characteristics are concerned. In one, the amplitude and phase are controlled by the RLC properties of the crystal in conjunction with a fixed series resistance, the second arm of the bridge consisting of a thermal combination for controlling the signal amplitude. In the Wien-bridge circuit, the series elements on one half of the bridge consist of the dual R-C combinations, and the elements in the other half of the bridge again include a thermal element for controlling signal amplitude.

Fig. 11-4. R-C selection circuit

The next two sections of this chapter analyze the properties of the typical forms of the feedback circuit for both inverting and non-inverting networks, and include some typical design analyses. They are followed by a discussion of time-delay oscillators based on the use of delay lines as the feedback network. A brief discussion of one- and two-port negative immittances is also included.

11.2 The Basic Feedback Circuit Inverting Form

The analysis of the basic ladder network (Fig. 11–5) without source or terminating impedance gives a considerable insight into the frequency-selective behavior of the phase-shift circuit. The series elements in this

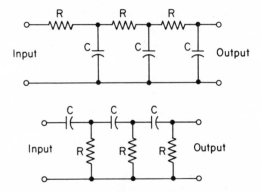

Fig. 11-5. Three-section R-C network — basic forms

network are identified as impedances, Z_i typically, and the shunt elements as Y_j. For simplicity, the Z_i's may be replaced by Y_i's for topological solution of the network and then the equation may be converted to include the series impedances by multiplication of the numerator and denominator of the appropriate impedance equation by the product of the series impedances.

Transistors, as tubes, are current-output devices, so that the form of network normally called for in the feedback path is the trans-impedance form. Several forms of the ladder network will be discussed in the next few paragraphs because a considerable amount of useful information can be gained thereby.

Topological techniques offer a convenient method for analyzing these coupling networks. A limited range of variations can then be made in input and output circuits without necessitating complete re-analysis. In addition, the process of analysis is simplified because of the elimination of unnecessary steps in the solution. The three impedance equations for the simplest configuration of three-section ladder network are

$$
\begin{aligned}
Z_I = [1 &+ Z_1 Y_2 + Z_1 Y_4 + Z_3 Y_4 + Z_1 Y_6 + Z_3 Y_6 + Z_5 Y_6 \\
&+ Z_1 Z_3 Y_2 Y_4 + Z_1 Z_3 Y_2 Y_6 + Z_1 Z_5 Y_2 Y_6 + Z_1 Z_5 Y_4 Y_6 \\
&+ Z_3 Z_5 Y_4 Y_6 + Z_1 Z_3 Z_5 Y_2 Y_4 Y_6]/[Y_2 + Y_4 + Y_6 \\
&+ Z_3 Y_2 Y_4 + Z_3 Y_2 Y_6 + Z_5 Y_2 Y_6 + Z_5 Y_4 Y_6 + Z_3 Z_5 Y_2 Y_4 Y_6]
\end{aligned} \tag{1}
$$

$$
\begin{aligned}
Z_T = 1/[Y_2 &+ Y_4 + Y_6 + Z_3 Y_2 Y_4 + Z_3 Y_2 Y_6 + Z_5 Y_2 Y_6 \\
&+ Z_5 Y_4 Y_6 + Z_3 Z_5 Y_2 Y_4 Y_6]
\end{aligned} \tag{2}
$$

$$
\begin{aligned}
Z_O = [1 &+ Z_3 Y_2 + Z_5 Y_2 + Z_5 Y_4 + Z_3 Z_5 Y_2 Y_4]/[Y_2 + Y_4 \\
&+ Y_6 + Z_3 Y_2 Y_4 + Z_3 Y_2 Y_6 + Z_5 Y_2 Y_6 + Z_5 Y_4 Y_6 + Z_3 Z_5 Y_2 Y_4 Y_6]
\end{aligned} \tag{3}
$$

Examination of the denominator of the transfer term shows that the values of the powers of (ZY) for the respective terms are zero, one, and two only. An R-C network formed from this combination of components, where either the Z's are resistive and the Y's are capacitive, or vice versa, cannot in any way develop 180° phase-shift and unity gain without having infinite amplification. The minimum exponent difference that can yield 180° phase shift with a finite amplification is three.

The denominator function, which represents a ladder network, has a frequency polynomial that can be solved in either of two forms, the one representing forward transmission, and the second, backward transmission. Essentially, the forward transmission mode is the impedance mode, with higher output impedance than input, and the backward transmission with a lower output impedance than input (higher output admittance). The denominator for the transfer function in Eq. (2) cannot be solved in useful form for either mode of transmission, as has already been shown. With the network modified by the inclusion of the input admittance, Y_0, however, the situation is completely changed, because either Y_0 can be factored out, and a solvable network established in terms of Z_1, Z_3, Z_5, Y_2, Y_4, and Y_6, or Y_6 may be factored out, and a similar solvable network established involving Z_1, Z_3, Z_5, Y_0, Y_2, and Y_4. These configurations are considered by Hooper and Jackets in their paper.[1]

The numerator of the input impedance function does have the required ratio of exponents of three because the range of terms is from a numeric, one, to a cubic product of Y and Z. The numerator function, however, generates only zeros of input or transmission, and consequently is of little use in frequency determination.

Consequently, without a shunt source admittance in parallel with the source current, this network is not satisfactory for use in R-C oscillators. In fact, it is easy to verify this by construction of an oscillator that utilizes the ladder network in this form. No amount of amplification will make available the required conditions for oscillation, and the oscillator will not function.

The addition of an input shunt admittance (Y_0 in Fig. 11–6), however, changes the situation appreciably. There are thirty-four terms each in the

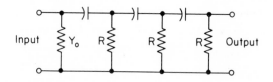

Fig. 11-6. Practical R-C ladder network (forward mode)

expressions for the input and output impedances when Y_0 is included, twenty-one being in the denominator, and a net of twenty in the transfer impedance. (The sign of the numerator thus is the negative of that of the denominator terms.) The equations are

$$
\begin{aligned}
Z_I = [1 &+ (Y_2 + Y_4 + Y_6)Z_1 + (Y_4 + Y_6)Z_3 + Y_6Z_5 \\
&+ (Y_2Y_4 + Y_2Y_6)Z_1Z_3 + (Y_2Y_6 + Y_4Y_6)Z_1Z_5 + Y_4Y_6Z_3Z_5 \\
&+ Y_2Y_4Y_6Z_1Z_3Z_5]/\langle Y_0[1 + Y_2Z_1 + Y_4(Z_1 + Z_3) \\
&+ Y_6(Z_1 + Z_3 + Z_5) + Y_2Y_4Z_1Z_3 + Y_2Y_6(Z_1Z_3 + Z_1Z_5) \\
&+ Y_4Y_6(Z_1Z_5 + Z_3Z_5) + Y_2Y_4Y_6Z_1Z_3Z_5] \\
&+ [Y_2 + Y_4 + Y_6 + Y_2Y_4Z_3 + Y_2Y_6(Z_3 + Z_5) \\
&+ Y_4Y_6Z_5 + Y_2Y_4Y_6Z_3Z_5]\rangle \quad\quad (4)
\end{aligned}
$$

[1] D. E. Hooper, and A. E. Jackets, "Current Derived Resistance-Capacitance Oscillators Using Junction Transistors," *Electronic Engineering*, August, 1956, p. 333.

$$Z_T = 1/\langle Y_0[1 + Y_2Z_1 + Y_4(Z_1 + Z_3) + Y_6(Z_1 + Z_3 + Z_5)$$
$$+ Y_2Y_4Z_1Z_3 + Y_2Y_6(Z_1Z_3 + Z_1Z_5) + Y_4Y_6(Z_1Z_5 + Z_3Z_5)$$
$$+ Y_2Y_4Y_6Z_1Z_3Z_5] + [Y_2 + Y_4 + Y_6 + Y_2Y_4Z_3$$
$$+ Y_2Y_6(Z_3 + Z_5) + Y_4Y_6Z_5 + Y_2Y_4Y_6Z_3Z_5]\rangle \tag{5}$$

The output impedance may be found from the input by making the following substitutions

$$Y_0 \to Y_6, \quad Y_6 \to Y_0, \quad Y_2 \to Y_4, \quad Y_4 \to Y_2, \quad Z_5 \to Z_1, \quad Z_1 \to Z_5 \tag{6}$$

This substitution is possible because of the completeness of the symmetry of the topology of the network.

In these equations, if Y_0 has the value zero, the expressions reduce to the previous form. If, however, Y_0 is given a value large enough that the second denominator bracket may be neglected, then the denominator of the transfer function is of order three, and the possibility of construction of a successful phase-shift network exists.

The elements of the network, that is, those in the Z group, and those in the Y group, are normally equal in immittance within each group, or they may be scaled in a manner that keeps the ratios of the immittances of corresponding elements in the Z and Y groups equal to the ratios for other corresponding elements. For equal immittances, that is, for $Y_2 = Y_4 = Y_6$ and $Z_1 = Z_3 = Z_5$, etc., and Y_0 is the source element, the denominator of the transfer function takes the form, where $Y_2 = j\omega C$ and $Z_1 = R$ and for a value of Y_0 large compared to Y_2 and $1/Z_1$

$$D = [1 + j\omega 6CR - \omega^2 5C^2R^2 - j\omega^3C^3R^3]Y_0 \tag{7}$$

The operating frequency is specified by the 180° phase-shift condition, that is, when the coefficient of the imaginary operator is zero and the real component is negative. This condition occurs when $\omega = \sqrt{6}/CR = \omega_0$. The corresponding value for the real components is -29, making necessary an amplification of -29 to offset the network gain of $-\frac{1}{29}$

The position of the capacitance and resistance elements in the basic ladder circuit has little effect on the operation of the circuit with the exception of a modification of the position of the multiplicative constant, the $\sqrt{6}$ above, which must be used with the values of capacitance and resistance to determine the operating frequency. The denominator expression given above is modified to its dual form when the resistor and the capacitor positions are interchanged, taking the form

$$D = Y_0[1 + (6/j\omega CR) - (5/\omega^2C^2R^2) - (1/j\omega^3C^3R^3)] \tag{8}$$

The imaginary part of this expression, when equated to zero and solved gives the radian frequency

$$\omega_0 = 1/RC\sqrt{6} \tag{9a}$$

For the other circuit, it was

$$\omega_0 = \sqrt{6}/RC \tag{9b}$$

And the real part again is -29. Thus, the effect of interchange of the positions of the capacitors and resistors is to shift the position of the factor $\sqrt{6}$, depending on whether the network is used as a low- or a high-pass filter.

If the numerator of the transfer function is imaginary instead of real (that is, Y_0 is imaginary instead of real), then the function of frequency discrimination and amplitude loss may be changed in the real and the imaginary parts of the bracket in Eqs. (7) and (8). This can change the $\sqrt{6}$ to a $\sqrt{5}$ in the untapered circuit, or the factor $[k^2 + 2k + 3]^{0.5}$ to $[2k + 3]^{0.5}$ in the tapered circuit.

When a taper is included in the immittances in such a way that the scaling on the resistances and capacitances are inverse to each other, then the component sizes are related by the equation

$$k = (Y_2/Y_4) = (Y_4/Y_6) = (Z_3/Z_1) = (Z_5/Z_3) \tag{10}$$

When these relations are substituted into the equation for the transfer impedance, the denominator takes the form for $Y_2 = j\omega C_2$ and $Z_1 = R_1$

$$
\begin{aligned}
D = Y_0\{ & 1 + j\omega[1 + k(1 + (1/k)) + k^2(1 + (1/k) + (1/k^2))]C_2R_1 \\
& - \omega^2[1 + k^2((1/k) + (1/k^2)) + k^3((1/k^2) + (1/k^3))]C_2^2R_1^2 \\
& - j\omega^3 C_2^3 R_1^3 \}
\end{aligned} \tag{11}
$$

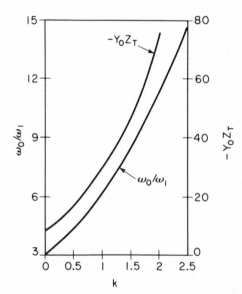

Fig. 11-7. Effect of taper "k" on network

The solution of this equation for the real and imaginary roots gives the above factors. The more important root equation is

$$\omega_0^2 = [k^2 + 2k + 3]/C_2^2R_1^2 = (k^2 + 2k + 3)\omega_1^2 \tag{12}$$

where the value of ω_1 is defined by the equation

$$\omega_1^2 = 1/C_2R_1 \tag{12a}$$

Substituting the root equation back into the denominator gives the forward impedance for the network in the form

$$\begin{aligned}
Z_T &= 1/Y_0[1 - 9 - 12k - 7k^2 - 2k^3] \\
&= 1/-Y_0[8 + 12k + 7k^2 + 2k^3]
\end{aligned} \tag{13}$$

Both the required amplification and the operating frequency are consequently a function of k, for any specified product C_2R_1. The value of the ratio ω_0/ω_1 and the value of the function $[8 + 12k + 7k^2 + 2k^3]$ as a function of k are shown in Fig. 11–7.

The feedback network can take an admittance form as well as an impedance form, in which case the input signal must have a low source impedance (Fig. 11–8). The output from the network may either be taken as the current flowing through Y_6, or it may be taken as the voltage across Y_6.

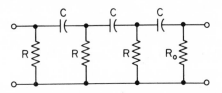

Fig. 11-8. Practical R-C ladder network (reverse mode)

One limitation applies to the Y_0 component of the network, in that it must include a conductance element to permit the passage of collector current. Under special conditions it is possible to avoid this constraint. These special cases are not considered here.

In the incorporation of R-C feedback networks into transistor oscillators, the output of a conventional transistor amplifier is best represented in the form of a current source. It is therefore desirable to use the trans-impedance form of a circuit. The output characteristics of this form of R-C circuit are poorly suited to use in the forward transfer configuration in which Y_6 is the final output element, because the input admittance of the transistor is high, and the output admittance of the network is small. The reverse-transfer configuration, in which Y_0, Y_2, and Y_4 are ladder elements, however, and in which Y_6 is large, is better suited to the design requirements. The denominators for the two modes of operation are

Forward

$$\begin{aligned}
D = Y_0[&1 + Y_2Z_1 + Y_4(Z_1 + Z_3) + Y_6(Z_1 + Z_3 + Z_5) \\
&+ Y_2Y_4Z_1Z_3 + Y_2Y_6(Z_1Z_3 + Z_1Z_5) \\
&+ Y_4Y_6(Z_1Z_5 + Z_3Z_5) + Y_2Y_4Y_6Z_1Z_3Z_5]
\end{aligned} \tag{14}$$

Reverse

$$D = Y_6[1 + Y_0(Z_1 + Z_3 + Z_5) + Y_2(Z_3 + Z_5) + Y_4Z_5$$
$$+ Y_2Y_4Z_3Z_5 + Y_0Y_2(Z_1Z_3 + Z_1Z_5)$$
$$+ Y_0Y_4(Z_1Z_5 + Z_3Z_5) + Y_0Y_2Y_4Z_1Z_3Z_5] \tag{15}$$

The first of these equations applies to either the equivalent transfer impedance or to the transfer admittance if Y_0 is large compared to the remaining admittances Y_1, Y_2, Y_3, Y_4, Y_5 and Y_6 as specified in Eqs. (4) and (5), whereas the second applies if Y_6 is large compared to the remaining admittances. For the forward-impedance circuit, the gain is determined in terms of the value of Z_0 divided by the bracket function, and for the backward-impedance circuit in terms of the value of Z_6 and the corresponding bracket function.

Emitter-followers may be required with the transistor amplifiers used with these oscillators if the network is used in the forward-admittance configuration (one provides the source signal for the network), or the forward-impedance configuration (it is used as a repeater for the output signal). If the network is used in the backward-impedance mode, correct matching of impedance levels results, but the limiting of amplitude of oscillation may be unsatisfactory. Emitter-followers are not essential if adequate limiting is obtained without them. The transistor is operating in the current-gain mode with this configuration, however, and as a result may provide poor waveform. When perfection of waveform is important, it is essential to use the forward-impedance mode with an emitter-follower to provide the input signal for the amplifier.

EXAMPLE 1.   Design 1000 cps R-C oscillators using as many as possible of the above configurations based on a transistor having a forward admittance, $g_{f'}$, of 30,000 μmhos, an input admittance of 150 μmhos, and a base-spreading resistance of 100 ohms. Assume that the other parameters of the device may be neglected, and assume that adequate oscillator limiting will occur in any configuration.   (In other words, make a linearized design; any of the designs described in Chapters Nine and Ten could be studied for nonlinearity problems.)

First the conditions required for the establishment of a forward-transfer oscillator for use with a transistor having a beta of 200 may be examined.

The range of voltage gain in the transistor is limited by the forward conductance of the device multiplied by the effective load resistance, which is here $1/g_i$, the input resistance. The minimum amplification will be $g_{f'}Z_0$, and the maximum $g_{f'}/g_{i'} = \beta$. The resistance required in the frequency-selection network must lie between Z_0 and $1/G_i$ and at the same time, the minimum permitted value for the expression $g_{f'}Z_0$ is 29. The following inequality expresses the relation

$$g_{f'}Z_0 \ll g_{f'}R_2 \leq g_{f'}/g_{i'} = \beta \qquad (16)$$

This simplifies to

$$29 \ll g_{f'}R_2 \leq 200$$

Evidently, these conditions cannot be met, because the ratio of the minimum to the maximum number is only seven. An emitter-follower amplifier is therefore required as a matching section between the output of the transfer network and the input of the active device.

If, on the other hand, the backward-transfer network is utilized, then the amplification of the feedback network is controlled by Z_6, which nominally may have a value of approximately 2000 ohms. The values of R_0, R_2, and R_4 would be greater than 5000 ohms, and the value of Z_6 would be reduced by loading to give a loop amplification of 40 to 50, more or less. Selection of values of R_0, R_2, and R_4 in the neighborhood of 10,000 or more ohms, and Z_6 to have a total of 750 ohms, including the transistor input, means that a forward conductance of approximately 40,000 μmhos is required. The corresponding value of Y_6 is 1333 μmhos, which is considerably more than the input admittance of the transistor, 200 μmhos. Consequently, a consistent design is obtainable under these conditions. The combined value for Y_6 should be as near an order-of-magnitude larger than G_i as possible.

The ladder elements, with resistive components of 10,000 ohms include capacitances of value 0.0065 mfd for the high-pass configuration, and 0.039 mfd for the low-pass configuration for the normal, untapered, network. The effect of network taper may now be considered.

The maximum value of k that can be permitted is determined by the current gain available in the active device. Although it might appear superficially that there was advantage in using a value of k appreciably greater than unity with the reverse-transfer network (Hooper's current feedback network), the limitations on the termination impedance, Z_6, offset any apparent advantages. The feedback loss increases so rapidly that the use of a value of k in excess of 2.50 is likely to introduce serious difficulties. A value of k of 0.5 is convenient for many ordinary applications, because then the feedback loss is 16, making an amplifier amplification of 16 necessary. The corresponding frequency factor is $\sqrt{4.25}$, or 2.060. This factor is in the numerator with low-pass networks, in the denominator with high-pass. In the backward-transfer mode, the network must have the high-pass configuration, because the source element, Y_0, is a part of the frequency-selection network instead of being a driver impedance, as with the forward-transfer configuration.

Multi-Section Ladders. As an example of multi-section ladders, a four-section ladder may be used for the frequency-determining feedback path. Such a network if properly terminated at either end, will have a single operating frequency, and since only 45° per section phase shift is required, it will not have any more loss than does a corresponding three-section tapered filter. The transfer equation for such a network is

$$Z_T = Z_0/[1 + 10ZY + 15Z^2Y^2 + 7Z^3Y^3 + Z^4Y^4$$
$$+ Z_0(4Y + 10Y^2Z + 6Y^3Z^2 + Y^4Z^3)] \tag{17}$$

where Y and Z are the network immittances, and Z_0 is either the input or the termination impedance, as required.

The simplest method of getting the coefficients for the terms of the transfer equations is by the establishment of an addition chain based on the continued-fraction expansion of the ladder network.[2] It takes the form:

Exponent of (YZ)

Function	0	1	2	3	4	5	6	7	8	9
Y_1	1									
F_1	1	1								
Y_2	2	1								
F_2	1	3	1							
Y_3	3	4	1							
F_3	1	6	5	1						
Y_4	4	10	6	1						
F_4	1	10	15	7	1					
Y_5	5	20	21	8	1					
F_5	1	15	35	28	9	1				
Y_6	6	35	56	36	10	1				
F_6	1	21	70	84	45	11	1			
Y_7	7	56	126	120	55	12	1			
F_7	1	28	126	210	165	66	13	1		
Y_8	8	84	252	330	220	78	14	1		
F_8	1	36	210	462	495	286	91	15	1	
Y_9	9	120	462	792	715	364	105	16	1	
F_9	1	45	330	924	1287	1001	455	120	17	1

In the table above, each row is formed from the two rows above it. To obtain Y_{j+1}, for example, the values of the coefficients for Y_j and F_j are added directly. Similarly, to find the coefficients for F_{j+1}, the coefficients for F_j are added to those for Y_{j+1} after Y_{j+1} has been multiplied by YZ to *shift each coefficient one column to the right.* The F term is the frequency-

---

[2] For a detailed discussion of this, see K. A. Pullen, Jr., "On the Properties of Ladder Networks," *BRL Report 1102*, Ballistic Research Laboratories, Aberdeen Proving Ground, Maryland, 1960.

determination term, and the Y term is the one whose value should be made negligible for efficient operation. In terms of these functions, the transfer impedance takes the form:

$$Z_T = Z_0/[F_j + Z_0 Y_j] \quad \text{or} \quad Z_T = Z_{2n}/[F_j + Z_{2n} Y_j] \tag{18}$$

where Y_j and F_j are the over-all ladder functions. A factor involving a function of k is also required when the network is tapered. The network design should be such that the second term in the bracket in Eq. (18) is small compared to the F_j term.

Modified Two-Section Ladder. There is one other phase-shift type circuit that is important because of its simplicity and freedom from loading effects. It is a modification of the two-section ladder, and it behaves as a three-section ladder with a low-impedance termination. The basic configuration is shown in Fig. 11–9. The input

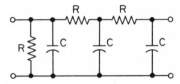

Fig. 11-9. Modified form of network

admittance in this arrangement consists of a parallel combination of a Y and a Z element, and the transfer impedance takes the form

$$Z_T = 1/[(Y + 1/Z)(1 + 3YZ + Y^2Z^2) + 2Y + Y^2Z]$$
$$= Z/[1 + 6YZ + 5Y^2Z^2 + Y^3Z^3] \tag{19}$$

If Z is resistive, the frequency-dependent terms are all in the denominator, and the resonant frequency is given by

$$\omega = \sqrt{6}/RC \tag{20}$$

The transfer resistance is $R/29$, the sign being negative. If, however, Z is capacitive, then the resonant frequency determined by

$$\omega = \sqrt{5}/RC \tag{21}$$

and the transfer impedance at this frequency is $5R/29$, positive, not negative. The operating frequencies are slightly different, and one is zero-phase, the other 180° phase. An emitter-follower on the output of the network is required to minimize the loading introduced by the amplifier.

11.3 Zero-Phase-Shift Networks

Networks having a maximum amplitude response at zero phase-angle may be used in conjunction with amplifiers having a phase-shift of either zero degrees or 360° to produce an additional form of R-C oscillator, of which the Wien-bridge oscillator is typical. This oscillator is somewhat critical in adjustment because of a relatively slow phase-shift with frequency in the neighborhood of maximum response. The most commonly used form of this network is shown in (A) in Fig. 11–10, and an additional form, which sometimes is useful, is shown in Fig. 11–10(B). There are a number of variations of this circuit in use, but their modes of operation usually reduce to one of the two forms shown above.

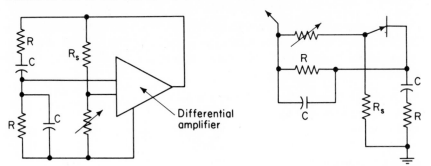

Fig. 11-10A. Simplified Wien-bridge oscillator

Fig. 11-10B. Emitter-coupled Wien-bridge configuration

These oscillators use amplifiers that have their gain stabilized closely to a fixed value, typically three, and use a thermistor bridge arrangement to provide the small amount of variation required to develop the loop-gain, somewhat greater than unity, needed to start the oscillator. A typical bridge circuit is shown in Fig. 11–11. The thermally-sensitive resistance, R_T, changes its resistance in the presence of signal, the change being in such a direction as to reduce the loop amplification, thereby stabilizing the operation and giving optimum waveform.

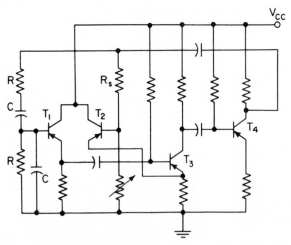

Fig. 11-11. Typical transistorized Wien oscillator

The feedback network for the zero-phase oscillator may be analyzed to give its input, its transfer, and its output impedances. The ordinary form of the Wien-bridge network is used as a voltage-transfer configuration, and as a result requires an emitter-follower used as a repeater. One of the other oscillators described in this section uses the same frequency-selection circuit in inverted form to control oscillation, and a third uses the configuration in a low-impedance circuit for generation of high-frequency signals.

The three basic equations for use with the Wien-bridge network of Fig. 11–11 are

$$Z_I = (Y_1Y_2 + Y_1Y_3 + Y_2Y_3 + Y_1Y_4 + Y_2Y_4)/[Y_1Y_2Y_3$$
$$+ Y_1Y_2Y_4 + Y_0(Y_1Y_2 + Y_1Y_3 + Y_2Y_3 + Y_1Y_4 + Y_2Y_4)]$$
$$\doteq R_0 \tag{22}$$

$$Z_T = Y_1Y_2/[Y_1Y_2Y_3 + Y_1Y_2Y_4 + Y_0(Y_1Y_2 + Y_1Y_3 + Y_2Y_3$$
$$+ Y_1Y_4 + Y_2Y_4)]$$
$$\doteq R_0/3 \tag{23}$$

$$Z_O = [Y_1Y_2 + Y_0(Y_1 + Y_2)]/[Y_1Y_2Y_3 + Y_1Y_2Y_4 + Y_0(Y_1Y_2$$
$$+ Y_1Y_3 + Y_2Y_3 + Y_1Y_4 + Y_2Y_4)]$$
$$\doteq (R + R_0 + 1/j\omega C)/3 \tag{24}$$

These equations hold as long as $R_0 \ll R$.

The principal design problem in connection with an oscillator of these general characteristics is getting it to start reliably at all frequencies over a range of many decades, and making certain that the net amplitude of oscillation is not a function of time or frequency after the initial build-up. The first condition can be achieved if the minimum initial starting amplification (closed-loop) is between 1.25 and 1.5, since then some gain margin is available, and the second requires that the amplification not reach large values compared to unity. In addition, the variation of the resistance of the thermal device with time must be slow compared to the minimum oscillation frequency.

A form of oscillator that is excellent for use at discrete frequencies or for use as a variable-frequency oscillator at

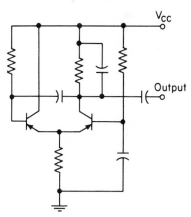

Fig. 11-12. Additional Wien-bridge oscillator

high frequencies is shown in Fig. 11–12. This oscillator makes use of current drive and provides an output voltage for use in exciting the amplifier. The output impedance for this network is comparatively high. The equations are

$$Z_I = (Y_3 + Y_4)/[Y_1Y_3 + Y_2Y_3 + Y_3Y_4 + Y_1Y_4 + Y_2Y_4]$$
$$\doteq (R + 1/j\omega C)/3 \tag{25}$$

$$Z_T = Y_3/[Y_1Y_3 + Y_2Y_3 + Y_3Y_4 + Y_1Y_4 + Y_2Y_4]$$
$$\doteq R/3 \tag{26}$$

$$Z_O = (Y_1 + Y_2 + Y_3)/[Y_1Y_3 + Y_2Y_3 + Y_3Y_4 + Y_1Y_4 + Y_2Y_4]$$
$$\doteq 2R/3 + 1/j3\omega C \tag{27}$$

Because the transfer impedance is dependent on the value of resistance in the frequency-selection circuit, variation of frequency can only be obtained by change in capacitance in this form of circuit. A variable capacitor may be used only if its minimum capacitance is relatively large compared to the input capacitance of the amplifier. This condition can be met with an emitter-follower input stage using a high-frequency transistor.

The extremely high trans-admittance available with transistors makes possible the use of very small values of R. The associated amplifier should be designed to have a trans-admittance that is degenerated to a value slightly greater than $3/R$ with the resistance selected for the network, and a small range of adjustment should be provided to permit the compensation for small errors in parts values.

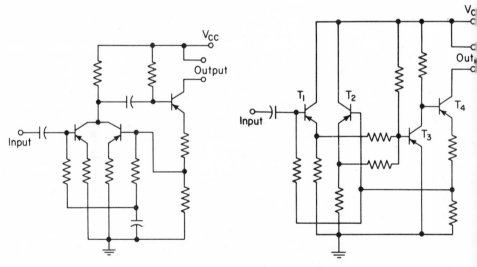

Fig. 11-13A. Stabilized forward admittance I

Fig. 11-13B. Stabilized forward admittance II

Two possible circuits for generating a stabilized forward admittance of the required value are shown in Fig. 11–13. The circuit (A) obtains stabilization through the comparison of two signal currents in transistors 1 and 2, whereas the circuit (B) obtains the stabilization through the comparison of two signal voltages and amplification of the difference in the difference amplifier. The first of the circuits is somewhat simpler, but has a smaller stability than the latter because its efficiency is dependent on the stability of the forward admittance of the individual transistors. However, because the stability and reproducibility of the forward admittance of transistors is rather good as long as the collector currents in the two transistors are equal, the balance may be expected to be good, possibly within five percent. The relations applying to Fig. 11–13 (A) are

$$G_f = 3[g_{f1}/(1 + \langle g_{i1} + g_{f1}\rangle R_e]g_{f3}R_L/[3\langle 1 + (g_{i3} + g_{f3})R\rangle$$
$$+ \langle g_{f2}/(1 + (g_{i2} + g_{f2})R_e)\rangle g_{f3}RR_L] \tag{28}$$

When $g_{f2}R_e \ll g_{f2}R_L$ and $g_{f3}R > 1$, this reduces to

$$G_f \doteq 3/R - 3\Delta g_f^2/g_{f1}^2 R \tag{29}$$

where $g_{f1}R_e \geqq 10$ and $g_{f2} - g_{f1} = \Delta g_f$. The transistor T_3 is used as an emitter-follower to make it possible to take full advantage of the available gain in the balance amplifiers. Otherwise, the value of R_L will not be sufficiently large compared to R_e to make Eq. (29) applicable.

The second circuit, which makes the comparison at the input through the use of an input emitter-follower and balance circuit, applies the difference voltage to the amplifier, and can consequently make full use of the amplification available in it. The emitter-followers used in the input comparison circuit have high inherent stability at signal frequency, a fraction of a percent or better.

The larger the undegenerated gain of the amplifier can be made, the smaller is the variation in over-all amplification. Circuits like those shown can be redesigned to provide Q multiplification for tuned circuits, and the effective Q available may be adjusted through the use of gain-adjustment circuits.

Automatic amplitude stabilization may be introduced into either of these amplifiers to provide self-limitation. In the first circuit, this is accomplished by decreasing the feedback voltage, and by placing either a negative-coefficient thermistor in the emitter of T_2 or a positive-coefficient device in the emitter of T_1. Either of these will disturb the balance in a manner to readjust the value of G_f as is required.

Amplitude stabilization may be introduced into the second amplifier in the balancing circuit through the use of a thermistor in the appropriate coupling circuit. Because it is possible to operate this balance circuit with no d-c in it, the sensitivity to signal level can be made considerably greater than is possible in designs in which the thermal element must pass both signal and static current. The principal problem in this circuit is the control of phase-shift, because phase delay is introduced as a result of capacitive loading on the balance detection terminal. The range of operating frequency of this circuit is limited by the effect of this phase-shift.

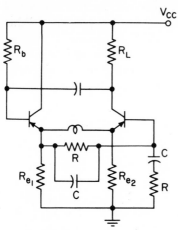

Fig. 11-14. Emitter-coupled oscillator

The role of the direct and the feedback paths in an oscillator may be interchanged successfully. An oscillator using a Wien-bridge in such a modification is shown in Fig. 11–14. The direct-feedback path in this circuit is through the voltage divider into the emitter of the amplifier transistor, whereas the frequency-selection path, by letting a cancelling component of voltage reach the base of the amplifier at all but the oscillation frequency, limits action to the desired frequency range. This configuration has the advantage that the two parts of the bridge are normally placed at the point of lowest impedance in the circuit, and the amplification is not limited by loading to the extent it might be otherwise.

With all sinusoidal oscillators, whether of energy-storage or of phase-shift type, the design procedure is based on analysis of the feedback network as a trans-impedance, and then coordination of the driving-point impedance characteristics of the network with its trans-impedance and with the trans-admittance of the active device(s) in the associated circuit. Determination of limiting conditions is based on the known nonlinear characteristics of the active devices. If available, the small-signal data are used for determination of the limiting conditions, or they may be approximated by a technique like the polynomial technique.

11.4 Negative Immittance Devices

The special amplifiers described for development of a fixed magnitude of gain in connection with the R–C oscillators above are special examples of what may be called negative immittance amplifiers. These amplifiers are used to supply the losses in a given circuit, thereby either increasing its efficiency or possibly increasing the selectivity of a circuit by providing part of the energy required by the circuit losses.

Just as there are two types of immittance, namely, impedance and admittance, there are two types of negative immittance, one of which is used to neutralize a shunt conductance in an associated circuit, and the other to neutralize a series resistance in an associated circuit. Except for the fact that negative immittance can only be developed over a narrow range, these two types would be indistinguishable. Typically, however, a negative admittance has characteristics similar to those shown in Fig. 11–15. Outside of a narrow range, the current flowing through the device increases relatively uniformly with increasing applied voltage, but within the critical range, an increase in voltage brings about a decrease of current. Devices and circuits having this property also have a shunt dynamic capacitance associated with them.

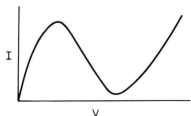

Fig. 11-15. Negative admittance

With negative impedance devices, outside the critical region the voltage across the device rises as the current through it rises, but within the critical range the voltage decreases with increase of current. These devices have a dynamic series inductance associated with them.

Negative immittance devices and negative immittance circuits may have either one or two ports (two or three terminals), the more usual ones having a single port. Among the exceptions, the Q-multiplier and the Clapp oscillator circuits are typical of negative admittance configurations having three terminals (Fig. 11–16). Most of the oscillators considered in Chapter Ten could have been analyzed as negative immittance circuits. The transfer, or two-port approach has been used in this book because it appears to simplify and clarify the dynamics of the circuits.

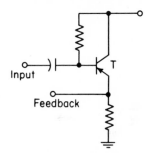

Fig. 11-16. Q-multiplication circuit

11.5 Time Delay Oscillators

There is another type of oscillator that is of considerable interest, though so far it has been relatively little used. This form of oscillator uses an artificial delay line as its frequency-establishing element. Either the transmitted signal can be used to perform the switching action, or a reflected signal may be used. The simplest circuit of this type is shown in Fig. 11–17. It uses a multivibrator having a normal switching time somewhat longer than that desired from the over-all circuit in conjunction with a delay line having somewhat dispersive characteristics. The delay in this line should increase with increasing frequency. The switching pulse from the emitter circuit is coupled into the delay line and used to initiate the reversal of the state of the multivibrator.

In spite of the bad waveform of this type of oscillator, its repetition rate is constant because of the relatively sharp rise in the output of the delay line allowing for but little variation in the switching instant. As long as the normal switching rate of the amplifier as a multivibrator is somewhat slower than the delay time in the delay line, operation will be at the minimum rate supportable by the line, and the frequency stability will be comparable with a good L-C oscillator.

The design of the active circuits for this application calls first for the design of a multivibrator having the appropriate repetition rate, and the insertion of a delay line to provide the required control action.

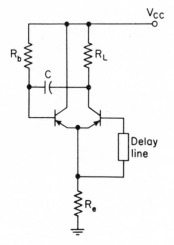

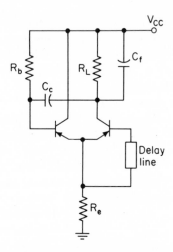

Fig. 11-17. Delay-line oscillator I

Fig. 11-18. Stabilized delay-line oscillator II

The delay line may be placed in other positions in the circuit as well as that shown in Fig. 11–17. It may be coupled from emitter to emitter; it may be inserted in any other position that will increase the total delay in the circuit by a fixed amount; or it may be arranged to provide a shunt-switching action as is generated by the circuit above. When the delay is placed in series with the main signal path, it is important that some reduction of high-frequency response be introduced to prevent the control from shifting from the fundamental rate to the second or a higher harmonic in a more-or-less random fashion. Some shunt capacitance across the amplifier load resistance can provide the required delay (Fig. 11–18).

11.6 Summary

The design of oscillators is the science of the interconnection of linear selective networks and nonlinear networks to cause a conversion of energy from a d-c source into a cyclic energy. Each section of the complete network may be analyzed in a fashion that permits interconnection without need for matching adjustments. That is, the design of each section is analyzed on the basis of the conditions that will apply when the sections are interconnected. The driving-point impedances, both input and output, are required for the linear network to make the design for the nonlinear section, and the transfer impedance is also required for the determination of the conditions of unity average loop amplification. The use of these data with the small-signal data on the active devices permits the adjustment of the amplification to the value required for oscillation to develop, and permits the determination of the conditions required for a given amplitude of oscillation to develop.

CHAPTER TWELVE

Design of Mixers and Converters

12.0 Introduction

Mixers and converters are used to shift the carrier frequency of a modulated wave without altering its modulation structure. A properly designed mixer or converter makes use of an unmodulated sinusoidal signal to vary the electrical characteristics of a nonlinear device in such a way that a second modulated signal, of considerably smaller amplitude, will experience a time variation of amplification. The modulation is thus transferred to a new carrier at the sum or the difference frequency, or one of their multiples. The mixer uses the nonlinear device solely for the multiplication action required to achieve the transfer, whereas the converter uses a single tube or transistor for both the oscillation and the multiplication functions.

12.1 Conversion Conductance

The value of conversion conductance or conversion gain developed by a circuit depends on the characteristics of the associated nonlinear device and also on the type of circuit with which the device is used. It also depends to a considerable extent on the manner of application, inasmuch as the amount of nonlinearity in the device may either be minimized or enhanced by fairly small variations in the circuit parameters. The next few paragraphs explain the determination of the conversion characteristics of several typical nonlinear behavior patterns, and following this discussion, some of the possible methods of taking maximum advantage of the conversion properties of practical devices are studied.

The simplest converter relation to analyze mathematically is the one in which the conversion conductance or the conversion gain is a linear function of the voltage from the reference oscillator. In this case, the gain relation may be written

$$K = K_0 + K_1 x \tag{1}$$

where $x = v_b/v_{\max} = \sin \omega_r t$ in the absence of input signal. The more correct form, including the signal, is

$$x = \sin \omega_r t + k_s \sin \omega_s t \tag{2}$$

where k_s is a function of time, and is the ratio of the amplitude of the desired signal and its accompanying noise to the amplitude of the reference signal, and ω_s and ω_r are the instantaneous angular frequencies of the composite signal and the reference voltages, respectively.

If Eq. (1) above is integrated to give the output voltage in terms of the input ratio, x, the result is

$$v_0 = V_a[K_0 x + 0.5 K_1 V_a x^2] \tag{3}$$

Next, the expression for x should be substituted, giving

$$v_0 = V_a K_0 x + 0.5 K_1 V_a^2 [\sin^2 \omega_r t + 2 \sin \omega_r t \\ \times k_s \sin \omega_s t + k_s^2 \sin^2 \omega_s t] \tag{4}$$

For mixer applications, the only term of importance is the sine-product term, consequently, the balance may be discarded

$$v_{0c} = 0.5 K_1 V_a^2 k_s [\cos (\omega_r - \omega_s)t - \cos (\omega_r + \omega_s)t] \tag{5}$$

It is more convenient to express the value of K_1 in terms of the greatest and the smallest values, K_p and K_n, than in terms of the derivative. Then $K_1 V_a$ takes the form

$$K_1 V_a = 0.5 (K_p - K_n) \tag{6}$$

Substituting, and recalling that the input signal voltage is $V_a k_s$ gives

$$v_{oc}/v_{is} = 0.25 (K_p - K_n)[\cos (\omega_r - \omega_s)t - \cos (\omega_r + \omega_s)t] \tag{7}$$

This equation shows that because v_{is} is the amplitude of the signal voltage, the output will be available at the radian frequencies, $(\omega_r - \omega_s)$ and $(\omega_r + \omega_s)$. Normally, all that is required to select the appropriate frequency is to introduce a frequency-selective circuit that develops sufficient impedance at the specified frequency to facilitate the transfer of energy to the following circuitry.

Although the development of mixing through linear variation of amplification (sometimes mis-called linear mixing) is probably the simplest way of obtaining moderate efficiency, it is by no means the only possible method of mixing, nor is it necessarily the best method of mixing. For example, it is only approximately half as efficient as the piecewise-linear mixer, which develops two fixed values of amplification over two ranges of bias

$$K = K_n; \quad v_i < 0$$
$$K = K_p; \quad v_i > 0 \tag{8}$$

This input relation gives a conversion efficiency of $K_c = 0.4244$, or a detection efficiency of 0.2122, rather than the 0.250 or 0.125 respectively for the square-law mixer or detector. The value of the conversion amplification can be up to twice the above values if diode-clamp mixing is used, and it may be up to three times the listed value if both diode clamping and peak (rather than average) mixing is produced. The table below indicates the range of conversion efficiencies that may be anticipated.

TABLE I

Conversion Amplification

Type of Mixing	Type of Output	Conversion Gain
Quadratic:		
$\quad K = K_0 + K_1 v_r$	Average	$0.25(K_p - K_n)$
Piecewise linear:		
$\quad K = K_p$ when $v_r \geqq 0$	Average	$0.42(K_p - K_n)$
$\quad K = K_n$ when $v_r < 0$	Peak	$0.5(K_p - K_n)$

Quadratic mixing is normally produced by transistors and tunnel diodes, and piecewise-linear by diodes under conditions of relatively large reference-voltage input.

12.2 Transistor Mixers

The basic requirement for mixer action with transistors is principally that the circuit must behave in a manner that will provide a varying amplification as a function of reference voltage, but a negligible variation as a function of the received signal. First, it is necessary to determine the conditions under which sufficient variation of amplification can be obtained to give effective mixing action. The amplification equation is

$$K = -y_{f'}R_L/[1 + y_{i'}(r_{b'} + R_s)(1 + y_c R_L) + y_0 R_L] \qquad (9)$$

where $y_{i'} = g_{i'} + j\omega C_{i'}$, and the terms in $y_0 R_L$ and $y_c R_L$ may be neglected. Eq. (9) then reads

$$K = -y_{f'}R_L/[1 + (g_{i'} + j\omega C_i)(r_{b'} + R_s)] \qquad (10)$$

In this equation, three of the parameters are proportional to the emitter current in the transistor, namely, $y_{f'}$, $g_{i'}$, and C_i. Consequently, for effective mixing, the second term of the denominator,

$$(g_{i'} + j\omega C_i)(r_{b'} + R_s)$$

must be less than or at most equal to unity. When ωC_i is small compared to $g_{i'}$ at the frequency chosen for use on the mixer or converter transistor, then the product $g_{i'}(r_{b'} + R_s)$ controls whether proper mixing can be obtained. If, however, the operating frequency is such that ωC_i is greater than $g_{i'}$, then the product $\omega C_i(r_{b'} + R_s)$ will control the operating behavior.

The two equations expressing the limitation on effective mixing indicate that two conditions must be fulfilled. The first of these is that the internal or source resistance of the source of input signal should be small, and the second is that the base-spreading resistance of the transistor also should be small. Only under conditions in which both of these factors are sufficiently small that the product terms are less than or approximately equal to unity will effective mixing be possible. These conditions may be stated as

$$
\begin{aligned}
g_{i'}(r_{b'} + R_s) &\leqq 1 \quad \text{or} \quad g_{i'}(2r_{b'}) \leqq 1 \\
\omega C_i(r_{b'} + R_s) &\leqq 1 \quad \text{or} \quad \omega C_i(2r_{b'}) \leqq 1
\end{aligned}
\qquad (11)
$$

If, then, the maximum value of R_s is set equal to $r_{b'}$, as indicated by the second equation of each group, the maximum operating current may be set in terms of the appropriate inequalities

$$C_i \leqq 1/2\omega r_{b'} \quad \text{or} \quad g_{i'} \leqq 1/2r_{b'} \qquad (12)$$

These two equations may be solved in terms of the nomograph, Fig. 12–1. The maximum forward conductance and the maximum emitter current may be read directly from the nomograph based on the assumption that the diffusion capacitance is approximately the total input capacitance of the transistor.

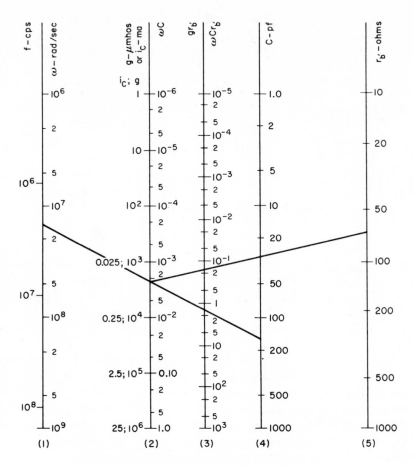

Note: if value of g on line 2 is forward conductance, g_f, then current scale may be used, not otherwise

Fig. 12-1. Calculation nomograph

These nomographs can be used to determine the maximum forward conductance that can be obtained efficiently in a transistor circuit. The required reference signal power for the mixer of Fig. 12–2 can be determined by reading the total peak-to-peak base voltage change, Δv_b, and the total peak-to-peak emitter current change, Δi_e. The input power then is

$$P_r = 0.125\,\Delta v_b \Delta i_e = 0.125\,\Delta v_b(\Delta i_b + \Delta i_c) \tag{13}$$

This amount of power must be made available to the emitter lead in the mixer if maximum mixing efficiency and the best possible noise figure are to result. The maximum conversion amplification is given by the equation

$$K_c = 0.25\,(Y_{fp} - Y_{fn})R_{LD} \tag{14}$$

where R_{LD} is the impedance at the output frequency, and Y_{fp} and Y_{fn} are the effective values of forward admittance. In this equation, one of the Y_f terms is the value at maximum current, and the other at minimum. Which is which depends on the polarity of the transistor.

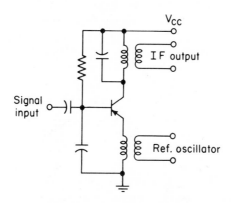

Fig. 12-2. Transistor mixer

The amplification of the mixer as a function of the bias voltage may be expressed in terms of an algebraic relation for the effect of source impedance

$$K = k_0(1 + x)/(1 + m + mx) \tag{15}$$

where the range for x is from -1 to $+1$, $k_0 = 0.5\, g_{f'\max}R_L$, $m = g_{i'\max}Z_s/2$, and $1 + 2m$ is the maximum value of the denominator as established in terms of $y_{i'}$, ω, C_i, and $r_{b'}$. The conversion amplification is expressed in terms of this equation, where $(K_p - K_n) = 2\,K_1$ is the total change of amplification with a negligible value of the parameter m. As long as the value of m is less than 0.5, the conversion conductance can be expressed in terms of the equation

$$K_c = \frac{0.25(K_p - K_n)}{(1 + m)^2} \langle 1 + [3m^2/5(1 + m)^2] \\ + [3m^2/7(1 + m)^4] + \ldots \rangle \tag{16}$$

This expression reduces to the normal function for $m = 0$, and the ratio of the bracket $\langle\ \rangle$ expression divided by $(1 + m)^2$ can be approximated by the expression

$$K_c = 0.25(1 + 0.6\, m^2)/(1 + m)^2 \tag{16a}$$

Consequently, the equation shows that the effect of the denominator term is to reduce the conversion amplification.

The mixer transistor may be used as its own oscillator, but the amount of conversion conductance that can be obtained under these conditions, if oscillator stability is important, is quite small. The reason for this condition is that good frequency stability requires the changes in amplification to be small over the operating cycle, whereas effective conversion action requires as large a change as possible. In addition, the larger the conversion amplification obtained for a given maximum forward conductance, the higher the over-all signal-to-noise ratio. This condition is typical of mixers, in that the noise is primarily noise generated in the IF passband, whereas the magnitude of the converted signal under linear conversion conditions is proportional to the total change of forward conductance.

EXAMPLE 1. Design a mixer for operation at five mc, using a 2N247 transistor in the configuration of Fig. 12-2. Take the collector supply voltage as ten volts, the value of $r_{b'}$ as 40 ohms, and the value of R_s may be left to be determined. The alpha-cutoff frequency for the 2N247 transistor is 30 mc.

First, the effective input capacitance corresponding to the alpha-cutoff frequency may be calculated. Assuming a maximum current of one ma, the approximate forward conductance is 0.04 mho, and the capacitance is

$$C_i = g_{f'}/\omega = 0.04/2 \times 10^8 = 2 \times 10^{-10} = 200 \text{ pfd}$$

At a frequency of-5 mc, this capacitance has a time constant with $r_{b'}$ of

$$C_i r_{b'} = 7 \times 2 \times 10^{-10} \times 40 = 8 \text{ nanoseconds}$$

The resulting value of m is 0.120 for a linear mixing circuit. If the source impedance of the signal circuit is kept sufficiently small, less than 100 ohms, for example, the behavior of the circuit should prove satisfactory.

The effect of $g_{i'}$ may also be checked as a matter of routine. The product of $r_{b'}$ and $g_{i'}$ is given by the equation

$$g_{i'} r_{b'} = 0.0008 \times 40 = 0.032$$

Consequently, the capacitance component is the one of importance in the limitation of the conversion amplification.

The magnitude of input signal from the reference oscillator to give full modulation of the transistor may be calculated. The required power is

$$P = 0.125 \,\Delta v_b \Delta i_e = 0.125 \times 0.130 \times 0.001 = 0.15 \text{ mw}$$

This amount of mixer power makes available up to 10,000 micromhos of conversion conductance. For a conversion gain of 30, the load impedance of the converter load is only a few ohms at the reference frequency.

The balance of the static design can now be completed. The average base current should produce a collector current of approximately 0.5 ma, and the collector current then varies from about 0.1 ma to a peak of one ma. The approximate value of base current required is eight μa.

The input circuit for the signal still must be designed. The average input conductance is approximately 400 μmhos, and the average input capacitance is approximately 100 pfd. Unless variable capacitance mixing is desired, it is necessary to minimize the effect of capacitance variation on the tuning of the input circuit. The nominal reactance level of 100 pfd at 5 mc is 200 ohms, a value much higher than can be tolerated in the circuit. It is necessary to reduce this reactance to a value which when resonated develops an effective source impedance less than forty ohms at the base if the conversion gain is not to be degraded significantly. Consequently, for a source reactance of one ohm at the base, the Q-factor circuit must not exceed 40 if R_s is to be forty ohms or less. A parallel capacitance of approximately 0.02 mfd in parallel with the base is required. Assuming a loaded Q of 40, and a nominal drive impedance for the tuned circuit of 1000 ohms, a capacitance step-down ratio of five is required if the unloaded Q of the tuned circuit is sufficiently large that the load current drawn by the base is small compared to the circulating or reactive current in the tuned circuit.

The fact that the nominal impedance level for the reference oscillator signal is 130 ohms does not necessarily mean that the source impedance to the emitter should be this high. Practically, it is desirable to keep the source impedance sufficiently small that the product $g_{f'}Z_r$ has a value considerably less than unity, particularly at signal and output frequencies. Because the average value of $g_{f'}$ is 0.02 mho, the value of Z_r should be less than 30 ohms.

12.3 Diode Mixers

The diode mixer is used under conditions in which transistors cannot be made to function satisfactorily. The diode has a series resistance component and a shunt capacitance component across the junction just as does a transistor, but the shunt capacitance may be only a hundredth of the diffusion capacitance of the transistor, and the series impedance may also be smaller by a factor of from two to ten. This combination of conditions makes the diode at least potentially able to operate as a mixer to a frequency a hundred to a thousand times as high as the transistor. The reference oscillator voltage required by the diode is from ten to twenty times that required of the transistor.

Diode mixing is generated by the use of the diode under piecewise-linear conditions developed on a large-signal basis. In effect, the diode acts as a switch, either turning the circuit on or turning it off. This switching, although it takes place in a range of one or two tenths of a volt, is not sufficiently sharp that the characteristics are strictly piecewise-linear with less than two to three volts of reference signal voltage.

The conversion amplification for the diode mixer is limited by the fact that in the forward direction the amplification is unity, and in the reverse direction, it is very nearly zero. For this reason, its value is appreciably less than unity, a maximum of 0.424 for the most commonly used circuit configurations. In spite of this, a diode can be convenient because a higher over-all amplification often can be obtained by the use of a diode under piecewise-linear conditions and following it by a transistor amplifier operating at the output frequency.

12.4 Diode Measurements

One of the problems in the use of diode mixers is the selection of devices capable of giving effective mixer action. The principal property of a diode that affects mixer action is its switch-off time. When any semiconductor diode is switched very rapidly from the forward to the reverse polarity, the diode current has a form similar to that shown in Fig. 12–3. The current in region A would not exist except for the time required to sweep out charge carriers.

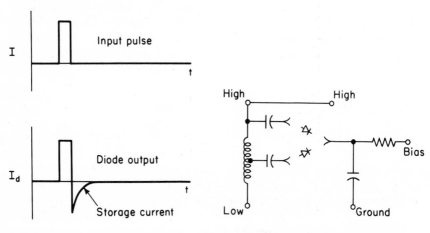

Fig. 12-3. Diode storage

Fig. 12-4. Diode test circuit using "Q-meter"

Diodes may be tested for the effect of the reverse-conduction loading shown in region A by the use of the circuit in Fig. 12–4 in conjunction with a conventional Q-meter. When this loading is present, if a diode with either no bias or reverse bias is coupled across a tuned circuit, a significant loss of Q-factor circuit can result. With a diode having small loss, the Q-reduction is normally very small.

12.5 Diode Amplifiers

Diodes can be used successfully as amplifiers if their characteristics include very small equivalent series resistance and a reasonably large capacitance change as a function of reverse bias voltage. Such amplifiers are known as parametric amplifiers. They take advantage of the fact that a variable capacitance can effect the tuning of a circuit. If the capacitance is controlled by a voltage of relatively high frequency and large amplitude, then the amplification of a low-frequency signal can be achieved.

The properties required of diodes for this application, aside from those of stable characteristics, are a large rate of variation of capacitance with injection voltage, and a relatively large value of positive bias for the initiation of the conducting region. In addition, the total voltage swing in the reverse direction to the Zener, or avalanche-breakdown voltage should be large.

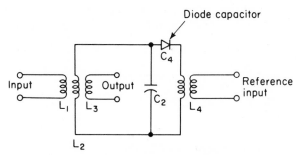

Fig. 12-5. Parametric amplifier

Suitable diodes for use in amplifier service may be found using the tester described in 12.5. The potentiometer varies the back-bias, and makes possible the measurement of effective capacitance as a function of the diode current. Diodes having a large capacitance variation, but introducing only small reductions of circuit Q-factor are essential for this application.

Either stable amplification or potentially unstable amplification may be obtained from variable-reactance diode circuits. If the reference injection frequency, ω_r, is large compared to the signal frequency, ω_s, two possible output frequencies normally are obtained from the variable-reactance amplifier, namely, $\omega_r + \omega_s$, and $\omega_r - \omega_s$. It is possible to obtain output at the frequency ω_s also if the proper operating configuration is selected. The limit on the amplification available at the frequency $(\omega_r + \omega_s)$ is sufficiently small that it seldom can be used, and the relatively more unstable operation at the lower frequency $(\omega_r - \omega_s)$ is usually used for developing a larger amplification.

The equation for amplification in the parametric amplifier may be derived either in terms of the active circuit including the parametric diode, or it may be derived in terms of the complete circuit, including input and output coupling. For the initial discussion, the simplified equation is the best to use, because the mutual coupling impedances play no significant part in the behavior of the circuit. The basic circuit, the current and voltage graphs, and the incidence matrices for the simplified parametric amplifier circuit are shown in Fig. 12–5. The trees (this derivation is being made topologically) are

y trees

$$yY_{L1}Y_{C2}, \quad yY_{C1}Y_{C2}, \quad yY_{L1}Y_{L2}, \quad yY_{C1}Y_{L2}, \quad yY_{L2}Y_{C2}$$

Other trees

$$Y_{L1}Y_{L2}Y_{C2}$$

From these trees, the transfer admittance and the voltage amplification for the network at fundamental frequency may be determined. After multiplication of both sets of trees by $Z_{L1}Z_{L2}$, the voltage gain is

$$K_v = 1/[(1 + Z_{L1}Y_{C1})(1 + Z_{L2}Y_{C2}) + Z_{L1}Y_{C2}] \tag{17}$$

When this is simplified by the substitutions

$$Z_{L1} = R_1 + j\omega_{L1}, \qquad Z_{L2} = R_2 + j\omega_{L2}$$
$$Y_1 = j\omega C_1, \qquad\qquad Y_2 = j\omega C_2 \tag{18}$$

and the further simplifications made that

$$\omega_s^2 = 1/L_1(C_1 + C_2), \quad \omega_s^2 L_2 C_2 \ll 1, \quad \text{and} \quad \omega_s R_2 C_2 < 1$$

the voltage gain is, at the angular frequency, ω_s

$$v_s = v_i/j\omega_s R_1(C_1 + C_2) = -jQ_s v_i \tag{19}$$

In a similar manner, the transfer gain for the reference frequency may be determined in terms of the trees of the reference-frequency network. The trees are

y_r trees

$$y_rY_{L1}Y_{L2}, \quad y_rY_{L1}Y_{C2}, \quad y_rY_{L2}Y_{C1}, \quad y_rY_{C1}Y_{C2}, \quad y_rY_{L2}Y_{C2}$$

Other trees

$$Y_{L2}Y_{C1}Y_{C2}, \quad Y_{L1}Y_{L2}Y_{C2}$$

Making the same simplification as before, the equation for voltage gain takes the form

$$K_{vr} = (1 + Z_{L1}Y_{C1})/[(1 + Z_{L1}Y_{C1})(1 + Z_{L2}Y_{C2}) + Z_{L1}Y_{C2}] \tag{20}$$

As in the previous case, this is the reference voltage developed across the capacitor C_2, which is varied by the applied voltage. If the two equations for voltage gain are solved for the output voltage across C_2 in terms of the input voltages, v_i and v_r, the sum of the two gives the total voltage generating intermixing across the variable capacitor. To determine the current or the voltage amplification that may be generated in the circuit, therefore, it is necessary to determine the ratio of the signal-frequency voltage generated with the reference-frequency signal applied, to that with the reference signal absent. The signal-frequency current may be determined from Eq. (19)

$$i_{c2s} = C_2 v_i / R_1 (C_1 + C_2) = \omega_s C_{20} Q_s V_i \sin \omega_s t \tag{21}$$

For this equation, the value of C_2 may be taken to be constant, or it may be expressed in terms of the constant part of the total capacitance

$$C_2 = C_{20} + C_{21} x, \qquad -1 \le x \le +1$$
$$x = v_t / V_{c2r} \tag{22}$$

(For a linear variation of capacitance, C_{21} is half the total change in value.)

The total change in C_2 is controlled by the magnitude of reference signal applied to the capacitor. The total instantaneous voltage across it is

$$v_t = (v_{c2r} + v_{c2s} + v_{c2rs})$$
$$v_t = -jQ_s V_i \sin \omega_s t + V_{c2rs} \sin \omega_{rs} t + (1 + Z_{L1} Y_{C1})$$
$$\times V_r \sin \omega_r t / [(1 + Z_{L1} Y_{C1})(1 + Z_{L2} Y_{C2}) + Z_{L1} Y_{C2}] \tag{23}$$

Because C_{21} is the average rate of change, the ratio of v_t / V_{c2r} must be used, where the value of V_{c2r} is given by the equation

$$V_{c2r} = V_r (1 + Z_{L1} Y_{C1}) / [(1 + Z_{L1} Y_{C1})(1 + Z_{L2} Y_{C2}) + Z_{L1} Y_{C2}]$$
$$= V_r / [1 + Y_{C2}(Z_{L2} + Z_{L1} / \langle 1 + Z_{L1} Y_{C1} \rangle)] \tag{24}$$

The mixing action that occurs in the reactance diode can either produce a voltage or a current modulation. Because resonant build-up is required in this circuit to develop the amplification, voltage injection at the idler frequency, $\omega_r - \omega_s$, is necessary for correct operation of the circuit. Consequently, the voltage developed across the reactance diode at idler frequency should be determined. In terms of the signal and reference voltages, it is formed from Eq. (24) and the expression:

$$v_{c2rs} = -C_{21} V_i \sin \omega_s t \sin \omega_r t / j \omega_s R_1 (C_1 + C_2)^2 \tag{25}$$

where the constant component of C_2, C_{20}, has been discarded in the expansion of $[1/(C_1 + C_2)]$ in power-series form. This expression may be converted to eliminate the j term in the denominator by performing the indicated integration of the sine $\omega_s t$ into a negative cosine term; the correct integration coefficient is already in the denominator. The equation then becomes

$$v_{c2rs} = C_{21}V_i \cos \omega_s t \sin \omega_r t / \omega_s R_1 (C_1 + C_2)^2 \tag{26}$$

Recognizing that $\sin \omega_r t \cos \omega_s t = 0.5 [\sin (\omega_r + \omega_s)t + \sin (\omega_r - \omega_s)t]$, the voltage introduced into the circuit at idler frequency becomes

$$v_{c2rs} = -C_{21}V_i \sin (\omega_r - \omega_s)t \, Q_s / 2(C_1 + C_{20}) \tag{27}$$

Now, at the idler frequency, $\omega_{rs} = (\omega_r - \omega_s)$, the circuit $L_2 C_2$ is tuned to resonance to maximize the idler current, which then is

$$i_{c2rs} = V_{c2rs}/R_2 = -C_{21}V_i \sin \omega_{rs} t \, Q_s / 2(C_1 + C_2)R_2 \tag{28}$$

This equation may be converted to the idler voltage across the capacitor by multiplication by $1/j\omega_{rs}C_2$, giving

$$v_{c2rs'} = Q_s Q_{rs} C_{21} V_i \cos \omega_{rs} t / 2(C_1 + C_2) \tag{29}$$

Now, this voltage introduces a signal-frequency component at the nonlinear capacitor. The resulting signal voltage is

$$(C_1 + C_2)V_{c2} = (C_{20} + C_{21}x)v_t$$

$$= C_{20} + C_{21}(\sin \omega_r t + (V_{rs}/V_{c2r}) \cos \omega_{rs} t)^2 V_{c2r}$$

Taking the conversion terms only gives

$$(C_1 + C_{20})V_{c2} = C_{21}(V_{c2r} \sin^2 \omega_r t + V_{rs}^2 \sin \omega_r t \cos \omega_{rs} t$$
$$+ V_{rs}^2 \cos \omega_{rs} t / V_{c2r})$$
$$\doteq C_{21}V_{rs} \sin \omega_s t = V_{c2s'}$$
$$= C_{21}Q_s Q_{rs} V_i / 2(C_1 + C_{20})^2 \tag{30}$$

The resonant voltage across the capacitor is

$$V_{c2rs''} = C_{21}^2 Q_s^2 Q_{rs} v_i / 2(C_1 + C_{20})^2$$

and the gain is

$$V_{c2s''}/V_{c2s} = C_{21}^2 Q_s Q_{rs} / 2(C_1 + C_{20})^2 \tag{31}$$

This is the approximate equation for the amplification of the parametric diode amplifier.

The proper behavior of this circuit requires that $C_1 > C_{20} > C_{21}$, with the result that the reference frequency is of necessity large compared to the signal frequency. Only then will the conditions assumed in the derivation prove valid. Based on these conditions, the amplification is a function of the circuit Q at the signal frequency and at the idler frequency also, and it depends on the numerical ratio of the different capacitances of the circuit.

EXAMPLE 2.   Design a parametric amplifier, assuming it is required to operate at 30 mc, and that its idler frequency has been selected as 300 mc. Design a possible circuit, assuming the static capacitance of the diode is 3 pfd, and its change, C_{21}, is 2 pfd.

The value of C_1 may be chosen as 25 pfd, giving an inductance of 1.2 μh for L_1. Similarly, the value for L_2 is approximately 0.08 μh. Selecting a value of Q_{1s} of 200, and 300 for Q_{2rs} gives a potential current gain of approximately 750. Because the input and output coupling links can be expected to drop the net values of Q_{1s} and Q_{2rs} to approximately 50 and 100 respectively, a maximum net gain of about 60 may be available at 30 mc. The reference frequency is 330 mc. The diode series resistance should be less than R_2, a fraction of an ohm.

Noise Figure.   The principal advantage of the parametric amplifier is its extremely small noise temperature, less than 100° Kelvin over the frequency range from approximately 10 mc to greater than 2000 mc. The parametric diodes currently available can be expected to function as amplifiers to frequencies of nearly 1000 mc, and future diodes may be expected to function effectively to even higher frequencies.

12.6 Complete Equations for Parametric Amplifiers

The general equations for the straight-through parametric amplifier (Fig. 12–6), including inductive input and output coupling, can be established topologically by the technique described by Coates and

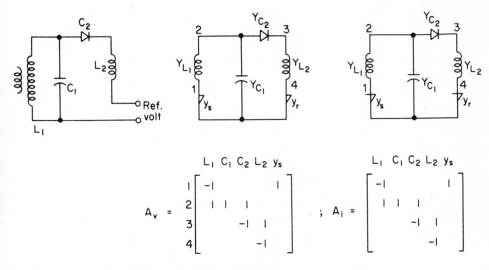

Fig. 12-6. Graphs of simplified parametric amplifier

Mayeda.[1,2] Using the series configuration, the equation for amplification may be established in the fashion described in Appendix III. A total of thirty-five trees are required in the solution, three in the transfer terms, and the balance in the denominator. In terms of admittances, the forward admittance equation reads

$$
\begin{aligned}
Y_f = &-Y_s Y_L y_{11} y_{22} y_{33} y_{12} y_{23} [y_{c2} y_{c4} + y_{c2} y_4 + y_{c4} y_4]/ \\
&[-y_{11} y_{22} y_{33} \langle (y_{23} y_{32} Y_s + y_{12} y_{21} Y_L)(y_{c2} y_{c4} + y_{c2} y_4 + y_{c4} y_4) \\
&- y_{12} y_{21} y_{23} y_{32} (y_{c4} + y_4) \rangle + (y_{11} y_{33} y_{12} y_{21} y_{23} y_{32} \\
&- y_{11} y_{22} y_{23} y_{32} Y_s Y_L + y_{12} y_{21} y_{23} y_{32} Y_s Y_L \\
&+ y_{22} y_{33} y_{12} y_{21} Y_s Y_L)(y_{c2} y_{c4} + y_{c2} y_4 + y_{c4} y_4) \\
&+ (y_{22} y_{12} y_{21} y_{23} y_{32} Y_s Y_L + y_{22} y_{12} y_{21} y_{23} y_{32} y_{33} Y_s \\
&+ y_{11} y_{22} y_{12} y_{21} y_{23} y_{32} Y_L)(y_{c4} + y_4) + (y_{33} y_{12} y_{21} y_{23} y_{32} Y_s \\
&+ y_{11} y_{12} y_{21} y_{23} y_{32} Y_L)(y_{c2} y_{c4} + y_{c2} y_4 + y_{c4} y_4)]
\end{aligned}
\tag{32}
$$

This equation may be multiplied through by $z_{11} z_{22} z_{33} z_{12} z_{21} z_{23} z_{32}$, and then the numerator and denominator are both divided by the product

$$
(y_{c2} y_{c4} + y_{c2} y_4 + y_{c4} y_4)(1 + z_{11} Y_s)(1 + z_{33} Y_L)
$$

to give the equation

$$
\begin{aligned}
Y_f = &-[z_{21}/(1 + z_{11} Y_s)][z_{32}/(1 + z_{33} Y_L)] Y_s Y_L/ \\
&[z_{22} + \langle (y_{c4} + y_4)/(y_{c2} y_{c4} + y_{c2} y_4 + y_{c4} y_4) \rangle - [\langle (z_{11}^2 z_{23}^2 \\
&+ z_{12}^2 z_{33}) Y_s Y_L/(1 + z_{11} Y_s)(1 + z_{33} Y_L) \rangle + z_{12}^2 Y_s + z_{23}^2 Y_L]]
\end{aligned}
\tag{33}
$$

In this equation, it is important to keep the negative term in the right-hand portion of the denominator relatively small so that the first two terms will control the amplification characteristics of the circuit. The second term actually introduces the required negative resistance and increases the amplification of the circuit. The way this action occurs is now considered.

The conversion of the second term requires transformation and substitution as follows

$$
\begin{aligned}
y_{c2} &= j\omega C_2, & y_{c4} &= j\omega(C_{40} + C_{41} x) \\
z_4 &= 1/y_4 = R_4 + j\omega L_4 + r_d, & z_{22} &= R_2 + j\omega L_2
\end{aligned}
\tag{34}
$$

where $x \doteq \sin \omega_r t$ and r_d is the damping introduced from the reference oscillator. Strictly, there is a component of frequency ω_s, the signal frequency, and $\omega_{rs} = (\omega_r - \omega_s)$, the idler frequency, also in x, but these terms

[1] C. L. Coates, "General Topological Formulas for Linear Network Functions," *IRE Transactions*, Vol. CT-5, No. 1.

[2] W. Mayeda, "Topological Formulas for Active Networks," *Interim Technical Report No. 8*, Contract DA-11-022-ORD-1983, University of Illinois, Urbana, 1958.

may be neglected because their magnitudes are small in comparison with the pump frequency, ω_r. Substituting gives

$$z_{22} + (y_{c4} + y_4)/(y_{c2}y_{c4} + y_{c2}y_4 + y_{c4}y_4)$$

$$= R_2 + j\omega L_2 + [\langle 1 + j\omega(C_{40} + C_{41}x)(R_4 + r_d + j\omega L_4)\rangle/$$
$$\langle j\omega C_2(1 + j\omega(C_{40} + C_{41}x)(R_4 + r_d + j\omega L_4)) + j\omega C_4\rangle]$$

$$= (R_2 + j\omega L_2) + \langle 1 + j\omega(C_{40} + C_{41}x)(R_4 + r_d + j\omega L_4)\rangle/$$
$$\langle j\omega(C_2 + C_{40} + C_{41}x)[1 + j\omega(C_2(C_{40} + C_{41}x)/\langle C_2 + C_{40} + C_{41}x\rangle)$$
$$(R_4 + r_d + j\omega L_4)]\rangle \tag{35}$$

Next it is necessary to expand the fraction in terms of the components that involve only C_{40} and those involving $C_{41}x$. When this is done, the equation takes the form

$$R_2 + j\omega L_2 + (1 + j\omega C_{40}(R_4 + r_d + j\omega L_4))/[j\omega(C_2 + C_{40}(1 + j\omega C_2$$
$$\times (R_4 + r_d + j\omega L_4)))] - j\omega C_{41}x/[j\omega\langle C_2 + C_{40}(1 + j\omega C_2$$
$$(R_4 + r_d + j\omega L_4))\rangle]^2 = z_{22} + (y_{c4} + y_4)/(y_{c2}y_{c4} + y_{c2}y_4 + y_{c4}y_4) \tag{36}$$

In this equation, the second and third terms cancel at signal frequency, ω_s, leaving the resonant resistance of L_2, and the value of the last, or conversion term to be determined. Neglecting the remaining terms, and taking

$$Y_f = I_s \sin \omega_s t/v_s = f(y)$$

gives

$$v_s = I_s \sin \omega_s t[R_2 - C_{41}x/j\omega[(C_2 + C_{40})(1 + \langle j\omega C_2 C_{40}$$
$$\times (R_4 + r_d + j\omega L_4)/(C_2 + C_{40})\rangle)]^2] \tag{37}$$

where the coupling terms have been neglected. These terms determine the negative immittance of the circuit. Multiplying through by $\sin \omega_s t$ and substituting for x gives

$$V_{c2s} = I_s(R_2 \sin \omega_s t - (\sin \omega_s t \sin \omega_r t/D)) \tag{38}$$

where D is given by the equation

$$D = [j\omega\langle(C_2 + C_{40})(1 + j\omega C_2 C_{40}(R_4 + r_d + j\omega L_4)/(C_2 + C_{40}))\rangle^2] \tag{39}$$

The expression (38) may be converted to a new form, remembering that $1/j\omega$ is indicative of an integration

$$v_{c2} = I_s(R_2 \sin \omega_s t + C_{41} \cos \omega_s t \sin \omega_r t/[2\omega_s(C_2 + C_{40})^2$$
$$\langle 1 + j\omega C_2 C_{40}(R_4 + r_d + j\omega L_4)/(C_2 + C_{40})\rangle^2]) \tag{40}$$

Because

$$\sin \omega_r t \cos \omega_s t = 0.5(\sin (\omega_r - \omega_s)t + \sin (\omega_r + \omega_s)t)$$

Eq. (40) may be rewritten as

$$v_{rs} = v_s C_{41} \sin \omega_{rs} t / [2\omega_s (C_2 + C_{40})^2 \langle 1 + j\omega C_2 C_{40}(R_4 + r_d + j\omega L_4)/$$
$$(C_2 + C_{40})\rangle^2] R_2 \tag{41}$$

where the terms involving fundamental signal frequency have been neglected, and only the signal frequency has been inserted in the denominator omega terms. The value of omega, which belongs in the inner bracket of the denominator is the idler angular frequency, ω_{rs}. The idler resonance condition may be introduced into the inner bracket, and it reduces to the form

$$j\omega_{rs} C_2 C_{40} \langle R_4 + r_d \rangle / (C_2 + C_{40})$$

giving the value of the idler voltage introduced into the idler circuit

$$v_{rs} = -v_s C_{41} \cos \omega_{rs} t / 2\omega_s \omega_{rs} R_2 (C_2 + C_{40}) C_2 C_{40} R_4 \tag{42}$$

The Q values for the signal and the idler circuits may be introduced into this equation, since they are

$$Q_s = 1/\omega_s R_2 (C_2 + C_{40})$$
$$Q_{rs} = (C_2 + C_{40})/\omega_{rs} C_2 C_{40}(R_4 + r_d) \tag{43}$$

Making the substitution gives

$$v_{rs} = -v_s C_{41} Q_s Q_{rs} \cos \omega_{rs} t / 2(C_2 + C_{40}) \tag{44}$$

Now, the total signal voltage across the variable capacitor is

$$v_t = V_s Q_s \cos \omega_s t + V_{rs} \cos \omega_{rs} t + V_{c4r} \sin \omega_r t$$
$$= -V_s Q_s [\cos \omega_s t + C_{41} Q_{rs} \cos \omega_{rs} t / 2(C_2 + C_{40})] + V_{c4r} \sin \omega_r t \tag{45}$$

This voltage may be applied to the nonlinear capacitor to give the resulting mixing components. Because a charge circulation at the sum and difference frequencies results from the capacitance variations, their excitation magnitudes may be determined in terms of the equation

$$(C_2 + C_{40})v_{c4} = (C_{40} + C_{41}x)v_t \tag{46}$$

Taking the nonlinear component gives the equation

$$(C_2 + C_{40})v_{c4} = C_{41}xv_t$$

Solving for v_{c4} and substituting for v_t gives

$$v_{c4} = C_{41}(\sin \omega_r t + \langle V_{rs} \cos \omega_{rs} t / V_{c4r} \rangle)^2 V_{c4r}/(C_2 + C_{40})$$
$$= C_{41} V_{c4r}(\sin^2 \omega_r t + 2V_{rs} \sin \omega_r t \cos \omega_{rs} t / V_{c4r})/(C_2 + C_{40}) \tag{47}$$

The resulting signal-frequency excitation voltage is

$$v_{c4s'} = C_{41}V_{rs} \sin \omega_s t / (C_2 + C_{40})$$
$$= C_{41}^2 Q_s Q_{rs} v_i / 2(C_2 + C_{40})^2 \qquad (48)$$

The resonant current resulting from this excitation voltage is

$$i_{s'} = v_{c4s'}/R_2 = C_{41}^2 Q_s Q_{rs}/2(C_2 + C_{40})^2 R_2 \qquad (49)$$

and the resonant voltage is

$$v_{c4s''} = C_{41}^2 Q_s^2 Q_{rs}/2(C_2 + C_{40})^2 \qquad (50)$$

Finally, the approximate voltage gain is

$$v_{c4s''}/v_{c4s} = C_{41}^2 Q_s Q_{rs}/2(C_2 + C_{40})^2 \qquad (51)$$

12.7 Tunnel Diode Mixers

Tunnel diodes can be used as mixers at extremely high frequencies, and, at least potentially, can be more efficient than conventional diodes in the application. They normally function as square-law devices, but they have an extremely high rate of curvature, and consequently require a relatively small magnitude of reference voltage. Normally they are biased in the positive-conductance region near zero bias, and are biased just sufficiently positive to make certain that the range of swing for the reference voltage will be from zero voltage to the voltage corresponding to the maximum negative conductance for the device (Fig. 12–7, point A).

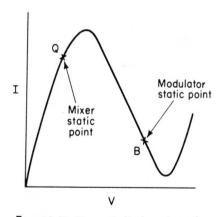

Relatively high conversion efficiency is available for these devices for two reasons, first because the conductance slope is higher than with conventional diodes, and second because of the increased change that results for a given peak value of conductance from the availability of both negative and positive values of conductance within a narrow voltage range.

Fig. 12-7. Tunnel diode mixer & modulator

Tunnel diodes can be used as modulators, and in functioning as modulators, can amplify an applied signal. In this application, the signal to be amplified is used to shift the static operating point of the diode, which is biased in the region B in Fig. 12–7. This shift changes the average negative conductance of the diode, which is also coupled to a tuned circuit tuned to a higher frequency than signal requiring amplification. The result of the shift is a variation of the oscillation amplitude of the diode oscillator of considerably greater magnitude than that of the applied signal. Rectification of the resulting carrier produces an amplified replica of the input signal.

The tunnel diode when used in the modulator mode will provide some of its own rectification, and may contribute some instability to the circuit. In addition, the amplification produced is not necessarily linear because of the variation of the device properties with bias. In spite of these features, however, it appears that the modulator mode is possibly one of the better ways to use the tunnel diode as an amplifier.

12.8 Product Detectors

Product detectors are of growing importance partly because they are essential components of phase detectors, and partly because they provide a superior method of separating signal from noise. Product detectors are actually special mixers because they detect by comparing the received signal with a sinusoidal signal of specified frequency. The frequency is equal to that of the carrier for amplitude modulation, or displaced somewhat from that of the carrier for CW or code signals.

Phase detectors are made from a pair of modulators or product detectors so connected that one signal is applied to both channels, whereas the other

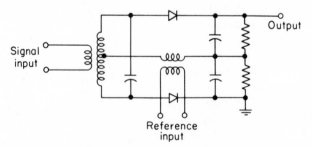

Fig. 12-8. Phase detector

is applied in push-pull (Fig. 12–8). The output of the two sections is so arranged that the net output voltage is a function of the phasor difference voltages developed in the two sections. With a phase angle of 90 degrees between the two input signals, the output is zero with a properly balanced circuit, and it increases nearly linearly with phase angle for difference angles between 90 degrees and 45 or 135 degrees, and then less rapidly with further changes.

These detectors are particularly useful in that they can recognize the signal independent of its accompanying noise, and can control the operation of additional circuits with nearly complete independence of the noise. For example, a phase detector may be used to maintain a locally generated signal in almost exact quadrature with respect to the received signal, and an additional phase detector, having its reference signal maintained at an angle 90 degrees out-of-phase with respect to the reference used in the main detector may be used to generate an AVC voltage that is almost completely immune to noise effects.

Diodes are normally selected for phase detectors, because balance in the active elements is of prime importance in these circuits. Transistors may be used for ordinary product detectors, however, because they give both excellent conversion and amplification when properly used. The design of product detectors using transistors follows the same pattern as is used for mixers. The problems encountered in the design of transistorized product detectors are greatly simplified compared to those encountered in the design of mixers because of the fact that often input capacitances and base-spreading resistance may be neglected in the design of low-frequency product detectors.

CHAPTER THIRTEEN

Transistor Multivibrators

13.0 Introduction

Multivibrators are oscillators having cycles in which instants of active instability are followed by periods of quiescence. The unstable condition is of the runaway nature, or is completely unstable in the mechanical sense. During the quiescent period, one or more active devices in the configuration are placed in an inactive condition through the shifting of the current and voltage on a control element, producing a condition of essentially zero amplification. An extremely large value of loop amplification may develop during the unstable period, causing nearly instantaneous switching of the circuit from one of the quiescent conditions to the other, or causing switching to a quasi-stable condition and then back to the quiescent condition.

The transistorized multivibrator is somewhat more complicated in behavior, and somewhat more complicated to design, than its vacuum-tube counterpart, primarily because of the effect of the series base-spreading resistance in the base lead of the device. The procedures already developed for design of tube multivibrators fortunately are applicable with minor modifications, however.[1] A familiarity with the basic principles of design discussed in these references is assumed in the discussion to follow.

The high input conductance of the base circuit of transistors under conduction conditions introduces curvature into the load lines, and also reduces the available gain from the transistors to a point where achievement of satisfactory oscillation conditions can be relatively difficult. For this reason, the use of emitter-followers as coupling devices is extremely common with transistor multivibrators, and related switching circuits.

The amount of saturation current drawn by the base of the conducting transistor may be as much as ten to fifty percent of the collector current, because the transistor is usually switched into a fully saturated condition. Unless the base circuit can pass the required current and the coupling capacitor can provide it momentarily, the switching of a transistor multivibrator can prove to be irregular and unreliable. The circuit of Fig. 13–1, in which the base bias is obtained directly from the collector supply, may not switch satisfactorily, particularly if the supply voltage is large and the

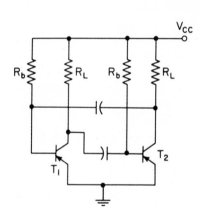

Fig. 13-1. Transistor multivibrator

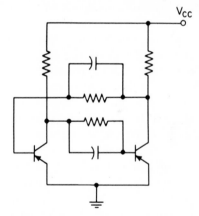

Fig. 13-2. Modified transistor multivibrator

load resistors and the base-bias resistors are large in value. The difficulty can usually be avoided by dropping the value of the base-bias resistors and returning them to the collectors of the alternate transistors, as in the circuit in Fig. 13–2. When this is done, the series resistance required between collector and base is sufficiently small that positive switching can be achieved.

[1] *Conductance Design of Active Circuits,* by K. A. Pullen, Jr. John F. Rider Publishers, Inc., New York, 1959.

K. A. Pullen, Jr., "Conductance Design of Relaxation Circuits," *IRE Transactions,* Convention Record, 1953.

The procedure for design of a multivibrator is first to make designs that assure stable operation of the transistors in the two quiescent states, and then to make the design capable of active transition. It is at least possible in theory to make two static designs and then find that the transition cannot occur either spontaneously or under excitation. This being the case, a rather careful check of the active conditions during the switching cycle is required. Regenerative switching cannot commence unless the loop amplification of the circuit exceeds unity by a considerable margin for a period sufficient to give an average amplification of unity over the complete period.

Nominally, regenerative switching in the circuit under discussion starts at unity loop amplification, but it is necessary to maintain such a value of amplification or more throughout the balance of the switching cycle if the regeneration is to continue. The loading of the conducting transistor on the partially-conducting one can be sufficiently heavy to limit the loop amplification to a value that is either about unity or even less than unity, with the result that the amplification available in the transistors must build up more rapidly than with tube circuits if reliable switching is to result.

The achievement of a satisfactory cutoff operating condition is comparatively simple unless reverse-breakdown can develop at low voltage in the base circuit of the transistor. (This can happen with diffused-base transistors.) The cross-coupling capacitor, which helps to provide the cutoff bias, has but little load on it as a result of the input conductance of the non-conducting transistor, so that cutoff decay is quite slow in occurring, and the change of base voltage required for cutoff, less than approximately 0.150 volt with respect to the emitter for small-signal transistors, is easily obtained.

The first step in design of the circuit to satisfy saturation conditions is to determine the minimum base current that can produce relatively heavy collector saturation. The average base current value may initially be selected to be half to three-fourths of this current. This initial value may require some readjustment when the effect of loading in the driven amplifier is considered. Fortunately, the amplifier driven by the saturated stage is biased to non-conducting conditions, and its input conductance is the leakage conductance of the base-to-emitter diode. For small-signal transistors, this conductance is usually less than 0.001 mho (over 1000 ohms). The load contours may take a form similar to that sketched in Fig. 13–3. Both a typical resistive load line and a possible form for the actual contour, somewhat exaggerated, are shown in this figure. The final average base current should be selected to be half of the average current flow along the high-impedance section of the load line between saturation and the turning point, and the base-bias circuit should be designed to provide the required base current.

The load line for collector currents less than the turning-point value of necessity must be nearly parallel to the contour of constant voltage, because the total load reflected from the saturated transistor to the output circuit of its companion is little greater than the value of the base-spreading resistances for the devices. As a first approximation, it may be assumed that the saturation-load condition develops primarily below the nominal value of current at the Q-point, and the slope of the contour shifts quickly

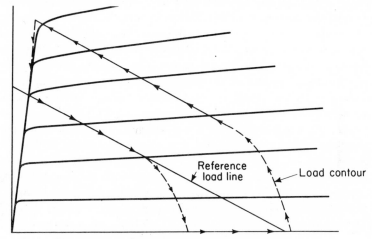

Fig. 13-3. Load contour path for multivibrator

to be parallel with the reference load line for higher currents. For this reason, the contour may be initially approximated by two lines, one of slope $r_{b'}$ through the point V_{CC}, O, and the second parallel to the reference load line through the selected collector saturation current and voltage. This approximate combination contour may be transferred to the input family, and the approximate small-signal data tabulated to permit the correction of the contour position.

The position of the critical turning points for the load contour are defined in terms of the product of the input conductance and load resistance. For this reason, it is important to note on both the input and the output contours the points at which the product $g_i R_L$ takes value such as 0.1, 0.2, 0.5, 1.0, 2.0, 5.0, 10, etc. These values determine the correction of the slope of the contour in terms of the equation

$$R_{LD} = R_L/(1 + g_i R_L) \qquad (1)$$

In this equation, the g_i is the input conductance for the transistor whose input is in parallel with R_L, namely the coupled transistor.

Corresponding points in the operation of the pair of transistors may be located on the contour curves because the input curves may be identified with one transistor, and the output curves with the other. It is necessary to use the saturation conditions as the starting point because this condition behaves as the equalizing condition. The saturation conditions on the input curves correspond to a non-conducting condition on the coupled transistor, and may be identified with the zero-current section of the output curves. Similarly, the low-current region on the input curves corresponds to the saturation conditions on the output curves.

If a detailed analysis, including capacitive effects, is made of the operating cycle of the transistor multivibrator, it turns out that their behavior is more complex than appears to be the case from the above discussion. The base current on the saturated transistor starts to decay along a modified exponential as soon as the associated transistor has been switched to the off-condition. The rise of the input resistance of the conducting transistor along with the sharp rise in collector voltage on the companion transistor, initially minimizes the decrease of base voltage, and maintains the conducting transistor in the "on" condition. After a short period, however, the collector voltage rise terminates, permitting a shift of the operating point of the conducting transistor toward non-conduction. When the weakly-conducting transistor draws sufficient current to make the loop-gain of the circuit unity, switching starts, and the slope of the load line begins to change as described above.

The curved load contours for switching in the two directions may not be identical because the entire action is modified by the action of the circuit capacitances and the internal variable capacitances of the devices as well. In addition, the switching to conduction on the input of the transistor is relatively more gradual with transistors than with tubes, particularly when compared to the width of the active amplification range for the device under comparatively low-current conditions. With transistors, the base voltage change required to shift operation from cutoff to the static operating point may be as small as 40 to 100 millivolts, and the range to carry the device into full saturation may be an additional 30 to 60 millivolts, whereas with a tube, the bias change over the active control area, with negligible grid current, may be several volts, and the additional saturation voltage may be a volt. The narrower range of active region with transistors is a consequence of the twenty-times higher transfer efficiency available.

Because of the continuous drain of base current in the conducting transistor, the equations for the calculation of the switching period for a transistor multivibrator differ appreciably from the equations developed for tube-type circuits. Examination of a typical set of input characteristics for a transistor shows, however, that as the operating point leaves the saturation region, the base-to-emitter voltage changes very slowly at first and the input load contour is often nearly horizontal during the corresponding period. The significant break in the slope of the load line occurs simultaneously on the two sets of curves.

Because the total change in the base voltage over the active part of the cycle of one of the transistors is only 100 to 200 millivolts, and the total voltage change in the collector circuit may be as much as ten volts, a considerable change of the collector voltage from the saturation value may occur before the transistor coupled to it can experience sufficient bias change to start it into the conduction region and bring about active switching. The typical waveforms to be expected in the conventional circuit are shown in Fig. 13–4.

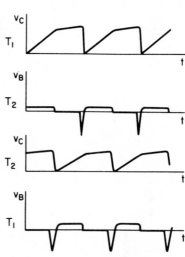

Fig. 13-4. Multivibrator waveforms (typical)

EXAMPLE 1. Design a multivibrator using the type 5001 (Hughes) transistor, and assume a supply voltage of seven volts. Use a static load resistance of 1400 ohms, draw the corresponding load line, and try different static points as the basis for the design.

Fig. 13–5 shows the reference load line for this example. Base current values of 20, and 40 μa may be selected for the static design values, and the operating characteristics expected from each may be determined. The approximate base-spreading resistance for this transistor is 270 ohms. Paralleling the value of $r_{b'}$ with the value of R_L, 270 ohms with 1400 ohms, gives 225 ohms. The effective load resistance therefore varies between 225 and 1400 ohms. The load line corresponding to 225 ohms is also plotted through V_{CC}, O on the figure.

The next step in design is the determination of the correct base-current value. The switching cycle may initially be assumed to be symmetrical, so that the base current for each transistor of the multivibrator is turned on for half the time. Evidently, the average base current during the conduction period for either transistor must be twice the over-all average value, giving the active base currents for the two conditions as 40 and 80 μa.

The voltage on the base of the transistor during conduction ($i_{b\ max} = 40\ \mu$a) is 172 mv, and for zero base current, 110 or less millivolts. This means that the change required for a base-current change of 40 μa is 62 millivolts. Further examination shows that 90 millivolts change is required with a current change of 80 microamperes.

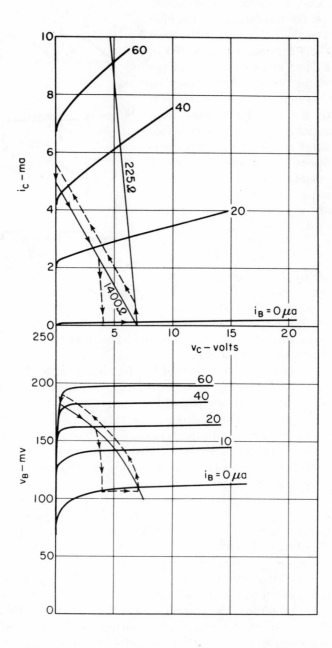

Fig. 13-5. Design of multivibrator for Example 1

Because of the short conduction time of a multivibrator compared to its period, active switching occurs at very small values of current in the initially-extinguished transistor. This also is the region of small forward conductance. With a large value of base-bias resistance, therefore, the capacitor that couples the collector of the non-conducting transistor to the base of the conducting transistor will quickly develop full supply voltage across itself because of the high base conductance in the conducting transistor. Consequently, the base voltage will drop rapidly and turn this transistor off unless the base biasing resistance is sufficiently small that an appreciable part of the required base current may flow through it. The time constant of this circuit depends on both the circuit capacitance and its resistances, and also on the base resistance of the transistor

$$C_c(R_L + R_b/\langle 1 + G_iR_b\rangle) = T \tag{2}$$

where R_L is the static load resistance, R_b is the base biasing resistance, and G_i is the effective input conductance for the transistor as given in Chapter Four. In this equation, the value for R_L is in the neighborhood of or less than 1000 ohms, and the typical value of G_i in the active region is as large as 0.002 mho or possibly larger. The result is to place a minimum value on the coupling capacitors below which the circuit does not function.

Suran has shown that the maximum operating frequency of a multivibrator is approximately equal to the noise-corner frequency.[2]

$$f_{n2} = f_m = f_\alpha/\sqrt{\beta + 1} \tag{3}$$

Using this frequency with the above equation and an approximate value of $1/G_i$ of 1000 ohms, the minimum value of the coupling capacitance, C_C, that can be used with the circuit is 150 pfd. In practice, the value used should be at least ten times this value unless special circuits are used.

Equation (2) shows that the rate of decay of the charge in the coupling capacitance is a function of the load resistance in series with the collector to which the capacitor is coupled. Normally, the value of R_b is sufficiently large that it has little effect on the value of the expression $R_b(1 + G_iR_b)$, and consequently its value should be selected based on the switching characteristics rather than on frequency-response characteristics.

Selection of the static operating point for the base circuit at a high value of base current rather than low is better for the following reasons:

1. Reduced sensitivity to device characteristics at high base current, particularly with saturation.

2. Ineffective clamping at high conduction unless the average current is high.

---

[2] J. J. Suran, and F. A. Reibert. "Two-Terminal Analysis and Synthesis of Junction Transistor Multivibrators," *IRE*, March, 1956.

3. Reduced total device dissipations with saturation.

4. Possibly somewhat faster switching.

The variation of current gain from device to device is less significant with multivibrators when the transistor is biased near the saturation region than when it is not, although even then the behavior is by no means independent of current gain. This reduced sensitivity is a result of the increased clamping under full conduction, since at saturation the base current increases sharply and thereby defines an endpoint more sharply. A sharp discontinuity in characteristics is required to produce accurate clamping. The reduced dissipation is a result of the lower voltage applied from collector to emitter in the saturation (negligible dissipation occurs when the device is cut off) and it is also a result of more rapid switching from the one state to the other. The more rapid switching is a result of increased loop amplification.

The fact that the transistor saturates sharply and then drifts out of the saturation condition means that the peak current flow will be appreciably greater than that which would be noted from finding where the base-current contour for twice the static base current approaches the saturation line. Averaging of the base current along the drift contour may be accomplished by the use of any of the averaging formulas, the Legendre or orthogonal method, the Fourier method, or any other convenient method. Although between switching episodes, there will be some curvature to the contour of current plotted as a function of time, it is comparatively small.

13.1 Loop Amplification

So far, no consideration has been given to the fact that the average loop gain of the multivibrator must equal unity over the operating cycle, as is necessary with any oscillator. During the switching period, the amplification of the circuit may reach values as high as several hundred or possibly even several thousand. The fact that the minimum amplification cannot be less than zero indicates that the conduction time during which the loop amplification is very high must of necessity be only a small fraction of the repetition period of the oscillator. This condition can be altered by capacitances in the transistors and in the circuit, because on an instant-by-instant basis the capacitances do decrease the effective amplification and at the same time alter the duration of the switching period. If the amplification is computed on an instant-by-instant basis, including the effects of both circuit and device capacitances, the switching time will be found to depend on the integrated amplification, and the times of completion of the switching function will also be found to be correct.

Much more rapid decay of charge occurs in the coupling capacitor connected to the base of the conducting transistor than in the one connected to its collector. This means that the collector voltage nearly reaches the supply voltage, after which the second transistor begins to switch on and the final rapid decrease occurs. This is quite different than is the situation with tube multivibrators, because the discharge of the coupling capacitor connected to the grid of the conducting tube leaves it in a state of full conduction, and negligible change of plate voltage occurs until conduction commences in the non-conducting tube.

13.2 Other Usable Configurations

The symmetrical multivibrator configuration just discussed is the basic configuration, and in one of its many modifications is possibly the most commonly used. Its waveform deficiency often makes the use of a different configuration desirable, namely, one which gives a more accurately formed square wave. One such configuration is the emitter-coupled multivibrator. This circuit in its tube arrangement is also the simplest one, giving a reasonably accurate square-wave output. Typical circuits for the tube and the transistor versions of this circuit are shown in Fig. 13–6.

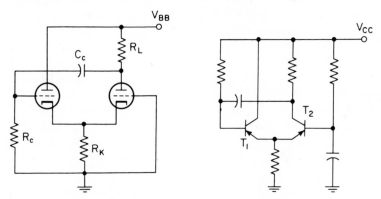

Fig. 13-6. Emitter-coupled multivibrator

The operating cycle of this circuit is somewhat different than that for the conventional symmetrical circuit, because in one state, the output transistor is operating at its static point, and in the other, its current is cut off. The input transistor either draws a decaying collector current, or is cut off, as shown in Fig. 13–7.

The duration times for each half of the cycle of this multivibrator are not necessarily equal. If the design is arranged so that the bias resistances of the circuits can be adjusted, however, the dwell-times can be made approximately equal for either polarity of the wave. Because the output transistor either is operating under static conditions, with a constant base current, or it is turned off, the waveform is very nearly square in shape.

The bias point for the output transistor should be placed reasonably near the saturation region, but need not be at full saturation. The bias point for the input transistor must be sufficiently high to yield a loop gain for the circuit having a peak value large compared to unity. If these conditions are fulfilled, and the coupling capacitor is sufficiently large to permit the oscillations to develop, then normal multivibrator action can be achieved.

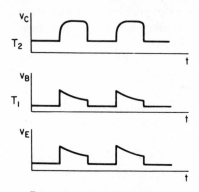

Fig. 13-7. Typical emitter-coupled waveforms

The emitter-follower action on the input transistor helps to reduce the input-conductance loading on the coupling circuit, making it possible to have an appreciable value of R_{b1} without having it swamped out by the input conductance. Consequently, the frequency can be controlled by the base-bias resistance to a much greater extent than is possible with the ordinary transistor multivibrator. Also the charge and decay of the capacitor is considerably less dependent on the input conductance of the transistor. The input resistance for the emitter-follower may appear to be as large as 50,000 or 100,000 ohms or more, making possible the use of a 10,000- to 20,000-ohm bias resistance. During the part of the cycle that the emitter-follower is conducting fully, the amplifier coupled to it is turned completely off, and the full multiplication of input impedance is available at the base of the follower. Consequently, the behavior of this circuit is almost identical with that of the corresponding tube multivibrator.

EXAMPLE 2. Design an emitter-coupled multivibrator using a 2N592 transistor. Determine a possible set of operating conditions, and select a set of component values that will assure multivibrator action. In addition, estimate the multivibrator period when the coupling capacitor has a capacitance of 0.02 mfd.

If 15 volts is taken as the supply voltage, 3000 ohms the load for the output stage, and a protective resistance of 2000 ohms is used in the collector circuit of the input transistor, the load contours shown in Fig. 13-8 result. The input transistor requires a load resistor to limit its dissipation, but this load resistor must be smaller than that for the output transistor because the current flow in the input transistor must be greater than that in the output to obtain proper switching action.

If the active base current for the output transistor is taken as 125 μa, the corresponding emitter-current flow is approximately 4.4 ma. If, now, an initial static emitter voltage is taken to be 0.5 volt with respect to the emitter-return, the required emitter-return resistance is 110 ohms. The base of transistor T_2 must be bypassed to ground (emitter-return) if effective switching is to result. The base voltage required is 175 mv greater than the emitter voltage, or 675 millivolts. To reduce the current in T_2 to zero, the base-to-emitter voltage must be reduced to less than 45 mv, or

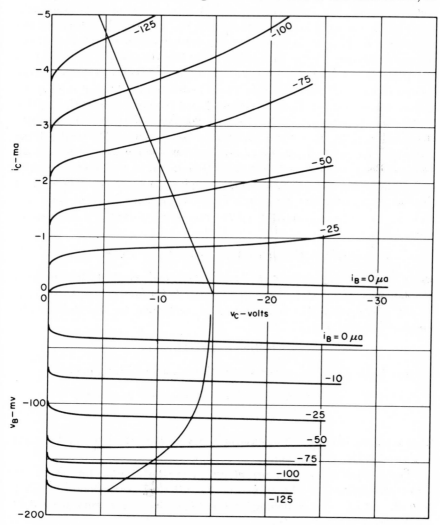

Fig. 13-8. Input load line for Example 2

the minimum emitter current during the conduction period for the input transistor, T_1, must be at least 25 percent greater than the static conduction current in the emitter of T_2. The time required for the emitter current to decay from its maximum value to the value that initiates conduction in T_2 is approximately half the over-all switching period of the circuit.

The calculation of the two quiescent periods for the two states of the multivibrator is relatively conventional. During the period for which T_1 is non-conducting, the discharge of C_C through R_L and R_{b1} controls the inactive period. The total voltage change at the base of T_1 is essentially equal to the voltage change across R_L in series with T_2. As a result of the conduction in T_1 prior to switching, the voltage across C_C is equal to the voltage difference, $V_{CC} - V_{bc}$, where V_{bc} is the voltage on the base of T_1 just prior to the initiation of switching. This voltage must be just large enough to block off conduction in T_2. It is determined by first setting the emitter voltage so that T_2 is extinguished, and then finding first the emitter current for T_1 required to develop the voltage and second the base-to-emitter voltage for T_1 to make the current flow possible. The total voltage V_{bc} is the sum of the resulting base-to-emitter voltage and emitter-return voltage. Because the base-bias resistor is returned to the collector supply rather than emitter, the total voltage applied to C_C is the difference of that across R_L and that across R_b. This voltage must decay to the value required to initiate conduction in T_1. The decay period is a function of the equation

$$t = (R_L + R_{b1})C_C \ln [(V_{cc} - V_d)/(V_{cc} - V_L + V_{bc})] \qquad (4)$$

where V_d is the voltage from the base of T_1 to emitter return for initiation of conduction of T_1, V_L is the voltage across T_2 for full conduction through it, and V_{bc} again is the base voltage at extinction for T_1. Because the nominal value of R_{b1} is

$$15/0.000125 = 120,000 \text{ ohms}$$

if input loading can be neglected, the time constant is approximately

$$t = 120,000 \times 10^{-8} \ln [(15 - 0.6)/(15 + 11 - 0.6)]$$
$$= 2.4 \times 10^{-3} \ln (1.7)$$

This is approximately 1.2 milliseconds. (Note that the 0.6 volt has been neglected in this calculation.)

The passive conduction period for T_1 is shorter than for T_2, as the input conductance of the transistor T_1 introduces considerable loading into the circuit. The switching time is approximately twenty percent of the value mentioned above.

The extremely small amount of voltage change required from base to emitter on a transistor, coupled with the over-all circuit characteristics of the emitter-follower, may make desirable the use of some additional series resistance in either the base or the emitter circuits of the transistors. An increase in the value of the emitter resistance, R_e, from 110 to 500 ohms is an effective way of increasing the range of voltage change, because the amplification of the circuit is still available, and the range of voltage that can be tolerated by the emitter-follower is greatly increased. With a 100-ohm emitter resistor and 1900 ohms protective load for T_1, the total change that can be developed in the emitter of the follower is 0.75 volt,

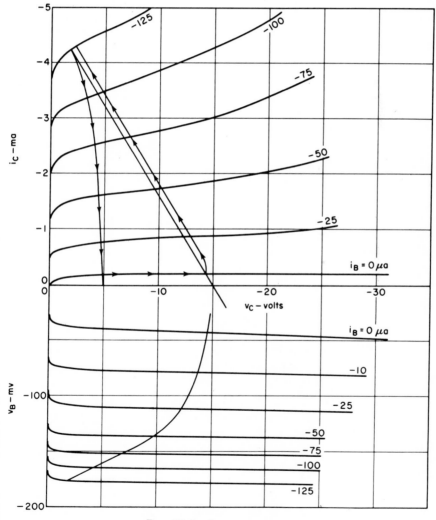

Fig. 13-9. Output contour

whereas with 500 ohms and protective load of 1500 ohms, the maximum change is 3.75 volts.

The load contour for the output transistor during its deactivation cycle follows the general pattern shown in Fig. 13–9. The collector voltage rises until the emitter-follower saturates, at which time the collector voltage remains approximately fixed, and the collector current, except for capacitor charging-current, drops to zero. The initiation of reversal cannot occur until the voltage across the capacitor approximately equals that between the collector supply terminal and the saturation voltage required on the base of T_1. Voltage decay at the base terminal then permits the emitter of the follower to drift downward in accordance with the discharge rate until the trigger level is again reached, this time in reverse direction. The total approximate discharge time constant is determined in terms of the rates, where $s_1 = 1/T_1$ and $s_2 = 1/T_2$

$$s_1 C_C (R_L + R_{b1}/\langle 1 + G_i R_{b1} \rangle) \doteq s_1 C_C (R_L + 1/G_i)$$

for $G_i R_{b1} > 1$ $\hspace{6cm}$ (5)

$$s_2 C_C (R_L + R_{b1}/\langle 1 + G_i R_{b1} \rangle) \doteq s_2 C_C (R_L + R_{b1})$$

where G_i is the input conductance of the emitter-follower. The first time constant is small compared to the second, because G_i limits the resistance component when it is large. The dwell times depend on the ratio of the nominal voltage change, Δv_0, to the actual switching change, Δv_1 or Δv_2, as required. If either of the Eqs. (5) are written as $s_1 R_1 C_1$ or $s_2 R_2 C_2$, then the times may be determined in terms of the equation

$$T_i = R_i C_i \ln (\Delta v_0/\Delta v_1) \qquad i = 1, 2 \hspace{3cm} (6)$$

Since, however, the value of R_i may vary with the bias value, strictly a step-by-step determination of T is required. As a first approximation, the formula used with tube multivibrators may be used.

Because the total current through the output transistor is 4.4 ma, and the emitter resistance is 500 ohms, the total base voltage on the transistor is $2.20 + 0.17 = 2.37$ volts. The bias resistance for the output transistor then is $12.6/0.000125 = 100,000$ ohms. For the input transistor, the static operating conditions may be set so that both transistors will draw approximately the same current if the coupling capacitor is removed; then the actual quiescent position may be altered somewhat to improve the equality of the two halves of the cycle. Taking both base currents equal to 110 μa, the emitter current for T_1 is about 4.2 ma, that for T_2, 3.9 ma, for a total of 8.1 ma, or a total emitter voltage of 4.05 volts. This is satisfactory because 110 μa through the 100,000-ohm resistors leaves the required 4.0 volts available for the bases of T_1 and T_2. The correct current is approximately

108.5 μa, and the emitter and base voltages are 4.0 and 4.17 volts respectively.

The bypass capacitor on the base of T_2 must be sufficiently large so that the base voltage does not change appreciably compared to the base bias range, which is about 100 millivolts. A ten-millivolt change during the quiescent period is the maximum that can be tolerated. If a repetition rate of 500 cycles per second is required, for example, the size of bypass capacitance may be determined in terms of the equation

$$CV = iT \tag{7}$$

where the half-cycle time, T, is 0.001 second, and i is half the average change in static current between the two quiescent periods. Solving for C gives

$$C = 100iT$$

where i is in amperes and T in seconds. For this example, the value of i is half of 125 μa, and the capacitance is between six and ten mfds.

The approximate amplification of the combination of the two transistors may be obtained by the use of the equation for the cathode-coupled amplifier as derived in *Conductance Design of Active Circuits*, Chapter 6.[3] It is

$$K = g_{f1}g_{f2}R_eR_L/[1 + (g_{f1} + g_{f2})R_e] \tag{8}$$

This amplification may be as large as 93 for the circuit under consideration, because the values of g_{f1} and g_{f2} are about 0.075 mho, and the net R_L for $R_e + R_L = 3000$ ohms is 2500 ohms. This condition occurs when the denominator is approximately $2g_fR_e$.

If the input conductance of the input transistor is calculated on the basis of $g_i = 0.001$ mho as an average value, the effective value is about 38 micromhos, considerably more than the ten micromhos selected for the bias resistor in the above analysis. This means that the circuit must be redesigned to accept a bias resistance of at most 10,000 ohms. This may be done in either of two ways, by dividing the bias resistance into a 10,000-ohm and a 90,000-ohm section, and placing a large bypass capacitor at the tap, the 10,000-ohm section being connected to the base, or by dividing the supply voltage to provide approximately six volts, bypassing the tap, and returning a base-bias resistance of about 10,000 to 20,000 ohms to the tap. The size of the bypass capacitor again should be chosen to keep the change to approximately 10 millivolts.

13.3 Other Arrangements

Probably the most useful modification that can be made in a transistorized multivibrator is the introduction of emitter-followers coupled to the col-

[3] See p. 297.

lectors of each of the amplifiers (Fig. 13–10). This arrangement makes the signal voltage available at low impedance instead of relatively higher impedance, and can increase the signal-output voltage available. These followers may be coupled directly to the collectors as in Fig. 13–10, or they may be used as coupling elements between the coupling capacitors

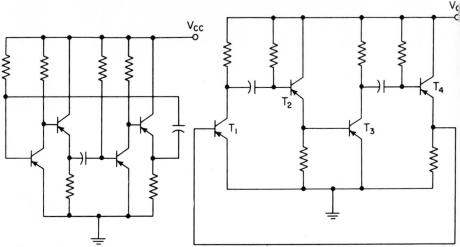

Fig. 13-10. Emitter-follower-coupled multivibrator-collector type

Fig. 13-11. Emitter-follower-coupled multivibrator-base Type II

and the base leads of the amplifier transistors as in Fig. 13–11. This modification makes possible the use of better operating conditions, since the R-C coupling network now has a considerably higher load impedance than otherwise. The result is a simplified design for low-frequency multivibrators. It has the disadvantage of requiring an additional voltage supply for the returns for the emitter resistors for the followers. It is a better configuration, however, because it makes possible the use of the base-bias resistors as the resistance component of the frequency-determining network.

The general procedure of design that has been described can be adapted to most forms of multivibrators, and the calculation of switching rate may be made by the method described in *Conductance Design of Active Circuits*.[4] The only change required is the substitution of the correct amplification equations. The calculation of the maximum repetition frequency may be made directly by the use of the equation for the noise-corner frequency as has been described by Suran and Reibert.[5]

[4] See p. 297.
[5] See p. 303.

CHAPTER FOURTEEN

Switching and Sampling Circuits

14.0 Introduction

Many switching circuits use multivibrators with resistive
return paths in parallel with the collector-to-base coupling
capacitors. The presence of these d-c paths makes possible
the locking of the circuit in either of its static states. The
discussion in this chapter starts with consideration of the
method of modifying an ordinary multivibrator to produce
a unit that requires a trigger pulse to switch it, the so-called
univibrator, or single-shot multivibrator. This discussion
is followed by a study of bi-stable, or flip-flop circuits.
Several different forms of each of these circuits are considered, and the means of controlling and triggering them
are also examined. A number of examples of the basic
methods of use of the various configurations are included,
among which is the control of a diode matrix by counting
circuits. The design of such diode matrices is discussed
briefly, and their use in the control of sampling circuits
described. In addition, Sec. 14.10 includes a brief explanation of a method of construction of bi-directional counting circuits, and explains how they may be made into
bi-directional decade counters. The chapter concludes with

a brief discussion of tunnel-diode switching circuits and a brief resume of the general contents of the Handbook.

14.1 Univibrators

The conversion of a multivibrator into a univibrator requires shift of the value of the bias current to the base of one of the transistors by an amount sufficient to reduce the over-all loop gain to a value less than unity. This requires an increase of base current in one transistor and a significant reduction in the current in the other. If the change is to be made in the simplest way possible, it is desirable to place a voltage divider in the base circuit for one transistor. This divider fixes the base voltage on the transistor, because otherwise an excessively large difference in resistance is required to obtain a completely quiescent condition. The result is loss of trigger sensitivity.

A typical circuit for a symmetrical univibrator is shown in Fig. 14–1. The transistor T_1 is blocked in the non-conducting condition by the action of the divider. The pulse shapes shown at the various points in the circuit indicate the relative magnitudes of the voltages. The pulse shapes assume positive direction for the collector voltage with respect to the emitter so that an increase in conduction may be indicated by an upward shift in base voltage. The triggering pulse may be introduced either on the non-conducting transistor, in which case the pulse tends to turn it on, or it may be introduced on the conducting transistor, in which case the pulse tends to turn it off.

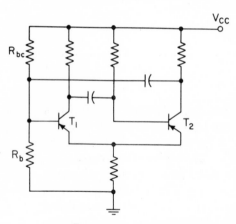

Fig. 14-1. Univibrator

The value of amplification during transition in each transistor is large enough so that free-running switching can occur unless one transistor is switched nearly completely non-conducting as explained above. Consequently, some common-bias resistance in the emitter return usually is required, and the fixed bias voltage shown in Fig. 14–1 is also required. Normally the one transistor is biased just beyond current cutoff to make certain that stray pulses will not trigger the circuit.

The introduction of the initiation voltage for the univibrator is best accomplished at a point outside the main switching path. Because both the bases and the collectors of the transistors are in the switching path for a conventional symmetrical univibrator, either one of the base-return leads or one of the emitters may be used for triggering, or a diode injection circuit may be used. Some of the possible positions for introduction of the control signal are shown in Fig. 14–2. Emitter-injection circuits are particularly convenient, because pulse integration is minimized.

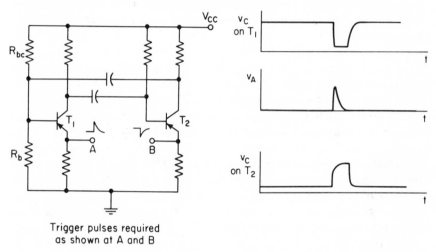

Trigger pulses required
as shown at A and B

Fig. 14-2. Univibrator triggering   **Fig. 14-3.** Voltage waveforms

If the injection is made into either one of the bases or one of the collectors of the transistors, even with isolating diodes, the behavior of the loop is altered by conductive loading during the activation period. The potential diagrams of the circuit shown in Fig. 14–2 are included in Fig. 14–3. In each of these potential diagrams, the collector potential is measured vertically upwards with respect to the emitter, so the relative polarity of the initiation pulses may be deduced directly.

The emitter bias used with the univibrator should be sufficiently large so that the resistance from the base to the emitter-return on the non-conducting transistor can be between 1000 and 10,000 ohms. With the lower value, an isolation resistance as shown in Fig. 14–4 may be desirable, but with the larger value, it is unnecessary. The base-bias resistance for the second base is made sufficiently small to place the second transistor in a saturation condition, and the emitter resistance is just sufficiently large to permit the cessation of current flow in the non-conducting transistor.

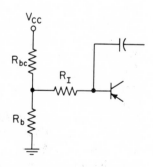

Fig. 14-4. Position of isolation resistance

EXAMPLE 1. A multivibrator is to be converted to a univibrator by the introduction of a divider circuit and a common-emitter bias resistance. The base-to-emitter voltage for current cutoff is 100 mv, and that for saturation is 200 mv. The divider circuit is to carry a current equal to the saturation base current in the conducting stage, namely, 80 μa. The collector saturation current is 7.0 ma, and the collector supply voltage is 10 volts. Design the modifications required to convert this circuit to a univibrator.

The series bias resistances for the base terminals of the two transistors as a multivibrator are between 100,000 and 120,000 ohms, because the resistance is about 12,000 ohms per volt, and the voltage is approximately nine volts. If the base-tap point for the non-conducting transistor, T_1, is placed 6000 ohms above ground, and a 5000-ohm additional leak resistance is used, the voltage at the base is approximately a half volt, the emitter voltage should also be a half volt. For a collector saturation current in the conducting transistor of 7.0 ma, the required emitter resistance then is 70 ohms, this resistance being bypassed by a large capacitor. An additional resistance of 30 ohms may be connected in series with either of the transistors as desired for the introduction of the trigger pulse. The collector load resistances are nominally 1360 ohms. A 1500-ohm resistor probably would be used.

The base-circuit configuration for T_2 is unchanged, the base return resistance remaining at 100,000 ohms, and the coupling capacitors of such a size that the required pulse duration results.

14.2 The Emitter-Coupled Univibrator

The emitter-coupled univibrator is closely related to the corresponding multivibrator, and is modified from it in an exactly similar manner as was the symmetrical univibrator. This circuit is particularly convenient in that it has a "loose" base connection that may be used for pulse injection.

This univibrator differs from the symmetrical one in that there are two different ways of setting up the trigger circuit, one for taking a positive pulse on the spare base connection, and one for taking a negative pulse. With the symmetrical circuit, it is only necessary to move the injection resistance from one emitter to the other, whereas with the emitter-coupled univibrator, it is necessary to shift the bias networks instead. If the base on T_1 is biased to conducting conditions, then a pulse having the same polarity as the collector voltage must be introduced into the injection base lead, whereas if the input base is biased to non-conducting, then the input pulse has opposite polarity from the collector voltage, Fig. 14–5.

The design of the bias-locking circuits for the emitter-coupled univibrator closely parallels that for the symmetrical type, but it differs in several important respects. In the first place, operation with the second transistor, T_2, non-conducting is better for generation of long pulses, because it makes possible the use of a larger R-C constant in the feedback path. Similarly, for high frequencies, a reverse situation may be some-

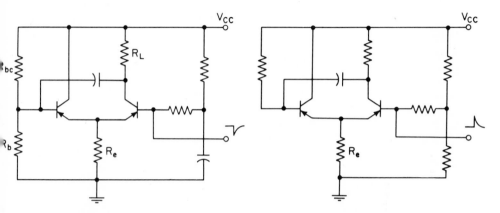

Fig. 14-5A. Emitter-coupled univibrator, Type I

Fig. 14-5B. Emitter-coupled univibrator, Type II

what better, because the value of the R-C constant is then reduced appreciably by the base input resistance. Otherwise, circuit conversion for opposite-polarity trigger pulses requires an interchange of the bias networks.

14.3 The Basic Bi-stable Circuit

When the coupling capacitors of any of the multivibrators described in Chapter Thirteen are paralleled with an appropriate resistance, and the bias circuits are modified to provide voltage division, a circuit that can be triggered into either of two states results (Fig. 14–6). The adjustment of the required bias circuits is somewhat critical, however, and as a result they require rather careful design. Otherwise, although the circuit may switch easily in one direction, it may prove to be considerably more difficult to switch in the reverse direction, and may behave more like a univibrator than a bi-stable circuit.

A typical circuit for one form of transistorized bi-stable circuit is shown in Fig. 14–6. In this circuit, the current flow through the bias path should be sufficient to provide the required base-saturation current for the conducting transistor with the other transistor in a non-conducting state. At the same time, it must not be large enough to limit the available loop amplification through excessive shunting of the output current through the auxiliary network. The design must be capable of functioning in the presence of the static collector current, I_{co}, of the transistor as well. For purposes of design, a shunt leakage resistance capable of passing appreciably more than the maximum value of I_{co} should be connected in parallel with the base-collector circuit of each transistor, and then the design made including this amount of leakage current. If the design can switch this load, then satisfactory operation of the circuit over the required temperature range can be expected.

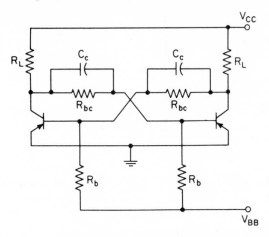

Fig. 14-6. Bistatic current

The base-emitter voltage required to place a transistor in saturation is relatively important in all switching circuits, and is critically important in some forms such as the DCTL circuits. If, for example, one transistor in a switching system is capable of conducting strongly with a value of base voltage for which it should be non-conducting, the circuit may block in one state. Likewise, if one of the transistors requires a larger bias voltage for the conducting state than the other, then the circuit will be more difficult to switch in one direction than the other, and circuit operation may be unsatisfactory. As long as the current gain in the transistors is sufficiently large to provide some margin in the switching current, it is not particularly important in typical circuits. In fact, frequently there will be no correlation whatsoever between transistors that function and the current gain as measured by a static test if the minimum required value is available.

Those who have worked with bi-stable circuits made with tubes are aware that the balance and values of the grid voltages with the tubes out of the socket must be adjusted correctly to provide efficient switching conditions. The same situation is true with the transistors and other components in the resistive cross-coupled flip-flop circuit. In addition, the transistors should have available a minimum current gain of at least ten along with matched values of base-to-emitter voltage. Small wonder, therefore, is it that the construction of a satisfactory bi-stable circuit using transistors is more difficult than making a similar circuit for use with tubes.

Sometimes a bi-stable circuit will be erratic in spite of everything seemingly being right, the current gains adequate, the voltages balanced, and the devices balanced. One of the most insidious causes of erratic operation under these conditions is an over-sensitive circuit. For example, it is possible for the circuit to be so sensitive that it switches not just the way that is intended, but it may also switch back on a single pulse. In other words, the circuit does not lock out after switching on a single pulse, but detects the tail of the pulse and accepts it as an additional trigger signal. This condition can easily develop with a circuit using steering diodes to direct the switching pulse. Shortening the duration of the switching pulse is one possible solution to this problem, but the shortening usually must be done by reduction of the base-return R component, and not the C component, of the coupling network.

The introduction of switching pulses is best achieved in either the collector or the emitter terminal of one of the transistors, not in the base circuit. If the pulses are introduced into a collector, steering diodes are normally used to route the pulse to the proper transistor. This pulse usually is a downward-directed pulse.

The pulses may also be introduced into the emitter circuit. In this case, an extremely low-impedance drive source is required, because the transistor loading is very heavy. Considerable additional circuitry is required for this mode of triggering, so it seldom is used. Emitter-injection is used in connection with the reversible decade counter described later, where it is used to reset the decade.

The minimum size coupling capacitor in the switching circuit is dependent primarily on the base-to-emitter capacitance, and through it on the noise-corner frequency. The required value of capacitance may be calculated in terms of the base-to-emitter voltage during conduction and the collector-to-emitter voltage during non-conduction, the minimum value being set by the value required to compensate the circuit response to constant delay as a function of frequency. If the capacitance selected for the coupling capacitor is larger than the minimum size, it overcompensates the circuit and speeds the switching somewhat. The actual value of capacitance selected should be at least twice the minimum value determined in terms of the equations

$$C_C/C_{be} = V_{bt}/(V_{cz} - V_{bt})$$
$$2\pi f_\alpha C_{be} = (g_{i'} + g_{f'})$$

(1)

where C_{be} and C_C are the base-to-emitter and the coupling capacitances, respectively, V_{cz} is the collector-to-emitter voltage of the transistor in the non-conducting state, and V_{bt} is the base-to-emitter voltage under conditions of full conduction.

The minimum capacitor size may be calculated in terms of the required charge in micro-micro-coulombs (pcb), because the charge may be reduced to a capacitance in terms of the base-to-emitter voltage, and the inverse ratio of the voltages used to correct for the potential division. The equation for the capacitance then takes the form

$$C_C = C_{be}V_{bt}/(V_{cz} - V_{bt}) = Q_s/(V_{cz} - V_{bt}) \qquad (2)$$

Data on Q_s are given by some manufacturers.[1] The use of the equation for the alpha-cutoff frequency enables the user to obtain a reasonably good approximate value for C_C at almost any condition in the operating range of the transistor, because the value of $(g_{i'} + g_{f'})$ in micromhos is approximately 39,000 times the emitter current in milliamperes.

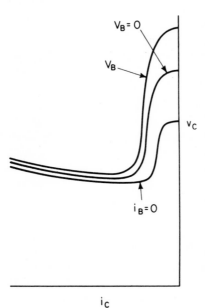

When large values of current are drawn through the transistors in a bi-stable circuit, and the supply voltage is reasonably near to the rated maximum value, it is possible for a phenomenon known as "latching" to occur. This phenomenon is caused by the avalanche-type behavior of the transistor at high values of collector voltage and current. The behavior of typical contours of constant base current for large values of v_C and i_C are shown in Fig. 14-7 (replotted from the RCA data-sheet on the 2N1300 transistor). The lines of constant base current, instead of turning approximately horizontal but continuing to rise slowly, actually dip to a lower voltage as the collector current increases, and then start to rise. When latching occurs, the transistor switches "off" to the higher-current lower-voltage intersection of the load-line crossings with the avalanche section of the base-current contour.

Fig. 14-7. Avalanche collector-voltage effect

---

[1] See the data sheet published by Radio Corporation of America on the 2N1300 transistor for further data on the Q_s method.

If the collector supply voltage is large enough that the load line crosses the base-current contour in the avalanche region, a stable operating point simulating the normal non-conducting conditions results, but it occurs at relatively high collector dissipation, and can cause the destruction of the transistor. Consequently, the collector supply voltage selected must be sufficiently small so that the load line will not cross the avalanche sections of the base-current contours. A circuit that may be used for the selection of satisfactory transistors not subject to this difficulty or for selection of a voltage for the collector supply for which latching will not occur is shown in Fig. 14–8. The value selected for V_{CC} should be less than the rated value of BV_{CE} and frequently less than half BV_{CB}, and it should exceed the finally selected voltage for the circuit by at least one or two volts. The push switch in Fig. 14–8 is closed to place the transistor in saturation. The voltmeter should read the

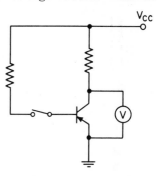

Fig. 14-8. Avalanche test set

same voltage after opening the switch as it did before closing it. Otherwise, latching is occurring and either the transistor or the voltage is unsuitable.

14.4 The Emitter-Follower Bi-stable Circuit

The simple bi-stable circuit just described is somewhat marginal in its operation, in that the base-loading through the cross-coupling network limits the switching speed and also limits the output power that can be developed by the circuit. This difficulty is commonly corrected by the use of emitter-followers either to drive the cross-coupling networks or the bases of the switching transistors. The use of the emitter-follower directly on the collector of the switching transistors is convenient for the development of switching pulses for a group of load transistors, whereas the use at the base input improves the switching properties of the circuit itself. The use of the followers at the bases of the switching transistors does not increase the load-driving characteristics unless the loads can be activated from the voltage available in the base circuit of the switch units.

Both of these configurations may require additional power input compared to the flip-flop circuit itself, but the power distribution is sufficiently more effective that the increase in requirement may be surprisingly small. Where power capabilities are adequate, the use of these coupling followers can be well worth-while. Design of the combined circuit is based directly on the design of the simple switching circuit and the design of emitter-followers.

EXAMPLE 2. Design a counting circuit using a 2N1300 transistor with a collector voltage of minus five volts and a base-return voltage of five volts. Calculate the minimum value of the cross-coupling capacitance.

An approximate replot of the static data provided with the 2N1300 transistor is included in Fig. 14–9. The input family given is only approximate, as the data given on the device show the variation of the base voltage for a given base current most effectively in the saturation region, but not as the curves break into the active area.

If a contour of constant collector current is super-imposed on the input family, it takes the form shown by the dash contour, showing that as the base current increases, so does the base voltage. The amount of variation of base voltage with large changes of base current in the saturation region (for a given value of collector current) is so small that the significance of the curves is really quite small for applications other than switching. For example, a base-current change from 0.5 ma to 5 ma with a fixed collector

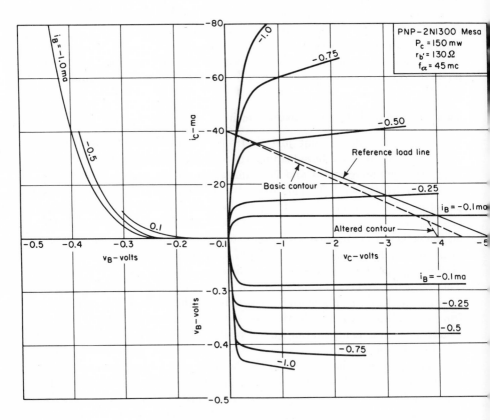

Fig. 14-9. Switch circuit calculation

current of 20 ma carries an accompanying change of 50 mv in base voltage. This change indicates a base-spreading resistance of less than ten ohms.

The resistive load contour for the switching circuit, neglecting the effect of the cross-coupling circuits, is drawn in a conventional fashion. The contour plotted in Fig. 14–9 corresponds to a resistive load of 125 ohms. This load line does not tell the whole story, however, because the coupling load must be included. This load both increases the load current in the resistor and decreases the available collector voltage. The circuit loading coupled to the collector of the conducting transistor is just that which results from current flow in the coupling network, whereas the loading coupled to the collector of the non-conducting transistor includes both the network and the input current for the base of the conducting transistor. The result is that the equivalent supply voltage is

$$V_{CC'} = [V_{CC}/(1 + G_C R_L)] + V_{BB}G_C R_L/(1 + G_C R_L) \qquad (3)$$

where R_L is the load resistance in the collector circuit, G_C is the instantaneous value of the conductance of the cross-coupling network, including the loading resulting from the input conductance of the other transistor, and V_{CC} and V_{BB} are the collector and the base supply voltages respectively. Because the polarities of the two supplies are usually different, and the second term is small in value, the effective collector supply voltage is somewhat less than the nominal value.

The conversion of the approximate load contour to the actual contour may be started at the saturation condition, because at that point, the value of $R_t = 1/G_C$ is equal to the sum of the resistances R_{CB1} and R_{B2}. The corrected value, $V_{CC'}$, is determined in terms of Eq. (3), and a process of integration back along the contour may be started. For the present problem, the current in the coupling network may be taken as 2 ma under saturation conditions. The total resistance ($R_{CB1} + R_{B2}$) is 2500 ohms. This gives a value of $V_{CC'} = -4.52$ volts, and the parallel combination of resistances is 119 ohms. The load contour corresponding to this condition may also be plotted as in Fig. 14–9 as long dashes. Neglecting the capacitance loading, transfer takes place along this line until the base of the second transistor starts to draw appreciable current. Then the value of R_t changes, and the slope of the corresponding part of the load contour changes to correspond to the new conditions. Because the first transistor now is non-conducting, conditions that will provide a specified base current to the second, conducting, transistor should be found. This is easily accomplished by setting $R_{BC1} = R_x$, $R_{B2} = 2500 - R_x$, and the saturation base current for the second transistor as I_{bt}. The resulting equations are

$$(R_L + R_x)I_{bt} = V_{CC} - V_{bt} \qquad (4)$$

$$(R_t - R_x)(I_t - I_{bt}) = (V_{bt} - V_{BB}) \qquad (5)$$

where I_t is the total current in the divider network. These equations may be solved for R_x, giving

$$R_x = [V_{CC} - V_{BB} + I_{bt}(R_t - R_L) -$$

$$\langle\sqrt{(V_{CC}-V_{BB})^2-2I_{bt}\times(R_t+R_L)(V_{CC}+V_{BB}-V_{bt})+I_{bt}^2(R_t+R_L)^2}\rangle]/2I_{bt} \quad (6)$$

Only the negative radical is used because the positive gives values of R_x greater than R_t.

If the radical is examined for the possible presence of zeros, it turns out that its value is always positive, and that it may have either a minimum or a maximum in the possible range of use. Differentiating the terms in the radical with respect to k, where k is defined in terms of the equation

$$kV_{CC} = I_{bt}(R_t + R_L)$$

gives the equation

$$(2k - 2)V_{CC}^2 - 2V_{BB}V_{CC} + 4V_{bt}V_{CC} = 0 \quad (7)$$

This reduces to the general relation for k

$$(V_{BB}/V_{CC}) - 2(V_{bt}/V_{CC}) = k - 1 \quad (8)$$

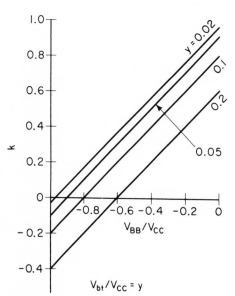

Fig. 14-10. Relation for voltage division

This equation is plotted in Fig. 14–10 for different values of the ratio V_{bt}/V_{CC}. Two particularly useful points are those for $V_{BB} = -V_{CC}$, for which case $k = -V_{bt}/V_{CC}$, and with $V_{BB} = 0$, giving a value of $k = 1 - \delta$, where δ is a small positive increment, or $\delta = -2V_{bt}/V_{CC}$.

For the circuit under consideration, therefore, the optimum value of k is small, approximately 0.08, but a somewhat larger value should be selected to make certain that the current gain is adequate. The saturation value of the base current is approximately 0.8 ma, and the corresponding base voltage, 0.400 volt. The total resistance of 2500 ohms and saturation current of 0.8 ma in the base correspond to a value of k of 0.4. The circuit may be redesigned for a resistance load, $(R_t + R_L)$, of 1000 ohms, giving a value of 0.16, possibly as close to the optimum as is practical without the use of emitter-followers.

The balance of this design is based on the value of the factor k of 0.40. Solving Eq. (6) for R_x gives a value of 1088 ohms, or nominally 1000 ohms, leaving 1500 ohms for R_{CB1} and R_{CB2}.

The collector voltage at which the variation of the load line from the reference sets in may be determined by finding the point at which the base voltage crosses the zero-base-current line. It is given by the equation

$$V_{ct} = (V_{bz} R_t / R_{b2}) + V_{BB}(1 - R_t / R_{b2}) \qquad (9)$$

where V_{bz} is the base voltage for zero base current, and V_{ct} is the corresponding value of collector voltage for the associated transistor. In this instance, with $v_B = 0.3$ volt, the transfer starts when the collector voltage has risen to 3.83 volts. At this point, the load contour curves away from the plotted linear contour. The total change of base voltage to full saturation is an additional 0.1 volt, corresponding to a further increase at the collector of 0.167 volt to 4.00 volts. The modified contour is sketched on the figure. The total voltage change is approximately 3.7 volts.

If emitter-followers are introduced for each of the coupling circuits, then the collector load resistance in series with each of the switching transistors may be increased, because only a small part of the switching power is drawn from the main switching transistors. The peak current through the switching transistors now may be limited to ten milliamperes, and the switching power for the coupling network drawn from the emitter-

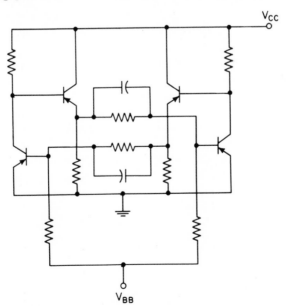

Fig. 14-11. Emitter-follower-coupled flip-flop

followers. The modified circuit is shown in Fig. 14–11. If, now, the total current through each emitter-follower is taken as twenty ma, the total resistance R_t is approximately 500 ohms. A total of 200 ohms of this resistance is between the emitter of the follower and the base of the switching transistor, and the balance of 300 ohms is placed between the base and the base supply. The maximum dissipation in the follower transistor is $0.010 \times 5 = 50$ mw, well within the 150 mw rating of the 2N1300 transistor at 25° C. The resulting value of k is

$$0.001 \times 500/5.0 = 0.1$$

approximately the optimum value. The required load resistor for the switching transistors is now 500 ohms instead of the former 125 ohms. Interestingly enough, the total power consumption is about the same as without the followers, because the modification makes possible a more effective use of the available energy. The gain in the emitter-followers is well over 0.75, the value at which an even trade of capacitance and resistance will occur between the base of the follower and the load resistance in the switching transistor, and the output impedance of the follower is so low that only the base-spreading resistance of the switching transistor limits the switching rate in the balance of the circuit.

14.5 Direct-Coupled Switching Circuits (DCTL)

The operating conditions for which k equals $1 - \delta$ in the example above correspond to what is sometimes called "direct-coupled transistor logic,"

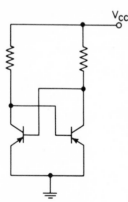

Fig. 14-12. Direct-coupled transistor flip-flop

or DCTL circuitry. These circuits differ in that the bases and the collectors of the switching transistors are cross-connected with no separating resistance or capacitance at all. Because of the direct connection, no base-return resistance is required, as can be verified from Fig. 14–12. This type of circuit can be used primarily because the voltage on the base terminal of the conducting transistor is greater with respect to its emitter than is its collector voltage, and in fact the collector voltage under conduction is slightly less than the base voltage required to cause current flow in the device. There may be as much as 200 to 300 mv difference between the two points under saturation conditions. Because of the large amount of base current that flows in the conducting transistor, only a few tenths of a volt change are developed between the off and the on states with DCTL circuits, with the result that although the basic switching circuit is simple, its control circuitry may be somewhat more critical than is required with standard circuits.

The principal problem with these circuits is one of getting adequate balance in the values of base voltage at which saturation and turn-off for the respective transistors occur. Because the total switching range is from a change as small as 50 mv to as much as 100 mv from start of conduction to saturation, to assure reliability it is desirable to have the values of base voltage of the respective transistors in a specific switching unit correspond to within approximately ten millivolts. No form of alpha tester can check this, since it is to a large extent dependent on the base-spreading resistance of the individual transistors. Fortunately, a simple testing device can be used for the purpose. Its basic circuit is shown in Fig. 14–13. With this device, the transistors to be used are adjusted, one-by-one, until a specified degree of saturation results, for example, a collector-to-emitter voltage of 0.200 volt, and the base voltage required to produce the condition is noted. Some types (code numbers) of transistors will be found to vary widely, whereas others

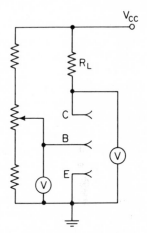

Fig. 14-13. Saturation voltage tester

may be formed into a small number of groups. If the transistors are coded and used in groups, with all of the transistors in critical position for a given individual circuit taken from the same group, this difficulty can be avoided. The groups are typically ten millivolts wide.

The small voltage change available from the DCTL flip-flop makes necessary the use of some auxiliary circuits for output and pulse-direction. These additional transistors to some extent offset the extreme simplicity of the flip-flop itself, but even so, the circuit can prove to be very useful. Possibly the simplest method of controlling the basic flip-flop is based on the circuit shown in Fig. 14–14. This circuit, one of several reported by Clark, obtains its pulse-direction through the use of collector clamping.[2] If either transistor T_2 or T_5 is in the conduction state, the corresponding T_1 or T_6 is unable to develop any voltage change, because its partner is saturated and limits the collector voltage change in the trigger transistor to a few tenths of a volt. With the transistor of the pair, T_2, or T_5, which is not in the conduction state, however, the full collector-supply voltage is available, and a strong trigger pulse can be formed. When a trigger pulse is introduced on the trigger line, therefore, it is routed into the proper side

[2] E. G. Clark, "DCTL Complementing Flip-Flop Circuits," 1957 Transistor and Solid State Circuits Conference, Philadelphia, Pa.

of the circuit and coupled into the switching circuit through the capacitor, thereby changing the state of the circuit.

The transistors used with this flip-flop are driven very hard into saturation, and consequently may not switch as rapidly as with some circuits. The circuit simplicity, however, may make its use desirable in place of a faster circuit. The output signal for triggering the succeeding stage may be extracted directly from either T_3 or T_4, or it may be obtained from either T_2 or T_5. In any case, the trigger signal should take the form of a pulse with this circuit.

The transistors T_2 and T_5 are included in the circuit to give the full voltage change of which the circuit is capable. The waveform available on the collectors of these transistors includes switching transients in addition to a reasonably rectangular waveform because of the fact that they are used for the introduction of the switch direction control signals. As a consequence, they may not have a sufficiently square waveshape for applications such as control of a diode matrix. The waveshape should be adequate for triggering an additional counter in a binary chain, however. Actually, a switching pulse for the next binary element in a chain probably could be obtained from the collector of either T_3 or T_4, because these transistors do switch sufficiently hard to pulse the control circuit of a succeeding stage.

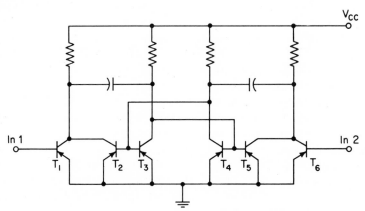

Fig. 14-14. Direct-coupled transistor logic binary

The main problems in the design of a complete functioning circuit based on Fig. 14–14 are two, first, the proper selection of the transistors, and second, the selection of the proper size of coupling capacitor for the interstage circuit. Empirically, the capacitance value should depend at least approximately on Eqs. (1) and (2), although loop amplification can act to increase the value required. For this reason, over-compensation is essential.

EXAMPLE 3.   Design a DCTL circuit for use with the 2N217 transistor, using a supply voltage of seven volts for the flip-flop itself. Take the alpha-cutoff frequency as 0.4 mc, and use a load resistance of 5600 ohms.

The only points in question in this circuit are the adjustment of the size of the coupling capacitor and the setting of the pulsing transistors so they will pulse the circuit properly. Based on a base voltage of 200 mv, and a voltage across C_C of five volts, the minimum coupling capacitance allowed by Eq. (2) is

$$C_C = (0.20/7) \times 2 \times 10^{-8} = 8 \times 10^{-10} \text{ pfd or 800 pfd}$$

Introducing a factor of four gives a value of 3200 pfd as a good starting point for design.

The base of the routing transistor should be biased to draw a few microamperes current, just enough to reduce the collector voltage to about ten percent less than its supply. Then the circuit will be sensitive to a low-impedance trigger voltage of between twenty and fifty millivolts, and it will pulse the output of the appropriate directing transistor sufficiently to switch the circuit. To determine the amplitude of input pulse required, it is only necessary to work backward from the desired change of collector current in the trigger amplifier.

14.6 Use of DCTL Circuits with Switching Matrices

One of the ideal applications of DCTL binary circuits is the control of switching matrices that are used to control and route signals from one set of inputs to a different set of outputs. This section describes the modifications that may be helpful in making the binary circuit control a matrix, and the next section discusses the design of diode matrices for use with the binaries. A later paragraph describes how such a circuit can be used to control the input of a telemeter modulator.

To achieve clean switching in any kind of switching circuit, it is necessary that the control signals be as free as possible of unwanted signals or noise. The transistors T_2 and T_5 in the DCTL circuit have rather good collector-voltage waveforms, but not sufficiently good for use with a switching matrix, because the voltage does vary from the nominal value during the switching transient. For this reason, an additional pair of repeater transistors may be used in parallel with T_2 and T_5, but they must have separate outputs to keep out the switching signals. The circuit shown in Fig. 14–15 serves the purpose excellently. The signals developed across the collector loads are excellent square waves and have ample amplitude to produce a precise switching action. Depending on the amount of loading developed in the matrix, the amplifier may be used directly, or it may be used to control an emitter-follower controlling the matrix.

The emitter-follower form of matrix control has proven to be nearly ideal, since the output voltage can be extremely stable, and also a type of transistor can be selected that causes the transistor to draw considerable current when it is providing power to the matrix. If the counter and signal-output circuits use PNP transistors, it is common for an NPN transistor to be required for the follower application. The amplifiers and the followers may be designed by the conventional methods already described.

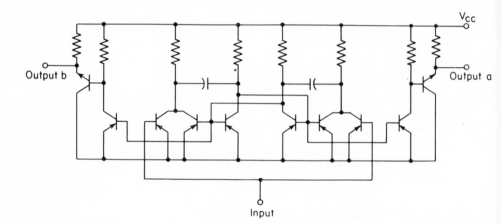

Fig. 14-15. Matrix-switching DCTL

14.7 Diode Matrices

Diode matrices are commonly used to convert the switching data generated by a binary counter to another counting base, such as sequential or decimal counting. These matrices may be made to perform either as "and" gates, in which case the matrix detects the fact that all of its inputs are in a specified state, usually referred to as the on or "and" state, or as "or" gates, in which case the matrix detects the fact that one or more of its inputs is in the "on" state. Typical simple "and" and "or" gate circuits are shown in Fig. 14–16. With the "and" gate, the output is clamped to the bias source except when all of its input terminals are biased to block conduction. When the blocking condition occurs, a specified signal may be transmitted through the gate with negligible loss, but otherwise the clamping action of one or more of the diodes prevents the transmission of the specified signal. On the other hand, with the "or" gate, the presence of an "on" state potential on any one of the inputs to the gate causes the transmission of the signal pulse.

The design of the logic for the diode matrix is an extremely complicated process that will not be discussed in this book because it is rather well described in some of the texts on computing machinery. A simple discussion of the process is included in *Transistor Electronics*, by Hurley.[3] It is of

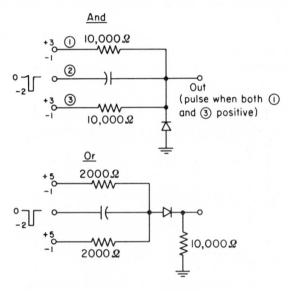

Fig. 14-16. "And" and "Or" diode circuits

particular importance to the user, however, to know the properties of diodes, which are important in the construction of effective switching matrices.

Ideally, the diodes used in making switching matrices should have infinite conductivity in the forward direction, and zero conductivity in the reverse direction. Practically, the conductivity in the reverse direction is considerably more important in diode matrices than that in the forward direction because only one diode may be in series with the signal path, whereas there may be large numbers of them in parallel. Some of the tree-type combining matrices use a smaller number of diodes for the same switching combinations, but have more series-connected diodes in their circuits. With them, the forward conductance can be more important.

The forward-to-reverse resistance ratio limits the number of diodes that can be used in a diode matrix without excessive loading developing from diode leakage. The nominal operating impedance for the square matrix may be estimated by determining the admittance

$$g_s = \sqrt{mg_f g_r} \qquad (10)$$

[3] *Transistor Electronics*, by R. B. Hurley. John Wiley & Sons, Inc., New York, 1959.

where m is the number of diodes connected to a given transmission path, and g_f and g_r are the average forward and reverse conductances, respectively. The value of g_s should be at most a hundredth to a thousandth of the value of g_f for minimum loading on the signal, and the series impedance between signal input and signal output should be approximately the reciprocal of g_s.

Evidently for a diode to be satisfactory for matrix use with at least ten diodes involved per output circuit, its reverse conductance should be less than a micromho. In the circuit shown in Fig. 14–17, the thirty-two

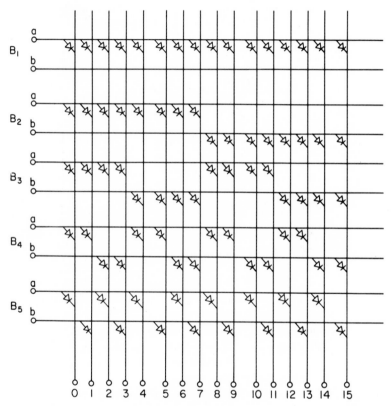

Fig. 14-17. Binary-consecutive matrix

output channels have five diodes per circuit, whereas the control circuits have sixteen diodes each. Fortunately, the source impedance level for the control circuits can be kept very small by the use of emitter-followers in the control circuits, so that the number of diodes per output is important, whereas the number per binary control path is relatively less important.

The diodes used for switching matrices, besides having a very large forward-to-back ratio and a high back-resistance, should be all-glass encased, and they should be as small as possible within the physical resistance and current limitations. Metal-case diodes tend to be unsatisfactory for this application because of the crowded structure necessary in matrices and the ever-present possibility of development of bridging shorts. In addition, some metal-cased diodes are somewhat deficient in reverse resistance, and are consequently of little use in switching matrices. Hermetic sealing is also important, because it is the most effective method of making certain that operating characteristics are stable with time.

The diode matrix may be used as a multiple switch, or it may be used as a signal combining and switching arrangement. If the matrix is used for combining pulse or a-c signals, then the number of diode gate circuits through which the signal must pass in reaching the output is relatively unimportant, whereas if the matrix is used for the selection of different individual d-c signals, then the number of diodes can be of considerable importance.

14.8 A Telemetering Commutator

The diode matrix, along with an oscillator and countdown circuit, can be used effectively in a static telemetering commutator for use in research

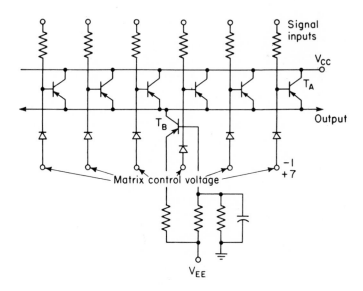

Fig. 14-18. Signal repeater

vehicles carrying magnetometers. Because of the sensitivity of the magnetometers, it is not possible to use mechanical commutators in this application, and commutation for a sequential telemeter requires some kind of an electronic network. The diode matrix, in simplified form, and its associated repeater network for repeating the input voltage in waveform and magnitude are shown in Fig. 14–18. In the form shown, no diode bias voltages are introduced in series with the main signal paths, just the base-to-emitter voltage for the repeater transistors, but it has the disadvantage that it is not possible to introduce any given signal into more than one input without interfering with operation of the circuit. Because repeated measurements within a normal switching cycle may be required at spaced intervals of time, the modification shown in Fig. 14–19 can be used with those channels for which multiple operation is required.

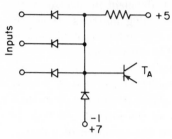

Fig. 14-19. Paralleling diode circuit

The interval of dwell on any one channel need not be limited to a single stepping period, but can be any binary multiple of it, two, four, eight, etc. Consequently, a great deal of flexibility is available in these units. In contrast to mechanical commutators, the duty factor of the transistorized commutator can be nearly 100 percent, because the series coupling impedances used between the signal source and the diodes provides the required isolation and permits simultaneous switching. The input impedance of the emitter-followers is sufficiently high and the diode impedance in the transient condition is sufficiently high that the series resistance has negligible effect on the circuit during signal transmission. During the block period, however, it prevents the application of a low-impedance short on the voltage source.

The emitter-follower circuit used in this commutator is interesting in that the transistor T_2, which is placed in the emitter return of T_1, is connected to provide a high dynamic impedance to the emitter of the transistor T_1, thereby making the output signal voltage almost exactly equal to the input signal voltage. The action of the diode matrix keeps all but a single one of the principal transistors T_{1j} in an inactive condition, thereby preventing the mixing of signals between channels.

The linearity of the repeater circuit with its two transistors and the matrix switch depends primarily on the back-resistance of the diodes used in the matrix. With diodes having back-resistances in the one to ten megohm range, it is possible to get linearities that are better than a half percent with a properly designed circuit.

14.9 Bi-Directional Counters

Normally, electronic counters based on flip-flop circuits are used to count in only one direction, but with minor changes, it is possible to make them bi-directional. The direction of count in a binary counter may be reversed by the transfer of the pulse-coupling network from outputs A to outputs B in Fig. 14–20. That this is the case may be seen from the counting diagrams shown in Fig. 14–21. The direction of progression of the counter with the couplings transferred is diametrically the opposite of that before transfer, and as a consequence, it constitutes a reversal of counting direction.

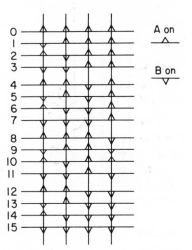

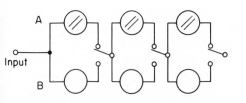

Fig. 14-20. Basic bi-directional counter

Fig. 14-21. Count in 4-binary counter

The introduction of a pair of "or" circuits between the two outputs of one counter binary unit and the input to the following binary can then select the routing of the pulses from one binary to the next if the two "or" circuits are switched in a complimentary manner, that is, the one passes signal when the other is switched off. Such a configuration can therefore form a bi-directional counter, the only additional requirement being that a sensing circuit be provided ahead of the counter to sense the sign of the count. These counters are useful for counting the difference between a reference frequency and an unknown frequency. If count pulses arrive once per period of the signal being counted, there is no possibility of detecting the polarity of the count, but if the drift of the signal with respect to a reference signal can be measured several times per period, then the direction of drift can be used to control the counting direction. The discussion of the logic of such a system is beyond the scope of this book.

The bi-directional counter may be made into a binary decade counter if a count combination is used that is completely symmetrical. Fortunately, such a combination can be found which will convert a four-bit counter into a scale-of-ten counter that has skew-symmetrical final-count values. Such a configuration may be based on the four-bit counter by taking the range of three through twelve from a zero through fifteen counter (Fig.

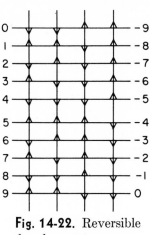

Fig. 14-22. Reversible decade counter

14–22). The counts on collector-group A are numbered zero through nine against the count numbers three through twelve, and the counts on collector-group B numbered from zero to minus nine against the count numbers twelve through three, namely, in the reverse order. The switching-level diagram shows that the count positions on Group B, for a given number, correspond exactly to the count in reverse direction, for the same given number, with that in group A.

The only remaining problem is to install two "and" circuits, one for each direction, which detect the counts of three-reverse and twelve-forward. These two "and" circuits reroute the counting pulse to the appropriate reset circuit, in the positive-counting direction to reset the counter from twelve to three, and in the negative-counting direction to reset the counter from three to twelve. If necessary, a lock-out circuit can also be installed to deactivate all count-transfer circuits during reset, thereby assuring reliable operation. One form the circuit might take is shown in Fig. 14–23.

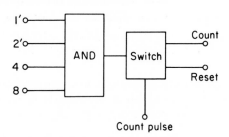

Fig. 14-23. Count routing circuit

14.10 Tunnel Diode Switches

The tunnel diode is an excellent example of a two-terminal switch that has great potential for use in computers. Its principal advantages are its small size, high speed, and small power consumption.

Tunnel diodes can be used in countdown circuits by arranging them to take advantage of the two stable states, A and B, in Fig. 14–24. To accomplish switching, it is necessary to trigger the operating conditions either from A through A' to B or from B through B' to A. Then either of the indicated switching cycles results.

To produce, from a single-pulse type, first a switch from A to B and then from B to A, a circuit somewhat like that shown in Fig. 14–25 is

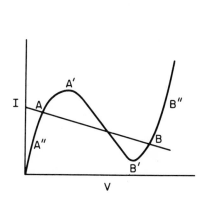

Fig. 14-24. Tunnel diode switch circuit

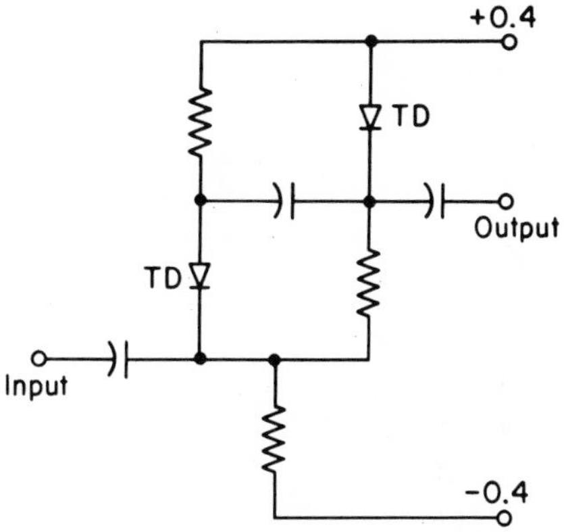

Fig. 14-25. Possible tunnel-diode bistatic circuit

required. If a negative pulse is applied to the input, and TD_2 is in the low-voltage condition, the pulse tends to take TD_2 from A to A' and TD_1 from B to B''. Diode TD_2 then switches to B and reduces the voltage across TD_1 so that diode voltage B' is reached and it switches also. The next pulse takes TD_1 from A to A' and switches TD_2 back in the process. Then standard diode routing techniques can be used to introduce an output pulse from this counter into additional circuits.

Tunnel diodes can be used as pulse-forming amplifiers because a voltage sufficient to change the diode bias from A to A' will switch it to state B, and one capable of shifting the bias from B to B' will return the diode to state A.

The load resistance selected for use with a tunnel diode should be of such a value that a small lock-out margin, typically 20 mv, is available at point A, and possibly 50 to 100 mv at point B. These values specify both the load resistance and the supply voltage. Because switching is controlled at point A, the margin at B must be sufficient to provide usable values of R_0 and R_1.

The capacitor C is the memory element for the circuit, and controls the direction of switching. It should be sufficiently large to permit completion of change of state and prevent multiple switching.

14.11 Summary

The two basic types of circuit design for use with active devices and with transistors in particular are the combination static-small-signal design, which is required with amplifiers of all types, and switching design, which is required with transfer-of-state circuits such as multivibrators, flip-flops, and other switching circuits. With the first of these types, small-signal data in some form for the active devices are required in addition to static data. Although it is possible to minimize the dependence on these small-signal data by the use of least-squares smoothing techniques, such as the orthogonal polynomial procedure considered in Appendix IV, much more adequate design can be obtained if the small-signal data are available. The first few chapters of this Handbook develop forms in which these data can be provided most effectively, considering the stability of the various parameters with operating conditions and the relations of the data to the operating characteristics of the devices as a function of voltage, current, and frequency. The following group of chapters develops the basic equations and design procedures depending on the selected admittance plus base-spreading resistance representation, and applies them by a consistent procedure to a variety of circuits. Particular attention is given to the subject of oscillator design and the coordination of the properties of the linear and the nonlinear parts of the circuit to determine the limiting conditions of stable operation. A detailed discussion of the design of electronic mixer circuits is included, including an analysis of the effect of amplification variation on the mixer action in the circuit.

The final two chapters have discussed the properties of circuits having a high degree of nonlinearity. The design objective with these circuits is to cause operation in two or more different states successively. The small-signal characteristics are important in these circuits only in that they make possible the calculation of the transition properties from one state to the other. Because it is seldom necessary to make detailed calculations of the loop amplifications, as a general rule the data required on these devices may be limited to static input and output data. Implicit data on some of the small-signal data are required; for example, the ratio of the forward transfer admittance to the input admittance in the current gain, and the sum of the conductances and the capacitances in the frequency limits such as the alpha-cutoff frequency, and the base-spreading resistance. Orthogonal techniques can give an adequate estimate of these parameters for use with switching circuits.

The appendices contain a compendium of symbols and definitions (Appendix I) and a derivation of the small-signal distortion equations (Appendix II). In addition they include a discussion of the use of topological techniques in the determination of driving-point and transfer equations for both linear and active circuits (Appendix III) and a discussion of the orthogonal method of approximating small-signal data (Appendix IV). Appendix V includes a bibliography of papers and books used in the preparation of this Handbook, and includes some notes on papers of particular significance in the development of the described techniques, and Appendix VI describes one of the better sets of curve data presently available. Appendix VII includes an assortment of curves on transistors in current use. These curves are organized in accordance with the principles of Chapters Two and Three, and, where possible, they include small-signal data as well as the static. The static data are readily obtainable with some of the standard transistor curve tracers. Appendix VIII includes a nomograph for small-signal calculations and a variety of problems grouped by chapters for classroom use.

APPENDIX I

List of Symbols

In this appendix, a tabulation of the symbols used in the handbook is made on an alphabetical basis, with both the meaning of the symbol and the first page on which it is used included. With each letter, first the lower-case and then the capitalized symbols are listed. The Greek alphabet symbols follow the English alphabet symbols. Numerical subscripts are listed first, followed by lower-case and capitalized subscripts.

Symbol	*Definition of Symbol*	*Page*
A	Arbitrary constant	59
b	Ratio of electron mobility to hole mobility	58
b_i	Input susceptance	50
$b_{i'}$	Input susceptance, intrinsic transistor	214
C	Capacitance	94
C'	Modified capacitance for Clapp oscillator	218
C_0, C_1, C_2, C_3, C_4	Orthogonal coefficients	227
C_{0c}, C_{2c}	Corrected orthogonal coefficients	227
C_{0b}, C_{1b}, C_{2b}	Orthogonal coefficients	247
C_{20}	Fixed capacitance	287
C_{21}	Capacitance change per unit voltage	287
C_{40}	Fixed capacitance	290
C_{41}	Capacitance change per unit voltage	290
C_{be}	Base-emitter capacitance	319
$C_{e0}, C_{e1}, C_{e2}, C_{e3}, C_{e4}$	Orthogonal static coefficients	374
C_i	Input capacitance of transistor	50
C_{k0}, C_{k1}, C_{k2}	Orthogonal small-signal coefficients	375
C_n	Neutralizing capacitance	202
C_o	Output capacitance of transistor	116
C_p	Primary capacitance	166
C_s	Secondary capacitance	166

Symbol	Definition of Symbol	Page
C_t	Specific temperature change, degrees/watt	161
C_c	Capacitance across coupling inductance	198
C_c	Collector capacitance	116
C_D	Diffusion capacitance	116
C_{Dp}	p-type diffusion capacitance	59
C_{Ln}	Negative limit contour	226
C_{Lp}	Positive limit contour	226
C_S	Standard capacitance	94
C_T	Transition capacitance	59
D	Percentage distortion	353
D	Denominator function	156
D'	Denominator function	156
e	Electron charge	5
E	Electron energy in electron-volts	6
E_g	Gap energy width	9
E_F	Fermi electron energy	7
f	Frequency	33
f_1	Minimum operating frequency, transformer amplifier	165
f_2	R-C limit frequency, transformer amplifier	167
f_{2a}	Transformer resonant frequency	166
$f_{2a'}$	Transformer resonant frequency	166
f_{2b}	Transformer resonant frequency	167
f_{2c}	Transformer resonant frequency	167
f_{max}	Maximum oscillation frequency, transistor	64
f_{n1}	Lower noise corner frequency	33
f_{n2}	Upper noise corner frequency	33
f_T	Gain-bandwidth product frequency	63
f_α	Alpha cutoff frequency	50
f_β	Beta cutoff frequency	50
$F(E)$	Fermi distribution function	6
g	Conductance	235
g_{11}	Input conductance	68
g_{12}	Reverse conductance	68
g_{21}	Forward conductance	68
g_{22}	Output conductance	68
g_4	Conductance	237
$g_{b'c}$	Feedback conductance, Giacoletto config.	70
$g_{b'e}$	Input conductance, Giacoletto config.	70
g_c	Modified output conductance or h_o	68
g_{ca}	Average value modified output conductance	68
g_{ce}	Output conductance, Giacoletto config.	68
g_{cn}	Negative limit value of g_c	115
g_{cp}	Positive limit value of g_c	115
g_{cs}	Static value of g_c	115
g_f	Forward conductance	48

Symbol	*Definition of Symbol*	*Page*
$g_{f'}$	Intrinsic forward conductance	31
$g_{f'\max}$	Maximum value of $g_{f'}$	281
g_{fa}	Average value of g_f	115
g_{fn}	Negative limit value of g_f	115
g_{fp}	Positive limit value of g_f	115
g_{fs}	Static value of g_f	115
g_i	Input conductance	48
g_{i0}, g_{i1}, g_{i2}	Values of input conductance	95
$g_{i'}$	Intrinsic input conductance	70
g_{ia}	Average value of input conductance	115
g_{in}	Negative limit value of input conductance	115
g_{ip}	Positive limit value of input conductance	115
g_{is}	Static value of input conductance	115
$g_{i'\max}$	Maximum value of $g_{i'}$	281
g_m	Transconductance, Giacoletto config.	70
g_o	Output conductance	48
g_{oa}	Average value of output conductance	115
g_{on}	Negative limit value of output conductance	115
g_{op}	Positive limit value of output conductance	115
g_{os}	Static value of output conductance	115
g_r	Reverse conductance	48
g_{Dp}	Diffusion conductance — p-type material	59
G	Conductance parameters	52
G_d	Shunt input conductance	217
h	Planck's constant	9
h_{11}	Input hybrid parameter	37
h_{12}	Reverse hybrid parameter	37
h_{21}	Forward hybrid parameter	37
h_{22}	Output hybrid parameter	37
h_f	Forward hybrid parameter	37
h_{fb}	Common-base forward hybrid parameter	50
h_{fc}	Common-collector forward hybrid parameter	69
h_{fe}	Common-emitter forward hybrid parameter	50
h_i	Input hybrid (impedance) parameter	37
h_o	Output hybrid (admittance) parameter	37
h_{ob}	C-B output hybrid parameter	69
h_{oc}	C-C output hybrid parameter	69
h_r	Reverse hybrid parameter	37
h_{rb}	C-B reverse hybrid parameter	69
h_{rc}	C-C reverse hybrid parameter	69
H	Hybrid parameters	37
i_b	Small-signal base current	38
i_c	Small-signal collector current	38
i_e	Small-signal emitter current	38
i_f	Current in feedback resistor	155
i_i	Input current	48

Symbol	*Definition of Symbol*	*Page*
i_o	Output current	115
i_s	Source current	115
i_B	Instantaneous total base current	115
i_{B1}	Instantaneous base current, condition 1	96
i_{B2}	Instantaneous base current, condition 2	96
i_C	Instantaneous total collector current	115
i_E	Instantaneous total emitter current	115
i_L	Instantaneous total load current	165
i_O	Instantaneous total output current	115
i_S	Instantaneous total source current	115
I_{ba}	Average base current	115
I_{bm}	Base current for maximum collector dissipation	115
I_{bn}	Negative limit base current	115
I_{bp}	Positive limit base current	115
I_{bt}	Saturation base current	323
I_{bz}	Base current when $I_{co} = i_C = -I_{bz}$	115
I_{ca}	Average collector current	115
I_{cm}	Collector current for maximum dissipation	115
I_{cn}	Negative limit collector current	115
I_{cp}	Positive limit collector current	115
I_{cr}	Peak dynamic collector current	127
I_{ct}	Peak collector current on static load line	127
I_{cz}	Collector nominal cutoff current I_{co}	115
I_{ea}	Average emitter current	115
I_{em}	Emitter current for maximum collector dissipation	115
I_{en}	Negative limit emitter current	115
I_{ep}	Positive limit emitter current	115
I_{ez}	Emitter current (zero value) minimum i_C condition	115
I_n	Negative limit current	226
I_{oa}	Average output current	115
I_{om}	Output current for peak dissipation	115
I_{on}	Negative limit output current	115
I_{op}	Positive limit output current	115
I_{oz}	Output current at collector cutoff	115
I_p	Positive limit current	226
I_s	Static current value	226
I_{sa}	Average source current	115
I_{sm}	Source current at peak dissipation	115
I_{sn}	Negative limit source current	115
I_{sp}	Positive limit source current	115
I_{sz}	Source current at collector cutoff	115
I_t	Total current in cross-coupling network	323
I_B	Base current	58
I_B	d-c value of base current	115
I_{BM}	Maximum value of signal base current	115
I_C	Collector current	58

Symbol	Definition of Symbol	Page
I_C	d-c value of collector current	115
I_{CM}	Maximum value of signal collector current	115
I_E	Emitter current	58
I_E	d-c value of emitter current	115
I_{EM}	Maximum value of signal emitter current	115
I_O	d-c output current	115
I_{OM}	Maximum value of signal output current	115
I_S	d-c source current	115
I_{SM}	Maximum value of signal source current	115
j	Imaginary operator for shifting phase by 90°	50
k	Boltzmann's constant	9
k	Arbitrary constant	161
k	Coefficient of coupling for inductors	250
k_c	Critical coupling coefficient	199
k	Ratio $I_{bt}(R_t + R_L)/V_{CC}$	324
k_0	Nominal amplification for mixer = $0.5\,g_{f'\text{max}}R_L$	281
K	Amplification	109
K_0, K_1, K_2	Legendre gain coefficients	229
K_a	Average amplification	115
K_i	Current gain	65
K_n	Negative limit amplification	115
K_p	Positive limit amplification	115
K_s	Static amplification value	115
K_S	Total stage amplification, R-F amplifier	200
K_v	Voltage amplification	65
K_{vr}	Voltage gain at reference frequency	286
K_{max}	Maximum amplification	207
K_{min}	Minimum amplification	207
L	Mean-free-path	26
L	Inductance	166
L'	Inductance modified by capacitor in Clapp oscillator circuit	218
L_1	Primary inductance	216
L_2	Secondary inductance	216
L_2, L_3	Oscillator inductances	237
L_n	Electron diffusion length	58
$L_{n'}$	Electron diffusion length, collector region	58
L_p	Hole diffusion length	58
L_{eff}	Effective inductance	250
L_C	Inductance of coupling coil	198
L_{C1}	Effective inductance in presence of C_C	199
L_L	Leakage inductance	166
L_T	Total inductance	240
m	Mass of electron	5
m	Has value $0.5\,g_{i'\text{max}}Z_s$	281
m_e^{γ}	Electron mass near edge of conduction band	9

Symbol	Definition of Symbol	Page
m_h^γ	Hole mass near edge of valence band	9
M	Mutual inductance	216
n	Number of electrons per unit volume	5
n	Exponent	59, 94
n	Order of orthogonal polynomial	227
n_e	Number of electrons per unit volume	9
n_h	Number of holes per unit volume	9
n_i	Number of thermally generated carriers per unit volume	10
n_i	Input turns	196
n_{iG}	Thermally generated carriers per unit volume in germanium	10
n_{iS}	Thermally generated carriers per unit volume in silicon	10
n_n	Number of electrons in n-type material	10
n_o	Output turns	196
n_p	Number of electrons in p-type material	16
n_p	Primary turns	166
n_s	Secondary turns	166
n_{eff}	Effective number of electrons per unit volume	5
p_i	Number of thermally generated holes per unit volume	16
p_n	Number of holes in n-type material	16
p_p	Number of holes in p-type material	16
pfd.	Picofarads or $\mu\mu$fd	195
P_c	Collector power dissipation	161
Q	Tuned circuit Q-factor	130
Q	Quiescent point or static point	178
Q_a	Quiescent point "a"	178
Q_b	Quiescent point "b"	178
Q_{rs}	Q-factor of parametric amplifier at its idler frequency	288
Q_s	Q-factor of parametric amplifier at its signal frequency	288
Q_s	Stored charge	320
Q_t	Unloaded tuned Q-factor	199
Q_c	Q-factor for coupling circuit	198
r_b	Base resistance	51
$r_{b'}, r_{bb'}$	Base-spreading resistance	29, 116
$r_{bo'}$	$r_{b'}$ at reference temperature, T_o	159
r_c	Collector resistance	51
$r_{c'}$	Collector series resistance	25
r_d	Resistance in Tee representation	51
$r_{e'}$	Emitter series resistance	28
r_i	Input resistance	51
r_m	Mutual resistance	51

Symbol	Definition of Symbol	Page
R	Resistance component	51
R'	Resistance	218
R_1, R_2, R_3	Resistances	235
R_b	Base resistance	187
R_{bc}	Feedback resistance	155
R_{c1}	Collector load resistance	155
R_{c2}	Collector load resistance (feedback)	155
Re	Real part of	213
$R_e, R_{e0}, R_{e1}, R_{e2}, R_{e3}$	Emitter resistances	187
R_n	Neutralizing resistance	202
R_s	Source resistance	65
R_x	Base-return resistance (unknown)	323
R_{CC}	Collector supply resistance	89
R_L	Load resistance	104
R_{L1}, R_{L2}	Specific load resistances	187
R_{LD}	Dynamic load resistance	127
R_S	Standard resistance	95
R_S	Resonant resistance	238
S_c	$\partial i_c / \partial I_{co} + 1$	156
S_{c1}	$\partial i_c / \partial I_{co}$	156
$S_{c1'}$	$\partial i_c / \partial v_{b'}$	156
S_e	$\partial i_e / \partial I_{co}$	156
$S_{e'}$	$\partial i_c / \partial v_{b'}$	156
t	Ratio of R_{LD}/R_L	127
t_f	Fall time	116
t_r	Rise time	116
t_s	Storage time	116
T	Absolute temperature	6
T	Time constant	303
T	Set of network trees	357
$2\text{-}T$	Set of network two-trees	368
T_o	Reference temperature	159
U	Unilateral gain	213
v_b	Signal component of base voltage	53
v_c	Signal component of collector voltage	53
v_e	Signal component of emitter voltage	53
v_{eb}	Signal component, emitter-base voltage	53
v_i	Input voltage, signal component	48
v_o	Signal component of output voltage	48
v_s	Signal component of source voltage	114
v_s	Signal voltage	286
v_B	Instantaneous total base voltage	114
v_C	Instantaneous total collector voltage	114
v_E	Instantaneous total emitter voltage	114
v_F	Fermi drift velocity	6
v_O	Instantaneous total output voltage	114

Symbol	Definition of Symbol	Page
v_S	Instantaneous total source voltage	114
V	Voltage	59
V	Internal trees of network	357
V_{ba}	Average base voltage	114
V_{be}	Base-emitter voltage, full conduction	308
V_{bm}	Base voltage at maximum dissipation	114
V_{bn}	Negative limit base voltage	114
V_{bp}	Positive limit base voltage	114
V_{bt}	Base voltage for saturation	319
V_{bz}	Base voltage for collector cutoff	114
V_{ca}	Average collector voltage	114
V_{cb}	Collector-to-base voltage	94
V_{cm}	Collector voltage at maximum dissipation	114
V_{cn}	Negative limit collector voltage	114
V_{cp}	Positive limit collector voltage	114
V_{ct}	Saturation collector voltage	325
V_{cz}	Collector voltage at cutoff	114
V_{ea}	Average emitter voltage	114
V_{em}	Emitter voltage at maximum dissipation	114
V_{en}	Negative limit emitter voltage	114
V_{ep}	Positive limit emitter voltage	114
V_{ez}	Emitter voltage at cutoff	114
V_n	Negative limit voltage	353
V_{oa}	Average output voltage	114
V_{on}	Negative limit output voltage	114
V_{op}	Positive limit output voltage	114
V_{oz}	Output voltage at cutoff	114
V_p	Positive limit voltage	353
V_{sa}	Average source voltage	114
V_{sn}	Negative limit source voltage	114
V_{sp}	Positive limit source voltage	114
V_{sz}	Source voltage at cutoff	114
V_B	Applied bias voltage	58
V_B	Static value of base voltage	114
V_{BB}	Base supply voltage	114
V_{BM}	Maximum value of base signal voltage	114
V_C	Applied collector voltage	58
V_C	Static value of collector voltage	114
V_{CC}	Collector supply voltage	114
V_{CM}	Maximum value of collector signal voltage	114
V_E	Static value of emitter voltage	114
V_{EE}	Emitter supply voltage	114
V_{EM}	Maximum value of emitter signal voltage	114
V_O	Static value of output voltage	114
V_{OM}	Maximum value of output signal voltage	114
V_{OO}	Output circuit supply voltage	114

Symbol	Definition of Symbol	Page
V_S	Static value of source voltage	114
V_{SM}	Maximum value of source signal voltage	114
V_{SS}	Source supply voltage	114
W	Base width in transistor	26
$W_{i,o}^{i,o}$	Driving-point two-trees	357
$W_{j,o}^{i,o}$	Transfer two-trees	357
x	Current ratio variable	207, 281
X	Reactance component	51
X_L	Load reactance	165
X_o	Link reactance	249
y	Source-sink admittance	286, 357
y_{11}	Input admittance	37
y_{12}	Reverse transfer admittance	37
y_{21}	Forward transfer admittance	37
y_{22}	Output admittance	37
y_c	Modified output admittance $= h_o$	37
y_{ca}	Average modified output admittance	115
y_{cn}	Negative limit value, y_c	115
y_{cp}	Positive limit value, y_c	115
y_{cs}	Static value, y_c	115
y_f	Forward admittance	37
$y_{f'}$	Intrinsic forward admittance	46, 57
y_{fa}	Average value of forward admittance	115
y_{fn}	Negative limit value of forward admittance	115
$y_{fo'}$	Forward admittance at reference temp.	159
y_{fp}	Positive limit value — forward admittance	115
y_{fs}	Static value, forward admittance	115
y_i	Input admittance	37
$y_{i'}$	Intrinsic input admittance	46, 57
y_{ia}	Average input admittance	115
y_{in}	Negative limit input admittance	115
$y_{io'}$	Input admittance at reference temp.	156
y_{ip}	Positive limit input admittance	115
y_{is}	Static value, input admittance	115
y_o	Output admittance	37
y_{oa}	Average output admittance	115
y_{on}	Negative limit output admittance	115
y_{op}	Positive limit output admittance	115
y_{os}	Static value output admittance	115
y_r	Reverse transfer admittance	37
y_r	Reference source-sink signal admittance	286
y_r	Feedback admittance	203
y_u	Equivalent total feedback admittance	203
Y	Y parameters	52
Y_0, Y_2, Y_4, Y_6	Shunt admittance elements of ladder network	259
Y_1, Y_3, Y_5	Series admittance elements	259

Symbol	Definition of Symbol	Page
Y_1, Y_2, Y_3, Y_4	Admittances	235
Y_0, Y_1	Coefficients of power-series expansion of admittance function	229
Y_{cp}	Primary-side shunt capacitive admittance	165
Y_{cs}	Secondary shunt capacitive admittance	165
Y_f	Over-all forward admittance	214
Y_{fa}	Over-all average forward admittance	244
Y_{fn}	Over-all negative-limit value, Y_f	244
Y_{fp}	Over-all positive-limit value, Y_f	244
Y_{fs}	Over-all static value, Y_f	244
Y_i	Over-all input admittance	173
Y_{max}	Maximum value of admittance, Y	229
Y_{min}	Minimum value of admittance, Y	229
Y_{pm}	Primary magnetizing admittance	165
Y_{sm}	Secondary magnetizing admittance	165
Y_t	Admittance equal to $1/(r_{b'} + R_s)$	360
Y_{LD}	Admittance equal to $1/Z_{LD}$	360
z	Turns-ratio, n_s/n_p	166
z_{11}	Input impedance	68
z_{12}	Reverse impedance	68
z_{12}	Mutual impedance	237
z_{21}	Forward impedance	68
z_{21}	Mutual impedance	237
z_{22}	Output impedance	68
z_{23}	Mutual impedance	237
z_{32}	Mutual impedance	237
z_f	Forward impedance	49
z_{fb}	Forward impedance, C. B.	69
z_{fc}	Forward impedance, C. C.	69
z_i	Input impedance	49
z_{ib}	Input impedance, C. B.	69
z_{ic}	Input impedance, C. C.	69
z_o	Output impedance	49
z_o	Output impedance	196
z_{ob}	Output impedance, C. B.	69
z_{oc}	Output impedance, C. C.	69
z_r	Reverse impedance	49
z_{rb}	Reverse impedance, C. B.	69
z_{rc}	Reverse impedance, C. C.	69
Z	Z parameters	51
Z	Relative impedance level	49
Z_2, Z_3	Impedances of network	237
Z_1, Z_3, Z_5, Z_7	Series impedances, ladder network	259
Z_i	Input impedance	235
Z_o	Crystal impedance	251
Z_r	Impedance at reference frequency	283

Symbol	Definition of Symbol	Page
Z_{LD}	Tuned or untuned load impedance	200
Z_T	Transfer impedance	235
α	Current gain	50
α_N	Forward current gain	116
α_I	Reverse current gain	116
β	Current gain	50
γ	Multiplication factor $0 < \gamma < 1$	95
γ_c	Current increment $\partial I_{co}/\partial T$	161
$\gamma(h)$	Hybrid factor $= 1 + h_f - h_r + \Delta(h)$	67
δ	Number $\ll 1$	324
$\Delta(g)$	Value is $g_i g_o - g_f g_r$	67
$\Delta(h)$	Value is $h_i h_o - h_f h_r$	67, 105
$\Delta(y)$	Value is $y_i y_o - y_f y_r$	67, 103
$\Delta(z)$	Value is $z_i z_o - z_f z_r$	67
Δf_o	Frequency increment	221
Δg_c	Total change in g_c	115
Δg_f	Total change in g_f	115
$\Delta g_{f'}$	Total change in $g_{f'}$	115
Δg_i	Total change in g_i	115
Δg_i	Total change in $g_{i'}$	115
Δg_o	Total change in g_o	115
Δi_b	Base current change	96
Δi_c	Collector current change	115
Δi_e	Emitter current change	115
Δi_o	Output current change	115
Δi_s	Source current change	115
Δv_b	Base voltage change	114
Δv_c	Collector voltage change	114
Δv_e	Emitter voltage change	114
Δv_o	Output voltage change	114
Δv_s	Source voltage change	114
Δy_c	Change in y_c	115
Δy_f	Change in y_f	115
$\Delta y_{f'}$	Change in $y_{f'}$	115
Δy_i	Change in y_i	115
$\Delta y_{i'}$	Change in $y_{i'}$	115
Δy_o	Change in y_o	115
ΔI_{co}	Change in I_{co}	161
ΔK	Change in amplification	115
ΔK_σ	RMS change in K in oscillator	219
ΔP_c	Change in collector dissipation	161
ΔT	Change in temperature	161
ΔV_{pos}	Positive voltage change from static	353
ΔV_{neg}	Negative voltage change from static	353
$\Delta \omega$	Radian frequency increment	215
$\Delta \omega_o$	Radian frequency increment	221

Symbol	*Definition of Symbol*	*Page*
λ_F	Mean-free-path	6
Λ	$\Lambda = (q/kT)$	58
μ	micro	
π	3.1415926	
σ	Conductivity	5
$\sigma(g)$	$g_i + g_f + g_r + g_o$	53
$\sigma(g')$	$g_{i'} + g_{f'} + g_{r'} + g_{o'}$	70
$\sigma(z)$	$z_i - z_f - z_r + z_o$	67
$\sigma(y)$	$y_i + y_f + y_r + y_o$	67
$\sigma(y')$	$y_{i'} + y_{f'} + y_{r'} + y_{o'}$	70
σ_i	Intrinsic conductivity	58
σ_n	n-type conductivity	58
σ_p	p-type conductivity	58
$\sigma_{p'}$	Collector p-type conductivity	58
$\sigma(R)$	Summation $r_{b'} + R_s + R_e$	142
σR	Summation $r_{b'} + R_s + R_L$	147
τ_F	Relaxation time	6
τ_p	Lifetime in PNP transistors (minority carriers)	59
ω	Radian frequency	50
ω_o	Nominal resonant radian frequency	215
ω_o	Ladder oscillator radian frequency	261
ω_1	Nominal R-C radian frequency ($\omega_1 RC = 1'$)	263
ω_a	Roll-off radian frequency knee, emitter follower	142
ω_b	Level-off radian frequency knee, emitter follower	142
ω_r	Reference radian frequency, parametric amplifier	285
ω_s	Signal radian frequency, parametric amplifier	285
ω_{rs}	Idler radian frequency, parametric amplifier	288

APPENDIX II

Derivation of Distortion Equations

The derivation of the equation for distortion of a nonlinear device in terms of voltage differences has been available for many years. The equation takes the form

$$D = 50(\Delta V_{pos} - \Delta V_{neg})/(V_p - V_n) \ \% \qquad (II-1)$$

The voltage differences in the two polarities, ΔV_{pos} and ΔV_{neg}, both represent averaged values of the amplification in the two directions, the one showing the average increase, and the other the average decrease. In this section, the distortion equations in terms of small-signal behavior are derived, based on an assumption of a linear variation of amplification with input voltage. Under these conditions, the distortion generated is principally a second-harmonic. First the variation of amplification with input signal should be established.

$$K = K_0 + K_1 v_b \qquad (II-2)$$

and the limiting values of amplification are given by the equations

$$K_p = K_0 + K_1 \Delta v_b, \qquad K_n = K_0 - K_1 \Delta v_b$$
$$\Delta v_b = V_{bp} - V_{bs} = V_{bs} - V_{bn} \qquad (II-3)$$

If Eq. (II-2) is integrated to give the output voltage, it gives

$$v_o = \int_{-\Delta v_b}^{\Delta v_b} K dv_b = \int_{-\Delta v_b}^{\Delta v_b} [K_0 + K_1 v_b] dv_b \qquad (II-4)$$

over the limits from $(-\Delta v_b)$ to $(+\Delta v_b)$. The result takes the form

$$v_o = K_0 v_b + K_1 v_b^2/2 \qquad (II-5)$$

before the substitution of the limits, and a similar form involving Δv_b after substitution.

The value of v_b may be expressed in terms of a sinusoidal input signal

$$v_b = V_B \sin \omega t$$

and then Eq. (II–5) takes the form

$$v_o = K_0 V_B \sin \omega t + (K_1 V_B^2 \sin^2 \omega t)/2 \tag{II–6}$$

$$= K_0 V_B \sin \omega t + 0.25 K_1 V_B^2 [1 - \cos 2\omega t] \tag{II–7}$$

From this last equation, the relation of the second harmonic to the fundamental is given by the equation

$$D = 100 K_1 V_B^2/4K_0 V_B = 25 K_1 V_B/K_0 \tag{II–8}$$

If, now, the limit amplifications, K_p and K_n, are defined by the following equations, assuming predominate second harmonic

$$K_p = K_0 + K_1 V_B, \qquad K_n = K_0 - K_1 V_B \tag{II–9}$$

The differences and sums of these equations are

$$K_p - K_n = 2K_1 V_B, \qquad K_p + K_n = 2K_0$$

Substituting these in Eq. (II–8) gives

$$D = 25(K_p - K_n)/(K_p + K_n)\% \tag{II–10}$$

The procedure for calculation of the third-harmonic component parallels that used above.

APPENDIX III

Topological Equation Derivation

The algebra involved in the derivation of the operating equations for transistor amplifiers is sufficiently complex that the use of simplifying methods of derivation can be very helpful. Flow graphs are useful for this purpose when only the transfer function is required, but other methods are required if both driving-point and transfer functions are required. One method that has proven extremely helpful in applications where both driving-point and transfer functions are required is the use of graph theory, or network topology, in the determination of the small-signal equations. Topological design is based on Kirchhoff's laws and several properties of "network trees."

1. With nodal networks, the self-admittance of the network may be expressed in terms of the quotient of the sum of tree products divided by the sum of the tree products for the network with the admittance terminals short-circuited.

2. A tree product is the product of a group of admittances so selected that each vertex is touched by at least one admittance and no closed paths or circuits are formed by the selected admittances.

3. The sum of the tree products includes all possible trees that can be formed using the given set of vertices.

4. No element of a tree (no branch) can appear more than once in any product in a network that contains no mutual inductance.

5. Active devices such as tubes or transistors have separate current and voltage representations; for example, the transconductance of a tube has a current element in the plate circuit, and a voltage element in the grid.

6. Trees for active circuits include some that may be called partial trees and others that are complete trees. Partial trees are ones found in

either the current or the voltage graph, but not on both, whereas complete trees appear on both. These complete trees may have different orientations for the two diagrams, but they have the same admittance components.

7. The relative orientations of the elements in the current representation and the voltage representation of a tree determines the sign of the tree. A series of transformations is made to determine the sign.

The application of these rules to the design of transistor circuits minimizes the probability of making errors of algebra because it establishes setup and checking routines that can be applied as the derivation is being made.

Basic Steps. The first step in the analysis of a circuit to obtain its driving-point or transfer immittance is the establishment of the composite circuit diagram. All passive elements may be represented as resistances in the usual way so that they are readily recognized, and then special symbols may be used to represent the special active elements, the current and voltage "immittances" that appear in the circuit. For transistors, the active elements are the trans-admittances, y_f and y_r. In addition, the input and output voltages and currents may be represented by the special symbols. Such a composite diagram for a simple transistor amplifier is shown in Fig. III–1.

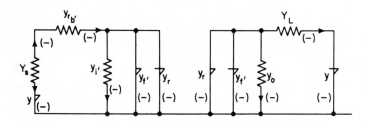

Fig. A-III-1. Topological diagram of transistor amplifier. Negative end of admittance indicated by arrowhead

Next, the composite diagram may be separated into a voltage graph and a current graph. Each of the passive elements is included in both graphs, but only voltage components are included in the voltage graph and current elements in the current graph. The special symbols shown in Fig. III–2 are required both for voltage and current components of admittances and also for source and sink elements.

The voltage source element has the same properties as are possessed by a battery, that is, when the voltage is reduced to zero (removal) a short circuit remains. The current-sink element, which behaves as an ammeter, also presents a short circuit on its removal. On the other hand, however, the current source and the voltage sink both disappear from in parallel with an admittance when they are removed, so that an open circuit results. The same general properties can, with some limitations, result with the trans-elements. With tubes and transistors, the elements are voltage sinks and current sources, and hence represent open circuits on removal, whereas with a mutual inductance, the elements are current sinks and voltage sources, and in this case behave as short circuits on removal. The direction and type of action must be considered.

Voltage   Current

|(+) |(+)

|(−) |(−)

Fig. A-III-2. Voltage and current source sink symbols (and transfer symbols)

The trees may now be tabulated for either the current or the voltage graph. The required number of trees is determined as described on page 365. If the number of trees corresponding to the maximum are tabulated, only part of them are trees for the full network. Each tree of one graph may be checked against the other graph, and those that form trees on both graphs are called complete trees, those that form circuits or other defective trees are called partial or incomplete trees. Each defective tree for one graph has a corresponding but different defective tree present in the companion graph. After the incomplete trees are discarded, the remaining trees are separated into two groups, one containing the source admittance element, y, and one not containing the source element. The complete topological equation for the network now reads

$$yW_{i,o}^{i,o} + V = T \qquad\qquad \text{(III–1)}$$

where T is the tree sum, V is the sum of the trees not involving the y element, and the W term the sum of the y-tree terms with the y factored out. Because the y representing the source element acts as a generator or power source, the equation may be solved for $(-y)$ to give $(T = 0)$

$$Y_{io,io} = (-y) = V/W_{i,o}^{i,o} \qquad\qquad \text{(III–2)}$$

The use of this equation and its equivalent for transfer networks for the derivation of driving-point and transfer immittance equations and the formation of its components is the subject for discussion in this Appendix.

The transfer admittance function may be determined in a similar manner. To set up the respective current and voltage networks for the determination of the trees for a transfer network, a source element is placed to activate the input terminal pair (in parallel if a current source and in series if a voltage) and a sink element is placed in the output circuit (in series with the load if a current sink, and in parallel with the load if a voltage). Then the trial trees may be determined from the current and voltage graphs, the partial trees eliminated, and the remaining trees sorted into those including y and those not including y as before. The transfer tree equation reads

$$yW + V = T_t \qquad\qquad (\text{III--3})$$

where the properties of W and V are dependent on whether the expression is for a transfer admittance or a transfer impedance. This equation is again equated to zero, because the y symbol represents both the energy source and the sink as before, and the solution for $(-y)$ again found

$$(-y) = V/W \qquad\qquad (\text{III--4})$$

If a voltage source and a current load are included in the circuit, the equation is for a transfer admittance, and the transfer term is in V, whereas if a current source and a voltage load are included in the circuit, the equation is for a transfer impedance and the transfer term is in the denominator, indicating that the transfer equation should be written as

$$(-1/y) = W/V \qquad\qquad (\text{III--5})$$

The denominators of Eqs. (III--4) and (III--5) are the internal network terms (typically

$$[1 + y_o R_L + y_{i'}(R_s + r_{b'})(1 + y_c R_L)]$$

for the common-emitter amplifier).

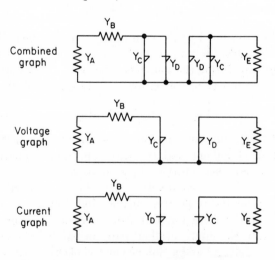

Fig. A-III-3. Voltage and current graphs

The polarity sign associated with an individual tree may be determined by establishing a transformation table, and determining the n mber of interchanges and sign changes required to bring the symbol arrangements into coincidence. The table is established by writing one column for each significant node of the network, and arranging the admittances of the tree so each admittance is used only once, and one of the admittances is in each column. There may be two different arrangements for the two graphs, and the sign is determined by the number of changes required to bring the positions and the polarities of the symbols to coincidence.

As an example, consider the current and voltage graphs shown in Fig. III–3. If the transposition table is prepared based on the tree $Y_B Y_C Y_D$, the table takes the form

	$Y_B Y_C Y_D$			
	1	2	3	
v	Y_B	Y_C	Y_D	
i	Y_B	Y_D	Y_C	
Transpose	Y_B	Y_C	Y_D	$(-1)^1$

It is necessary to transpose the C and D terms in the current row to produce coincidence with the voltage row, and, because one sign change is required, the term has a negative polarity, giving a negative tree. If the total number of sign changes, including one for each individual transposition and one for each final sign reversal is even, the sign of the tree is positive, if odd, then negative.

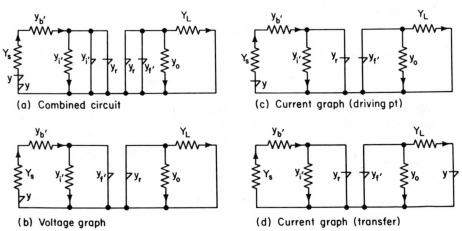

(a) Combined circuit

(b) Voltage graph

(c) Current graph (driving pt)

(d) Current graph (transfer)

Fig. A-III-4. For Example 1

EXAMPLE 1. Derive the equations for input admittance and voltage gain for a simple transistor amplifier whose combined circuit graph is shown in Fig. III–4(a). Assume that the series resistance R_t in the base lead includes both the base-spreading resistance, $r_{b'}$, and the series source resistance, R_s, and determine the equation for $R_s = 0$.

First the voltage and current graphs are drawn as shown in (b) and (c) in Fig. III–4. Directions are assigned on an arbitrary basis to each passive resistance because these signs are used in the polarity determination for the trees. Otherwise the symbols for passive resistances are conventional. The transfer elements and the source and sink elements use the special symbols shown in Fig. III–2. The complete set of partial trees for the voltage graph may now be tabulated for the driving-point (input) admittance

y terms:

$$yY_tY_L, \quad yy_{i'}Y_L, \quad yy_oY_t, \quad yy_{i'}y_o, \quad yy_{f'}y_r,$$

$$yy_{i'}y_r, \quad yy_{f'}y_o, \quad yy_{f'}Y_L, \quad yy_rY_t$$

Other terms:

$$Y_ty_{i'}Y_L, \quad Y_ty_{i'}y_o, \quad Y_ty_{f'}y_r,$$

$$Y_ty_{i'}y_r, \quad Y_ty_{f'}y_o, \quad Y_tY_Ly_{f'}$$

In each of these groups, those in the first row represent full trees, and the second row partial trees of the voltage graph. The corresponding partial trees of the current graph are

y terms:

$$yy_{i'}y_{f'}, \quad yy_ry_o, \quad yy_rY_L$$

Other terms:

$$Y_ty_{i'}y_{f'}, \quad Y_ty_ry_o, \quad Y_tY_Ly_r$$

Writing the quotient for $(-y)$, but using all positive signs between terms gives the equation

$$(-y) = [Y_ty_{i'}Y_L + Y_ty_{i'}y_o + Y_ty_{f'}y_r]/[Y_tY_L + y_{i'}Y_L$$
$$+ y_oY_t + y_{i'}y_o + y_{f'}y_r] \tag{III–6}$$

where the last term in each bracket will be shown to have a negative sign.

The signs of the various terms may now be determined as demonstrated above

yY_ty_o			yY_tY_L			$yy_{i'}y_o$		
1	2	3	1	2	3	1	2	3
$v\ y$ y	$-Y_t$	y_o	y	$-Y_t$	Y_L	y	$y_{i'}$	y_o
$i\ y$ y	$-Y_t$	y_o	y	$-Y_t$	Y_L	y	$y_{i'}$	y_o
(+)			(+)			(+)		

$yy_{i'}Y_L$			$yy_{f'}y_r$			$Y_ty_{f'}y_r$		
1	2	3	1	2	3	1	2	3
$v\ y$ $y_{i'}$	Y_L		y	$y_{f'}$	y_r	Y_t	$y_{f'}$	y_r
$i\ y$ $y_{i'}$	Y_L		y	y_r	$y_{f'}$	Y_t	y_r	$y_{f'}$
(+)			(−)			(−)		

The terms in the first four of these tables are identical, so the signs of all the corresponding trees are positive. The last two tables both required one interchange to make them identical, so the trees are negative. All other terms can be shown to be positive, giving the driving-point admittance as

$$Y_{is} = [y_{i'}(1 + y_cR_L)]/[1 + y_oR_L + y_{i'}R_t(1 + y_cR_L)] \qquad \text{(III-7)}$$

where both numerator and denominator have been multiplied by R_tR_L and the delta factor has been replaced by $y_{i'}y_c$. If R_s is allowed to go to zero, R_t becomes $r_{b'}$, and this equation then reduces to

$$Y_i = [y_{i'}(1 + y_cR_L)]/[1 + y_oR_L + y_{i'}r_{b'}(1 + y_cR_L)] \qquad \text{(III-8)}$$

Reference to Eq. (4–23) in Chapter Four shows that this is the equation previously derived.

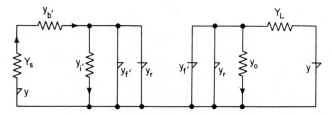

Fig. A-III-5. Combined transfer graph for Example 1

The principal change required in the derivation of the transfer admittance is the moving of the y element in the current graph to a position in series with Y_L (Fig. III–5a). The trees having y as a factor are unchanged for the transfer problem: only the remaining terms are changed. The only one representing a complete tree is

$$y_{f'}Y_tY_L$$

The polarity of this term is of interest. The table for its determination is

	$y_{f'}Y_tY_L$			
	1	2	3	
v	Y_t	$y_{f'}$	Y_L	
i	$-Y_L$	$-Y_t$	$y_{f'}$	
T_1	$y_{f'}$	$-Y_t$	$-Y_L$	$(-)$
T_2	$-Y_t$	$y_{f'}$	$-Y_L$	$(-)^2$
S	Y_t	$y_{f'}$	Y_L	$(-)^4$

thus giving a positive sign for the term.

Figure III–5(b) shows the graph configuration for the determination of the transfer impedance. The complete trees for this network are

y terms: $\qquad\qquad -yy_{b'}y_{f'}$

Other terms:

$$Y_sY_Ly_{b'}, \quad y_{b'}y_{i'}Y_L, \quad y_{b'}y_oY_s, \quad Y_sy_{i'}Y_L,$$
$$y_{b'}y_{i'}y_o, \quad y_{b'}y_{f'}y_r, \quad Y_sy_{i'}y_o, \quad Y_sy_{f'}y_r$$

The transfer equation, introducing the correct signs, takes the form

$$(-y) = [1 + y_oR_L + y_{i'}(R_s + r_{b'})(1 + y_cR_L)]/[-y_{f'}R_sR_L] \quad \text{(III–9)}$$

The transfer impedance then is

$$(-1/y) = -y_{f'}R_sR_L/[1 + y_oR_L + y_{i'}(R_s + r_{b'})(1 + y_cR_L)] \quad \text{(III–10)}$$

The corresponding transfer admittance is

$$(-y) = y_{f'}/[1 + y_oR_L + y_{i'}(R_s + r_{b'})(1 + y_cR_L)] \quad \text{(III–11)}$$

The only difference other than sign between these equations is the presence of R_sR_L in the numerator of Eq. (III–10) and its absence in (III–11).

Significantly, the only negative terms in the driving-point admittance terms or the internal terms of the transfer immittance are those involving the $y_{f'}y_r$ factor. These two graph elements interchange on the current and the voltage graphs, and require an odd number of exchanges to bring them into coincidence. The voltage-gain equation is obtained by multiplying Eq. (III–11) by R_L, and the current-gain equation by multiplying Eq. (III–10) by Y_L.

EXAMPLE 2. As a further example of the use of the topological method, the equations for the common-base amplifier may be derived, showing the ease with which the complications otherwise present may be avoided. The complete correct relations for this amplifier are given in Eqs. (9), (13), (14), (19), (25), (26), (27), (28), and (29) in Chapter Four. The difficulty results in taking account of the effect of base-spreading resistance.

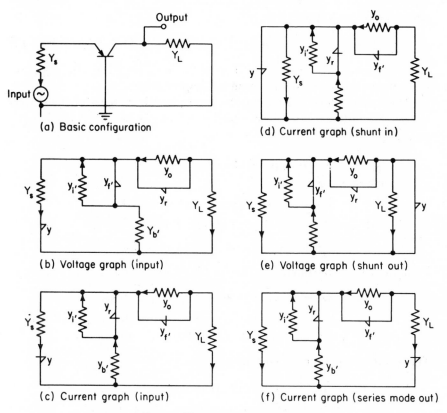

Fig. A-III-6. For Example 2

The basic network and the various graphs are shown in Fig. III–6. The complete trees for the input admittance are

y terms:

$$yY_sy_{f'}y_r, \quad yY_sy_{i'}y_o, \quad yY_sy_{b'}y_o, \quad yY_sy_{i'}Y_L,$$

$$yy_{b'}y_{i'}y_o, \quad yy_{b'}y_{f'}y_r, \quad yy_{b'}y_{f'}Y_L, \quad yy_{b'}y_oY_L, \quad yy_{i'}y_oY_L,$$

$$yy_{f'}y_rY_L, \quad yy_{b'}y_{i'}Y_L, \quad yy_{b'}y_rY_L, \quad yY_sy_{b'}Y_L$$

Y_s terms:

$$Y_sy_ry_{b'}y_{f'}, \quad Y_sy_{b'}y_{i'}y_o, \quad Y_sy_{b'}y_{i'}Y_L, \quad Y_sy_{b'}y_{f'}Y_L,$$

$$Y_sy_{b'}y_rY_L, \quad Y_sy_{b'}y_oY_L, \quad Y_sy_{i'}y_oY_L, \quad Y_sy_{f'}y_rY_L$$

In terms of these trees, the input admittance is

$$Y_{is} = [\sigma(y) + y_{i'}y_c(r_{b'} + R_L)]/[1 + y_o R_L + \sigma(y)R_s$$
$$+ y_{i'}r_{b'} + y_{i'}y_c(r_{b'}R_s + r_{b'}R_L + R_s R_L)] \qquad \text{(III–12)}$$

and, with $R_s = 0$, it is

$$Y_i = [\sigma(y) + y_{i'}y_c(r_{b'} + R_L)]/[1 + y_o R_L + y_{i'}r_{b'}(1 + y_c R_L)] \quad \text{(III–13)}$$

after multiplication by $R_s r_{b'} R_L$. If $r_{b'}$ is taken as zero, then the equation simplifies to the corresponding form in Chapter Four.

The forward-current gain may be determined by the use of the graphs in Figs. III–6(d) and (e). The complete trees may be tabulated as follows

y terms:

$$yy_{b'}y_{f'}, \quad yy_{b'}y_o, \quad yy_{i'}y_o, \quad yy_{f'}y_r$$

Other terms:

$$Y_s y_{b'} Y_L, \quad y_{b'} y_{i'} Y_L, \quad y_{b'} y_{f'} Y_L, \quad y_{b'} y_r Y_L,$$
$$y_{b'} y_o Y_L, \quad Y_s y_{i'} Y_L, \quad Y_s y_{b'} y_o, \quad Y_s y_{i'} y_o, \quad Y_s y_{f'} y_r,$$
$$Y_L y_{i'} y_o, \quad Y_L y_{f'} y_r, \quad y_{b'} y_{i'} y_o, \quad y_{b'} y_{f'} y_r$$

From these trees, the following transfer admittance equation may be formed

$$(1/Z_f) = (-y) = [1 + \sigma(y)R_s + y_{i'}r_{b'} + y_o R_L$$
$$+ y_{i'} y_c (r_{b'} R_L + r_{b'} R_s + R_s R_L)]/[(y_{f'} \qquad \text{(III–14)}$$
$$+ y_o) + y_{i'} y_c r_{b'}]R_s R_L$$

The resulting equation for current gain is

$$K_i = [(y_{f'} + y_o) + y_{i'} y_c r_{b'}]R_s/[1 + \sigma(y)R_s$$
$$+ y_{i'}r_{b'} + y_o R_L + y_{i'} y_c (r_{b'} R_L + r_{b'} R_s + R_s R_L)] \qquad \text{(III–15)}$$

The output voltage is divided by the load resistance to convert the output signal to current and give the current gain.

The transfer admittance for the same circuit and its voltage gain may both be established from a corresponding set of complete trees

y terms:

$$y Y_s y_{b'} y_o, \quad y Y_s y_{b'} Y_L, \quad y Y_s y_{i'} y_o, \quad y Y_s y_{i'} Y_L,$$
$$-y Y_s y_{f'} y_r, \quad yy_{b'} y_{i'} y_o, \quad -yy_{b'} y_{f'} y_r, \quad yy_{i'} y_{b'} Y_L, \quad yy_{b'} y_{f'} Y_L,$$
$$yy_{b'} y_r Y_L, \quad yy_{b'} y_o Y_L, \quad yy_{i'} y_o Y_L, \quad -yy_{f'} y_r Y_L$$

Other terms:

$$Y_s y_{b'} y_{f'} Y_L, \quad Y_s y_{b'} y_o Y_L, \quad Y_s y_{i'} y_o Y_L, \quad -Y_s y_{f'} y_r Y_L$$

The equations for the transfer admittance and voltage gain resulting from these trees are

$$(-y) = [(y_{f'} + y_o) + y_{i'}y_c r_{b'}]/[1 + \sigma(y)R_s + y_{i'}r_{b'}$$
$$+ y_o R_L + y_{i'}y_c(r_{b'}R_L + r_{b'}R_s + R_s R_L)] \qquad \text{(III–16)}$$

$$K = [(y_{f'} + y_o) + y_{i'}y_c r_{b'}]R_L/[1 + \sigma(y)R_s + y_{i'}r_{b'}$$
$$+ y_o R_L + y_{i'}y_c(r_{b'}R_L + r_{b'}R_s + R_s R_L)] \qquad \text{(III–17)}$$

Tree Determinations. One of the critical problems in the use of the topological method is the calculation of the number of trees required in the establishment of one of the immittance expressions. Knowing this number precisely is helpful in that once the specified number of trees is found, the search can be terminated.

The "maximum" number of trees is determined by establishing a determinant having $(v - 1)$ rows and columns, where v is the number of vertices. The diagonal numbers in this determinant give the number of elements, on either the current or the voltage graph, contacting the specified vertex, and the off-diagonal terms are the negatives of the number of elements coupling two vertices directly. In the voltage graph (Fig. III–4b), for example, the determinant takes the form, where T_M indicates the maximum

$$T_M = \begin{vmatrix} 2 & -1 & 0 \\ -1 & 3 & 0 \\ 0 & 0 & 3 \end{vmatrix} = 15$$

This maximum number gives the total number of trees and partial or incomplete trees in the specified network. The minimum number of trees in general may be called T_m, and in particular may be represented as T_i, T_b, T_f, or T_o. This number is the difference in the total positive and total negative trees in the network. The T_i is used to identify the number of trees in the input immittance for the network, the T_b the number in the basic network with the y-factor eliminated, the T_f the number of trees in the transfer immittance for the network, and T_o the number of trees in the output immittance. The difference between T_b and T_f may be either positive or negative, depending on whether or not there is a phase reversal in the transfer immittance. The magnitude of the difference indicates the number of terms in the transfer part of the immittance function if terms involving the delta-factor are omitted. Because the delta-factor terms include equal numbers of positive and negative trees, they are not counted in the procedures to be described.

The establishment of the minimum number of trees for any network requires first the establishment of the incidence matrices for both the current and the voltage graphs. The incidence matrix for a chosen graph contains $(v - 1)$ rows, one less than the number of vertices, and the one eliminated is usually that having the most connections (the ground). The number of columns in this matrix is equal to the number of elements of the chosen graph, and one column is assigned to each element. After the rows have been assigned numbers corresponding to the vertices of the graph, the identification of the connection pattern is introduced by identifying by plus or minus one the fact that a given admittance contacts a specified vertex, and by zero the fact that it does not. The origin end of the admittance, in accordance with the arrowhead symbol, has the positive unity, and the terminal the negative unity.

After the incidence matrix has been formed, it can be noted that there are at most two non-zero entries in any column, and the number of entries in a given vertex row gives the number of elements incident at the vertex. Because one of the entries on many of the elements may be to the common ground, many columns may have only one entry.

After both the current and the voltage incidence matrices have been formed from a corresponding current and voltage graph, the product of the two may be formed to give the required tree determinant

$$T_m = A_i \times A_v^t \qquad (\text{III–18})$$

where A_i is the current incidence matrix, and A_v^t is the transpose of the voltage incidence matrix.* The correct combination of A_i and A_v may be formed for any of the forms of network desired, and the calculation (III–18) made. Extra terms corresponding to the delta-factor terms may be added, and the separation of trees from partial trees started.

The approximate number of terms involving the delta-factor may be estimated directly from the graph configuration. In driving-point admittances, there is normally a delta-factor term in the numerator if there is a non-zero impedance connected across the port opposite to that at which the admittance is being determined. Likewise, there is a delta-factor term in the denominator only if there is an external impedance at the point of measurement and a non-zero terminating impedance on the opposite port. The presence of a return impedance like an emitter-degeneration resistance for a common-emitter amplifier, or base-spreading resistance in the common-base amplifier makes available additional delta-factor combinations, for

* If the matrices to be multiplied are

$$A = \begin{pmatrix} a & b \\ c & d \end{pmatrix}, \qquad B = \begin{pmatrix} e & f \\ g & h \end{pmatrix}$$

then the product $A \times B^t$ is defined by the equation

$$A \times B^t = \begin{pmatrix} ae + bf & ag + bh \\ ce + df & cg + dh \end{pmatrix}$$

example, input-output, input-return, and output-return, which appear in the denominator.

In the transfer function, all the delta-factor terms in the denominator of the driving-point admittance are present, and a term may be present in the transfer factor if a return impedance is present, but not otherwise. The sign of the term resulting from a return impedance must be checked, as it may or may not be the same as the balance of the transfer terms.

EXAMPLE 3. Establish the incidence matrices for the transfer admittance condition with the common-emitter amplifier, and determine the minimum number of trees, T_f. Also determine the basic number of trees, T_b.

The incidence matrices are

$$
A_i = \begin{array}{c} \\ 1 \\ 2 \\ 3 \end{array}
\begin{array}{ccccccc}
y & Y_t & y_{i'} & y_{f'} & y_r & y_o & Y_L \\
\left[\begin{array}{ccccccc}
1 & 0 & 0 & 0 & 0 & 0 & -1 \\
0 & -1 & 1 & 0 & 1 & 0 & 0 \\
0 & 0 & 0 & 1 & 0 & 1 & 1
\end{array}\right]
\end{array}
$$

$$
A_v = \begin{array}{c} 1 \\ 2 \\ 3 \end{array}
\left[\begin{array}{ccccccc}
1 & 1 & 0 & 0 & 0 & 0 & 0 \\
0 & -1 & 1 & 1 & 0 & 0 & 0 \\
0 & 0 & 0 & 0 & 1 & 1 & 1
\end{array}\right]
$$

The product of these matrices gives a determinant in the form

$$
T_f = \begin{vmatrix} 1 & 0 & -1 \\ -1 & 2 & 1 \\ 0 & 1 & 2 \end{vmatrix} = 3 + 1 = 4
$$

Because the circuit contains both an input and an output resistance, there is one delta-factor term in the denominator of the expression, but none in the numerator.

The value of T_b is obtained by deleting the y column from both of the incidence matrices, and recalculating. However, because one of the vertices is eliminated by the removal of the y element, only two rows remain, namely, rows two and three. The tree determinant is

$$
T_b = \begin{vmatrix} 2 & 1 \\ 1 & 2 \end{vmatrix} = 3
$$

This result shows that the transfer term is positive. The signs of the respective trees may be calculated from the product of incidence matrices by deleting all columns not corresponding to the tree, in both matrices, and then multiplying. If the tree is negative, the matrix has a negative unity value. If it is positive, the matrix value is plus unity, and if the configuration is not a complete tree, the product has the value zero.

In circuits having the general ladder form but considerable complexity, it is possible to build the trees from sections or building blocks. Because the over-all combination must possess the properties of a tree, it is necessary to determine the kind of building blocks that can be used. The principal components for the construction of complex trees include smaller trees, two-trees of at least four types, and three-trees. The types of two-trees are:

1. One-terminal-pair two-trees, that is, networks having a single tree connected to each of the terminals and one connecting branch or element between the trees missing. Each vertex touches at least one tree element, and one tree may consist of a single vertex.

2. Two-terminal-pair (two-port) two-trees, which show two-tree properties at both ports. They are designated by the symbol 2-T, as are the two-trees in 1.

3. Two-port two-trees having two-tree properties only at the left-hand port. They are designated 2L-T.

4. Two-port two-trees having two-tree properties at the right-hand port. They are designated as 2R-T. It is also possible to establish definitions for multi-port two-trees.

The three-tree is similar to the two-tree except that with it the network is separated into three individual trees. This configuration requires a minimum of two ports.

A two-tree or a three-tree has either two or three trees, respectively, as constituent parts, and each vertex of the network forming the two- or three-tree is located on one of the tree components. Null-trees, or isolated vertices, as well as more complex trees may be included in the set.

When a network is separated into sections in the determination of the complete tree set, all possible tree combinations of each type should be tabulated, and then the sums of the tree configurations of each type determined. For a two-tree, the product representing one term of the sum is the product of the two component trees, and a three-tree the product of the three individual component tree products. Only certain types of configurations may be used together, as otherwise circuits may be developed. Some of the permitted combinations are listed below.

T	$2-T$		T	$2L-T$	
T	$3-T$	T	$2-T$	$2-T$	T
$2R-T$	T		$2R-T$	$2-T$	T
$2-T$	$2R-T$	T	$2R-T$	$2R-T$	T
$2-T$	T	$2-T$	$2R-T$	T	$2L-T$

The use of network partitioning in determining the over-all tree sum is best shown by an example.

EXAMPLE 4.   Use partitioning to determine the complete tree sum function for the three-section ladder network with input admittance shown in Fig. III–7(a). To do this, partition the network as shown in Fig. III–7(b).

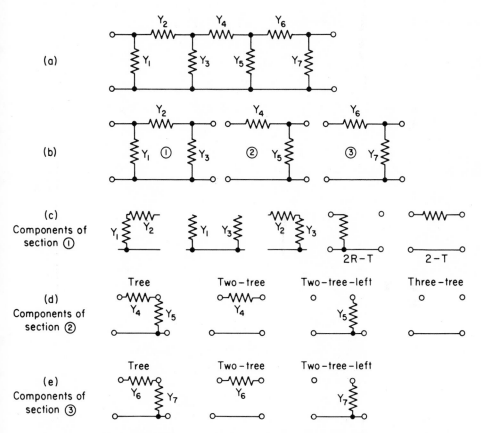

Fig. A-III-7. Use of tree partitioning for Example 4

The pi section, (1) of this network, can form the three trees shown in Fig. III–7(c), and two two-trees, one of the R variety and the other a standard one-port two-tree. Section (2), the left "ell" section, can form a tree, a pair of two-trees, or a three-trees. Similarly, Sec. (3) can form either a tree or two two-trees. The possible forms for all of these structures are shown in Fig. III–7(d).

The tree combinations that result are tabulated

$$T_1 \times 2 - T_2 \times 2 - T_3 \quad = (Y_1Y_3 + Y_1Y_2 + Y_2Y_3)Y_4Y_6$$

$$T_1 \times 2 - T_2 \times 2L - T_3 = (Y_1Y_3 + Y_1Y_2 + Y_2Y_3)Y_4Y_7$$

$$T_1 \times 2L - T_2 \times 2L - T_3 = (Y_1Y_3 + Y_1Y_2 + Y_2Y_3)Y_5Y_7$$

$$T_1 \times 2L - T_2 \times 2 - T_3 = (Y_1Y_3 + Y_1Y_2 + Y_2Y_3)Y_5Y_6$$

$$T_1 \times 3 - T_2 \times T_3 \quad = (Y_1Y_3 + Y_1Y_2 + Y_2Y_3)Y_6Y_7$$

$$2 - T_1 \times 2 - T_2 \times T_3 \quad = Y_2Y_4Y_6Y_7$$

$$2R - T_1 \times T_2 \times 2 - T_3 \quad = Y_1Y_4Y_5Y_6$$

$$2R - T_1 \times T_2 \times 2L - T_3 = Y_1Y_4Y_5Y_7$$

$$2R - T_1 \times 2 - T_2 \times T_3 \quad = Y_1Y_4Y_6Y_7$$

$$2 - T_1 \times T_2 \times 2 - T_3 \quad = Y_2Y_4Y_5Y_6$$

$$2 - T_1 \times T_2 \times 2L - T_3 \quad = Y_2Y_4Y_5Y_7$$

APPENDIX IV, PART A

Use of Legendre and Orthogonal Polynomials

The conversion of either curves or discrete data into a form in which they can express a relation in terms of a relatively small number of expressions is best done in terms of some form of orthogonal functions rather than in terms of a power series. Unless the property of orthogonality is used, an increase of accuracy through the addition of an extra element requires a complete revision of the previous solution. This orthogonality property is the factor that makes Fourier analysis useful, and it likewise is the factor that makes possible rapidly converging solutions with a minimum of work using any of the common polynomials, Legendre, orthogonal, Bessel, Laguerre, Hermite, Jacobi, and others. The discussion in this section is limited to the application of Legendre and orthogonal polynomials in the determination of spectral components directly from an input-output relation or an input-amplification relation.

Orthogonal functions have the property that the sum or integral, as applicable, of the products of two different functions of the set has a value zero. A summation, or integral, of the product of the function being represented and one of the polynomials resolve the function into components that are proportional to the components of the representing set. Because it is frequently convenient to expand transfer functions in terms of power series, the following tables permit direct conversion of the series into its corresponding orthogonal representation. An expansion table for functions varying over the range $-1 < x < +1$ and a table for functions having zero value over the range $-1 < x < 0$ follow.

TABLE I

Expansions for Complete Functions

Ord/Exp	0	1	2	3	4	5	6
0	1.00	0	1/3	0	1/5	0	1/7
1	0	1.00	0	3/5	0	3/7	0
2	0	0	2/3	0	4/7	0	10/21
3	0	0	0	2/5	0	4/9	0
4	0	0	0	0	8/35	0	24/77
5	0	0	0	0	0	8/63	0
6	0	0	0	0	0	0	16/231

TABLE II

Expansions for One-Sided Functions

Ord/Exp	0	1	2	3	4	5	6
0	1/2	1/4	1/6	1/8	1/10	1/12	1/14
1	3/4	1/2	3/8	3/10	1/4	3/14	3/16
2	0	5/16	1/3	5/16	2/7	25/96	5/21
3	−7/16	0	7/48	1/5	7/32	2/9	3/16
4	0	−3/32	0	9/128	4/35	9/64	12/77
5	11/32	0	−11/384	0	11/320	4/63	11/128
6	0	13/256	0	−13/1280	0	13/768	8/231

The diagonal of the matrix of numbers in Table I is a dividing line between diagonal-type rows that are alternatively zeros and a series of numbers and a series of diagonal rows all of whose numbers are zeros. This is a consequence of the orthogonality relations of the polynomials. All polynomials above zero order are orthogonal with a constant, because the zero-order polynomial is in fact a constant. Similarly, all polynomials above the first are orthogonal with respect to a function that is linear in x, and so on with higher orders.

An example of the usefulness of this set of tables is shown by the development of the polynomial expansion of the function

$$f(x) = (1 + x)/(1 + k + kx) \qquad (IV–1)$$

If an attempt is made to expand this function directly by integration, the resulting integrals become extremely difficult to handle, since logarithmic terms develop. If, however, the function is first expanded in a power series, the resulting series may readily be handled by Table I unless $|kx| >$ $(1 + k)$. Then the series is a diverging series. Because the maximum value of k is likely to be less than unity, and the range for x is from minus unity to plus unity, the maximum value of the ratio $kx/(1 + k)$ is one-half. The expansion then will converge, and the series takes the form

$$f(x) = [1/(1 + k)] + [1/(1 + k)]^2 x - [k/(1 + k)^3]x^2 + \ldots \quad \text{(IV-2)}$$

From this equation, the following values for the K's in the coefficient equations, Eqs. (IV-7) may be determined,

$$K_0 = [1/(1 + k)] - [k/3(1 + k)^3] - [k^3/5(1 + k)^5] - \ldots$$

$$K_1 = [1/(1 + k)^2] + [3k^2/5(1 + k)^4] + [3k^4/7(1 + k)^6] + \ldots$$

$$K_2 = -[2k/3(1 + k)^3] - [4k^3/7(1 + k)^5] - \ldots \quad \text{(IV-3)}$$

$$K_3 = 2k^2/5(1 + k)^4 + \ldots$$

$$K_4 = -[8k^3/35(1 + k)^5] + \ldots$$

From these equations and the fact that the conversion gain is $0.5K_1$, (Eq. 12-5), the conversion conductance can be determined from the equation for K_1 above. Evidently, the larger the value of k, the degeneration, the lower the conversion conductance, because the correction terms make a maximum of twenty percent increase, whereas the $1/(1 + k)^2$ multiplier reduces the conductance by as much as a factor of four.

Table II may be used for the reconstruction of Table I, in which case the terms whose sum of order and exponent is odd are zero, and even are non-zero, or it may be used for the construction of a table in which the sign of the function in the negative range is positive also. Then the terms for which the sum of order and exponent is even are zero-valued, and the value of the odd order twice that given in Table II. The coefficients for a Legendre expansion of a given continuous function $f(x)$ over any selected interval may be found from the equation

$$C_n = [(2n + 1)/2] \int_{-1}^{1} f(x)P_n(x)dx \quad \text{(IV-4)}$$

where the interval over which $f(x)$ is non-zero may extend from minus one to plus one, or the function may be zero over part of the range. The coefficients in the two tables were determined by the use of this equation.

The expressions for each of the polynomials, $P_n(x)$, may be substituted, one at a time, in Eq. (IV-4), along with the function $f(x)$ and the appropriate value of n to determine the multiplying factor to be used in representing a given function. The first few polynomials are

$$P_0(x) = 1, \qquad P_1 = x, \qquad P_2(x) = 0.5(3x^2 - 1)$$
$$P_3(x) = 0.5(5x^3 - 3x), \qquad P_4(x) = 0.125(35x^4 - 30x^2 + 3)$$
$$P_5(x) = 0.125(63x^5 - 70x^3 + 15x)$$
$$P_6(x) = 0.0625(231x^6 - 315x^4 + 105x^2 - 5) \tag{IV-5}$$
$$P_7(x) = 0.0625(429x^7 - 693x^5 + 315x^3 - 35x)$$
$$P_8(x) = 0.0078125(6435x^8 - 12012x^6 + 6930x^4 - 1260x^2 + 35)$$

In these equations, it should be remembered that x may be replaced by its equivalent, $x = \cos \theta$ to give the equations as a trigonometric multi-angle series, and they can also be written as power series if desired. The multi-angle (Chebycheff-form) equations are

$$P_0(\theta) = 1, \qquad P_1(\theta) = \cos \theta, \qquad P_2(\theta) = 0.25(3 \cos 2\theta + 1)$$
$$P_3(\theta) = 0.125(5 \cos 3\theta + 3 \cos \theta)$$
$$P_4(\theta) = 0.015625(35 \cos 4\theta + 20 \cos 2\theta + 9)$$
$$P_5(\theta) = 0.0078125(63 \cos 5\theta + 35 \cos 3\theta + 30 \cos \theta) \tag{IV-6}$$
$$P_6(\theta) = 0.001953125(231 \cos 6\theta + 126 \cos 4\theta + 105 \cos 2\theta + 50)$$
$$P_7(\theta) = 0.0009765625(429 \cos 7\theta + 231 \cos 5\theta + 189 \cos 3\theta$$
$$+ 175 \cos \theta)$$
$$P_8(\theta) = 0.00006103525625(6435 \cos 8\theta + 3432 \cos 6\theta$$
$$+ 2772 \cos 4\theta + 2520 \cos 2\theta + 1225)$$

The decimals may be rounded off as desired, because not more than three significant figures should be required in normal applications.

These values for the successive polynomials in terms of $n\theta$ may be substituted for the polynomial form, giving the unknown function in terms of the polynomials. The resulting equation gives the amplification of the respective harmonics in terms of the coefficients. The coefficients may be arranged in terms of either the amplification function or the output function to give the harmonic amplitudes. In addition, conversion equations may be written in a form to convert from one set of coefficients to the other. These various sets are

Basic output function form:

$$E_0 = C_{e0} + C_{e2}/4 + 9C_{e4}/64 + 50C_{e6}/512 + 1225C_{e8}/16{,}384$$
$$E_1 = C_{e1} + 3C_{e3}/8 + 15C_{e5}/64 + 175C_{e7}/1024$$
$$E_2 = 3C_{e2}/4 + 5C_{e4}/16 + 105C_{e6}/512 + 2520C_{e8}/16{,}384$$
$$E_3 = 5C_{e3}/8 + 35C_{e5}/128 + 189C_{e7}/1024 \tag{IV-7}$$
$$E_4 = 35C_{e4}/64 + 63C_{e6}/256 + 693C_{e8}/4096$$
$$E_5 = 63C_{e5}/128 + 231C_{e7}/1024$$

Derived gain form:

$$K_0 = C_{e1} + 9C_{e3}/4 + 225C_{e5}/64 + 1225C_{e7}/256$$

$$K_1 = 3C_{e2} + 45C_{e4}/8 + 525C_{e6}/64$$

$$K_2 = 15C_{e3}/4 + 105C_{e5}/16 + 4725C_{e7}/512$$

$$K_3 = 35C_{e4}/8 + 945C_{e6}/128 + 10395C_{e8}/1024 \tag{IV-8}$$

$$K_4 = 315C_{e5}/64 + 2079C_{e7}/256$$

$$K_5 = 693C_{e6}/128 + 9009C_{e8}/1024$$

The corresponding equations based on the input-gain relation are

Basic gain form:

$$K_0 = C_{k0} + C_{k2}/4 + 9C_{k4}/64 + 25C_{k6}/256 + 1225C_{k8}/16{,}384$$

$$K_1 = C_{k1} + 3C_{k3}/8 + 15C_{k5}/64 + 175C_{k7}/1024$$

$$K_2 = 3C_{k2}/4 + 5C_{k4}/16 + 105C_{k6}/512 + 315C_{k8}/2048$$

$$K_3 = 5C_{k3}/8 + 35C_{k5}/128 + 189C_{k7}/1024 \tag{IV-9}$$

$$K_4 = 35C_{k4}/64 + 63C_{k6}/256 + 693C_{k8}/4096$$

$$K_5 = 63C_{k5}/128 + 231C_{k7}/1024$$

The corresponding derived input-output relation is

$$E_{k1} = C_{k0} - C_{k2}/8 - C_{k4}/64 - 5C_{k6}/1024 - 35C_{k8}/16{,}384$$

$$E_{k2} = C_{k1}/4 - C_{k3}/16 - 5C_{k5}/512 - 7C_{k7}/2048$$

$$E_{k3} = C_{k2}/8 - 5C_{k4}/128 - 7C_{k6}/1024 - 21C_{k8}/8192$$

$$E_{k4} = 5C_{k3}/64 - 7C_{k5}/256 - 21C_{k7}/4096 \tag{IV-10}$$

$$E_{k5} = 7C_{k4}/128 - 21C_{k6}/1024 - 33C_{k8}/8192$$

$$E_{k6} = 21C_{k5}/512 - 33C_{k7}/2048$$

Orthogonal polynomials are used instead of the Legendre form when the data are known at equally-spaced discrete points. These polynomials are closely related to the Legendre polynomials, and can be manipulated by identical procedures with the exception that the integration is replaced by a summation. Polynomials based on discrete data are of particular use with active devices because of the form in which their characteristic curve data are provided.

The equations for evaluation of the coefficients may be given in terms of summations, or they may be expressed in terms of matrix products. The parallelism with the evaluation for Legendre polynomials is best shown in terms of the summations, but actual calculations are best made in terms of matrix representation. The summation form of the coefficients are

$$C_{kn} = |\,P_n(0)\,| \sum_{h=0}^{K} K(h)P_n(h) / \sum_{h=0}^{K} [P_n(h)]^2$$

$$C_{en} = |\,P_n(0)\,| \sum_{h=0}^{K} E(h)P_n(h) / \sum_{h=0}^{K} [P_n(h)]^2$$

(IV–11)

The first term on the right-hand side of each of these equations is required to give a dimensionally correct value for the coefficient. With it present the coefficient is dimensionally identical with the function being represented.

When the raw data give the functional behavior in terms of an input-output relation, then the second equation of (IV–11) is used for determining the coefficients. The equations based on the basic output function are used for the input-output analysis, and the derived-gain equations for the gain and admittance. When the data are given in terms of the input-amplification relation, then the first of Eqs. (IV–11) is used for the coefficients, and the basic gain and derived output form of the equations are used.

IV-1. The Conversion of the Gain-Form of the Coefficients into the Equivalent Admittance or Impedance. To determine the admittance components, for example, the input variable is taken as input voltage, and it is rescaled to have a range from minus one to plus one; the output variable is then taken as output current. The "amplification" is determined with the Eqs. (IV–11), and it gives the magnitude of the current in terms of the arbitrary input scale of plus or minus one. If, therefore, the current magnitudes determined from the Eqs. (IV–7) through (IV–10) are given in amperes, and the values are divided by the voltage increment corresponding to the voltage interval from zero to either plus or minus unity, the quotients are admittances. The equations typically take the form

$$Y_j = E_j/\delta v$$

(IV–12)

where δv is half the difference of the voltages v_p and v_n. If the output variable is selected as a voltage, then a voltage gain results. An impedance or a current gain may be determined by the use of a current as the input variable.

In Eqs. (IV–11) for the coefficients, the value of the denominator is always known once the number of data points is known and the order of n is selected. Consequently, the value of the denominator summation may be called S_j, and its value is included in the listings of the tabular values for the orthogonal polynomial, $P_n(h)$. Also, the following relation can be given for the extreme values $P_n(0)$ and $P_n(k)$, where $k + 1$ is the total number of data points used in the summation

$$| P_n(0) | = | P_n(k) | \qquad \text{(IV–13)}$$

The tabular values of the discrete polynomials differ from Legendre polynomials in two significant ways, first in that the numbers are tabulated as integers rather than as decimals, and second that the endpoint values may not have a magnitude greater than all interior points, as is the case with the Legendre polynomials. For large numbers of data points and small polynomial order, the end values may have the greatest magnitude, however, as the polynomials then have characteristics closely approaching those of the Legendre polynomials. The development of orthogonal polynomials is clearly explained in Milne, *Numerical Calculus.*[1]

The matrix procedure for calculation of the basic coefficients for use in the equations for the component amplitudes is based on Eqs. (IV–11). In the following matrix equation, the order of the individual matrices are indicated under each matrix, and those which are diagonal in form (all elements of $[a_{ij}]$ for which $i \neq j$ are identically zero) are identified by a D placed above the matrix. The equation is

$$\overset{D}{[S_j]} \times [C_j] = \overset{D}{[|P_j(0)|]} \times [P_j^t(x)] \times [f(x)] \qquad \text{(IV–14)}$$
$$\underset{m \times m}{} \underset{m \times 1}{} \underset{m \times m}{} \underset{m \times (2n+1)}{} \underset{(2n+1) \times 1}{}$$

Because the matrix $[S_j]$ is non-singular, the equation may be solved for $[C_j]$ to give

$$[C_j] = [S_j]^{-1} \times [|P_j(0)|] \times [P_j^t(x)] \times [f(x)] \qquad \text{(IV–15)}$$

The second and third matrices on the right-hand side of the equation may be combined into one matrix, thereby simplifying the calculation. Whereas the tabulations of these polynomials usually are based on $P_j(h)$, the tables of values herein are those of the product of $| P_j(0) |$ and $P_j(h)$, and they are identified by the symbol, $R_j(h)$. The resulting matrix equation is

$$[C_j] = \overset{D}{[S_j]^{-1}} \times [R_j^t(h)] \times [f(h)] \qquad \text{(IV–16)}$$
$$\underset{m \times 1}{} \underset{m \times m}{\phantom{[S_j]^{-1}}} \underset{m \times (2n+1)}{} \underset{(2n+1) \times 1}{}$$

where $[S_j]^{-1}$, because of its diagonal form, may be written in either form

$$[S_j]^{-1} = [1/S_j] \qquad \text{(IV–17)}$$

The tables of polynomial numbers listed in this appendix give the values of R_j^t and S_j, where the variable j gives the order of the polynomial and

[1] *Numerical Calculus*, by W. M. Milne. Princeton University Press, 1949.

indicates the number of the row in R_j^t, and the h, which ranges from 0 to k, identifies the specific point at which a given measurement was made. The columns of R_j^t correspond to the respective data points.

For the benefit of the reader who is unfamiliar with the process of matrix multiplication, the following example is included. When the matrices a_{ij} and b_{jk} are to be multiplied, the first step is to be sure that they are arranged to place the common index (in this example, j) on the left matrix so that it specifies the columns, and on the right matrix so that it identifies the rows. The number of columns of the left matrix must equal the number of rows of the right matrix. Then successive pairs of numbers, the one taken consecutively across the desired row of the left matrix and the other taken consecutively down a selected column of the right matrix, are multiplied, and the sums added. If these matrices are

$$a_{ij} = \begin{bmatrix} a_{11} & a_{12} & a_{13} & a_{14} \\ a_{21} & a_{22} & a_{23} & a_{24} \end{bmatrix} \quad b_{jk} = \begin{bmatrix} b_{11} & b_{12} & b_{13} \\ b_{21} & b_{22} & b_{23} \\ b_{31} & b_{32} & b_{33} \\ b_{41} & b_{42} & b_{43} \end{bmatrix} \quad \text{(IV–18)}$$

then the product is given by terms in the form

$$a_{i1}b_{1k} + a_{i2}b_{2k} + a_{i3}b_{3k} + a_{i4}b_{4k} \quad \text{(IV–19)}$$

In this matrix made from terms of the form (IV–19), the possible values for i are 1 and 2, and those for k are 1, 2, and 3. The final matrix has two rows and three columns, and the four-by-four dimensions on the component matrices have disappeared into the summations. Such a product summation may readily be prepared on a desk calculator.

As an example of the use of these procedures, the average current flow and the components of current change may be determined, and the corresponding admittance components evaluated.

A circuit is required to provide an average current of 90 microamperes, and the following values of current flow as a result of equal increments of applied voltage

V_b, mv	100	110	120	130	140	150	160	170	180
I_b, μa	10	20	35	55	80	110	145	185	230

The nominal static point may be selected at 140 millivolts and 80 microamperes, and the exact average currents for different ranges of base voltage, 120 to 160, 110 to 170, and 100 to 180, may be determined by the use of Tables VI, VII, and VIII. The calculations for the range 110 to 170 millivolts are

$$
\begin{bmatrix} C_{e0} \\ C_{e1} \\ C_{e2} \\ C_{e3} \\ C_{e4} \\ C_{e5} \end{bmatrix}
=
\begin{bmatrix}
\tfrac{1}{7} & & & & & \\
& \tfrac{1}{28} & & & & \\
& & \tfrac{1}{84} & & & \\
& & & \tfrac{1}{6} & & \\
& & & & \tfrac{1}{154} & \\
& & & & & \tfrac{1}{84}
\end{bmatrix}
\times
\begin{bmatrix}
1 & 1 & 1 & 1 & 1 & 1 & 1 \\
9 & 6 & 3 & 0 & -3 & -6 & -9 \\
25 & 0 & -15 & -20 & -15 & 0 & 25 \\
1 & -1 & -1 & 0 & 1 & 1 & -1 \\
9 & -21 & 3 & 18 & 3 & -21 & 9 \\
1 & -4 & 5 & 0 & -5 & 4 & -1
\end{bmatrix}
$$

$$
\times
\begin{bmatrix}
20 \\ 35 \\ 55 \\ 80 \\ 110 \\ 145 \\ 185
\end{bmatrix}
$$

$$
=
\begin{bmatrix}
\tfrac{1}{7} & & & & & \\
& \tfrac{1}{28} & & & & \\
& & \tfrac{1}{84} & & & \\
& & & \tfrac{1}{6} & & \\
& & & & \tfrac{1}{154} & \\
& & & & & \tfrac{1}{84}
\end{bmatrix}
\times
\begin{bmatrix}
630 \\ -2310 \\ 1050 \\ 0 \\ 0 \\ 0
\end{bmatrix}
=
\begin{bmatrix}
90 \\ -82.5 \\ 12.5 \\ 0 \\ 0 \\ 0
\end{bmatrix}
$$

The values of C_{e3}, C_{e4}, and C_{e5} all are zero for all of the sets of data as a result of the square-law relation selected for the input-output ratio. The values of the various important parameters and coefficients may be tabu-lated as follows

ΔV_b	40	60	80
C_{e0}	85	90	96.4
C_{e1}	55	82.5	110
C_{e2}	5.0	12.5	26.3
I_a	86.25	93.1	103.0
G_0	2750	2750	2750
G_1	750	1250	1977
$0.5\Delta V_b$	20	30	40

Evidently, the corrections can be important on all of the values. The conductance values are in micromhos, and the average current, I_a is in microamperes. A little practice in conjunction with either a desk calculator or a slide rule and the user can make calculations such as these in much less time than is required to measure the corresponding results.

The tables of values for $R'_j(h)$ and S_j follow.

TABLES OF ORTHOGONAL POLYNOMIALS

TABLE III

$R_j^t(h);\quad 2n+1=4$

h	0	1	2	3
j = 0	1	1	1	1
1	9	3	-3	-9
2	1	-1	-1	1
3	1	-3	3	-1

S_j

j =	0	1	2	3
0	4			
1		20		
2			4	
3				20

TABLE IV

$R_j^t(h);\quad 2n+1=5$

h	0	1	2	3	4
j = 0	1	1	1	1	1
1	2	1	0	-1	-2
2	2	-1	-2	-1	2
3	1	-2	0	2	-1
4	1	-4	6	-4	1

S_j

j =	0	1	2	3	4
0	5				
1		5			
2			7		
3				10	
4					10

TABLE V

$R_j^t(h);\quad 2n+1=6$

h	0	1	2	3	4	5
j = 0	1	1	1	1	1	1
1	5	3	1	-1	-3	-5
2	25	-5	-20	-20	-5	25
3	5	-7	-4	4	7	-5
4	1	-3	2	2	-3	1
5	1	-5	10	-10	5	-1

S_j

j =	0	1	2	3	4	5
0	6					
1		14				
2			84			
3				90		
4					28	
5						252

TABLE VI

$R_j^t(h)$ *for* $2n + 1 = 7$

h	0	1	2	3	4	5	6
$j = 0$	1	1	1	1	1	1	1
1	9	6	3	0	−3	−6	−9
2	25	0	−15	−20	−15	0	25
3	1	−1	−1	0	1	1	−1
4	9	−21	3	18	3	−21	9
5	1	−4	5	0	−5	4	−1

S_j

$j =$	0	1	2	3	4	5
0	7					
1		28				
2			84			
3				6		
4					154	
5						84

TABLE VII

$R_j^t(h)$ *for* $2n + 1 = 8$

h	0	1	2	3	4	5	6	7
$j = 0$	1	1	1	1	1	1	1	1
1	7	5	3	1	−1	−3	−5	−7
2	7	1	−3	−5	−5	−3	1	7
3	49	−35	−49	−21	21	49	35	−49
4	7	−13	−3	9	9	−3	−13	7
5	7	−23	17	15	−15	−17	23	−7

S_j

$j =$	0	1	2	3	4	5
0	8					
1		24				
2			24			
3				264		
4					88	
5						312

TABLE VIII

$$R_j^t(h) \text{ for } 2n + 1 = 9$$

h	0	1	2	3	4	5	6	7	8
j = 0	1	1	1	1	1	1	1	1	1
1	4	3	2	1	0	−1	−2	−3	−4
2	28	7	−8	−17	−20	−17	−8	7	28
3	98	−49	−91	−63	0	63	91	49	−98
4	14	−21	−11	9	18	9	−11	−21	14
5	4	−11	4	9	0	−9	−4	11	−4

S_j

j =	0	1	2	3	4	5
0	9					
1		15				
2			99			
3				495		
4					143	
5						117

TABLE IX

$$R_j^t(h) \text{ for } 2n + 1 = 10$$

h	0	1	2	3	4	5	6	7	8	9
j = 0	1	1	1	1	1	1	1	1	1	1
1	27	21	15	9	3	−3	−9	−15	−21	−27
2	6	2	−1	−3	−4	−4	−3	−1	2	6
3	294	−98	−245	−217	−84	84	217	245	98	−294
4	162	−198	−153	27	162	162	27	−153	−198	162
5	6	−14	1	11	6	−6	−11	−1	14	−6

S_j

j =	0	1	2	3	4	5
0	10					
1		110				
2			22			
3				1430		
4					1430	
5						130

In the remaining tables, only even values of n are used, and only half of the table is presented. The balance of the table is symmetrical or anti-symmetrical with respect to the part listed, symmetry being indicated by the letter S, and anti-symmetry by AS. Each additional term is the negative of the corresponding listed term when the symbol is AS. With the symbol S the signs are the same. For example, in Table X, the series of numbers for $j = 2$ are 75, 25, -5, -30, -45, -50, and, completing the series, -45, -30, -5, 25, and 75. Those for $j = 3$ are 30, -6, -22, -23, -14, 0, and 14, 23, 22, 6, and -30 for the additional terms.

TABLE X

$R_j^t(h)$ for $2n + 1 = 11$

h	0	1	2	3	4	5	Sym.
$j = 0$	1	1	1	1	1	1	S
1	5	4	3	2	1	0	AS
2	75	30	-5	-30	-45	-50	S
3	30	-6	-22	-23	-14	0	AS
4	18	-18	-18	-3	12	18	S
5	3	-6	-1	4	4	0	AS

S_j

$j =$	0	1	2	3	4	5
0	11					
1		22				
2			286			
3				143		
4					143	
5						52

TABLE XI

$R_j^t(h)$ for $2n + 1 = 13$

h	0	1	2	3	4	5	6	Sym.
$j = 0$	1	1	1	1	1	1	1	S
1	18	15	12	9	6	3	0	AS
2	22	11	2	-5	-10	-13	-14	S
3	11	0	-6	-8	-7	-4	0	AS
4	891	-594	-864	-486	99	576	756	S
5	242	-363	-198	121	286	220	0	AS

S_j

$j =$	0	1	2	3	4	5
0	13					
1		91				
2			91			
3				52		
4					6188	
5						3094

TABLE XII

$R_j^t(h)$ for $2n + 1 = 15$

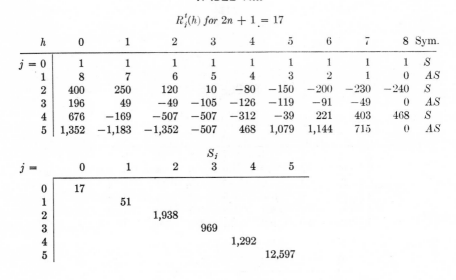

h	0	1	2	3	4	5	6	7	Sym.
j = 0	1	1	1	1	1	1	1	1	S
1	7	6	5	4	3	2	1	0	AS
2	91	52	19	−8	−29	−44	−53	−56	S
3	637	91	−245	−406	−427	−343	−189	0	AS
4	1,001	−429	−869	−704	−249	251	621	756	S
5	11,011	−12,584	−10,769	−484	8251	11,000	7425	0	AS

S_j

j =	0	1	2	3	4	5
0	15					
1		40				
2			408			
3				3,060		
4					6,460	
5						116,280

TABLE XIII

$R_j^t(h)$ for $2n + 1 = 17$

h	0	1	2	3	4	5	6	7	8	Sym.
j = 0	1	1	1	1	1	1	1	1	1	S
1	8	7	6	5	4	3	2	1	0	AS
2	400	250	120	10	−80	−150	−200	−230	−240	S
3	196	49	−49	−105	−126	−119	−91	−49	0	AS
4	676	−169	−507	−507	−312	−39	221	403	468	S
5	1,352	−1,183	−1,352	−507	468	1,079	1,144	715	0	AS

S_j

j =	0	1	2	3	4	5
0	17					
1		51				
2			1,938			
3				969		
4					1,292	
5						12,597

$R_j(h)$ for $2n + 1 = 13$

h	0	1	2	3	4	5	6	7	8	9	Sym.
j = 0	1	1	1	1	1	1	1	1	1	1	S
1	27	24	21	18	15	12	9	6	3	0	AS
2	51	34	19	6	-5	-14	-21	-26	-29	-30	S
3	408	136	-56	-178	-240	-252	-224	-166	-88	0	AS
4	5,508	-612	-3,492	-4,077	-3,186	-1,512	378	2,043	3,168	3,564	S
5	102	-68	-98	-58	3	54	79	74	44	0	AS

	0	1	2	3	4	5
j = 0	19					
1		190				
2			266			
3				2,090		
4					33,649	
5						874

TABLE XV

$R_j^t(h)$ for $2n + 1 = 21$

h	0	1	2	3	4	5	6	7	8	9	10	Sym.
j = 0	1	1	1	1	1	1	1	1	1	1	1	S
1	10	9	8	7	6	5	4	3	2	1	0	AS
2	18,050	12,635	7,790	3,515	-190	-3,325	-5,890	-7,885	-9,310	-10,165	-10,450	S
3	285	114	-12	-98	-149	-170	-166	-142	-103	-54	0	AS
4	49,419	0	-26,010	-34,680	-31,365	-20,706	-6,630	7,650	19,635	27,540	30,294	S
5	65,892	-32,946	-58,956	-44,506	-13,396	18,071	40,018	47,923	41,548	23,868	0	AS

	0	1	2	3	4	5
j = 0	21					
1		77				
2			100,947			
3				1,518		
4					301,070	
5						533,715

APPENDIX IV, PART B

Trapezoidal Corrections

In theory one might expect the Legendre and the orthogonal procedures to yield identical results, and in fact when the value of n is sufficiently large, they do converge to common values. Because electronic problems often take a form that makes available only a limited group of data this convergence cannot be assured, and it is convenient to be able to estimate the corrections for the various coefficients to give the results as determined on the basis of Legendre polynomials with continuous data.

The results obtained using the orthogonal values based on the tables included in Part A of this appendix often give results that are good enough for routine applications. In fact, error only shows up conclusively when an attempt is made to fit data calculated on the basis of a specified relation known in closed form to an orthogonally equivalent solution. Separate correction is required for the even-order terms and for the odd-order terms because of the way the odd-order coefficients zero out in the calculation of an even-order coefficient, and vice versa.

The correction multipliers may be set up in a matrix form and used to correct the coefficients to those of the corresponding Legendre coefficients. This matrix is useful because of the triangular form of its entries. The coefficients take the form shown in Table XVI. Similar coefficients for correction of exponents of five and greater may be prepared. For example, the order five-exponent-five coefficient is

$$C_{5c} = 4n^4 C_5 / (2n - 1)(2n - 3)(n - 1)(n - 2) \qquad \text{(IV-20)}$$

The proper means of analysis for the determination of the respective coefficients is to introduce a power-series with arbitrary coefficients, both in closed form and numerically, and determine from the resulting expressions the correct conversion equations for correcting the terms. The coefficients should convert the numerical values to the forms given in Table I of this appendix.

TABLE XVI

Coefficient Correction Table

Ord/Exp	0	1	2	3	4
0	C_0	0	$\dfrac{[f(q)+nC_0]}{(n+1)}$	0	$f(q)+\dfrac{nC_2}{2n-1}+\dfrac{C_4[108n^4-594n^3-1540n^2-1985n-930]}{24(2n-1)^2(2n-3)(n-1)}$
1	0	C_1	0	$C_1-\left[\dfrac{C_3(3n-1)}{(2n-1)(n-1)}\right]$	0
2	0	0	$\dfrac{2n^2C_3}{(2n-1)}$	0	$\dfrac{2nC_2}{(2n-1)}-\dfrac{5C_4}{3}\left[\dfrac{180n^3+308n^2+397n+186}{(2n-1)^2(2n-3)(n-1)}\right]$
3	0	0	0	$\dfrac{2n^2C_3}{(2n-1)(n-1)}$	0
4	0	0	0	0	$\dfrac{4n^3C_4}{(2n-1)(2n-3)(n-1)}$

APPENDIX I.V, PART C

Elliptical Load Lines

Orthogonal analysis techniques may also be used in the evaluation of the circuit properties of a transistor-reactive-load operating combination. The principal requirement that must be fulfilled by the circuit for the technique to be described to apply is that the load contour have what may be called central symmetry, that is, on each radial through the center, or static Q-point, the displacement to one side of the center is exactly equal to the displacement to the other side of the center.

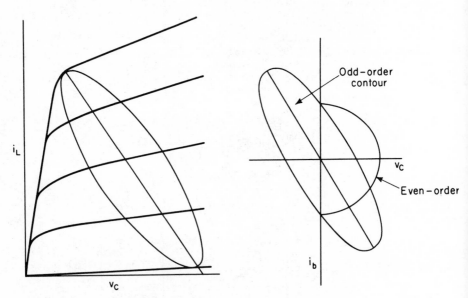

Fig. A-IV-1. Basic elliptic contour

Fig. A-IV-2. Replotted contour

The first step in the analysis of an elliptic contour is to tabulate the current and voltage data at the successive base-current contours, and to make an orthogonal analysis of one of the two sections of the contour from one bias limit to the other limit. The result will be expressed in terms of a complete set of coefficients of order zero, one, two, three, up through some number commonly five. The odd coefficients represent the in-phase components of the relation, and may be kept unchanged. The even coefficients are re-assembled into a curved contour like the original one, except that a new central plotting point is selected at one of the extremities. This process is indicated graphically in Figs. IV–1 through IV–4. Figure IV–1 shows the original contour with the bias curves superimposed. Figure IV–2 shows the result of replotting the curve as a function of bias current, and also shows the position of the contour formed by the odd-order components. Replotting in effect reconstitutes the contour by plotting differences from the odd-order contour, thereby bending it down to the horizontal axis. The differences are plotted above and below this contour as the axis. The even-order contour resulting has altered limits, since the Q-point on one side is taken as one limit, that on the other side as the second limit, and the point of intersection of the even-contour with the axis is taken as the new Q-point. The replotted curve is shown in Fig. IV–3.

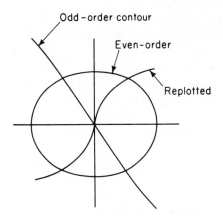

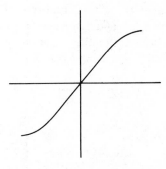

Fig. A-IV-3. Separated contours

Fig. A-IV-4. Replotted and rescaled even contour

The scale used for plotting this contour may now be altered to provide the correct quadrature relation (Fig. IV–4). The scale selected for the replotting must be one which will give proper emphasis to the respective values, so that the final curve will properly fit the available data. The process is explained in some detail in Chapter 12, *Radio Engineering Handbook*.[1]

The relation among the various data points for the symmetric and the asymmetric portions of the contour may readily be expressed in terms of arc-trigonometric relations. In effect, the symmetric or in-phase portion uses points linearly spaced in terms of the base-current spacing, and the asymmetric portion in terms of the complementary arc-function. The data points are associated in terms of Table XVII. In this table, $n\Delta i$ is the total magnitude of the bias excursion either side of the Q-point.

TABLE XVII

Direct and Quadrature Angle Relations

Direct		Quadrature	
Angle	*Bias Increment*	*Angle*	*Bias Increment*
Arcsin 0	0	Arccos 0	$n\Delta i$
Arcsin $1/n$	Δi	Arccos $1/n$	$\Delta i \sqrt{n^2 - 1}$
Arcsin $2/n$	$2\Delta i$	Arccos $2/n$	$\Delta i \sqrt{n^2 - 4}$
Arcsin $3/n$ etc.	$3\Delta i$	Arccos $3/n$ etc.	$\Delta i \sqrt{n^2 - 9}$
Arcsin 1	$n\Delta i$	Arccos 1	0

These direct and quadrature coefficients are independently combined to give the magnitudes of the direct and the quadrature components of each harmonic in accordance with Eqs. (IV-7). The harmonic-time multiplier for the direct components take the form $\cos k\omega t$, where k is the harmonic order, and $\cos (k\omega t + 90°)$ for the quadrature components.

---

[1] *Radio Engineering Handbook*, K. Henney, Editor; Chapter 12, "Nonlinear Circuits," by K. A. Pullen, Jr., McGraw-Hill Book Co., New York, 1959.

APPENDIX V

Bibliography

The bibliography that follows in this appendix lists a large number of the references consulted in the process of preparing this book. In general, only the title, author, and source is given, but for some articles or references considered to contain particularly important material bearing on the development of this book, brief notes on the contents have been included. This list is by no means all-inclusive, but it may prove helpful to the reader.

The list is divided into some sixteen different categories to facilitate locating different items, and is further subdivided alphabetically according to authors. The individual topics are:

1. Diode technology	9. Tuned amplifiers
2. Semiconductor technology	10. Transistor oscillators
3. Transistor technology	11. Transistorized regulated power supplies
4. Transistor characteristics	12. Transistorized computing circuits
5. General circuits	13. Transistor pulse circuits
6. Stabilization	14. Transistor noise
7. D-C amplifiers	15. Transistor circuits
8. A-C amplifiers	16. General nonlinear elements

Detailed reference has been made to these sources as required, and only brief reference where little direct use has been made of the material.

The following list includes some of the books that may prove useful to the reader for correlative reading. With the exception of *Conductance Design of Active Circuits,* none of them consider transistor circuit design on a coordinated basis, but they contain much useful basic data on the devices or on semiconductor physics.

De France, Joseph J.: *Electron Tubes and Semiconductors,* Prentice-Hall, Inc., Englewood Cliffs, N. J., 1958.

Dekker, Adrianus J.: *Solid State Physics,* Prentice-Hall, Inc., Englewood Cliffs, N. J., 1957.

Henney, Keith, Editor: *Radio Engineering Handbook*, McGraw-Hill Book Co., New York, 1959. Of particular interest are Chaps. 10 and 12.

Kron, Gabriel: *Tensor Analysis of Networks*, John Wiley & Sons, Inc., New York, 1938. This book and other related books by the same author give a good exposé of the basis for the topological method.

Lo, Arthur W., Richard O. Endres, Fred D. Waldhauer, and Chung-Chih Cheng: *Transistor Electronics*, Prentice-Hall, Inc., Englewood Cliffs, N. J., 1955.

Middlebrook, R. D.; *An Introduction to Junction Transistor Theory*, John Wiley & Sons, Inc., New York, 1957.

Pressman, Abraham I.: *Design of Transistorized Circuits for Digital Computers*, John F. Rider Publisher, Inc., New York, 1959.

Pullen, Keats A., Jr.: *Conductance Design of Active Circuits*, John F. Rider Publisher, Inc., New York, 1959.

Riddle, Robert L., and Marlin P. Ristenbatt: *Transistor Physics and Circuits*, Prentice-Hall, Inc., Englewood Cliffs, N. J., 1958.

Smith, Charles V. L.: *Electronic Digital Computers*, McGraw-Hill Book Co., New York, 1959.

van der Ziel, Albert: *Solid State Physical Electronics*, Prentice-Hall, Inc., Englewood Cliffs, N. J., 1957. This book is an excellent treatment of the basic electronics of semiconductors.

Van Valkenburg, Mac E.: *Network Analysis*, Prentice-Hall, Inc., Englewood Cliffs, N. J., 1955. An excellent treatment.

Weed, Herman R., and Wells L. Davis: *Fundamentals of Electron Devices and Circuits*, Prentice-Hall, Inc., Englewood Cliffs, N. J., 1959.

DIODE TECHNOLOGY

Anders, R. J., and E. L. Steele: "A Medium Power Silicon Rectifier," *IRE Trans.* PGED, Wescon, 1957, p. 73.

Armstrong, H. L.: "Some Reasons for Nonsaturation of Reverse Current in Junction Diodes," *IRE Trans.* PGED, April 1958, p. 66.

———: "On the Switching Transient in the Forward Conduction of Semiconductor Diodes," *IRE Trans.* PGED, April 1957, p. 111.

Barnes, F. S.: "The Forward Switching Transient in Semiconductor Diodes," *Proc. IRE*, July, 1958.

Belovitch, V.: "Effect of Rectifier Capacitance on the Conversion Loss of Ring Modulators," *IRE Trans.* PGCT, March 1955, p. 41.

Bergson, A., "Silicon Diode Application Notes," *Electronic Design*, 5 March 1958, p. 58.

Bisson, D. K.: "A Medium Power Silicon Controlled Rectifier," *IRE Trans.* PGED, Wescon, 1958.

Bogue Electric Co.: "Standard Base Silicon Rectifiers," *Electronic Design*, June 1955, p. 36.

———: "High Power Silicon Rectifier," *Electronic Design*, 15 March 1957, p. 24.

Carman, J. N., and W. R. Sittner: "Thermal Properties of Semiconductor Diodes," *IRE Trans.* PGED, Conv. Rec., 1955, p. 105.

Cutler, M., and H. M. Bath: "Surface Leakage Current in Silicon Fused Junction Diodes, *Proc. IRE*, Jan. 1957, p. 39.

Davies, L. W.: "Low-High Conductivity Junctions in Semiconductors," *Proc. Physical Society*, Sec. B, Sept. 1, 1957, p. 885.

Finnegan, F.: "Junction Diodes — Features and Applications," *IRE Trans.* PGED, Jan. 1955, p. 51.

Firle, T. E.: "Some Silicon Junction Diode Recovery Phenomena," *IRE Trans.* PGED, Wescon, 1957, p. 90.

Forster, J. H., and P. Zuk: "Millimicrosecond Diffused Silicon Computer Diodes," *IRE Trans.* PGED, Wescon, 1958, p. 122.

Golahny, Y.: "Silicon Diodes as Logarithmic Elements," *Electronics*, Aug. 1, 1957, p. 196.

Gossick, B. R.: "A Note on the Small-Signal Amplitude Transient Response of P-N Junctions," *Proc. IRE*, Feb. 1956, p. 259.

Henderson, J. C., and J. R. Tillman: "Minority Carrier Storage in Semi-Conductor Diodes," *Jour. IEE*, Mar. 1957, p. 162.

Henkels, H. W.: "Germanium and Silicon Rectifiers," *Proc. IRE*, June 1958, p. 1086.

Hewlett, C. W.: "Method of Making P-N Junction Semiconductor Units," Patent 2,780,559, Feb. 1957.

Hughes, H. E., J. H. Wiley, and P. Zuk: "Diffused Silicon Diodes — Design Characteristics, and Aging Data," *IRE Trans.* PGED, Wescon, 1957, p. 80.

Lehovic, K., A. Marcus, and K. Schoeni: "Current-Voltage Characteristics and Hole Injection Factor of Point Contact Rectifiers in the Forward Direction," *IRE Trans.* PGED, Jan. 1956.

Matare, H. F.: "Grain Boundaries and Transistor Action," *IRE Trans.* PGED, Conv. Rec., 1955, p. 113.

Rediker, R. H., and D. E. Sawyer: "Very Narrow Base Diode," *Proc. IRE*, July 1957, p. 944.

Rudenberg, H. G.: "Developments in Silicon Junction Diodes and Power Rectifiers," *IRE Trans.* PGED, Conv. Rec., 1955, p. 125.

Shockley, W.: "The Theory of P-N Junctions in Semiconductors and P-N Junction Transistors," *Bell System Tech. Jour.*, July 1949, p. 435.

Thornton, C. G., and L. D. Hanley: "A New High Temperature Silicon Diode," *IRE Trans.* PGED, Conv. Rec., 1954, p. 84.

————: "A High-Temperature Silicon Diode," *Proc. IRE*, Feb. 1955, p. 186.

Uhlir, A., Jr.: "Two-Terminal P-N Junction Devices for Frequency Conversion and Computation," *Proc. IRE*, Sept. 1956, p. 1183.

————: "Diode Function Generator Design, A Russian Translation," *Electronic Design*, 1 Sept. 1956, p. 92.

————: "High Power Silicon Rectifier," *Electronic Design*, 1 July 1957, p. 58.

————: "Zener Diode Characteristics," *Electronic Design*, 19 Mar. 1958, p. 26.

SEMICONDUCTOR TECHNOLOGY

Aldrich, R. W., and T. A. Lesk: "The Double-Base Diode: A Semiconductor Thyratron," *IRE Trans.* PGED, Feb. 1954, p. 24.

Brattain, W. H., and G. L. Pearson: "History of Semiconductor Research," *Proc. IRE,* Dec. 1955, p. 1794.

Chang, S. S. L.: "Relation between Ratio of Diffusion Lengths of Minority Carriers and Ratio of Conductivities," (letter), *Proc. IRE,* July 1957, p. 1019.

Cutler, M.: "Point-Contact Rectifier Theory," *IRE Trans.* PGED, July 1957, p. 201.

Dill, F., Jr., and L. Depian: "Semiconductor Capacitance Amplifier," *IRE Trans.* PGED, Conv. Rec., 1956, p. 172. Discusses parametric amplification using semiconductor diodes.

Fletcher, N. H.: "The High-Current Limit for Semiconductor Junction Devices," *Proc. IRE,* June 1957, p. 862.

Fritts, R. W.: "High-Voltage Semimetal Thermocouples," *Electronic Design,* 28 May 1958, p. 28.

Giacoletto, L. J.: "Junction Capacitance and Related Characteristics Using Graded Impurity Semiconductors," *IRE Trans.* PGED, July 1957, p. 207.

Hannay, N. B.: "Recent Advances in Silicon," *Progress in Semiconductors,* I, John Wiley & Sons, Inc., 1956, p. 3.

Hurley, R. B.: "Flow-Line Analysis," *Electronic Industries,* April 1957, p. 52.

————: "Avalanche Flow-Line Analysis," *Electronic Industries,* June 1957, p. 101.

Lin, H. C., and R. E. Crosby: "A Determination of Thermal Resistance of Silicon Junction Devices," *IRE Convention Record,* Part 3, Vol. 5, 1957, p. 22.

Low, G. G. E.: "A Method of Evaluating Surface State Parameters from Conductance Measurements," *Proc. Physical Society,* Sec. B, Dec. 1, 1956, p. 1331.

Prim, R. C., and W. Shockley: "Joining Solutions at the Pinch-Off Point in Field-Effect Transistors," *IRE Trans.* PGED, Dec. 1953, p. 1.

Schwarz, R. F., and J. F. Walsh: "The Properties of Metal-to-Semiconductor Contacts," *Proc. IRE,* Dec. 1953, p. 1715.

Shockley, W.: "Electrons, Holes, and Traps," *Proc. IRE,* June 1958, p. 973.

Smits, F. M.: "Formation of Junction Structures by Solid-State Diffusion," *Proc. IRE,* June 1958, p. 1049.

Suran, J. J.: "Low-Frequency Circuit Theory of the Double-Base Diode," *IRE Trans.* PGED, April 1955, p. 40.

————: "Small-Signal Wave Effects in the Double-Base Diode," *IRE Trans.* PGED, Jan. 1957, p. 34.

Van Horn, H. B., and W. Y. Stevens: "Determination of Transient Response of a Drift Transistor," *IBM Journal of Research and Development,* Apr. 1957, p. 189.

Willardson, R. K.: "New Semiconductor Materials," *Battelle Technical Review,* Aug. 1957, p. 8.

TRANSISTOR TECHNOLOGY

Aldrich, R. W., R. H. Lanzl, D. E. Maxwell, J. O. Percival, and M. Walduer: "An 85 Watt Dissipation Silicon Power Transistor," IRE Fall PGED Meeting, 1957.

Aldrich, R. W., and M. Walduer: "Medium Power Silicon Transistors," *Proc. National Conf. Airborne Electronics*, May 1955, p. 353.

Avakian, A.: "Germanium NPN Junction Transistor Triodes," (with D. M. Unger), *Proc. IRE*, April 1958, p. 783.

Baker, D. W.: "High-Frequency Germanium NPN Tetrode," *IRE Trans.* PGED, Conv. Rec., 1956, p. 143. Gives admittance and capacitance values and has good bibliography.

Beatty, H. J., and R. E. Swanson: "High-Speed, High-Current PNP and NPN Drift Transistors," IRE Fall PGED Meeting, 1957.

Bowe, J. J.: "A New Higher Ambient Transistor," *IRE Trans.* PGED, July 1956, p. 121. Introduction of 3% Si into Ge increases Fermi gap to 0.83 ev from 0.72 ev.

————: "Silicon-Germanium Transistors," *Electronic Equipment*, Sept. 1957, p. 26.

Brower, W. C., and C. E. Earheart: "70 mc. Silicon Transistor," IRE Fall PGED Meeting, 1957.

Brown, J. S., and T. P. Sylvan: "Silicon Unijunction Transistor," *Electronic Design*, 8 Jan. 1958, p. 56; 22 Jan. 1958, p. 30.

CBS-Hytron: "Low-Cost Power Transistors," *Electronic Design*, 1 Nov. 1956, p. 24.

Chang, C. M.: "An NPN High-Power Fast Germanium Core Driver Transistor," IRE Fall PGED Meeting, 1957.

Chang, H. C., and J. Philips: "Germanium Power Switching Devices," *IRE Trans.* PGED, Jan. 1958, p. 13.

Clark, M. A.: "Power Transistors," *Proc. IRE*, June 1958, p. 1185.

Cornelison, B., and W. A. Adcock: "Transistors by the Grown-Diffused Technique," *IRE Trans.* PGED, Wescon, 1957, p. 22. Describes grown-diffused techniques for reduction of series impedances, giving values of $r_{ee'} = 0.5\omega$, $r_{b'} = 150\omega$, $r_{cc'} = 60\omega$.

Delco Mfg. Co.: "Switching Transistor," *Electronic Design*, 1 Mar. 1957, p. 62.

Ditrick, N. H.: "High Frequency Germanium Transistors," *Proc. IRE National Conf. Aeronautical Electronics*, May 1957, p. 371.

Drapkin, H.: "Microforms for Semiconductors," *Electronic Design*, 15 July, 1957, p. 110.

Dwork, L., C. Huang, and H. W. Palmer: "Some Application Aspects of the Tetrode Transistor," *IRE Trans.* PGED, Feb. 1954, p. 7.

Emeis, R., and A. Herlet: "The Blocking Capability of Alloyed Silicon Power Transistors," *Proc. IRE*, June 1958, p. 1216.

Emeis, R., A. Herlet, and E. Spenke: "The Effective Emitter Area of Power Transistors," *Proc. IRE*, June 1958, p. 1220.

Flaherty, P., G. Freedman, P. Kaufmann, D. Root, D. Spittlehouse, W. Waring *et al.:* "A New Five-Watt, Class A, Silicon Power Transistor," *IRE Trans.* PGED, Conv. Rec., 1958, p. 77.

Fletcher, N. H.: "Note on 'The Variation of Junction Transistor Current Amplification Factor with Emitter Current,' " *Proc. IRE*, Oct. 1956, p. 1475.

————: "Junction Transistor for K. W. Pulses," (letter), *Proc. IRE*, Apr. 1957.

Gaertner, W. W.: "Design Theory for Depletion Layer Transistors," *Proc. IRE*, Oct. 1957, p. 1392.

Green, M.: "The Gaussistor — A Solid-State Electronic Valve," *IRE Trans.* PGED, July 1956, p. 133.

Griswold, D. M., and V. J. Cadre: "Use of the RCA 2N384 Drift Transistor as a Linear Amplifier," *IRE Trans.* PGED, Conv. Rec., 1958, p. 49.

Gudmundson, R. A., W. P. Waters, A. L. Wannlund, and W. V. Wright: "Recent Developments in Silicon Fusion Transistors," *IRE Trans.* PGED, Jan. 1955, p. 63.

Hebb, M. H.: "New Frontiers in Solid-State Physics," *Electronic Design*, 15 July 1957, p. 25.

Henkels, H. W.: "Transistor High-Level Injection and High-Current Switches," *Proc. National Electronics Conf.*, Oct. 1957, p. 13.

Henkels, H. W., and T. P. Nowalk: "High-Power Silicon Transistors," *IRE Trans.* PGED, Wescon, 1958, p. 157.

Henkels, H. W., and G. Strull: "Very-High-Power Transistors with Evaporated Aluminum Electrodes," *IRE Trans.* PGED, Oct. 1957, p. 291. Typical values $y_i = 0.033$ mho, $y_f = 1.4$ mho, $y_c = 0.01$ mho.

Jenny, D. A.: "The Status of Transistor Research in Compound Semiconductors," *Proc. IRE*, June 1958, p. 959.

Kestenbaum, A. L., and N. H. Ditrick: "Design, Construction and High-Frequency Performance of Drift Transistors," *RCA Review*, March 1957, p. 12.

Kestenbaum, A. L., and J. W. Englund: "A Drift Transistor for High-Frequency Applications," *Proc. National Electronics Conf.*, 1956, p. 668.

Klamack, J. J., and A. J. Wahl: "Factors Affecting Reliability of Alloy Junction Transistors," *Proc. IRE*, April 1956, p. 494.

Kordalewski, A. P.: "PNP Transistor with High-Current Amplification Forward and Reverse," *Proc. National Electronics Conf.*, 1956, p. 481.

Kroemer, H.: "Theory of a Wide-Gap Emitter for Transistors," *Proc. IRE*, Nov. 1957, p. 1535.

Lesk, I. A., and R. E. Gonzalez: "High Frequency Transistors by the Diffused-Meltback Process Employing Three Impurities," IRE Fall PGED Meeting, 1957.

————: "Germanium and Silicon Transistor Structures by the Diffused-Meltback Process Employing Two or Three Impurities," *IRE Trans.* PGED, July 1958, p.121.

Lin, H. C., and R. E. Crosby: "A Determination of Thermal Resistance of Silicon Junction Devices," *IRE* Conv. Rec. PGED, Part 3, Vol. 5, 1957.

Mackintosh, I. M.: "Three-Terminal PNPN Transistor-Switches," *IRE Trans.* PGED, Jan. 1958, p. 10.

Macnee, A. B.: "Approximating the Alpha of a Junction Transistor," *Proc. IRE*, Jan. 1957, p. 91.

Maupin, J. T.: "Tetrode Power Transistor," *IRE Trans.* PGED, Jan. 1957, p. 1.

Miller, L. E.: "The Design and Characteristics of a Diffused Silicon Logic Amplifier Transistor," *IRE Trans.* PGED, Wescon, 1958, p. 132.

Mitchell, A., and L. Lapidus: "High-Current Switching Times for a PNP Drift Transistor: Numerical Analysis on IBM 704 Digital Computer," *IRE Trans.* PGED, Conv. Rec., 1958, p. 157.

Moll, J. L.: "Junction Transistor Electronics," *Proc. IRE*, Dec. 1955, p. 1807.

Moll, J. L., and M. Tannenbaum: "PNPN Transistor Switches," *Proc. IRE*, Sept. 1956, p. 1174.

Molozzi, A. R., D. F. Page, and A. R. Boothroyd: "Measurement of High-Frequency Equivalent Circuit Parameters of Junction and Surface Barrier Transistors," *IRE Trans.* PGED, April 1957, p. 120. An excellent bridge for measurement of $r_{b'}$ and f_α is discussed.

Mooers, H. T.: "Recent Developments in Power Transistors," *IRE Trans.* PGED, Jan. 1955, p. 63. Shows need for input data in terms of v_b.

Mueller, C. W., and J. Hilibrand: "The Thyristor — A New High-Speed Switching Transistor," *IRE Trans.* PGED, Jan. 1958, p. 2.

Nelson, J. T., J. E. Iwerson, and F. Keywell: "A Five-Watt 10 mc Transistor," *Proc. National Conference Aeronautical Electronics*, May 1957, p. 380.

————: "A Five-Watt 10 mc Transistor," *IRE Trans.* PGED, Wescon, 1957, p. 28.

Orman, C., and L. White: "Diffused Emitter and Collector PNP and NPN Silicon Medium-Power Transistors," IRE Fall PGED Meeting, 1957.

Pankove, J. I.: "Transistor Fabrication by the Melt-Quench Process," *Proc. IRE*, Feb. 1956, p. 185.

Pankove, J. I., and C. W. Mueller: "A PNP Triode Alloy Junction Transistor for R. F. Amplification," *IRE Trans.* PGED, Feb. 1954, p. 6.

Philips, A. B., and A. M. Intrater: "A New High-Frequency NPN Silicon Transistor," *IRE National Conv. Rec.* PGED, 1957, p. 3.

Prince, M. B.: "High-Frequency Silicon-Aluminum Alloy Junction Diode," *IRE Trans.* PGED, Oct. 1955, p. 8.

Pritchard, R. L. "Two-Dimensional Current Flow in Junction Transistors at High Frequencies," *Proc. IRE*, June 1958, p. 1152.

————: "Advances in the Understanding of the P-N Junction Triode," *Proc. IRE*, June 1958, p. 1130.

Raytheon Mfg. Co.: "High-Frequency Transistors," *Electronic Design*, Feb. 1955, p. 32.

Reich, B.: "What is the Status of Transistors?" *Electronic Design*, 15 July 1957, p. 24.

Rittman, A. D., and T. J. Miles: "High-Frequency Silicon Alloy Transistor," *IRE Trans.* PGED, April 1956, p. 78.

Rittman, A. D., G. C. Messenger, R. A. Williams, and E. Zimmerman: "Microalloy Transistor," *IRE Trans.* PGED, April 1958, p. 49.

Saby, J. S.: "Transistors for High-Power Application," *IRE Trans.* PGED, Conv. Rec., 1954, p. 80.

Sardella, J. J., and R. C. Wonson: "A New High Frequency Diffused-Base NPN Silicon Transistor," *IRE Trans.* PGED, Conv. Rec., 1958, p. 68.

Schenkel, H., and H. Statz: "Junction Transistors with Alpha Greater than Unity," *Proc. IRE*, March 1956, p. 360.

Schwartz, R. S., and B. N. Slade: "A High-Speed PNP Alloy-Diffused Drift Transistor for Switching Applications," IRE Fall PGED Meeting, 1957.

Sparks, J. J., and R. Beaufoy: "The Junction Transistor as a Charge-Controlled Device," (letter), *Proc. IRE*, Dec. 1957, p. 1740.

Statz, H., and R. A. Pucel: "The Spacistor, a New Class of High-Frequency Semiconductor Devices," *Proc. IRE*, March 1957, p. 317.

Statz, H., R. A. Pucel, and C. Lanza: "High-Frequency Semiconductor Spacistor Tetrodes," *Proc. IRE*, Nov. 1957, p. 1475.

Stewart, R. F., B. Cornelison, and W. A. Adcock: "High-Frequency Tetrodes," *IRE Trans.* PGED, Conv. Rec., 1956, p. 166. Discusses the active unilateral gain of a transistor.

Stewart, R. F.: "High-Performance Silicon Tetrode Transistors," *Proc. IRE*, July 1957, p. 1019.

Talley, H. E.: "A Family of Diffused-Base Germanium Transistors," *IRE Trans.* PGED, Wescon, 1958, p. 115. Contains useful data on 2N509, 2N537, 2N694, 2N559 transistors.

Tannenbaum, M., and D. E. Thomas: "Diffused Emitter and Base Silicon Transistors," *Bell System Tech. Jour.*, Jan. 1956, p. 1.

Tarui, Y.: "Transistor Complementary Symmetry," *Electronics*, Sept. 1, 1957, p. 200.

Thomas, D. E.: "A Point-Contact Transistor VHF-FM Transmitter," *IRE Trans.* PGED, April 1954, p. 43.

Thomas, D. E., and G. C. Dacey: "Application Aspects of the Germanium Diffused-Base Transistor," *IRE Trans.* PGCT, March 1956, p. 22. Data on spreading resistances and capacitances of mesa transistors.

Thornton, C., J. Roschen, and T. Miles: "An Improved High-Frequency Transistor," *Electronic Industries*, July 1957, p. 47.

Thornton, C., J. McCotter, and J. Angell: "Ultra-High-Speed Switching Transistor," IRE Fall PGED Meeting, 1957.

Thornton, C., and J. Angell: "Technology of MADT Transistors," *Proc. IRE*, June 1958, p. 1167.

Wannlund, A. L., and W. P. Waters: "A Silicon PNP Fused-Junction Transistor," *IRE Trans.* PGED, Wescon, 1957.

Warner, R. M., Jr.: "A New Passive Semiconductor Element," *IRE Trans.* PGED, Conv. Rec., 1958, p. 43.

Warner, R. M., Jr., and W. C. Hittinger: "A Developmental Intrinsic-Barrier Transistor," *IRE Trans.* PGED, July 1956, p. 157.

Westberg, R. W., and T. R. Robillard: "Complementary High-Speed Power Transistors for Computer and Transmission Applications," *IRE Trans.* PGED, Wescon, 1957, p. 14.

Wolff, E. A., Jr.: "Diffused 50 Watt Silicon Power Transistors," *IRE Trans.* PGED, Wescon, 1957, p. 40.

Zierndt, C. H., Jr.: "A Hermetically Sealed PNP Fused Junction Transistor for Medium Power Applications," *IRE Trans.* PGED, Feb. 1954, p. 47. Gives data on hermetic sealing.

————: "Transistor Design," *Electronic Design*, 15 Oct. 1956, p. 22.

————: "Transistors Can Be Reliable," *Electronic Design*, April 1, 1957, p. 22.

————: "Industrial Preparedness Studies on Transistors and Rectifiers," *Electronic Design*, 15 Sept. 1956, p. 116.

————: "A New Family of Transistor Switching Circuits," *Electronic Design*, 1 April 1957, p. 46.

————: "High-Power Silicon Transistor," *Electronic Design*, 15 June 1957, p. 42.

————: "Russian Transistors," *Electronic Design*, 15 July 1957, p. 150.

————: "Power Tetrode Transistor," *Electronic Design*, 1 Oct. 1957, p. 40.

————: "Silicon Unijunction Transistor," *Electronic Design*, 15 Nov. 1957, p. 112.

————: "Highest Frequency Transistors Cover Entire VHF Spectrum," *Electronic Design*, 1 Dec. 1957, p. 34.

————: "Composite Germanium-Silicon Power Transistor," *Electronic Design*, 16 April 1958, p. 86.

————: "The Intrinsic Barrier Transistor," *Electronic Design*, 28 May 1958, p. 98.

————: "Transistors and Their Applications, A Bibliography," *IRE Trans.* PGED, August 1954, p. 40. This is a very important listing of the papers on transistors published prior to 1954.

TRANSISTOR CHARACTERISTICS

Alcock, B. J.: "A Four-Pole Analysis for Transistors," *Electronic Engineering*, Oct. 1958, p. 592. Uses matrices with r parameters.

Almond, J., and R. J. McIntyre: "The Equivalent Circuit of a Drift Transistor," *RCA Review*, Sept. 1957, p. 361.

Alsborg, D. A.: "Transistor Metrology," *IRE Trans.* PGED, Aug. 1954, p. 12. Gives an excellent discussion on the problem of data organization and presentation. It is updated in this volume.

Armstrong, H. L.: "A Theory of Voltage Breakdown of Cylindrical P-N Junctions, with Applications," *IRE Trans.* PGED, Jan. 1957, p. 15.

Armstrong, H. L., E. D. Metz, and I. Weiman: "Design Theory and Experiments for Abrupt Hemispherical P-N Junction Diodes," *IRE Trans.* PGED, April 1956, p. 86.

Baker, R. H.: "Boosting Transistor Switching Speed," *Electronics*, March 1, 1957, p. 190.

Baldinger, E., W. Czaja, and M. Nicolet: "Influence of Nonideal Emitter Barriers on the Characteristics of Junction Transistors," *Helvetica Physica Acta*, Dec. 1956, p. 428.

Balter, L. M.: "More Definitive Symbols," *Electronic Design*, 1 Sept. 1956, p. 28.

Bangart, J. T.: "The Transistor as a Network Element," *IRE Trans.* PGED, Feb. 1954, p. 7.

Bashkow, T. R.: "Effect of Nonlinear Collector Capacitance on Collector Current Rise Time," *IRE Trans.* PGED, Oct. 1956, p. 167.

Bell, N. W.: "Small-Signal Analysis of Floating-Junction Transistor Switch Circuits," *IRE Trans.* PGED, Oct. 1955, p. 10.

Boothroyd, A. R., and J. Almond: "A Bridge for Measuring the AC Parameters of Junction Transistors," *Proc. IEE*, Part III, Sept. 1954, p. 314.

Burgess, R. E.: "Emitter-Base Impedances of Junction Transistors," *Journal of Electronics*, Nov. 1956, p. 301.

Chu, G. Y.: "A New Equivalent Circuit for Junction Transistors," *IRE Trans.* PGCT, Conv. Rec., 1954, p. 135. Develops the Giacoletto circuit.

Clark, M. A.: "Optimum Design of Power Output Transistors," *IRE Trans.* PGED, Conv. Rec., 1956, p. 151.

Coffey, W. N.: "Sweeper Determines Power-Gain Parameter," *Electronics*, March 1, 1957, p. 201.

Credle, A. B.: "Effects of Low Temperature on Transistor Characteristics," Transistor Conference, Feb. 1957.

Cripps, L. G.: "Transistor Cutoff Frequency Measurement," *Proc. IRE*, April 1958, p. 781. Discusses error in f_α measurement due to $r_{b'}$ and C_{ce}.

Early, J. M.: "Design Theory of Junction Transistors," *Bell System Tech. Jour.*, Nov. 1953, p. 1271.

———: "Design Theory of Junction Transistors," *Bell System Tech. Jour.*, May 1954, p. 517.

Easley, J. W.: "The Effect of Collector Capacity on the Transient Response of Junction Transistors," *IRE Trans.* PGED, Jan. 1957, p. 6.

Ebers, J. J., and J. L. Moll: "Large-Signal Behavior of Junction Transistors," *Proc. IRE*, Dec. 1954, p. 1761.

Enenstein, N. H., and M. E. McMahon: "Pulse Response of Junction Transistors," *IRE Trans.* PGED, June 1953, p. 5. Discusses in detail the relation of pulse and sinusoidal response for transistor amplifiers.

Enenstein, N. H.: "A Transient Equivalent Circuit for Junction Transistors," *IRE Trans.* PGED, Dec. 1953, p. 37.

Eshelman, C. R.: "Variation of Transistor Parameters with Temperature," *Semiconductor Products*, Jan.-Feb. 1958, p. 25.

Follingstad, H. G.: "An Analytical Study of z, y, and h Parameter Accuracies in Transistor Sweep Measurements," *IRE Trans.* PGED, Conv. Rec., 1954, p. 104. This is possibly one of the most important papers yet published on the selection of small-signal parameters. The common-emitter y parameters are equal to or superior in accuracy to the h parameters on the basis of data provided.

————: "Complete Linear Characterization of Transistors from Low through Very-High Frequencies," *IRE Trans.* PGI (Instrumentation), March 1957, p. 49.

Gaertner, W. W.: "Temperature Dependence of Junction Transistor Parameters," *Proc. IRE*, May 1957, p. 662.

Gaertner, W. W., E. Ahlstrom, H. Mette, and C. Loscoe: "The Current Amplification of a Junction Transistor as a Function of Emitter Current and Junction Temperature," *Proc. IRE*, Nov. 1958, p. 1875.

General Electric Co.: *The General Electric Transistor Manual*, General Electric Co., Liverpool, N. Y., 1959.

Giacoletto, L. J.: "Junction Transistor Equivalent Circuits and Vacuum Tube Analogy," *Proc. IRE*, Nov. 1952, p. 1490.

————: "Equipments for Measuring Junction Transistor Admittance Parameters for a Wide Range of Frequencies," *RCA Review*, June 1953, p. 269.

————: "The Study and Design of Alloyed Junction Transistors," *IRE Trans.* PGED, Conv. Rec., 1954, p. 99. This paper emphasizes the importance of $r_{b'}$ in the behavior of the transistor, and uses the equivalent π circuit.

————: "Comparative High-Frequency Operation of Junction Transistors Made of Different Semiconductor Materials," *IRE Trans.* PGED, Conv. Rec., 1955, p. 133. The unilateral gain is derived in terms of the equivalent π network.

Glenn, A. B., and I. Joffe: "Investigation of Power Gain and Transistor Parameters as Functions of Temperature and Frequency," *IRE Trans.* PGED, Conv. Rec., 1956, p. 157. Analyzes complete π network for transistor.

Goldich, N. H.: "Automatic Curve Tracing Aids Transistor Circuit Design," *Electronic Design*, 1 July 1956, p. 28.

Greenberg, L. S., Z. A. Mortowska, and W. W. Happ: "A Method of Determining Impurity Diffusion Coefficients and Surface Concentrations of Drift Transistors," *IRE Trans.* PGED, April 1956, p. 97.

Greene, R. D.: "Characteristics and Some Applications of Fused Junction PNP Germanium Transistors for High-Frequency Use," *IRE Trans.* PGED, Conv. Rec., 1955, p. 138.

Griffith, L. A.: "Power Transistor Temperature Rating," *Electronic Design*, June 1955, p. 22.

Grinich, V. H.: "Two Representations for a Junction Transistor in the Common-Collector Configuration," *IRE Trans.* PGCT, March 1956, p. 63.

Grinich, V. H., and R. N. Noyce: "Switching Time Calculations for Diffused Base Transistors," *IRE Trans.* PGED, Wescon, 1958, p. 141.

Hall, R. A.: "A 1 kc/s Junction Transistor T-Parameter Measurement," *Electronic Engineering*, Feb. 1958, p. 82.

Hayes, A. E., Jr.: "Transistor Formulas Use h-Matrix Parameters," *Electronics*, Feb. 28, 1958, p. 81.

Hempel, R. A.: "A Transistor Tester for the Experimental Labs," *Electronic Industries*, Feb. 1958, p. 58.

Hurley, R. B.: "Scheme for Designating Semiconductors," *Electronic Design*, 1 Sept. 1956, p. 26.

———: "Designing Transistor Circuits — Small-signal Parameters and Equivalent Circuits," *Electronic Equipment*, Nov. 1957, p. 28.

Hyde, F. J., and R. W. Smith: "An Investigation of the Current Gain of Transistors at Frequencies up to 105 mc.," *Proc. IEE*, Part B, May 1958, p. 221.

Jochems, P. J. W., O. W. Memelink, and L. J. Tummers, "Construction and Electrical Properties of a Germanium Alloy-Diffused Transistor," *Proc. IRE*, June 1958, p. 1161.

Johnson, R. C.: "Transient Response of a Drift Transistor," *Proc. IRE*, May 1958, p. 830.

Kulke, B., and S. L. Miller: "Accurate Measurement of Emitter and Collector Series Resistances in Transistors" (letter), *Proc. IRE*, Jan. 1957, p. 90.

Lefkowitz, H.: "Nomogram for Some Transistor Parameters," *Electronic Design*, 15 Oct. 1956, p. 62.

Lehovic, K., A. Marcus, and K. Schoeni: "Current-Voltage Characteristics and Hole Injection Factor of Point-Contact Rectifiers in the Forward Direction," *IRE Trans.* PGED, Jan. 1956, p. 1.

Lohman, R. D.: "A Transistor Analog," *IRE Trans.* PGCT, Conv. Rec., 1954, p. 118.

Lovering, W. F., and D. B. Britten: "A Simple Transistor Bridge," *Inst. Elect. Engr.* (British) *Paper* 2247M, Jan. 1957.

Macdonald, J. R.: "Solution of a Transistor Transient-Response Problem," *IRE Trans.* PGCT, March 1956, p. 54.

Mackintosh, I. M.: "The Electrical Characteristics of Silicon PNPN Triodes," *Proc. IRE*, June 1958, p. 1229.

Matz, A. W.: "Variation of Junction Transistor Current Amplification Factor with Emitter Current," *Proc. IRE*, May 1958, p. 616.

Middlebrook, R. D.: "A New Junction-Transistor High-Frequency Equivalent Circuit," *IRE Trans.* PGCT, Conv. Rec., 1957, p. 120.

Moll, J. L., and I. M. Ross: "Dependence of Transistor Parameters on the Distribution of Base-Layer Resistivity," *Proc. IRE*, Jan. 1956, p. 72.

Molozzi, A. R., D. F. Page, and A. R. Boothroyd: "Measurement of High-Frequency Equivalent Circuit Parameters of Junction and Surface Barrier Transistors," *IRE Trans.* PGED, April 1957, p. 120. Paper gives good methods of measuring $r_{b'}$, f_{α}, and related parameters. Includes good bridge designs for the measurements.

Mortenson, K. E.: "Junction Transistor Temperature as a Function of Time," *Proc. IRE*, April 1957, p. 504.

Mullard, Ltd.: *Mullard Technical Handbook*, Vol. 4, Mullard, Ltd., London, England.

Penfield, P., Jr.: "Transistor Formulas," *Electronic Industries*, April 1957, p. 68.

Pritchard, R. L., and W. N. Coffey: "Small-Signal Parameters of Grown-Junction Transistors at High Frequencies," *IRE Trans.* PGED, Conv. Rec., 1954, p. 89. Shows some limitations of h-parameters and the complexity of representation of $r_{b'}$ at high frequencies. Discusses high-frequency measurements.

Pritchard, R. L.: "Effect of Base-Contact Overlap and Parasitic Capacities on Small-Signal Parameters of Junction Transistors," *Proc. IRE*, Jan. 1955, p. 38.

———: "Frequency Response of Theoretical Models of Junction Transistors," *IRE Trans.* PGCT, June 1955, p. 183.

———: "Electric Network Representation of Transistors," *IRE Trans.* PGCT, March 1956, p. 5. Discusses h, y, and z representation of transistors. Good bibliography.

———: Measurement Considerations in High-Frequency Power Gain of Junction Transistors," *Proc. IRE*, Aug. 1956, p. 1050.

———: "Transistor Tests Predict High-Frequency Performance," *Electronic Industries*, March 1957, p. 62.

Pullen, K. A., Jr., and R. G. Roush: "Using Contour Curves in Transistor Circuit Design," *Electronic Design*, July 1955, p. 22.

Pullen, K. A., Jr.: "Transistor Contour Curves," *Electronic Design*, 1 July 1956, p. 40.

Pullen, K. A., Jr., and C. E. Shafer: "A Transistorized Telemetering Commutator for Data Transmission," National Telemetering Conference, June 4, 1958.

Pullen, K. A., Jr.: "Identifying Scope Displays," *Electronic Design*, July 9, 1958.

Raytheon Manufacturing Co.: *Technical Manual on Transistors*, Raytheon Manufacturing Co., Waltham, Mass.

Reich, B.: "Transistor Thermal Resistance Measurement," *Electronic Design*, 1 Dec. 1956, p. 20.

———: "Hot Junctions and Collector Cutoff Current," *Electronic Industries*, July 1957, p. 55.

———: "Temperature Sensitivity of Current Gain in Power Transistors," *IRE Trans.* PGED, July 1955, p. 180.

Riddle, R. L.: "Hybrid Parameters for Grounded Emitter Amplifiers with Feedback," *Electronic Design*, 1 April 1956, p. 30.

Rudenberg, H. G.: "On the Effect of Base Resistance and Collector-to-Base Overlap on the Saturation Voltages of Power Transistors," *Proc. IRE*, June 1958, p. 1304.

Saunders, N. B.: "Silicon or Germanium?" *Electronic Design*, July 1955, p. 34.

———: "Using a Curve Tracer for Transistor Circuit Design," *Electronic Design*, 15 July 1957, p. 46.

Scarlett, R. M., and R. D. Middlebrook: "An Approximation to Alpha of a Junction Transistor," *IRE Trans.* PGED, Jan. 1956, p. 25. Uses two-time-constant approach.

Schauwecker, H. E.: "Transistor H-F Cutoff Nomograph," *Electronics*, May 9, 1958, p. 88.

Scithers, G. H.: "Variability of Some Characteristics of a Group of Fused Junction Transistors," Stanford Electronics Research Lab. Report No. TR 92, Sept. 1955.

Sylvan, T. P.: "Conversion Formulas for Hybrid Parameters," *Electronics*, April 1, 1957, p. 188.

Stephanson, W. L.: "Transistor Cutoff Frequency," *Electronic and Radio Engineer*, Feb. 1958, p. 69.

Stern, A. P.: "Considerations on the Stability of Active Elements and Applications to Transistors," *IRE Trans.* PGCT, Conv. Rec., 1956, p. 46.

Suran, J. J.: "Transient Response Characteristics of Unijunction Transistors," *IRE Trans.* PGCT, Sept. 1957, p. 267.

————: "Low-Frequency Circuit Theory of the Double-Base Diode," *IRE Trans.* PGED, April 1955, p. 40.

Thomas, D. E., and J. L. Moll: "Junction-Transistor Short-Circuit Current Gain and Phase Determination," *Proc. IRE*, June 1958, p. 1177.

Thornton, C. G., and C. D. Simmons: "A New High-Current Mode of Transistor Operation," *IRE Trans.* PGED, Jan. 1958, p. 6.

Valvo, GMBH: *Valvo Berichte*, Valvo, GMBH, Hamburg, Germany.

Valvo, GMBH: *Valvo Halbleiter Handbuch*, Valvo, GMBH, Hamburg, Germany.

Other Manufacturers' Data Sheets: Sylvania, CBS Hytron, RCA, Texas Instruments, Fairchild, General Transistor, Delco, Motorola, Philco and others.

Wahl, A. J.: "A Three-Dimensional Analytic Solution for Alpha of Alloy-Junction Transistors," *IRE Trans.* PGED, July 1957, p. 216. Gives a Bessel expansion for α in terms of I functions.

————: "An Analysis of Transistor Base-Spreading Resistance and Associated Effects," IRE Fall PGED Meeting, 1957.

————: "An Analysis of Base Resistance for Alloy Junction Transistors," *IRE Trans.* PGED, July 1958, p. 131.

Ward, E. E.: "Measurement of the Impedance Parameters of Junction Transistors," British *Journal of Applied Physics*, Aug. 1957, p. 329.

Warner, R. M., J. M. Early, and G. T. Loman: "Characteristics, Structure, and Performance of a Diffused-Base Germanium Oscillator Transistor, Mesa," *IRE Trans.* PGED, July 1958, p. 127. Describes transistor with $r_{b'}$ of 35 ohms, $f_\alpha = 600$ mc.

Webster, W. M.: "On the Variations of Junction Emitter Current Amplification Factor with Emitter Current," *Proc. IRE*, June 1954, p. 194.

Weitzsch, F.: "Germanium-Dioden in Fernsentaengern," *Valvo Berichte*, Band II, 1956, p. 49.

————: "Zur Theorie des Ratiodetektors," *Valvo Berichte*, Band II, 1956, p. 159.

————: "p-n-p Flaechentransistoren — Kompendium," *Valvo Berichte*, Band III, Heft 1, Heft 3.

Young, C. W.: "Transistor Conversion Nomographs," *Electronic Equipment*, Nov. 1957, p. 26.

Zawels, J.: "High-Frequency Parameters of Transistors and Valves," *Electronic Engineering*, Jan. 1958, p. 15.

————: "On Base-Width Modulation and the High-Frequency Equivalent Circuit of Junction Transistors," *IRE Trans.* PGED, Jan. 1957, p. 17.

————: "Bridge for Yielding Directly Transistor Parameters," *IRE Trans.* PGED, Jan. 1958, p. 21.

Zierdt, C. H., Jr.: "Reliability of Heremtically Sealed Transistors," *Electronic Design*, June 1955, p. 32.

Zuleeg, R.: "Effective Collector Capacitance in Transistors," *Proc. IRE*, Nov. 1958, p. 1878.

————: "Diffused-Base Transistors," *Electronic Design*, 1 March 1956, p. 76.

————: "High-Frequency PNP Transistor — RCA," *Electronic Design*, 1 Nov. 1956, p. 48.

————: "Report on Transistor Reliability," *Electronic Design*, 1 Dec. 1956, p. 100.

————: "Transistor Equivalent Circuit" (abstract), *Electronic Design*, 1 Jan. 1957, p. 118.

————: "The Junction Transistor as a Network Element at Low Frequencies," *Philips Technical Review*, July 1957, p. 98.

————: "Equivalent Circuits for Transistors" *Electronic Design*, 1 Dec. 1957, p. 112.

————: "Determination of Transistor Lead-In Resistance" (abstract), *Electronic Design*, 22 Jan. 1958, p. 122.

————: "Non-Destructive Transistor Punch-Through Test," *Electronic Design*, 5 Feb. 1958, p. 30.

GENERAL CIRCUITS

Bevitt, W. D.: "Hybrid Auto Radios," *Electronic Design*, 1 Aug. 1956, p. 24.

Brailsford, H. D.: "Commutatorless DC Motor Using Transistors," *Electronic Design*, July 1955, p. 40.

Hatton, R. W.: "Saving Tantalum Capacitors," *Electronic Design*, 11 June 1958, p. 144.

Ibsen, S. C.: "Transistor Test Equipment Survey," *Electronic Design*, 15 July 1957, p. xix.

Loofbourrow, K. E.: "Hybrid Radio," *Electronic Design*, Oct. 1955, p. 48.

Mason, S. J.: "Power Gain in Feedback Amplifiers," *IRE Trans.* PGCT, June 1954, p. 20. This very important paper develops the dimensionless form for unilateral gain in an active device.

Prensky, S. D.: "Current Trends in Transistor Radios," *Electronic Design*, 15 July 1956, p. 48.

Pullen, K. A., Jr.: "Designing Cathode-Coupled Amplifiers Using Conductance Curves," *Electronic Design*, 15 Jan. 1956, p. 24.

———: "Designing Cascode Amplifiers with G-Curves," *Electronic Design*, 1 May 1956, p. 26.

———: "Design Techniques Using Conductance Curves — Degenerative Amplifiers," *Electronic Design*, 1 Oct. 1956, p. 32.

———: "Guides to Tube Selection," *Electronic Design*, 1 Nov. 1956, p. 26.

———: "Oscillator Design Techniques Using Conductance Curves," *Electronic Design*, 15 May 1957, p. 34.

———: "Design of Mixers Using Conductance Curves," *Electronic Design*, 1 June 1957, p. 32.

———: "Tiny Transistor Assemblies," *Electronic Design*, 15 July 1957, p. 38.

———: "Ideas For Design — Identifying Polaroid Records and Driftless Emitter Follower," *Electronic Design*, 1 Nov. 1957, p. 108.

———: "Amplifier in a Thermos Bottle," *Electronic Design*, 15 Nov. 1957, p. 92.

———: "Interference-Free Switching," *Electronic Design*, 8 Jan. 1958, p. 102.

"Tube-Transistor Radio," *Electronic Design*, July 1955, p. 48.

STABILIZATION

Bahrs, G. S.: "Stable Amplifiers Employing Potentially Unstable Transistors," *IRE Trans.* PGCT, Wescon, 1957, p. 185.

Boxall, F. S.: "Base-Current Feedback in Transistor Power Amplifier Design," *IRE Trans.* PGCT, Wescon, 1957, p. 20.

Cramwinckel, A.: "Transistor Operating Point Stabilization," *Philips Technical Review*, Jan. 1957, p. 100.

de Woolf, N.: "Rating Transistors to Prevent Runaway," *Electronic Design*, Feb. 1955, p. 28.

Ghandhi, S. K.: "Analysis and Design of Transistor Bias Networks," *Proc. NEC*, 1956, p. 491.

———: "Bias Considerations in Transistor Circuit Design," Transistor Conference, Feb. 1957.

———: "Bias Considerations in Transistor Circuit Design," *IRE Trans.* PGCT, Sept. 1957, p. 194.

Hurley, R. B.: "What Type of Degenerative Feedback for Transistors?" *Electronic Design*, 15 June 1956, p. 22.

Johnson, L. B.: "DC Stabilization of Junction Transistors," *Electronic Applications Bulletin*, Mullard Semiconductor Division, Sept. 1957, p. 151.

Lin, H. C.: "Thermal Stability of Junction Transistors and its Effect on Maximum Power Dissipation," *IRE Trans.* PGED, Sept. 1957, p. 202.

Murray, J. S.: "Transistor Bias Stabilization," *Electronic and Radio Engineer*, May 1957, p. 161.

Murray, R. P.: "Transistor Bias Circuits," *Electronic Industries*, Nov. 1957, p. 75.

Nikolayenko, N. S.: "An Amplifier Using Directly-Coupled Transistors," *Radiotechnika*, Feb. 1958.

Penfield, P., Jr.: "Protecting Power Transistors from Thermal Runaway," *Electronic Industries*, Feb. 1958, p. 79.

Prugh, T. A.: "Minimizing Gain Variations with Temperature in R-C Coupled Transistor Amplifiers," (letter), *Proc. IRE*, Dec. 1956, p. 1880.

Schenkerman, S.: "Designing Stability into Transistor Circuits," *Electronics*, Feb. 14, 1958, p. 122.

Soble, A. B.: "Thermistor Compensation of Transistor Amplifiers," *IRE Trans.* PGCT, Sept. 1957, p. 290.

Stuart-Monteith, G.: "Temperature Stability of Transistor Amplifiers," *Electronic Engineering*, Dec. 1956, p. 544.

Wheeler, A. J.: "Thermistors Compensate Transistor Amplifiers," *Electronics*, Jan. 1, 1957, p. 169.

———: "Improved Transistor Biasing," *Electronic Design*, 1 Sept. 1957, p. 102.

———: "Stabilizing Emitter Current," *Electronic Design*, 11 June 1958, p. 151.

D-C AMPLIFIERS

Beneking, H., K. H. Kupferschmidt, and H. Wolf: "Transistorized DC Measuring Amplifier," *Elektronische Rundshau*, Oct. 1956, p. 268.

Burton, P. L.: "A Transistor DC Chopper Amplifier," *Electronic Engineering*, Aug. 1957, p. 393.

Chaplin, G. B. B., and A. R. Owens: "Some Transistor Input Stages for High-Gain DC Amplifiers," *Jour. IEE*, July 1957, p. 429.

———: "Transistors in High-Gain DC Amplifiers," *Jour. IEE*, Feb. 1958, p. 88.

———: "A Transistor High-Gain Chopper-Type DC Amplifier," *Proc. IEE*, B, May 1958, p. 258.

Depian, L.: "A Stabilized DC Differential Transistor Amplifier," *Communication and Electronics*, May 1958, p. 157.

Ghandhi, S. K.: "Darlington's Compound Connection for Transistors," *IRE Trans.* PGCT, Sept. 1957, p. 291.

Holford, K.: "DC Amplifier Using Transistors and a Silicon Bridge Modulator," *Mullard Technical Communication*, June 1957, p. 126.

Hurley, R. B.: "Designing Transistor Circuits — DC Amplifiers," *Electronic Equipment*, March 1957, p. 34.

————: "Designing Transistor Circuits — Automatic Gain Control," *Electronic Equipment*, June 1957, p. 22.

Hurtig, C. R.: "Constant-Resistance AGC Attenuator for Transistor Amplifiers," *IRE Trans*. PGCT, June 1955, p. 191.

Lefkowitz, H.: "DC Feedback Equations for Transistor Amplifiers," *Electronic Design*, April 16, 1958, p. 52.

Lindsay, J. E., and H. J. Woll: Design Considerations for Direct-Coupled Transistor Amplifiers," *RCA Review*, Sept. 1958, p. 433. Can improve stability by optimizing source impedance. Relations for doing so given.

Lloyd, D. J.: "A Simple Transistor Amplifier for Energizing a Hall Multiplier," *Electronic Engineering*, Sept. 1958, p. 560.

Lyon, J. A. M., R. R. Jenness, C. B. Hassan, and W. C. Wang: "Temperature Stabilization of Direct-Coupled Transistor Amplifiers Utilizing Differential Stages," *Proc. NEC*, 1956, p. 505.

New London: "Transistorized Voltmeter," *Electronic Design*, 15 May 1956, p. 30.

Slaughter, D. W.: "The Emitter-Coupled Differential Amplifier," *IRE Trans*. PGCT, March 1956, p. 51.

Stanton, J. W.: "A Transistorized DC Amplifier," *IRE Trans*. PGCT, March 1956, p. 65.

————: "Designing Transistor DC Amplifiers," *Electronic Design*, Dec. 15, 1956, p. 20.

Verma, J. K. D.: "Low-Noise 30 mc Amplifier," *Review of Scientific Instruments*, May 1958, p. 371.

Wells, W. W.: "Transistor Voltage Standards," *Electronic Design*, 5 March 1958, p. 50

A-C AMPLIFIERS

Abraham, R. P.: "A Wide-Band Transistor Feedback Amplifier," *IRE Trans*. PGCT, Wescon, 1957, p. 10.

Adashko, J. G.: "The Regeneration Method in the Design of Transistor Amplifier Stages," *Electronic Design*, 15 April 1957, p. 134.

Anouchi, A. Y., and W. F. Palmer: "Randomly-Selected Transistor Output Pairs," *IRE Trans*. PGCT, Wescon, 1957, p. 27.

Anzalone, P.: "A High-Input-Impedance Transistor Circuit," *Electronic Design*, 1 June 1957, p. 38.

Bachmann, A. E.: "Transistor Low-Noise Preamplifier with High Input Impedance," Solid-State Circuits Conference, 1957.

Bahrs, G. S.: "Stable Amplifiers Employing Potentially-Unstable Transistors," *IRE Trans*. PGCT, Wescon, 1957, p. 72.

Baird Associates: "Transistor Mixer Amplifier," *Electronic Design*, 15 August 1956, p. 48.

Blecher, F. H.: "Basic Principles for Single-Loop Transistor Feedback Amplifiers," *IRE Trans*. PGCT, Sept. 1957, p. 145.

————: "Transistor Multiple-Loop Feedback Amplifiers," Program, NEC, 1957.

Bramley, J.: "Circuit Design for Transistor Interchangability," *Electronic Design*, 15 Oct. 1956, p. 26.

Brown, W. L.: "Common-Emitter Transistor Video Amplifiers," *Proc. IRE*, Nov. 1956, p. 1561.

Burr-Brown Research Corp.: "AC Decade Amplifier," *Electronic Design*, 15 Nov. 1956, p. 48.

Dion, D. F.: "Common-Emitter Transistor Amplifiers," *Proc. IRE*, May 1958, p. 920.

Grinich, V. H.: "An Eighty-Volt-Output Transistor Video Amplifier," *IRE Trans·* PGCT, March 1956, p. 61.

Gurnett, K. W., and R. A. Hilbourne: "Distortion Due to the Mismatch of Transistors in Push-Pull Audio-Frequency Amplifiers," *Proc. IEE*, Part C, Sept. 1957, p. 471.

Horowitz, I. M.: "R-C Transistor Network Synthesis," *Proc. NEC*, 1956, p. 818.

———: "R-C Transistor Network Design," *Electronic Design*, 1 August 1957, p. 28.

Hurley, R. B.: "Designing Transistor Circuits, Video Amplifiers," *Electric Equipment* May 1957, p. 26.

———: "Designing Transistor Circuits — Negative Feedback for Transistor Amplifiers," *Electronic Equipment Engineering*, Feb. 1958, p. 42.

———: "Designing Transistor Circuits — A Universal Amplifier," *Electronic Equipment Engineering*, May 1958, p. 32.

Jorysz, A.: "Transistor Circuit Design with Intermediate Terminal Connections," *Electronic Design*, 1 July 1956, p. 34.

Librascope Corp.: "Transistor Servo Amplifiers," *Electronic Design*, Sept. 1955, p. 40.

Loofbourrow, K. E.: "Class B Operation of Transistors," *Electronic Design*, Part I, July 1955, p. 28; Part II, Aug. 1955, p. 34.

Mark, M.: "Cooling of Power Transistors," *Electronic Design*, 1 Nov. 1957, p. 46.

McKinley, D. W. R., and R. S. Richards: "Transistor Amplifier for Medical Recording," *Electronics*, Aug. 1, 1957, p. 161.

Melehy, M. A.: "Transistor Push-Pull Audio Amplifier Theory," Program NEC, 1957.

Miller, C. B.: "Transistor Q-Multiplier for Audio Frequencies," *Electronics*, May 9, 1958, p. 79.

Minneapolis-Honeywell: "Power Transistors," *Electronic Design*, Jan. 1955, p. 44.

Minton, R.: "Circuit Considerations for Audio-Output Stages Using Power Transistors," *IRE Trans.* PGCT, Conv. Rec., 1957, p. 169 (Pt 7).

———: "Class A Transistor Power Amplifier Design," *Electronic Design*, Part I, 15 July 1957, p. 50; Part II, 15 Sept. 1957, p. 24.

Molynoux, L.: "A Transistor Cardio-Tachometer," *Electronic Engineering*, March 1957, p. 125.

Montgomery, G. F.: "High-Input-Impedance Transistor Amplifier," *Electronic Design*, Aug. 6, 1958, p. 48.

Mooers, H. T.: "Design Procedures for Power Transistors," *Electronic Design*, Part I, July 1955, p. 58; Part II, Sept. 1955, p. 42; Part III, Oct. 1955, p. 52.

Nisbet, T. R.: "The 'Resisting' Transistor for Servo Design," *Electronic Design*, 2 April 1958, p. 14.

Purton, R. F.: "Transistor Amplifiers: Common-Base vs. Common-Emitter," ATE Jour., April 1958, p. 157.

Roy, R.: "Transistorized High-Frequency Chopper Design," *Electronic Design*, Aug. 6, 1958, p. 52.

Sallen, R. P., and E. L. Key: "A Practical Method of Designing R-C Active Filters," *IRE Trans.* PGCT, March 1955, p. 74.

"Simplified Equivalent Circuits for Transistor Amplifiers," (Russian translation), *Electronic Design*, 1 Dec. 1956, p. 96.

Spilke, J. J., Jr.: "A Multistage Video-Amplifier Design Method," *IRE Trans.* PGCT, Wescon, 1957, p. 54.

Stewart, J. L.: "Bandwidth Limitations in Equalizers and Transistor Output Circuits," *IRE Trans.* PGCT, March 1957, p. 5.

Sutcliffe, H.: "A Transistor Demodulator," *Electronic Engineering*, March 1957, p. 140.

Vallese, L. M.: "Unilateralized Common-Collector Transistor Amplifier," *Proc. NEC*, Oct. 1957.

————: "Unilateralized Common-Collector Transistor Amplifier" (letter), *Proc. IRE*, Nov. 1957, p. 1548.

Waldhauer, F. D.: "Wide-Band Feedback Amplifiers," Solid-State Circuits Conference, 1957.

————: "Wide-Band Feedback Amplifiers," *IRE Trans.* PGCT, Sept. 1957, p. 178.

Wheatley, C. F.: "Class B Complementary-Symmetry Audio Amplifiers," *Electronic Design*, Aug. 6, 1958, p. 32.

————: Feedback Transistor Circuits," *Electronic Design*, 15 July 1957, p. 158.

————: "Nonlinear Distortion in Transistor Amplifiers" (abstract), *Electronic Design*, Jan. 22, 1958, p. 124.

————: International Electronic Research Co., "Transistor Heat Sinks," *Electronic Design*, 5 March 1958, p. 56.

————: "Transistorized Audio Amplifier from 12 V. Supply," *Electronic Design*, March 19, 1958, p. 107.

TUNED AMPLIFIERS

Baker, D. W.: "High-Frequency Circuits Use Meltback Tetrodes," *Electronics*, June 1, 1957, p. 177.

Cheng, C. C.: "Neutralization and Unilateralization," *IRE Trans.* PGCT, June 1955, p. 138, A *very, very* important paper.

Chow, W. F. and D. A. Paynter: "Series-Tuned Methods in Transistor Radio Circuitry," Solid-State Circuits Conference, Feb. 1957.

———: "Series-Tuned Methods in Transistor Radio Circuitry," *IRE Trans.* PGCT, Sept. 1957, p. 174.

DeSautels, A. N.: "Transistorized Phase Discriminators," *Electrical Engineering*, April 1957, p. 278.

Englund, J. W., and A. L. Kestenbaum: "Circuit Considerations for High-Frequency Amplifiers Using Drift Transistors," *IRE Trans.* PGCT, Conv. Rec., 1957.

Gibbons, J. F.: "Design of Alignable Transistor Amplifiers," Stanford Report, 1958.

Holmes, D. D.: "A Six-Transistor Portable Receiver Employing a Complementary-Symmetry Output Stage," *IRE Trans.*, Part 3 Conv. Rec., 1957, p. 193.

Hurley, R. B.: "Designing Transistor Circuits — Tuned Amplifiers," *Electronic Equipment*, Part I, July 1957, p. 14; Part II, Aug. 1957, p. 20.

Jannson, L. E.: "High-Frequency Amplification Using Junction Transistors," *Mullard Technical Communication*, Semiconductor Lab., Oct. 1957, p. 174.

Proudfit, A., K. M. St. John, C. R. Wilhelmsen, and R. J. Farber: "Tetra-Junction Transistor Receiver Circuits," *IRE Trans.*, Part 3 Conv. Rec., 1957, p. 199.

Pullen, K. A., Jr.: "RF and IF Amplifier Design with Conductance Curves," *Electronic Design*, 1 Feb. 1957, p. 48.

Raper, J. A. A.: "A Transistorized IF Amplifier-Limiter," *IRE Trans.* PGCT, March 1956, p. 67.

Stern, A. P.: "Stability and Power Gain of Tuned Transistor Amplifiers," *Proc. IRE*, March 1957, p. 335.

———: "Design of Wide-Band Transistor Amplifiers," *Electronic Design*, 15 March, 1957, p. 98.

TRANSISTOR OSCILLATORS

Armstrong, H. L., and F. Reza: "Synthesis of Transfer Functions by Active R-C Networks," *IRE Trans.* PGCT, June 1954, p. 8.

———: "Transistor Tuned Oscillators," *Electronics*, Feb. 1, 1957, p. 218.

Bradmiller, R. W.: "Stable Transistor Oscillator," U. S. Patent 2,810,073, October 15, 1957.

Cote, A. J., Jr.: "Matrix Analysis of Oscillators and Transistor Applications," *IRE Trans.* PGCT, Sept. 1958, p. 181.

Cripps, L. G.: "Low-Frequency Transistor Oscillators, *Mullard Technical Communication*, March 1957, p. 44; also *Electronic Applications Bulletin*, May 1957.

Drouilhet, P. R., Jr.: "Predictions Based on the Maximum Oscillator Frequency of a Transistor," *IRE Trans.* PGCT, June 1955, p. 178. This is an important fundamental paper.

Dulberger, L. H.: "Transistor Oscillator Supplies Stable Signal," *Electronics*, Jan. 31, 1958, p. 43.

Francini, G.: "Evaluation of Oscillator Quality, *IRE Trans.* PGCT, Sept. 1955, p. 261.

Gedney, G. A. and G. M. Davidson: "Crystal Oscillator Has Variable Frequency," *Electronics*, Feb. 14, 1958, p. 118.

Guene, R.: "Use of Thermistors for Thermal Drift Compensation," *Annales de Radio-electricite*, Oct. 1956, p. 317.

Hellerman, H.: "Notes on Transistor R-C Oscillators," private communication, 1958.

Herzog, W.: "Loading of Transistor Oscillators," *Electronic Design*, Aug. 6, 1958, p. 190.

Hooper, D. E., and A. E. Jackets: "Current-Derived R-C Oscillator Using Junction Transistors," *Electronic Engineering*, Aug. 1956, p. 333.

Hurley, R. B.: "Designing Transistor Circuits — Sinusoidal Transistor Oscillators," *Electronic Equipment*, Part I, Sept. 1957, Part II, Oct. 1957. Treats usual linearized problem.

Hyde, F. J., and R. W. Smith: "Transistor Relaxation Oscillations," *Electronic Engineering*, May 1957, p. 234.

Jensen, J. L.: "An Improved Square-Wave Oscillator Circuit," *IRE Trans.* PGED, Sept. 1957, p. 276.

Keonjian, E.: "Stable Transistor Oscillator," *IRE Trans.* PGCT, March 1956, p. 38.

Melehy, M. A., and M. B. Reed: "Junction-Transistor Oscillators," *Program NEC*, 1957.

Page, D. F.: "A Design Basis for Junction Transistor Oscillator Circuits," *Proc. IRE*, June 1958, p. 1271.

Paynter, D. A.: "An Unsymmetrical Square-Wave Power Oscillator," *IRE Trans.* PGCT, March 1956, p. 64.

Pritchard, R. L.: "Negative Resistance Oscillator," Patent 2,777,065, Jan. 8, 1957.

Pullen, K. A., Jr.: "Design of Oscillators," *Electronic Design*, Part I, 1 July 1957, Part II, 15 July 1957, p. 40.

Sohrabji, N.: "R-C Filters and Oscillators Using Junction Transistors," *Electronic Engineering*, Dec. 1957, p. 606.

Strutt, M. J. O., and S. F. Sun: "Experimental and Theoretical Investigation of Semi-conductor Hall-Effect Oscillators," *Archiv der Elektrischen Ubertragung*, June 1957, p. 261.

Sylvan, T. P.: "Design Fundamentals of Unijunction-Transistor Relaxation Oscillators," *Electronic Equipment*, Dec. 1957, p. 20.

Witt, S. N., Jr.: "Designing Oscillators for Greater Stability," *Electronics*, Nov. 1957, p. 180.

————: "Designing Transistorized Meacham-Bridge Oscillators," *Electronics Buyers' Guide*, June 1957, pp. R46-48.

————: "High-Frequency Transistor Oscillator," *Electronic Design*, 1 Oct. 1957, p. 98.

————: "Single Transistor Frequency Standard," *Electronic Design*, July 1955, p. 46.

————: "Transistor Oscillator for 8 mc.," *Electronic Design*, 14 May 1958, p. 176.

TRANSISTORIZED REGULATED POWER SUPPLIES

Aspinwall, D.: "Low Voltage Stabilizer," *Electronic Engineering*, Sept. 1957, p. 450.

Brown, T. H., and W. L. Stephenson: "A Stabilized DC Power Supply Using Transistors," *Electronic Engineering*, Sept. 1957, p. 425.

Deuitch, D. E., and H. J. Paz: "A Phase-Regulated Transistor Power Supply," *IRE Trans.* PGCT, Sept. 1957, p. 279.

Guiffrida, J., and W. O. Hamlin: "Transistorized 25 Volt Regulated Power Supply," *Electronic Design*, Jan. 15, 1957, p. 28.

Hurley, R. B.: "Designing Transistor Circuits — DC Regulators," *Electronic Equipment*, April 1957, p. 20.

Johnson, K. C.: "A Power Supply Stabilizer Using Transistors" (letter), *Electronic Engineering*, Feb. 1957, p. 95.

Keller, J. W., Jr.: "Regulated Transistor Power Supply Design," *Electronics Buyers' Guide*, June 1957, p. R54.

Kopaczek, T. F.: "Design of Transistor Regulated Power Supplies," *Proc. IRE*, Aug. 1958, p. 1537.

Lohr, J. F.: "Transistorized Static Inverter Design," *Electronic Design*, 16 April 1958, p. 58.

Lowry, H. R.: "Transistorized Regulated Power Supplies," *Electronic Design*, Part I, Feb. 15, 1956, p. 38; Part II, March 1956, p. 32.

Middlebrook, R. D.: "Design of Transistor Regulated Power Supplies," *Proc. IRE*, Nov. 1957, p. 1502.

Moody, N. F., and C. D. Florida: "Some New Transistor Bistable Elements for Heavy-Duty Operation," *IRE Trans.* PGCT, Sept. 1957, p. 241.

Reich, B.: "Report on Power Transistors for Converters," *Electronic Design*, Mar. 15, 1957, p. 22.

Sherr, S., P. Levy, and T. Kwap: "Design Procedures for Semiconductor Regulated Power Supplies," *Electronic Design*, 15 April 1957, p. 22.

Sherr, S., and P. Levy: "Design Considerations for Semiconductor Regulated Power Supplies," *Electronic Design*, 15 July 1956, p. 22.

Schorr, M. G.: "Transistorized Power Sources," *Electronic Design*, 15 Nov. 1956, p. 40.

Universal Atomic: "Transistorized Power Supply," *Electronic Design*, Aug. 1955, p. 42.

van de Stadt, W.: "High-Current Low-Tension Transistor Stabilizers" (letter), *Electronic Engineering*, July 1957, p. 352.

———: "Simple Transistorized 1% Voltage Regulator," *Electronic Design*, 25 June 1958, p. 71.

———: "Rapid Design of Transistorized Regulated Power Supplies," *Electronic Design*, 19 March 1958, p. 104.

TRANSISTORIZED COMPUTING CIRCUITS

Aranson, A. I., and C. F. Chong: "Monovibrator Has Fast Recovery Time," *Electronics*, Dec. 1957, p. 158.

Carlson, A. W.: "Junction Transistor Counters," *Electronic Design*, 1 March 1957, p. 28.

Clark, E. G.: "DCTL Complementing Flip-Flop Circuits," Solid-State Circuits Conference, Feb. 1957.

Clark, E. G.: "Direct-Coupled Transistor Logic Complementing Flip-Flop Circuits," *Electronic Design*, 15 June 1957, p. 34; 1 Aug. 1957, p. 34.

Cubic Corp.: "Dual Function NPN-PNP Flip-Flop," *Electronic Design*, 1 Dec. 1957, p. 32.

Henle, R. A., and J. L. Walsh: "The Application of Transistors to Computers," *Proc. IRE*, June 1958, p. 1240.

Hurley, R. B.: "Transistor Data for Logical Circuit Design," *Electronic Industries*, Oct. 1957, p. 60.

Mangan, B. A.: "Read and Write Transistor Circuits for Magnetic Drums," *Electronic Design*, 5 Feb. 1958, p. 42.

McMahon, R. E.: "Designing Transistor Flip-Flops," *Electronic Design*, Oct. 1955, p. 24.

Rapp, A. K., and S. Y. Wong: "Transistor Flip-Flops for Digital Computers," *Electronic Buyers' Guide*, June 1957, p. 24.

Rowe, W. D.: "Transistor NOR Circuit Design," *Electronic Design*, 1 April 1957, p. 48.

Rowe, W. D.: "Transistor NOR Circuit Design," *Electronic Design*, 5 Feb. 1958, p. 26.

Saunders and Co.: "Transistor Clock," *Electronic Design*, Nov. 1955, p. 34.

Schauwecker, H. E.: "Design of a Transistorized Monostable Multivibrator," *Electronic Equipment*, Dec. 1957, p. 40.

Wolfendale, E., L. P. Morgan, and W. L. Stephenson: "The Junction Transistor as a Computing Element," *Electronic Engineering*, Part I, Jan. 1957, p. 2; Part II, Feb. 1957, p. 83; Part III, March 1957, p. 136.

————: "Transistorized Magnetic Core Memory" (abstract), *Electronic Design*, 1 Sept. 1956, p. 98.

TRANSISTOR PULSE CIRCUITS

Carlson, A. W.: "Frequency Division with Semiconductor Devices," *Electronic Design*, 15 July 1957, p. 34.

Chernof, J.: "Design Features of a Transistor Sweep Circuit," *Electronic Equipment*, July 1957, p. 22.

Daddario, A. S.: "Transistor Blocking Oscillator Circuits," *Electronic Equipment*, June 1958, p. 55.

Hurley, R. B.: "Designing Transistor Circuits — Switching Statics," *Electronic Equipment Engineering*, June 1958, p. 42.

Jackets, A. E.: "A Method of Sharpening the Output Waveform of Junction Transistor Multivibrator Circuits," *Electronic Engineering*, June 1958, p. 371.

Pederson, D. O.: "Regeneration Analysis of Junction Transistor Multivibrators," *IRE Trans.* PGCT, June 1955, p. 171.

Pullen, K. A., Jr.: "Conductance Curve Design of Relaxation Circuits," *IRE Trans.* PGCT, Conv. Rec., 1953.

———: "Conductance Curve Design of Relaxation Circuits," *Electronic Design*, Sept. 1955, p. 24.

Sard, E. W.: "Junction Transistor Multivibrators and Flip-Flops," *IRE Trans.* PGCT, Conv. Rec., 1954.

Smith, M.: "Transistor Switching Circuits," *Electronic Design*, 1 Oct. 1957, p. 24.

———: "Overlap Method Makes Fast Pulses in Transistor Circuits," *Electronic Design*, 28 May 1958, p. 44.

Stassior, R. A.: "Pulse Applications of a Diffused-Meltback Silicon Transistor," *Electronic Equipment*, July 1957, p. 18.

Suran, J. J., and F. A. Reibert: Two-Terminal Analysis and Synthesis of Junction Transistor Multivibrators," *IRE Trans.* PGCT, March 1956, p. 26. Shows use of piece-wise linearization and proves maximum switching rate of multivibrator is $\sqrt{f_\alpha f_\beta}$. Good discussion.

Suran, J. J.: "Multivibrators — Design of Junction-Transistor Multivibrators by Driving-Point Impedance Methods," *IRE Trans.* PGCT, Conv. Rec., 1957, p. 2.

———: "Transistor Monostable Multivibrators for Pulse Generation," *Proc. IRE*, June 1958, p. 1260.

Sylvan, T. P.: "Applications of Unijunction Transistor Relaxation Oscillators," *Electronic Equipment Engineering*, May 1958, p. 51.

Vallese, L. M.: "Transient Analysis of Second-Order Flip-Flops," *Communications and Electronics*, May 1957, p. 161.

TRANSISTOR NOISE

Anouchi, A. Y.: "Measuring Noise Figures of Transistor Amplifiers," *Proc. IRE*, March 1958, p. 619.

Brophy, J. J., and A. R. Reinberg: "Internal Noise of Transistor Amplifiers," *Review of Scientific Instruments*, Nov. 1957, p. 965.

Chenette, E. R.: "Measurement of the Correlation Between Flicker and Noise Sources in Transistors," *Proc. IRE*, June 1958, p. 1304.

Coffey, W. N.: "Behavior of Noise Figure in Junction Transistors," *Proc. IRE*, Feb. 1958, p. 495.

Guggenbuhl, M. J. O.: "Theory and Experiments on Shot Noise in Semiconductor Junction Diodes and Transistors," *Proc. IRE*, June 1957, p. 839.

Hanson, G. H., and A. van der Ziel: "Shot Noise in Transistors," *Proc. IRE*, Nov. 1957, p. 1538.

Haus, H. A., and R. B. Adler: "Invariants of Linear Noisy Networks," *IRE Trans.* PGCT, Conv. Rec., 1956, p. 53.

Jackson, R. B., and A. K. Walton: "Abnormal Noise in Junction Transistors During Secondary Ionization," *Proc. Physical Society*, Sec. B, Feb. 1957, p. 251.

Middlebrook, R. D.: "Optimum Noise Performance of Transistor Input Circuits," Solid-State Circuits Conference, Feb. 1958.

Nielson, E. G.: "Behavior of Noise Figure in Junction Transistors," *Proc. IRE*, July 1957, p. 957.

Uhlir, A., Jr.: "High-Frequency Shot Noise in P-N Junctions," *Proc. IRE*, April 1956, p. 557.

van der Ziel, A.: "Theory of Shot Noise in Junction Diodes and Junction Transistors," (letter), *Proc. IRE*, July 1957, p. 1011.

———: "Theory of Junction Diode and Junction Transistor Noise," *Proc. IRE*, March 1958, p. 589. Simplified theory.

———: "Noise in Junction Transistors," *Proc. IRE*, June 1958, p. 1019. Excellent treatment of noise.

———: "Noise in Mixer Tubes," *Proc. IRE*, July 1958. Discusses relation of average noise to average over cycle with white noise input.

van Vliet, K. M.: "Noise in Semiconductors and Photoconductors," *Proc. IRE*, June 1958, p. 1005.

Walker, J. M., Jr.: "Noise Figures in Semiconductor Dielectric Amplifiers," *IRE Conv. Rec.*, Part 3, 1957, p. 14.

TRANSISTOR CIRCUITS

Angell, J. B., and F. P. Keiper, Jr.: "Circuit Applications of Surface-Barrier Transistors," *Proc. IRE*, Dec. 1953, p. 1709.

Armstrong, H. L.: "A Treatment of Cascaded Active Four-Terminal Networks with Application to Transistor Circuits," *IRE Trans.* PGCT, June 1956, p. 138.

Beck, K. H.: "An N-Stage-Series Transistor Circuit," *IRE Trans.* PGCT, March 1956, p. 44.

Burnett, J. R.: "A Synthesis Procedure for Linear Transistor Circuits," *IRE Trans.* PGCT, Conv. Rec., 1954, p. 125.

Chow, W. F.: "Transistor Superregenerative Detection," *IRE Trans.* PGCT, March• 1956, p. 58.

Cooke-Yarborough, E. H.: *Introduction to Transistor Circuits*, Interscience Publishers, New York, 1958.

DeClaris, N.: "Driving-Point Impedance Function of Active Networks," *IRE Trans.* PGCT, Conv. Rec., 1956, p. 26.

DeSautels, A. N.: "Using Transistors in Demodulator Circuits," *Electronic Design*, 28 May 1958, p. 24; 11 June 1958, p. 52.

Didinger, G. H.: "Operating Transistors at Higher Voltages," *Electronic Design*, July 1955, p. 44.

Farber, R. J., A. Proudfit, K. M. St. John, and C. R. Wilhelmsen: "Tetrajunction Transistor Simplifies Receiver Design," *Electronics*, April 1, 1957, p. 148.

Finn, D. L., and B. J. Dasher: "Graphical Analysis of Transistor Circuits," *IRE Trans.* PGCT, Conv. Rec., 1956, p. 68.

Ghandhi, S. K.: "Darlington's Compound Connection for Transistors," *IRE Trans.* PGCT, Sept. 1957, p. 291.

Gordon, S. H.: "Application of Transistors to Ordnance Electronics," *Electronic Equipment*, Aug. 1957, p. 40.

Horowitz, I. M.: "Active Network Synthesis," *IRE Trans.* PGCT, Conv. Rec., 1956, p. 38.

Huang, C., M. Marshall, and B. H. White: "Field-Effect Transistor Circuit Design," *Electronic Design*, Part I, July 1955, p. 38: Part II, Oct. 1955, p. 42.

Hurley, R. B.: "Designing Transistor Circuits — Gain and Impedance," *Electronic Equipment*, Dec. 1957, p. 28.

Jones, D. D.: "British Transistor Applications," *Electronic Design*, July 1955, p. 54.

Karp, M. A.: "A Transistor D-C Negative Immittance Converter," *Proc. NEC*, 1956, p. 469.

Larky, A. I.: "Negative Impedance Converters," *IRE Trans.* PGCT, Sept. 1957, p. 124.

Lommasson, T. E., and K. D. Hardin: "Designing Transistorized Test Equipment," *Electronic Design*, 1 July 1956, p. 46.

Markarian, H.: "Network Partitioning Techniques Applied to the Synthesis of Transistor Amplifiers," *IRE Trans.* PGCT, Conv. Rec., 1954, p. 130.

Mathies, J. M.: "Common-Base Transistor Equivalent Circuits for Wide-Band Applications," Stanford University, June 1957.

Milnes, A. G.: "Transistor Circuits and Applications," *Proc. IEE*, Part B, Nov. 1957, p. 565.

Norden-Ketay Corp.: *Transistor Analyzer*, July 1957.

Pearlman, A. R.: "Some Properties and Circuit Applications of Super-Alpha Composite Transistors," *IRE Trans.* PGED, Jan. 1955, p. 25.

Pecher, H.: "The Admittance Matrix of Passive and Active Networks," *Archiv der Elektrischen Übertragung*, Nov. 1956, p. 494.

Quantum Electronics Corp.: "Transistorized Transistor Analyzer," *Electronic Design*, July 1955, p. 36.

Saunders, N. B.: "Designing Reliable Transistor Circuits," *Electronic Design*, Part I, March 1955, p. 24; Part II, April 1955, p. 36.

Shekel, J.: "Matrix Representation of Transistor Circuits," *Proc. IRE*, Nov. 1952, p. 1493.

Stern, A. P.: "Transistor-Simulated Reactances," *Electronic Design*, 5 March 1958, p. 24.

Stewart, J. L.: "Bandwidth Limitations in Equalizers and Transistor Output Circuits," *IRE Trans.* PGCT, March 1957, p. 5.

Stockman, H.: "Three Output Immittance Theorems," *Electronic Industries*, Jan. 1958, p. 153.

Sullivan, J. D., and I. F. Barditch, "Transistor Impedance Changer," *Electronic Industries*, Jan. 1958, p. 77.

Sylvan, T. P.: "Flow-Graph Analysis of Transistor Circuits," *Semiconductor Products*, Jan-Feb. 1958, p. 38.

Van Overbeek, A. J. W. M.: "Transistor Mixing Circuit," U. S. Patent No. 2,775,705, issued Dec. 25, 1956.

Wellsand, R.: "A Voltage-Gain Nomogram for Transistor Circuit Design," *Electronic Design*, 15 July 1957, p. 56.

Westcott, J. H.: "The Introduction of Constraints into Feedback System Design," *IRE Trans.* PGCT, Sept. 1954, p. 39.

————: "Transistor Circuit Developments," *Electronic Design*, 15 May 1956, p. 56.

————: "Some Russian Transistor Applications," *Electronic Design*, 1 July 1956, p. 90.

————: "Ideas for Design — Transistor Circuits," *Electronic Design*, 1 Feb. 1957, p. 90.

————: "Transistor TV Deflection System," *Electronic Design*, 15 April 1957, p. 140.

————: "Transistorized Phase Discriminator," *Electronic Design*, 15 May 1957, p. 139.

————: "Evaluating Tubes and Transistors in Airborne Electronic Equipment," *Electronic Equipment*, Aug. 1957, p. 46.

————: "Transistor Modulator, Low Cost," *Electronic Design*, 22 Jan. 1958, p. 104.

————: "Transistorized Electronic Filter," *Electronic Design*, 11 June 1958, p. 100.

GENERAL NONLINEAR ELEMENTS

Duinker, S.: "General Properties of Frequency Converting Networks," *Philips Research Review*, Feb. 1958, p. 37.

Haber, F., and B. Epstein: "The Parameters of Nonlinear Devices from Harmonic Measurements," *IRE Trans.* PGED, Jan. 1958, p. 26.

Hegedus, B. J.: "E and I Regulation with Nonlinear Resistors," *Electronic Design*, 15 Dec. 1956, p. 32.

Rowe, H. E.: "Some General Properties of Nonlinear Elements, II Small-Signal Theory," *Proc. IRE*, May 1958, p. 850.

————: "What the Russians Are Writing — Mathematics of Nonlinear Distortion," *Electronic Design*, 1 July 1956, p. 92.

————: "Nonlinear Function Generators Using Piecewise-Linear Approximation," *Electronic Design*, Sept. 15, 1957, p. 166.

Storm, H. F.: "Applications of Nonlinear Magnetics," *Electronic Design*, 14 May 1958, p. 60; other parts, 19 Feb. 1958, p. 32, 19 Mar., p. 44, and 16 Apr. p. 62.

Some additional references, largely reports, follow:

Beatie, R. N.: "A Lumped Model Analysis of Noise in Semiconductor Devices," *Stanford Electronics Lab.*, TR 1505-1, 1959.

Caughey, D. M., and G. T. Lake: "Noise in Transistor Amplifiers," Defense Research Telecommunications Establishment, *DRTE Report* 1019, 1959.

Cobbold, R. S. C.: "The Charge Storage in a Junction Transistor During Turnoff in the Active Region," *DRTE Report* 5083-4, 1958.

———: "The Decay Time of Minority Carriers in the Base of Junction Transistors," *DRTE Report* 1004, 1959.

Davis, E. M., Jr.: "Sensitivity of Active Networks to Variations in Internal Parameters," *Stanford Electronics Lab.*, TR 47, 1958.

Fernandez-Yanyez, A. Mas: "The Effects on the Limiting Process of Asymmetry in a Transistor Limiter," *Stanford Electronics Lab.*, TR 755-1, 1959.

Gerig, J. S.: "A Method for Evaluating the Effects of Transistor Parameter Spread," *Stanford Electronics Lab.*, TR 1503-1, 1959.

Griffith, P. G.: "Lumped Models of Drift Transistors for Large Signals," *Stanford Electronics Lab.*, TR 1501-1, 1959.

Hamilton, D. J.: "A Theory for the Transient Analysis of Avalanche Transistor Pulse Circuits," *Stanford Electronics Lab.*, TR 1701-1, 1959.

Hamilton, D. J., and J. Gibbons, and W. Shockley: "Physical Principles of Avalanche Transistor Pulse Circuits," *Stanford Electronics Lab.*, TR 53, 1959.

Heffner, H., and G. Wade: "Gain Bandwidth and Noise Characteristics of the Variable-Parameter Amplifier," *Stanford Electronics Lab.*, TR 28, 1958.

Hoehn, G. L., Jr.: "Semiconductor Comparator Circuits," *Stanford Electronics Lab.*, TR 43, 1958.

Linville, J. G.: "Lumped Models of Transistors and Diodes," *Stanford Electronics Lab.*, TR 48, 1958.

Martin, Carlos: "Junction-Transistor Circuits for Square-Wave Generation," *Stanford Electronics Lab.*, TR 78, 1954.

Mayeda, W.: "Topological Formulas for Active Networks," *University of Illinois EERL* ITR-8, ORD-1983, 1958. This report is basic to the topological method used herein.

Mayeda, W., and S. Seshu: "Topological Formulas for Network Functions," *University of Illinois EERL*, ITR-3, ORD-1983, 1956. This report is basic to the topological method used herein.

Paddock, J. P.: "Transistor Measurements Using the Indefinite Admittance Matrix," *Stanford Electronics Lab.*, TR-20, 1957. Gives important parameter relations.

Pritchard, R. L., *et al.*: "Transistor Internal Parameters for Small-Signal Representation," *Proc. IRE*, April, 1961, p. 725.

Pullen, K. A.: "The Application of Polynomial Expansions in the Analysis of Nonlinear Circuits," *Ballistic Research Labs. Report* 1057, 1958. Gives basic orthogonal polynomial data.

————: "Principles of Information Engineering," *Ballistic Research Labs. Memo. Report* 1193, 1959. Discusses basic information problem.

————: "The Use of Network Topology with Active Circuits," *Ballistic Research Labs. Report* 1096, 1960. Includes a good discussion of the topological method; also a good bibliography.

————: "On the Properties of Ladder Networks," *Ballistic Research Labs. Report* 1102, 1960. Analyzes properties of ladder networks used with R-C oscillators.

Regis, D.: "VHF and UHF Measurements on Certain Micro-Alloy Diffused-Base and Mesa Transistors," *DRTE Report* 1020, 1959. Shows desirability of use of delay operator with g_f.

Regis, D., and G. T. Lake: "Derivation of an HF Equivalent Circuit for Drift Transistors Using Y Parameter Measurements," *DRTE Report* 1034, 1960. Excellent derivation of properties, including delay factor.

Reich, H. J.: *Functional Circuits and Oscillators*, D. Van Nostrand Co. Princeton, N. J., 1961. An excellent detailed treatment of the subjects of Chapters Nine through Eleven.

Roush, R. G., and F. Hamburger, Jr.: "Final Report on Transistor Test Bridge Developed under Contract DA-36-034-ORD-1419," *John Hopkins University ICR Report*, 1955. An excellent design and discussion.

APPENDIX VI

A Discussion of Available Extended Data

The data provided by some manufacturers on their transistor devices are of an excellence that makes worthwhile a detailed examination of their form and also a comparison against representing equations. The curve data on two transistors typical of advanced presentation are described in this appendix, and their form compared to the equations derived by Regis and Lake.[1] The transistor curves in question have been extracted from *Valvo Handbuch*, Halbleiter, 1960. Any one of a number of other foreign or American device manufacturers might equally well have been selected.

The transistors in question are the OC30 and the OC170, the former presenting an excellent example of static data for low-frequency operation, and the latter an outstanding example of data for high-frequency operation. The tabular data provided on these devices are not discussed here other than to state that they too tend to be more complete than those provided as a general practice.

Certain differences in symbolism exist between standard practice in the United States and in Europe, making desirable the presentation of the following equivalence table. (Table I).

Priming of the parameters listed indicates an intrinsic value within the basic transistor in the U.S. system. The European practice for designating the common electrode, a designation which may not be required if techniques in this book are followed, is to follow the above with an *e*, *b*, or *c* to indicate a common emitter, base, or collector. The *e* subscript is omitted in this book, but the *b* and the *c* subscripts are used for the common-base and the common-collector configurations as required.

---

[1] D. Regis, and G. T. Lake, "Derivation of an HF Equivalent Circuit for the Drift Transistor Using Y Parameter Measurements," *DRTE Report* 1034, Ottawa, Canada, 1960.

TABLE I

Equivalent Symbols

Voltage:

U.S.	v_C	v_B	V_{CC}	V_{BB}	V_{EE}	V_s	v
Europe	U_{CE}	U_{BE}	U_O	U_{bat}		U_g	U

Current: *Resistance:*   *Power:*

U.S.	i_B	i_C	i_E	$r_{b'}, r_{bb'}$	P_c	P_i	P_o
Europe	I_B	I_C	I_E	$r_{bb'}$	N_C	N_i	N_o

Tot. Inp. Power: *Crit. Freq.*   *Gain:*

U.S.	——	f_α	f_β	f_T	K	K_i
Europe	$N=,\ N_{bat}$	$f_{\alpha b}$	$f_{\alpha e}$	$f_{(\alpha e=1)}$	v_{ue}	v_{ie}

Parameters:

U.S.	$y_i = g_i + jb_i = g_i + j\omega C_i$ $y_f = g_f + jb_f = g_f + j\omega C_f$
Europe	$y_{11} = g_{11} + jb_{11} = g_{11} + j\omega C_{11}$ $y_{21} = g_{21} + jb_{21} = g_{21} + j\omega C_{21}$
U.S.	$y_r = g_r + jb_r = g_r + j\omega C_r$ $y_o = g_o + jb_o = g_o + j\omega C$
Europe	$y_{12} = g_{12} + jb_{12} = g_{12} + j\omega C_{12}$ $y_{22} = g_{22} + jb_{22} = g_{22} + j\omega C_{22}$

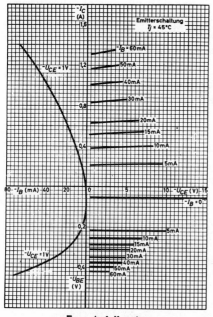

Fig. A-VI-1A

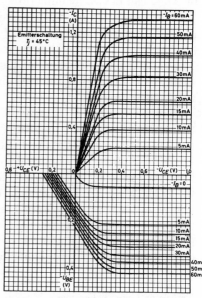

Fig. A-VI-1B

Two families of basic curves are provided on the OC30 transistor, Fig. VI–1, part (a) presenting the general group, and part (b) the low-voltage group. These two sets both include a collector family of curves and a base family in the form. In addition, the set in part (a) contains two other curves, one of base current as a function of collector current with a fixed collector voltage in the second quadrant, and a contour of base current against base voltage for fixed collector voltage in the third quadrant. The collector family is in the first quadrant, and the base family in the fourth. The two curves in the second and third quadrants represent data at the same collector voltage, and can be used for approximating both the beta and the forward conductance of the device, but at relatively low accuracy.*

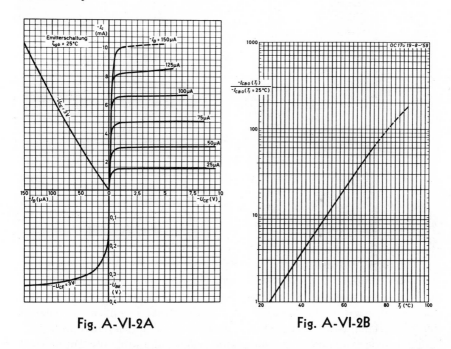

Fig. A-VI-2A   Fig. A-VI-2B

In addition to these families of basic curves, contours are also provided for the determination of the base current with an open emitter return and the emitter current with an open base return, Fig. VI–1(c). These data are helpful in the determination of the stability of a circuit using the device. Because the change in floating-potential of the base with temperature is known theoretically, a contour expressing this relation is only needed if the theoretical values for some reason do not give accurate results. The nominal values for this, given by Nosov and Khazanov, are

* Curve data courtesy of Amperex Electronic Corp.

-0.0023 volt per degree for germanium and -0.0020 volt per degree for silicon.[2]

The static data presented on these curves are consequently adequate for static design problems. They have only one limitation — the small-signal data are rather inaccessible.

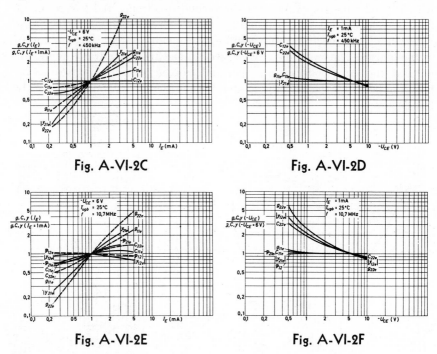

Fig. A-VI-2C   **Fig. A-VI-2D**

Fig. A-VI-2E   **Fig. A-VI-2F**

The data provided for the OC170 transistor in Fig. VI–2 are possibly the most complete the writer has seen. Only the base-input contours are missing in the static data. The small-signal data are nearly complete, but the coordination of the different data is somewhat inconvenient. One of the small-signal correction contours, that for g_{22e}, is missing on graph (2d). This curve is available on the remaining graphs, and probably can be used to correct for the missing contour.

Graph (2g) is particularly interesting in that it gives considerable information on the variation of the device parameters as a function of frequency. The behavior of all but two of the curves is as might be expected; the two worthy of further discussion are the curves for g_{11e} (g_i) and g_{22e} (g_o). As explained by Regis and Lake, the rise in the value of g_{11e} with frequency is due to the shunting-out of the internal conductance of the input by

[2] Y. R. Nosov, and B. I. Khazanov. "Temperature Stabilization of Transistor Voltage Amplifiers," *Radiotechnika*, Febuary, 1958.

the input capacitance. The conductance remaining is that due to base-spreading resistance. The frequency at which the conductance rise initiates is between the beta-cutoff frequency and the upper noise-corner frequency, fn_2. The increase in g_{22e} is a result partially of the time delay due to diffusion and drift introduced by y_{21e} through the effect of $r_{b'}$. If base-spreading resistance is zero, this increase would be zero.

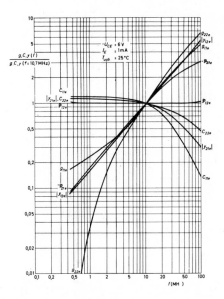

Fig. A-VI-2G

As a matter of interest, it is convenient to include the equations derived by Regis and Lake for representation of curves similar to those shown in Fig. VI-2(g). This representation, although derived for drift transistors, gives a good indication of the behavior of many common types of transistors. The equations, in the terminology of this book, are

$$y_i = (g_{i'} + j\omega C_{i'})/[1 + r_{b'}(g_{i'} + j\omega C_{i'})]$$

$$y_f = [g_{f'} \exp{(-j\pi f/4f_a)}]/[1 + r_{b'}(g_{i'} + j\omega C_{i'})]$$

$$y_r = -(g_{r'} + j\omega C_{r'})/[1 + r_{b'}(g_{i'} + j\omega C_{i'})]$$

$$y_o = g_{o'} + j\omega(C_{o'} + C_{o''}) + \frac{[g_{f'}(g_{r'} + j\omega C_{r'}) \exp{(-j\pi f/4f_a)}]r_{b'}}{[1 + r_{b'}(g_{i'} + j\omega C_{i'})]}$$

$$y_c = g_{o'} + j\omega(C_{o'} + C_{o''}) + \frac{[g_{f'}(g_{r'} + j\omega C_{r'}) \exp{(-j\pi f/4f_a)}]}{(g_{i'} + j\omega C_{i'})}$$

In these equations, the prime values correspond to those for the intrinsic transistor for which $r_{b'}$ is zero, and the double-prime capacitance is the capacitance between the collector lead and the base lead. At low frequencies, the value of y_o may be represented by $y_{o'}$ or conversely.

The curve for g_{11e} on graph (2g) levels to a constant value as the frequency is reduced, a condition not recorded on the contour. It turns horizontal rather sharply below a frequency of 0.5 mc. Similarly, the curve for g_{22e} turns horizontal at reduced values of frequency, but off the lower limit of the graph scale.

Superficially it would appear that the high-frequency values of g_{22e} or g_o should be only a few times greater than the low-frequency value. This is not the case as a result of the relatively large value of $C_{r'}$ and the effect of exp $(-j\pi f/4f_a)$, shifting the reactance into a conductance component. This fictitious conductance causes g_{22e} to continue to rise for over a decade increase of frequency, and causes the change to be of several orders of magnitude as can be noted on (2g).

APPENDIX VII

Characteristic Curves for Solid-State Devices

A collection of characteristic curves on semiconductor devices is included in this section to help the reader apply small-signal techniques to typical problems for solid-state devices. Some of these curves include superposed contours of the small-signal parameters and as a result lend themselves directly to the solution of problems in which reliability is an important factor. The balance of the devices are represented in terms of static characteristics, but, because of the coordinated form of the curves, approximations to the small-signal data can be made by the least-squares fitting techniques described in Appendix IV.

Power contours for half- and full-rated collector dissipation have been included when they fall within the scope of the curves being presented. These contours are also helpful in assuring reliable operation. Where extreme reliability and stability are essential, however, additional drift tests with a sweep-type tester can be helpful. The technique described in Chapter Three, using contours of constant base current as a function of base voltage and collector voltage, is most helpful for these tests. The transistor is operated in the repetitive-sweep condition for a few seconds, and then the base-drive current is removed. The drift of the zero-current contour, as the transistor cools, serves as a measure of the stability. The total power dissipated may be increased in steps until moderate to severe drifting occurs. The maximum steady-state dissipation then is approximately 15 percent of the peak value indicated on the curves.

Additional families of curves on transistor devices may be obtained easily with an analyzer such as the Tektronix Model 575, and photographs made from the curves may be replotted in the form presented in this appendix. Little difficulty will be encountered if adequate spread can be obtained for the input contours. The zero-suppression circuit described facilitates the preparation of the input family as required.

The reader should note that the curves presented are typical for ordinary production units of the specified code number, but may not necessarily be typical of the bogey, or ideal, transistor of the specified type. As a consequence, the data provided should be treated as being approximate, and an operating margin should be provided to allow for the variations which must be expected among typical devices such as those measured. Where the number of samples have permitted, and sufficient manufacturer's data have been available, the samples have been sorted to find the device in the group most nearly like the specifications. Otherwise, the unit measured has been selected partly on the basis of the one appearing to be the most representative of the group available. In particular, the degree of stability was weighted heavily in the process of selection.

The improvement of solid-state devices is continuing sufficiently rapidly so that even if the enclosed curves did represent ideal devices at the time of measurement, the passage of a few months or years can be expected to bring about sufficient improvements with the result that new curves should have to be taken to determine the characteristics of the devices then in production. This is particularly true if large numbers of the devices are required or if the reliability of the circuits using transistors is an important consideration.

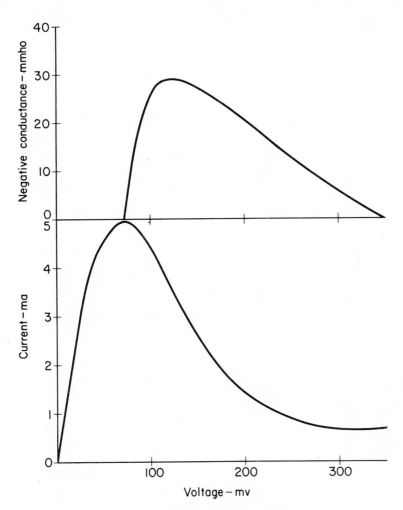

Fig. A-VII-1. ZJ56A-47(GE)

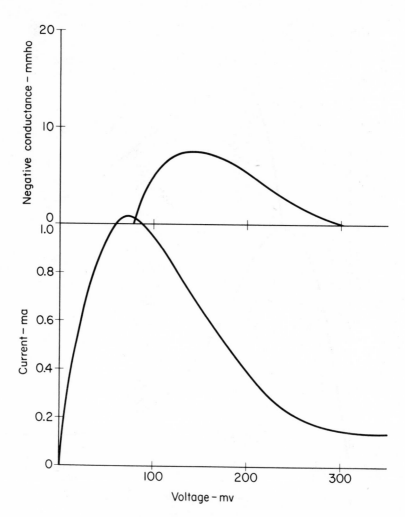

Fig. A-VII-2. ZJ56-013(GE)

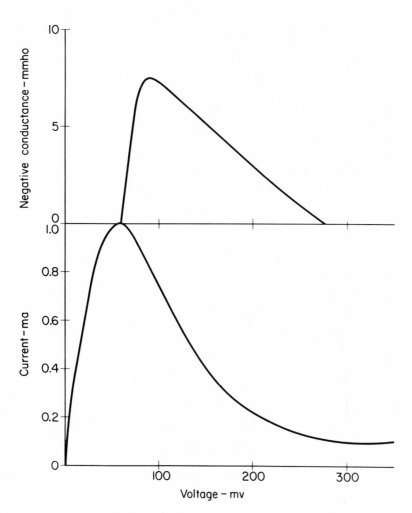

Fig. A-VII-3.   ZJ56-017(GE)

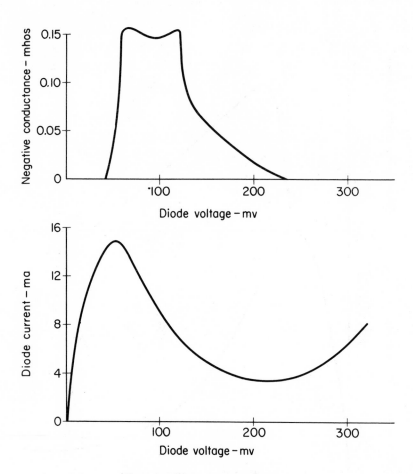

Fig. A-VII-4. TD-2(GT)

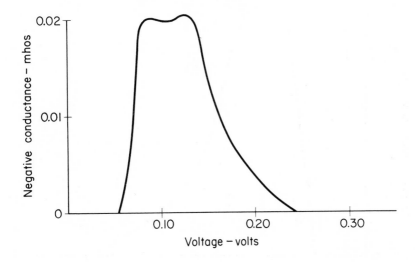

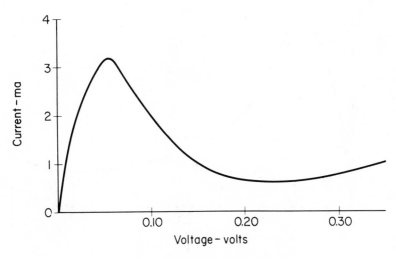

Fig. A-VII-5.   Orange dot (RCA)

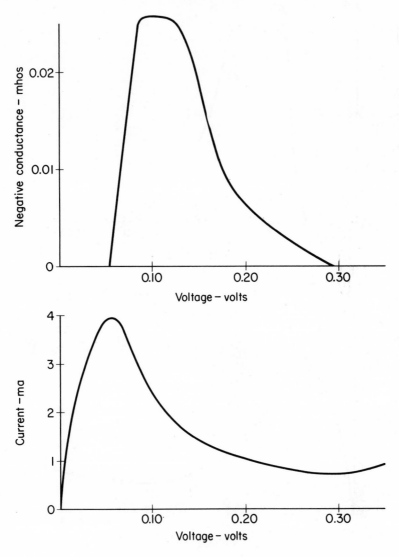

Fig. A-VII-6.   Yellow dot (RCA)

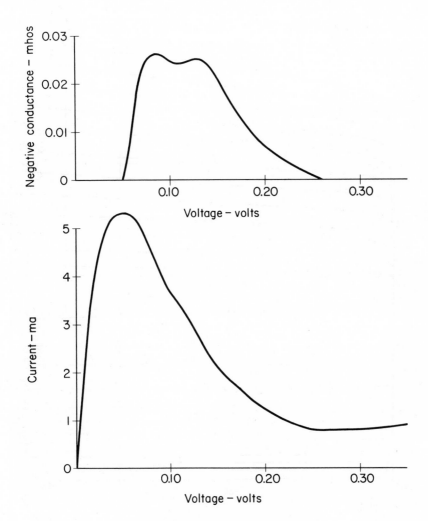

Fig. A-VII-7. Blue dot (RCA)

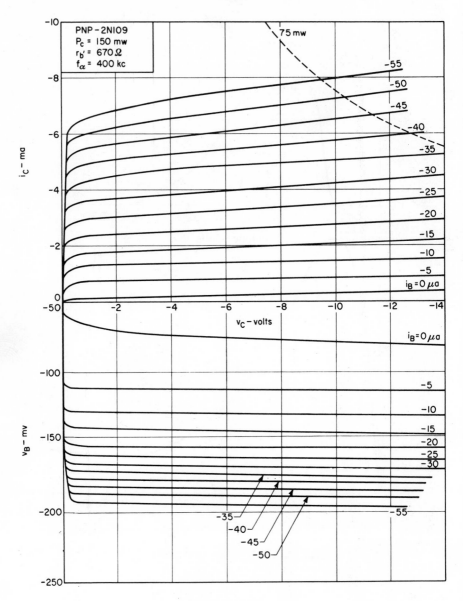

Fig. A-VII-8

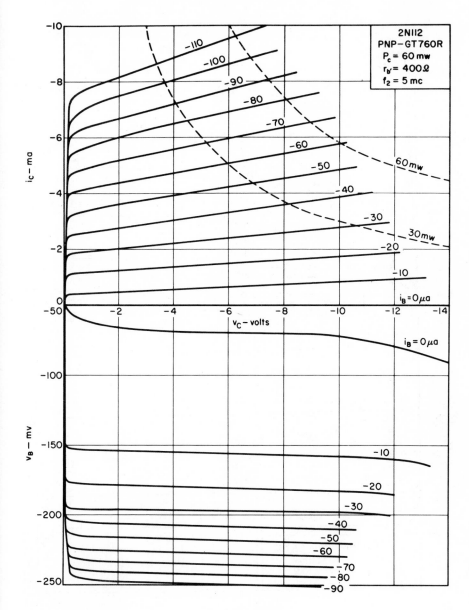

Fig. A-VII-9

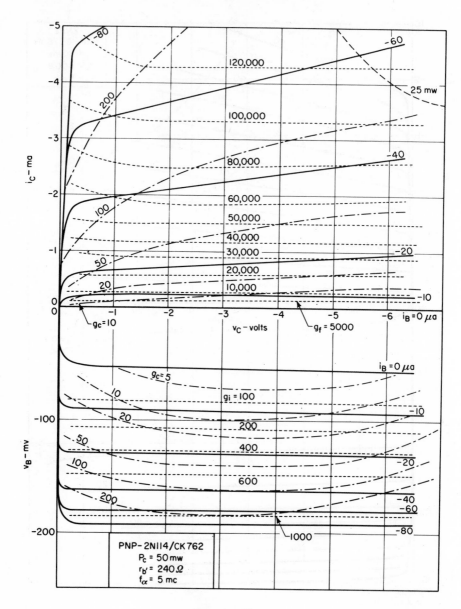

Fig. A-VII-10

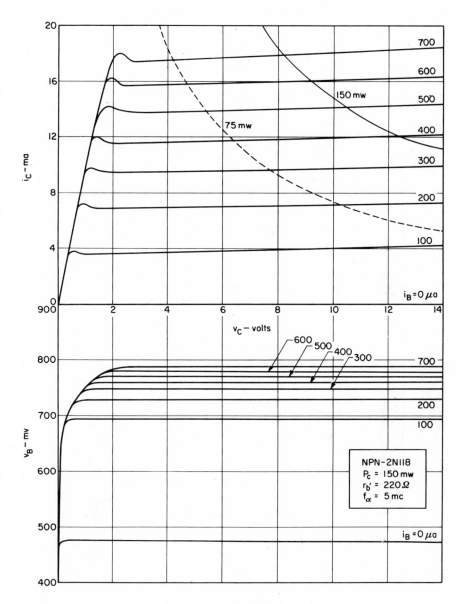

Fig. A-VII-11

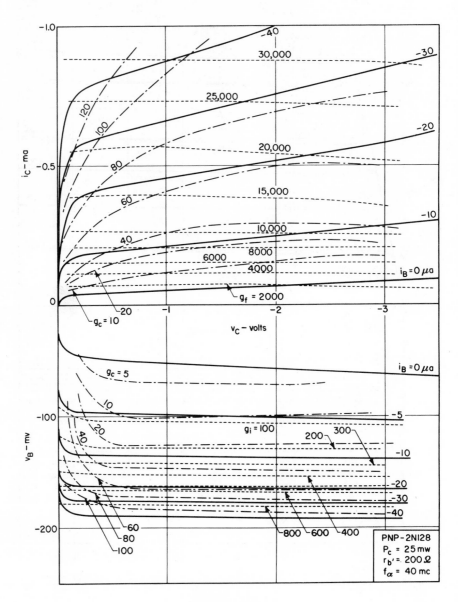

Fig. A-VII-12

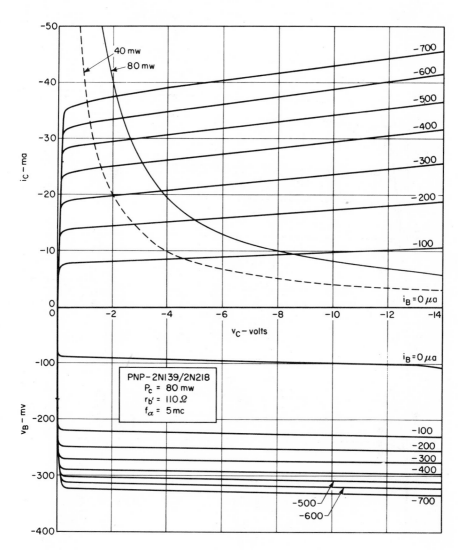

Fig. A-VII-13

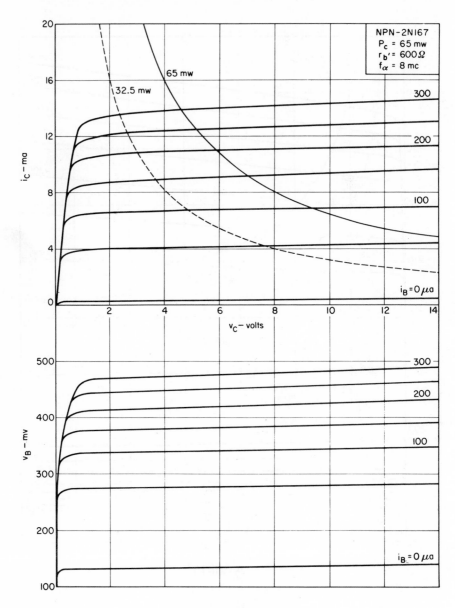

Fig. A-VII-14

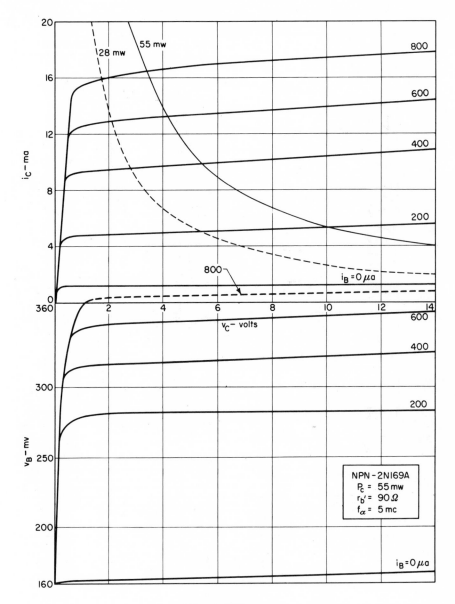

Fig. A-VII-15

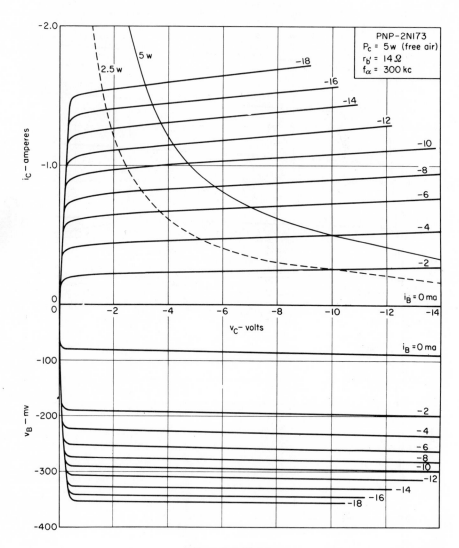

Fig. A-VII-16

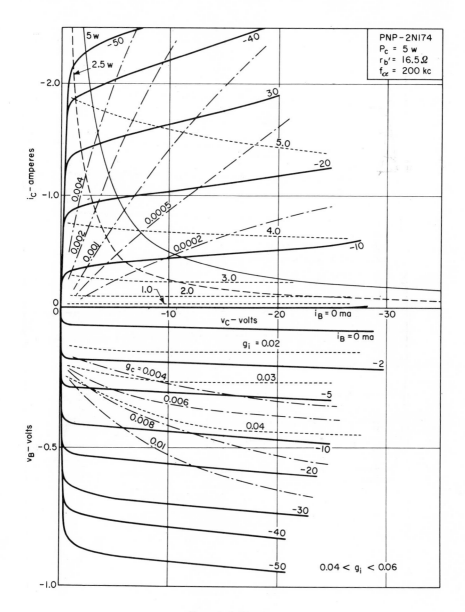

Fig. A-VII-17

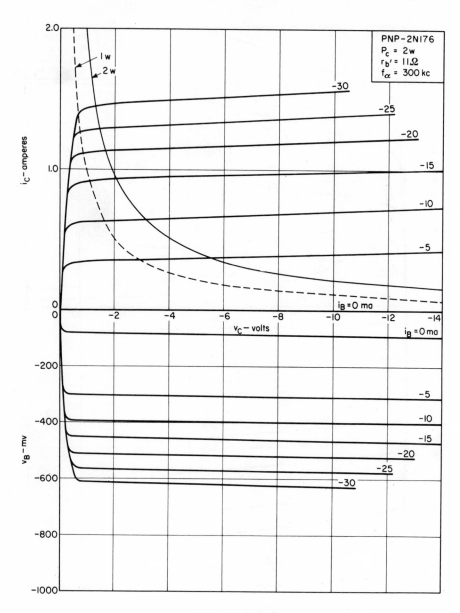

Fig. A-VII-18

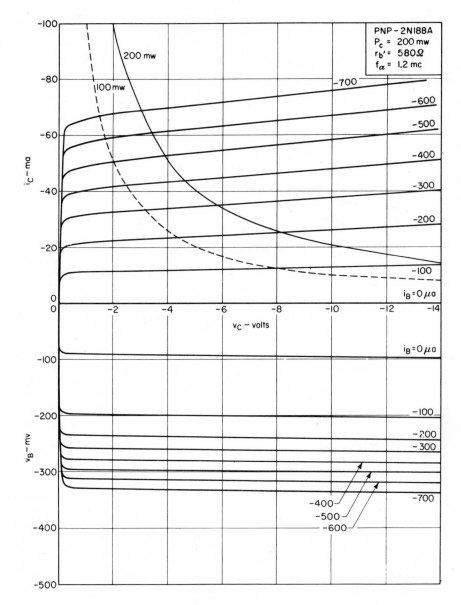

Fig. A-VII-19

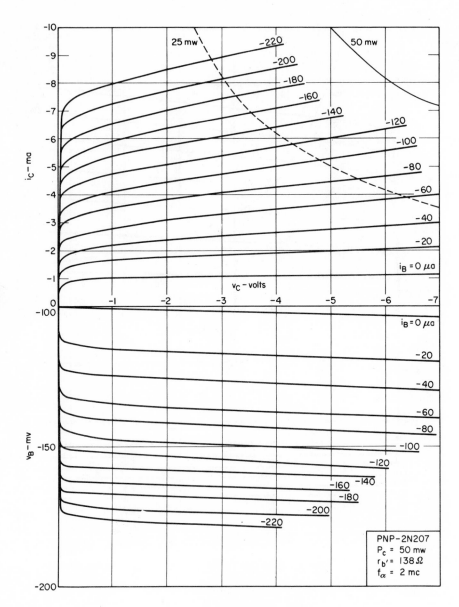

Fig. A-VII-20

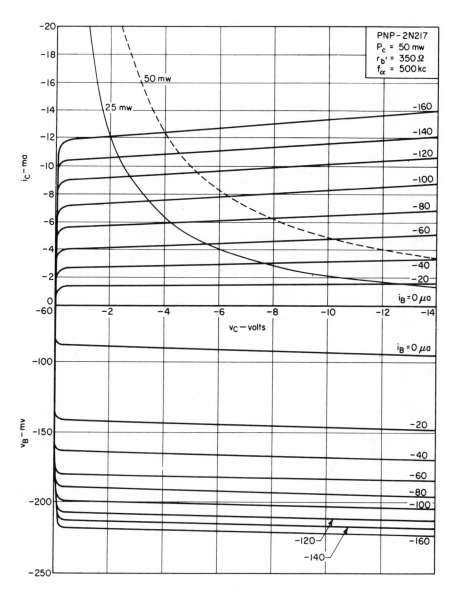

Fig. A-VII-21

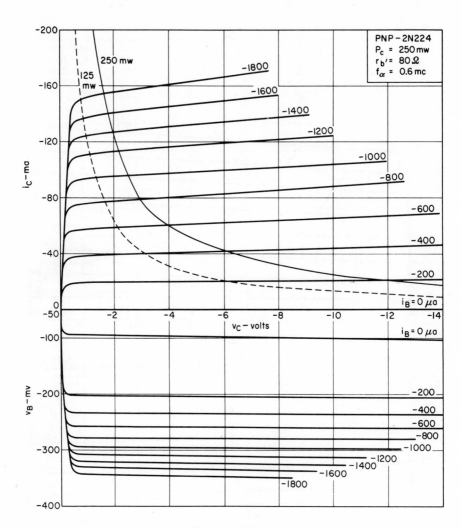

Fig. A-VII-22

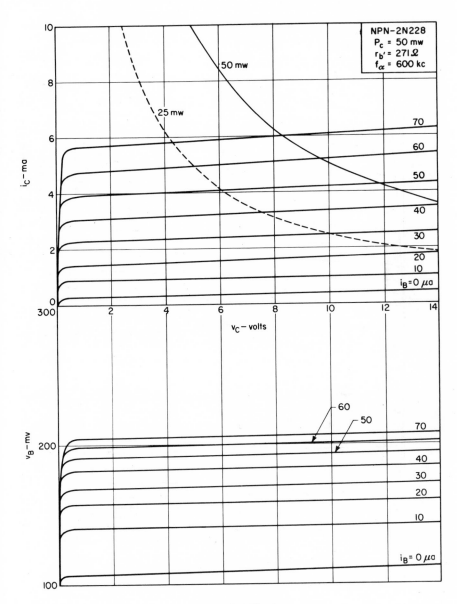

Fig. A-VII-23

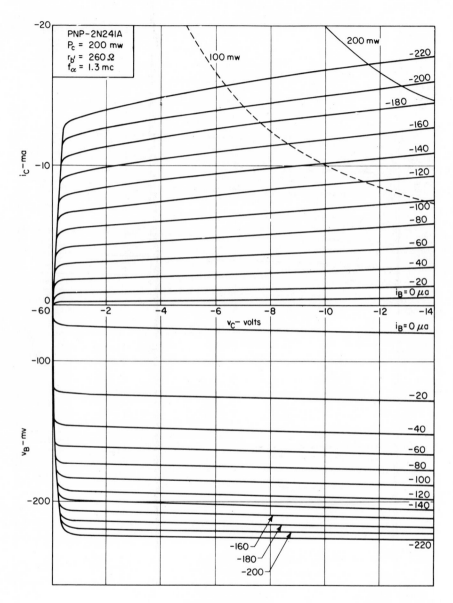

Fig. A-VII-24

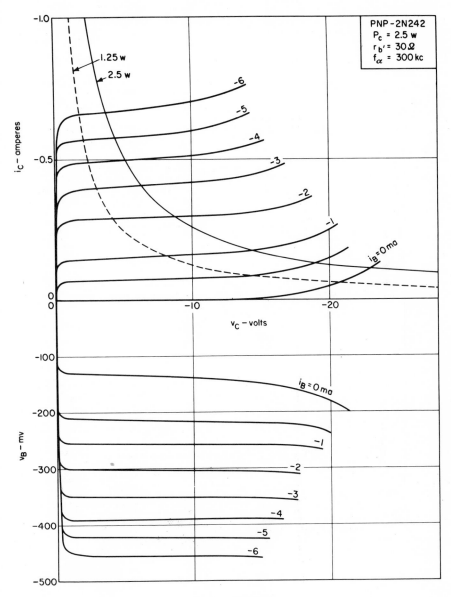

Fig. A-VII-25

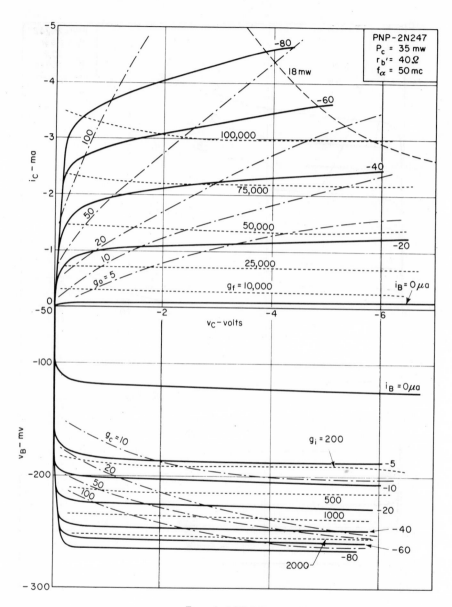

Fig. A-VII-26

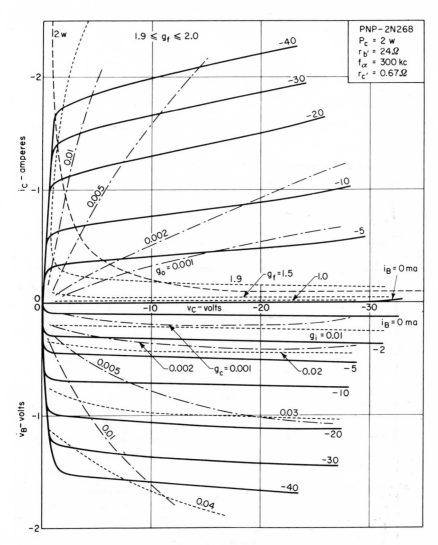

Fig. A-VII-27

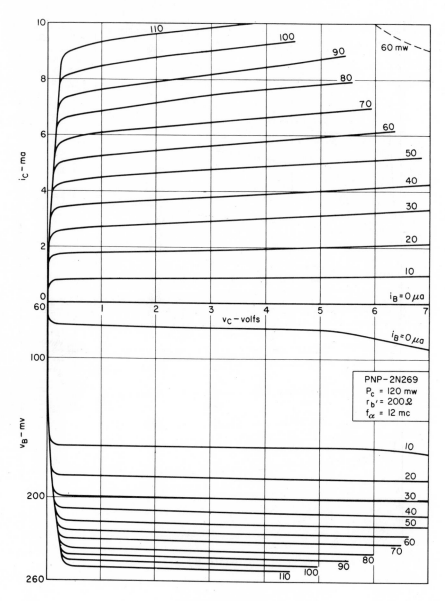

Fig. A-VII-28

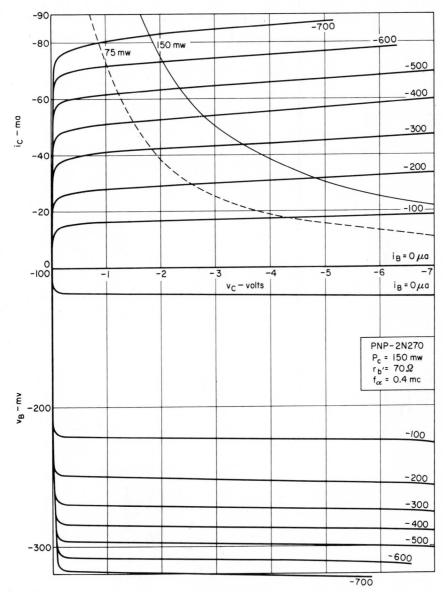

Fig. A-VII-29

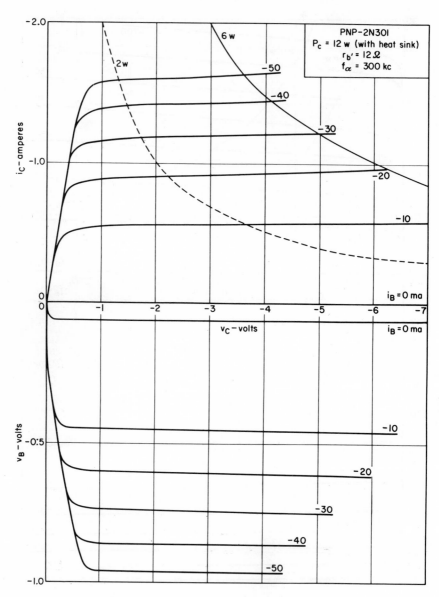

Fig. A-VII-30

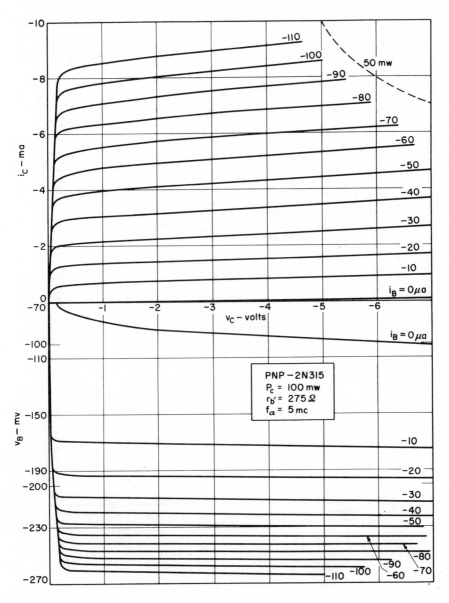

Fig. A-VII-31

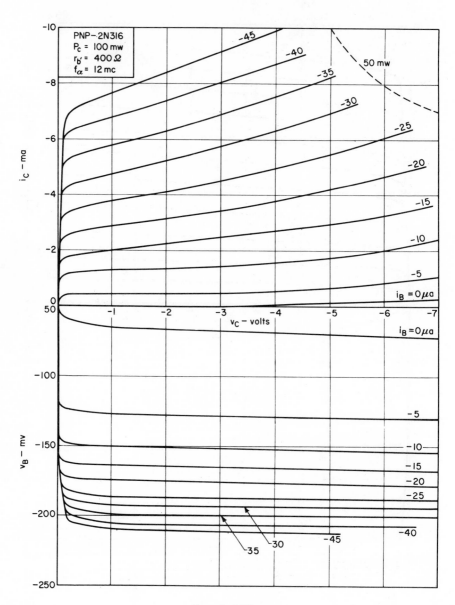

Fig. A-VII-32

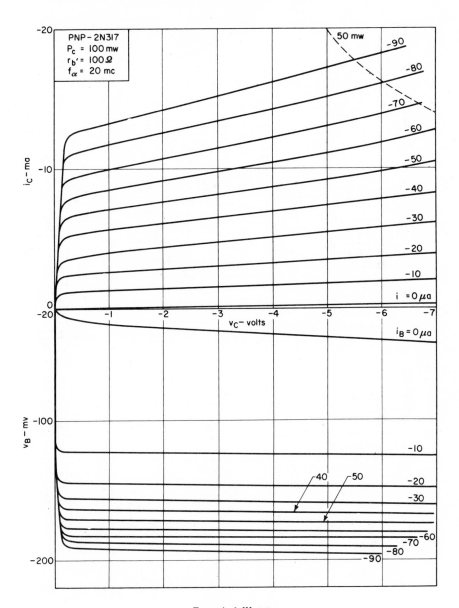

Fig. A-VII-33

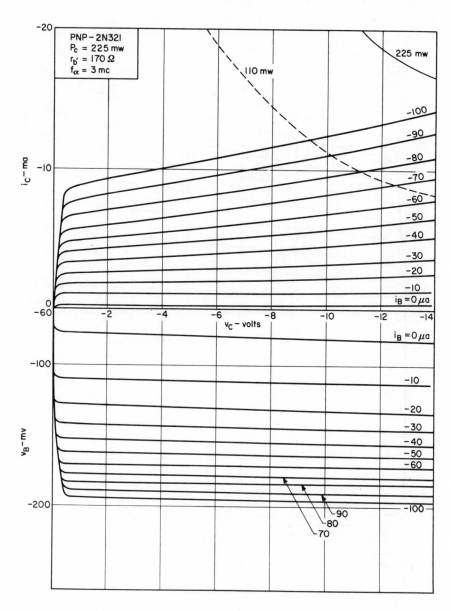

PNP–2N321
$P_c = 225$ mw
$r_{b'} = 170\ \Omega$
$f_\alpha = 3$ mc

Fig. A-VII-34

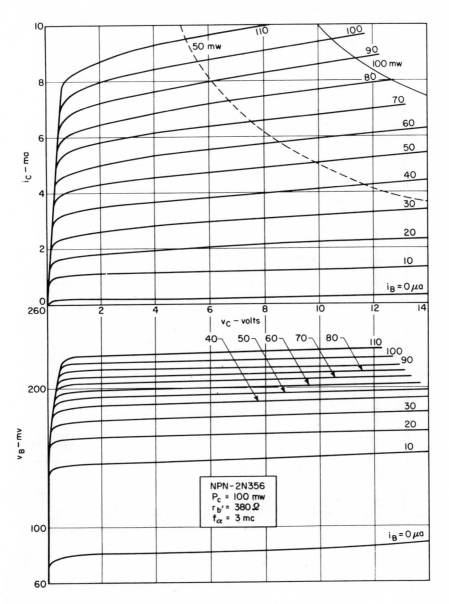

Fig. A-VII-35

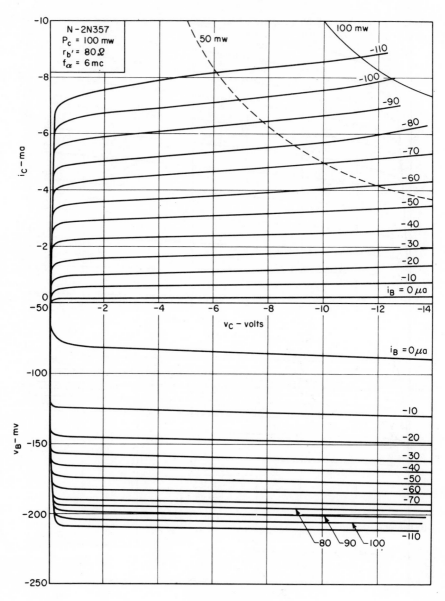

Fig. A-VII-36

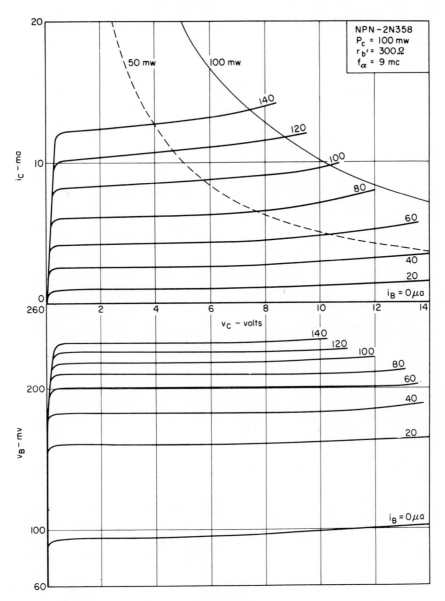

Fig. A-VII-37

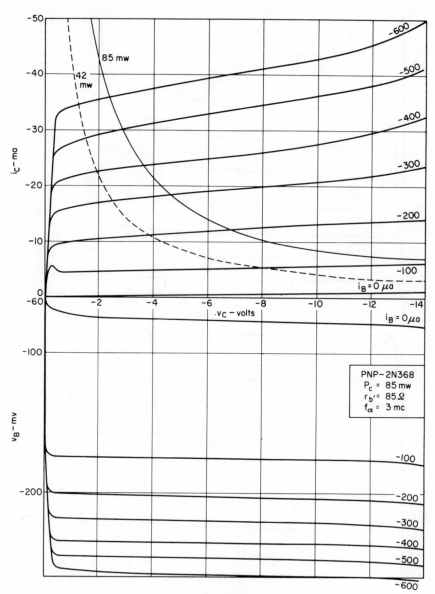

Fig. A-VII-38

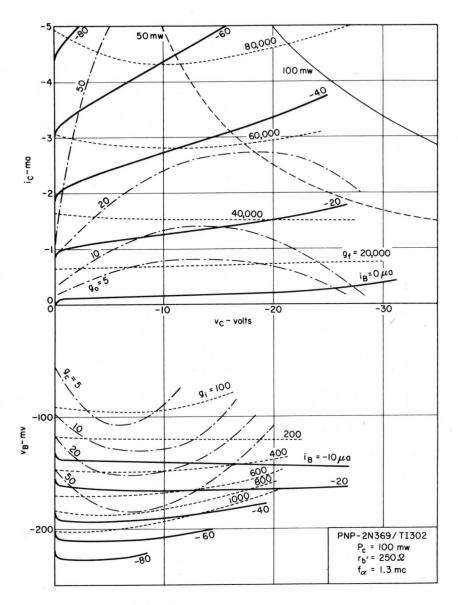

Fig. A-VII-39

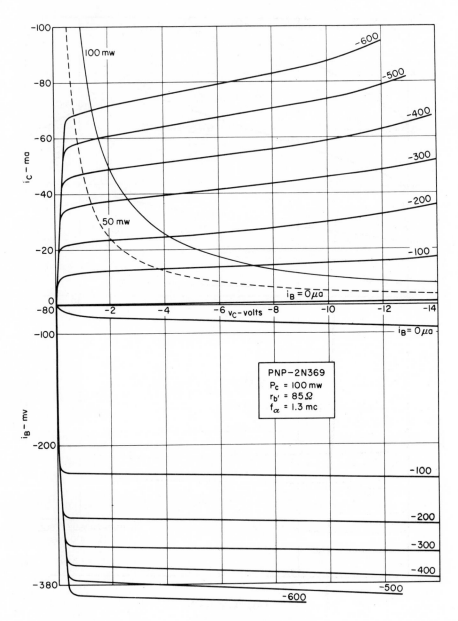

Fig. A-VII-40

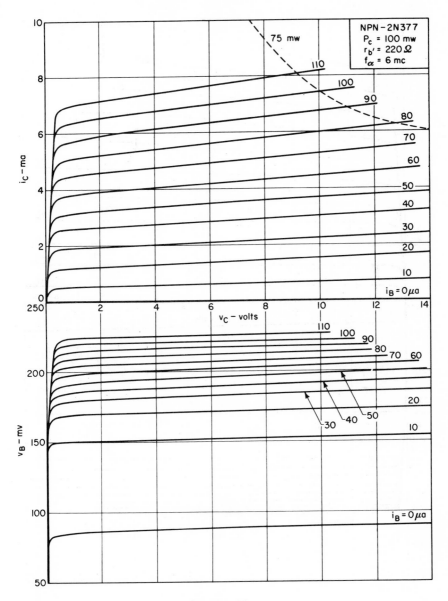

Fig. A-VII-41

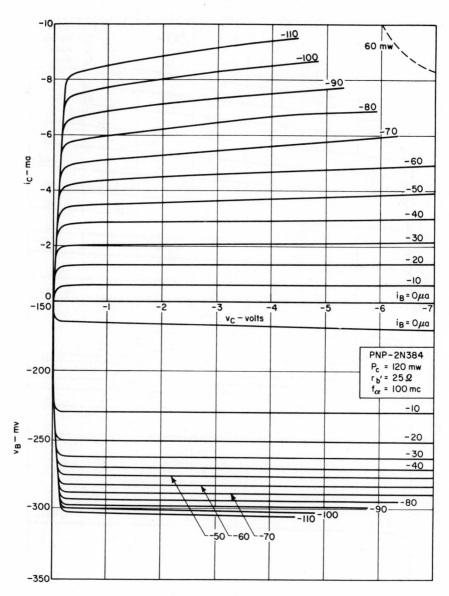

Fig. A-VII-42

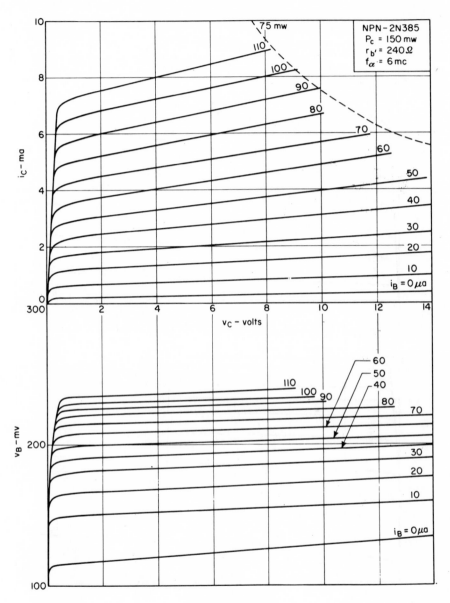

Fig. A-VII-43

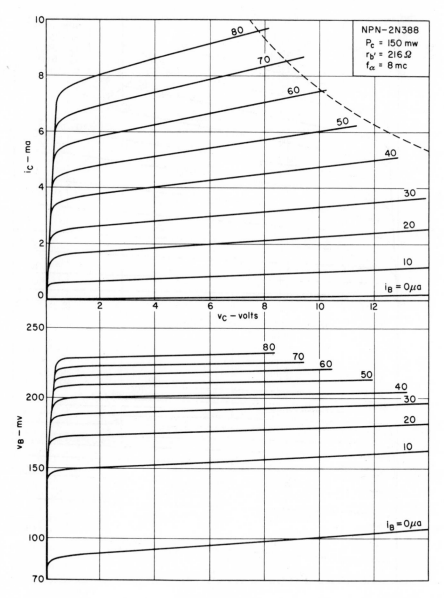

Fig. A-VII-44

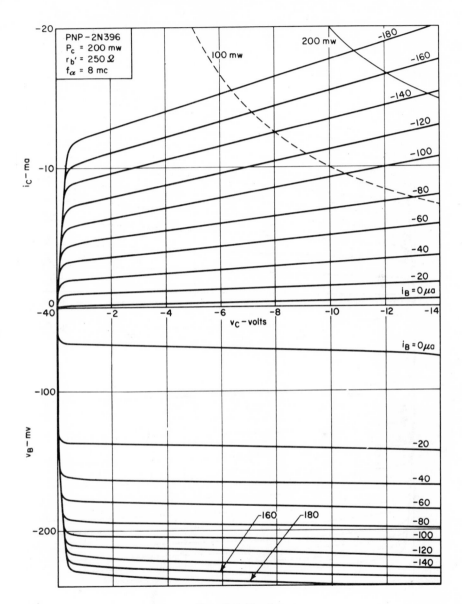

Fig. A-VII-45

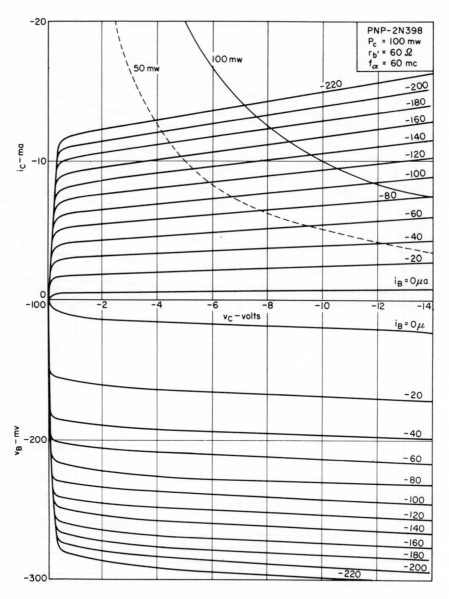

Fig. A-VII-46

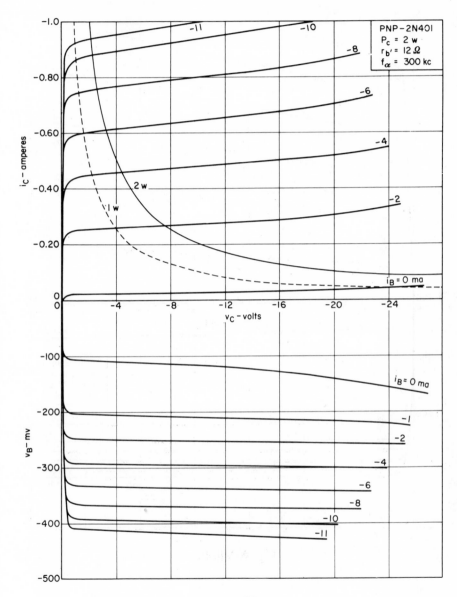

Fig. A-VII-47

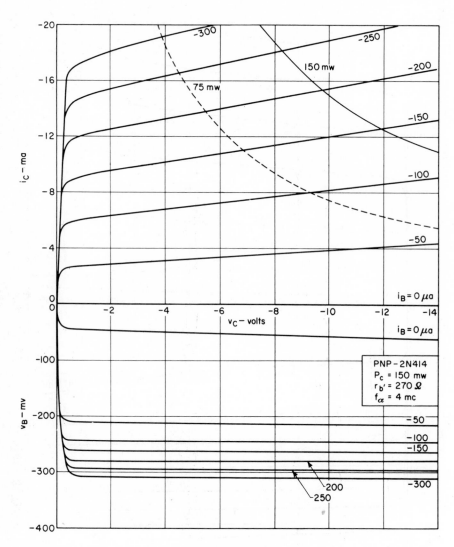

Fig. A-VII-48

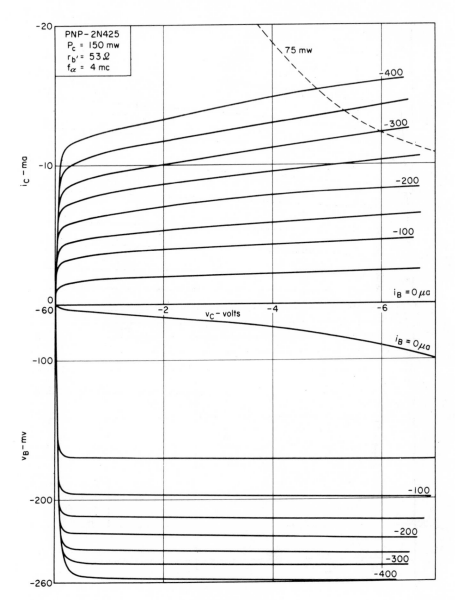

Fig. A-VII-49

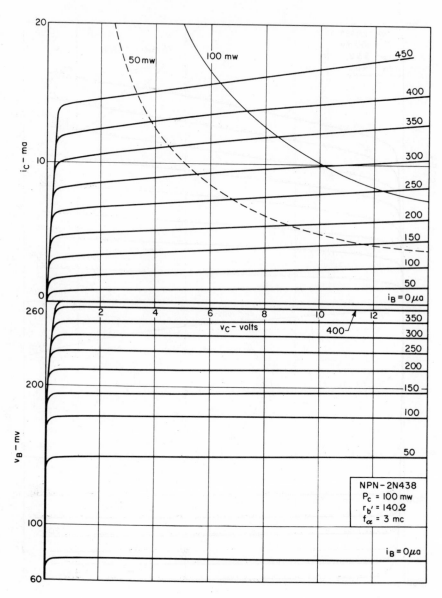

Fig. A-VII-50

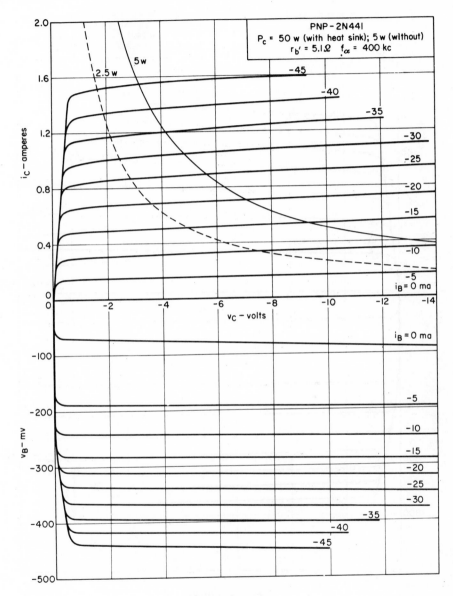

Fig. A-VII-51

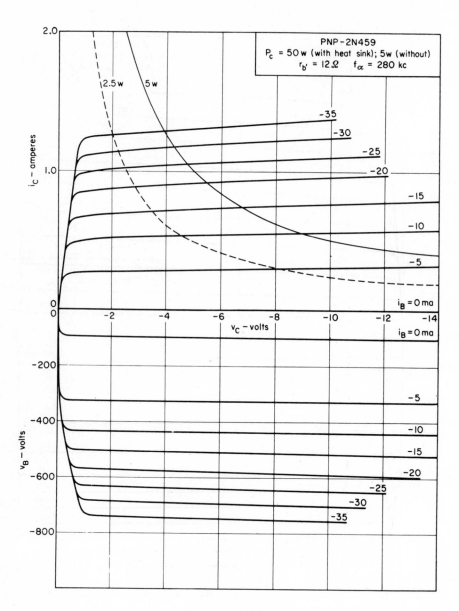

Fig. A-VII-52

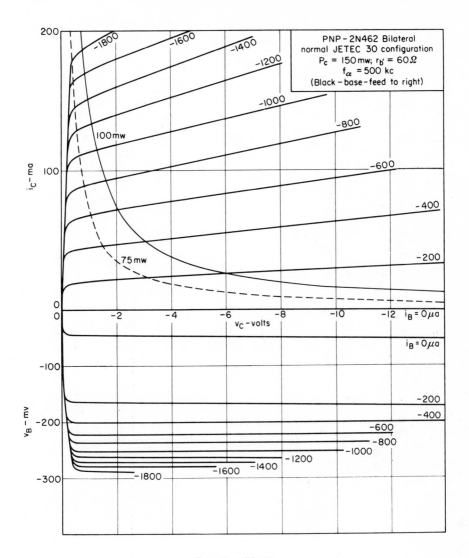

PNP – 2N462 Bilateral
normal JETEC 30 configuration
$P_c = 150\,mw$; $r_b' = 60\,\Omega$
$f_\alpha = 500\,kc$
(Black – base – feed to right)

Fig. A-VII-53

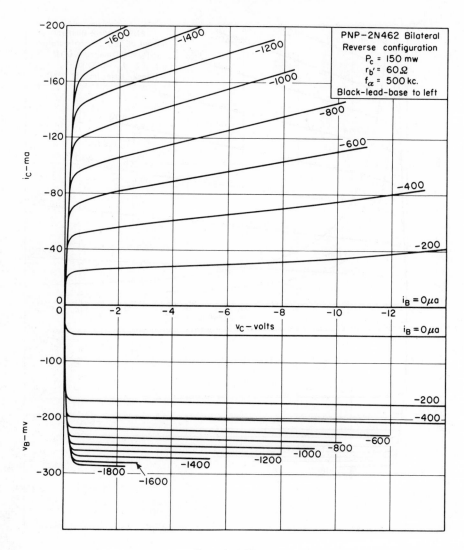

Fig. A-VII-54

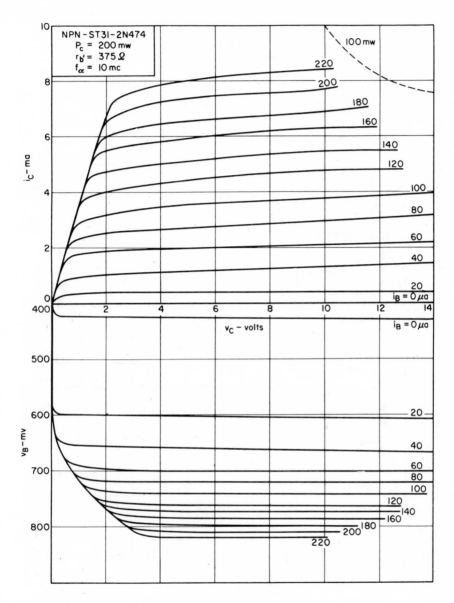

Fig. A-VII-55

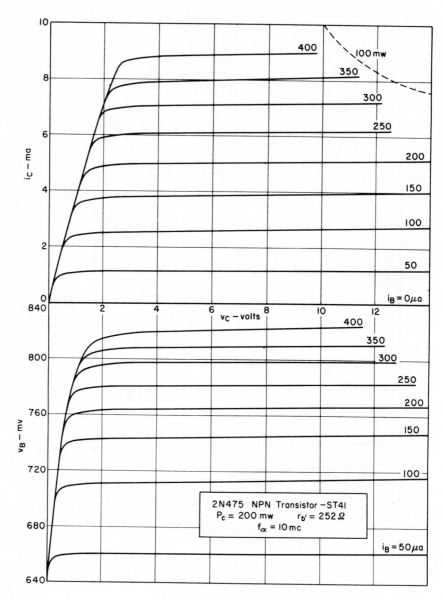

Fig. A-VII-56

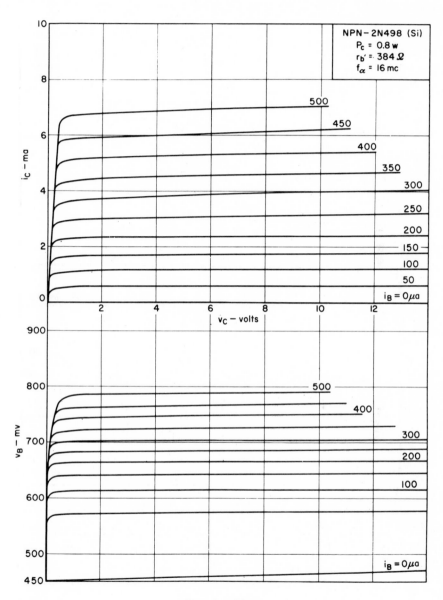

Fig. A-VII-57

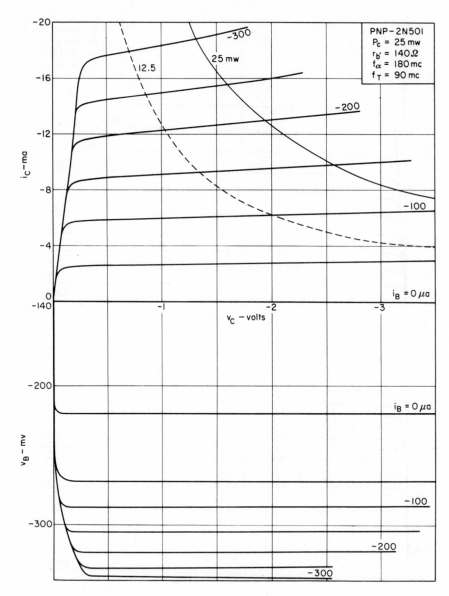

Fig. A-VII-58

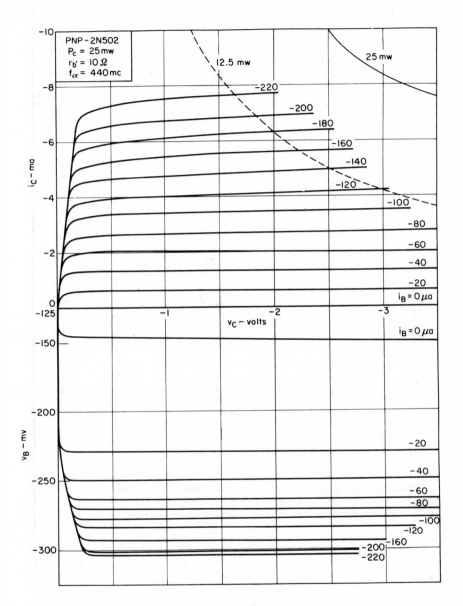

Fig. A-VII-59

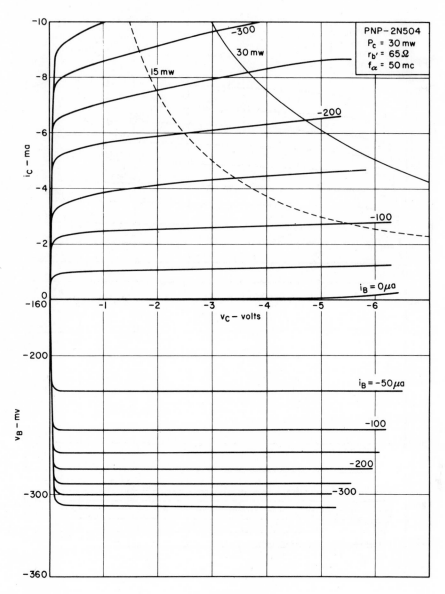

Fig. A-VII-60

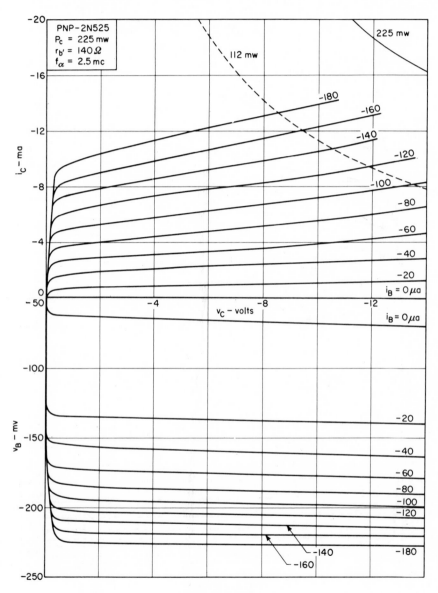

Fig. A-VII-61

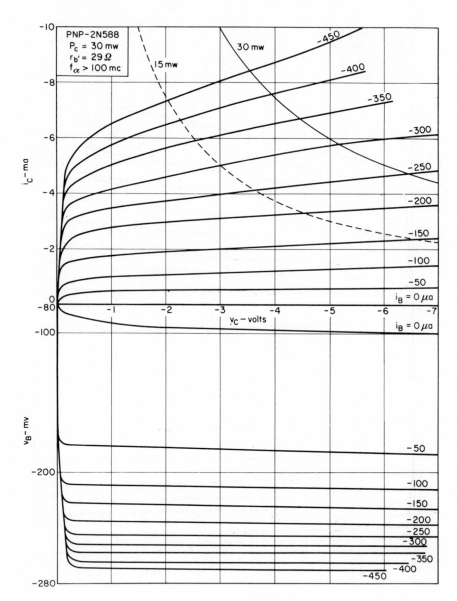

Fig. A-VII-62

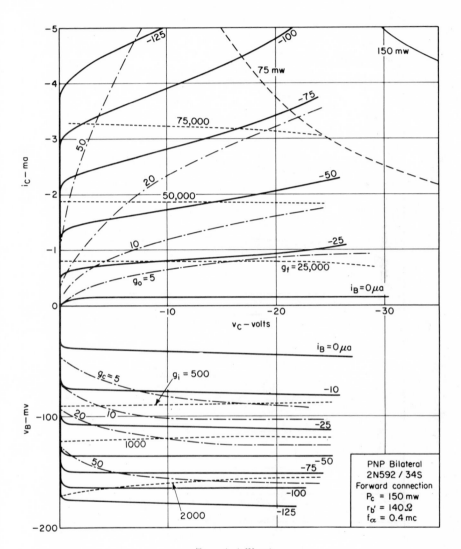

Fig. A-VII-63

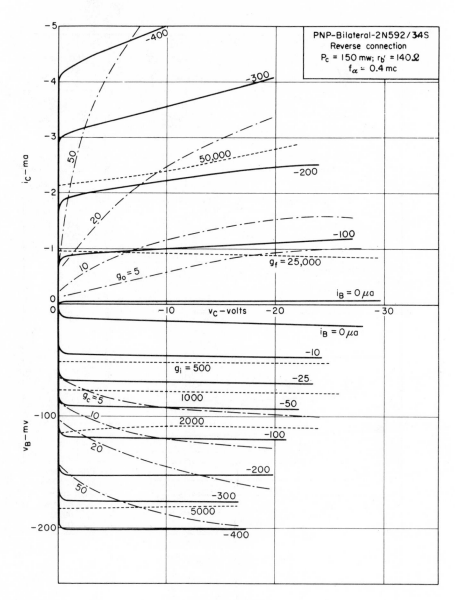

Fig. A-VII-64

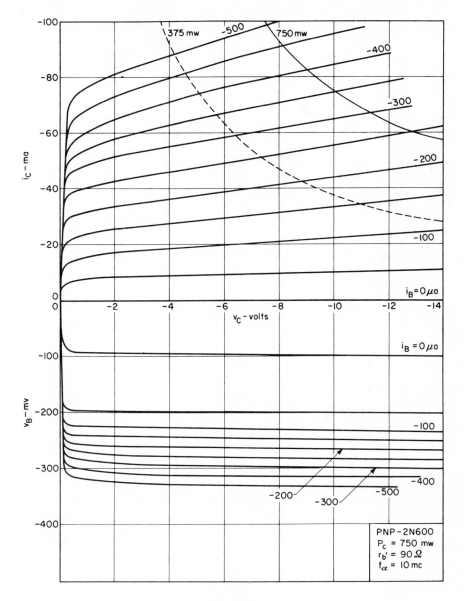

Fig. A-VII-65

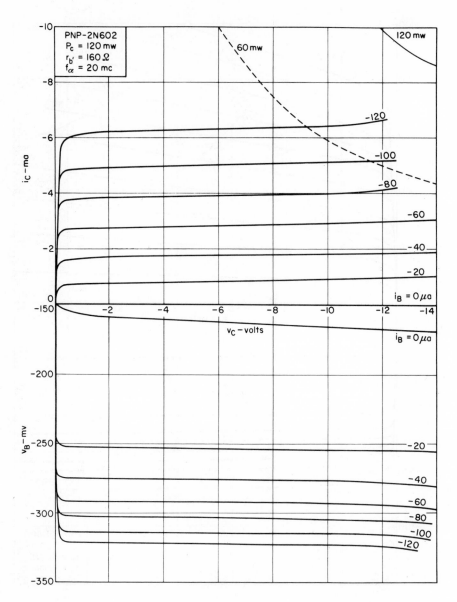

Fig. A-VII-66

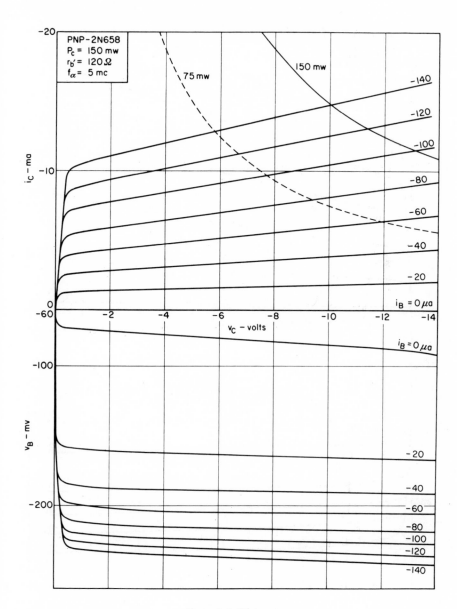

Fig. A-VII-67

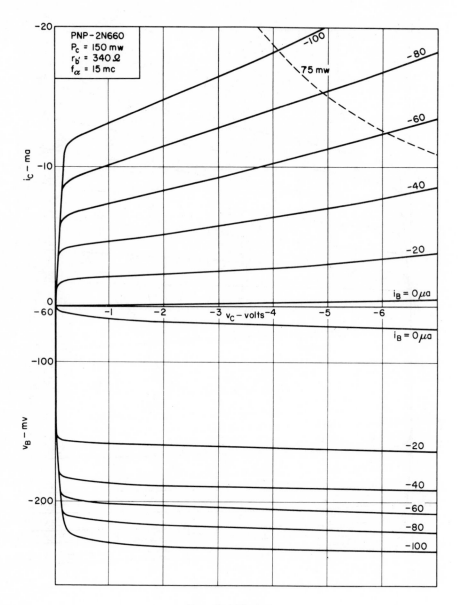

Fig. A-VII-68

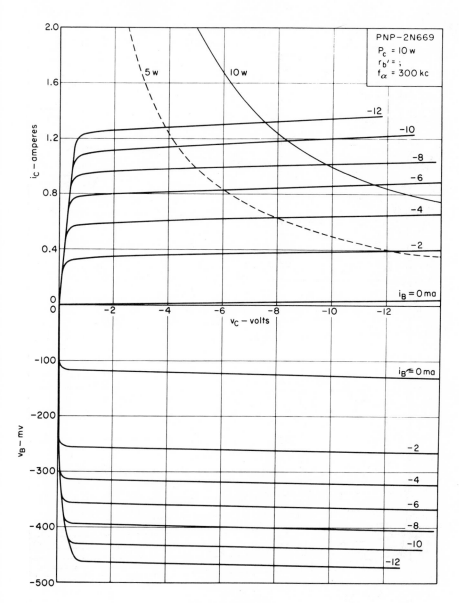

Fig. A-VII-69

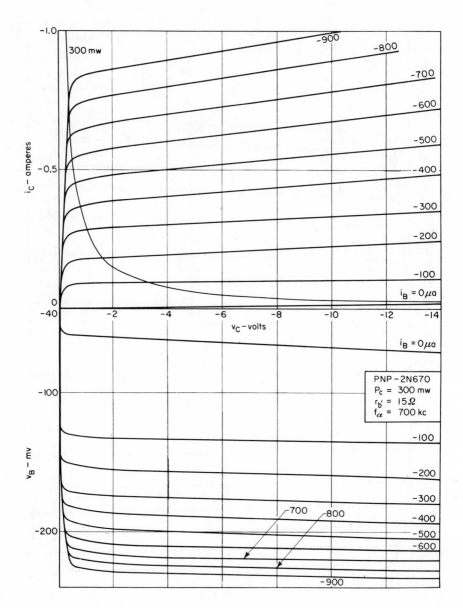

Fig. A-VII-70

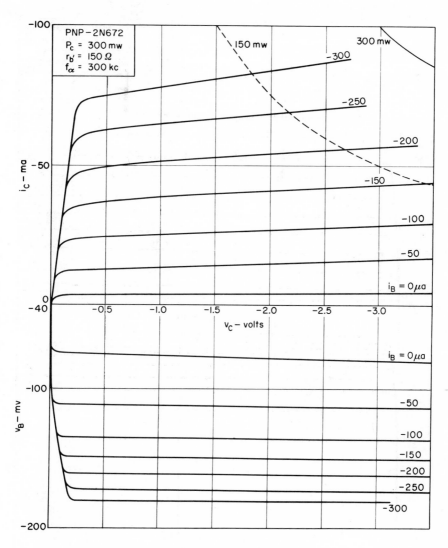

Fig. A-VII-71

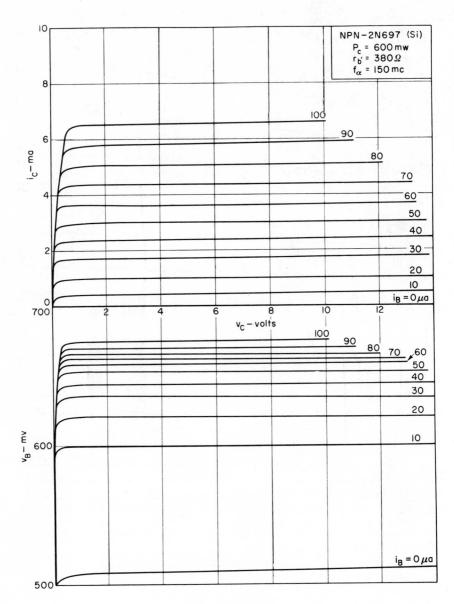

Fig. A-VII-72

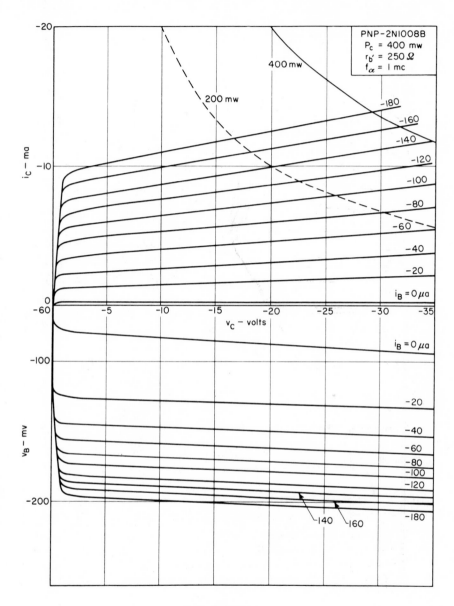

Fig. A-VII-73

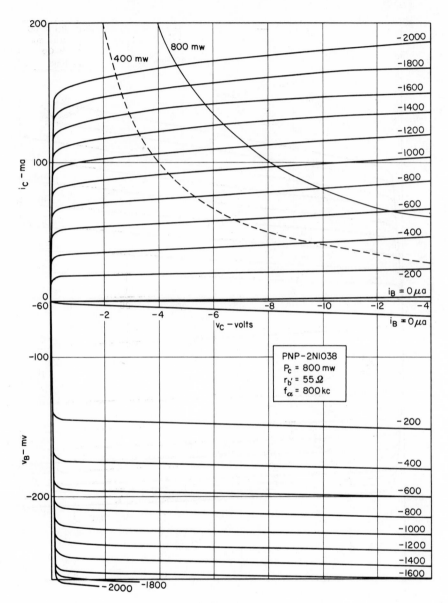

Fig. A-VII-74

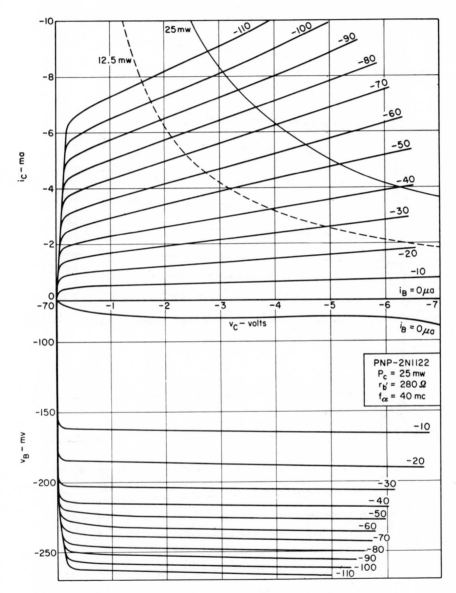

Fig. A-VII-75

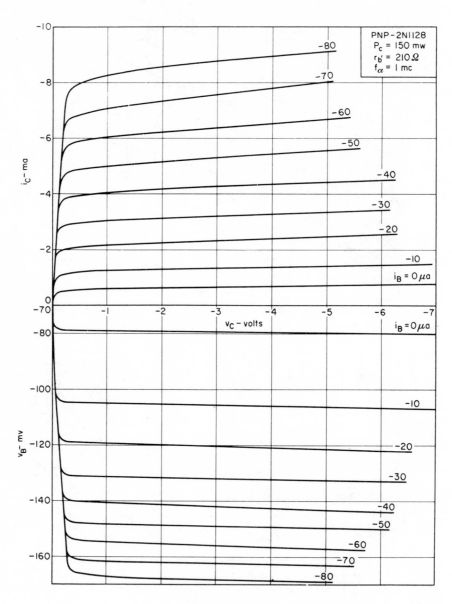

Fig. A-VII-76

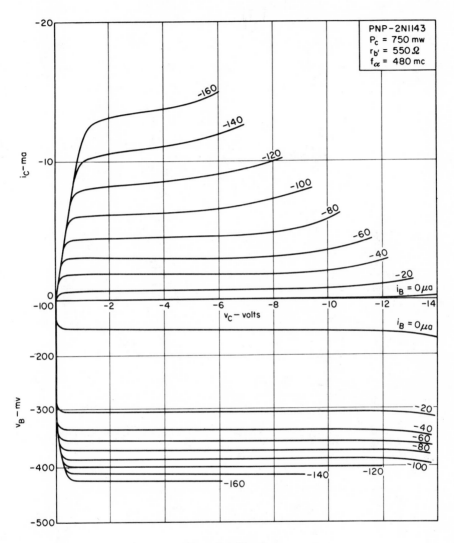

Fig. A-VII-77

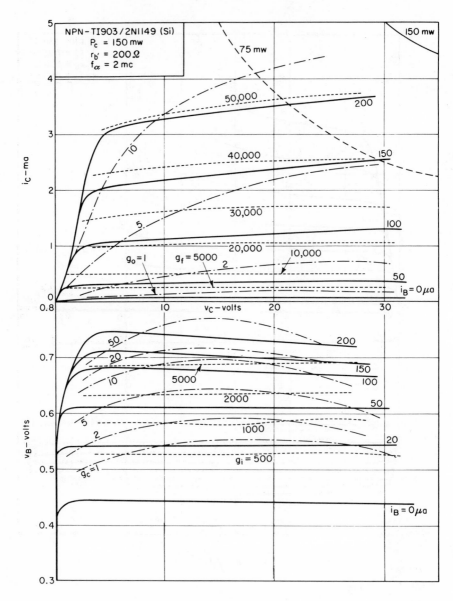

Fig. A-VII-78

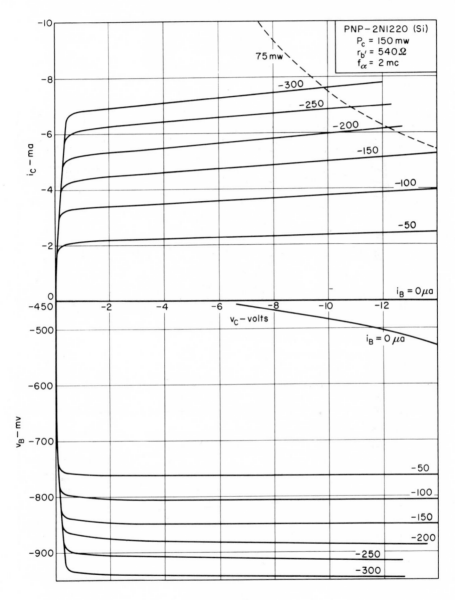

Fig. A-VII-79

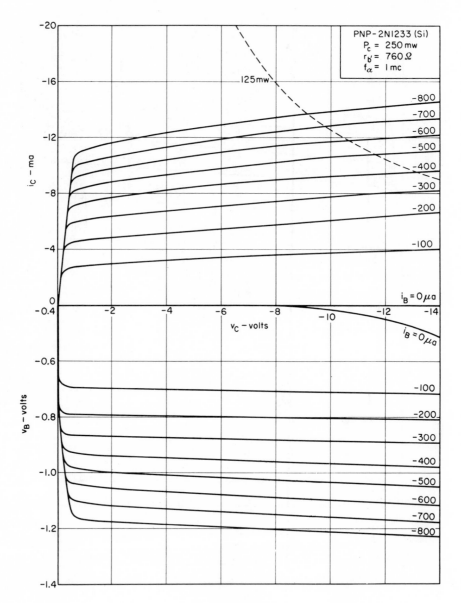

Fig. A-VII-80

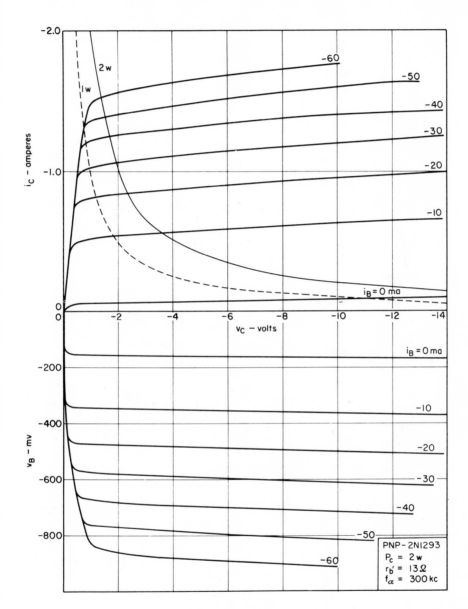

Fig. A-VII-81

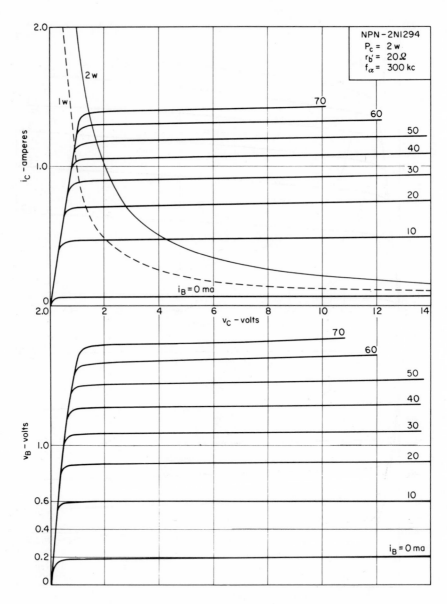

Fig. A-VII-82

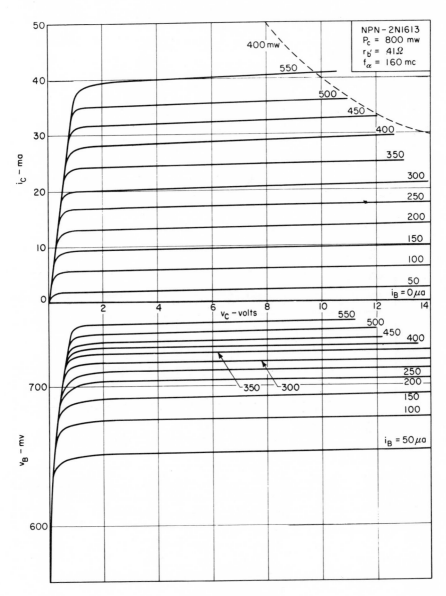

Fig. A-VII-83

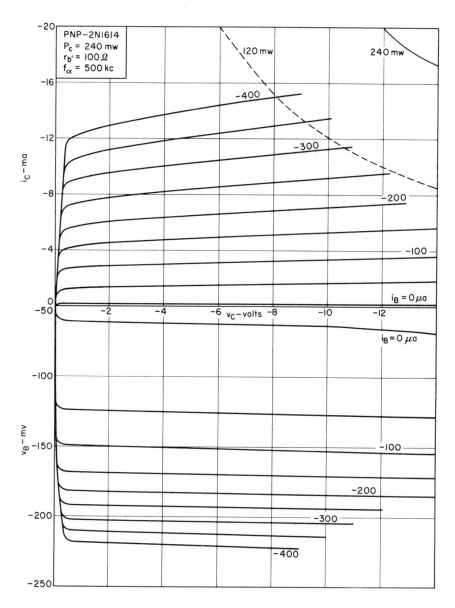

Fig. A-VII-84

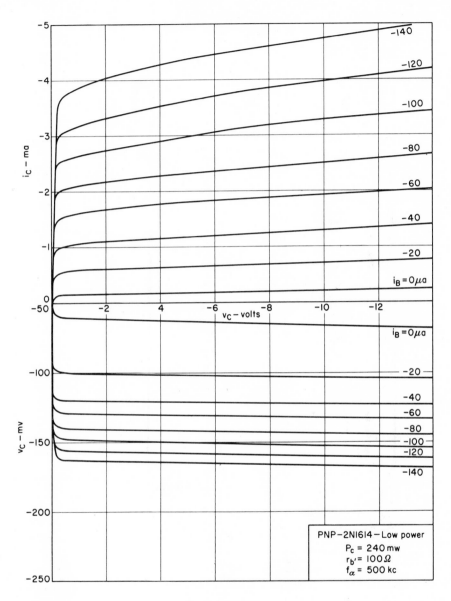

Fig. A-VII-85

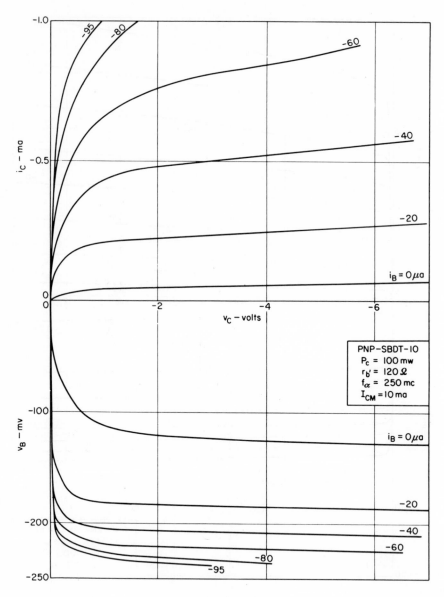

Fig. A-VII-86

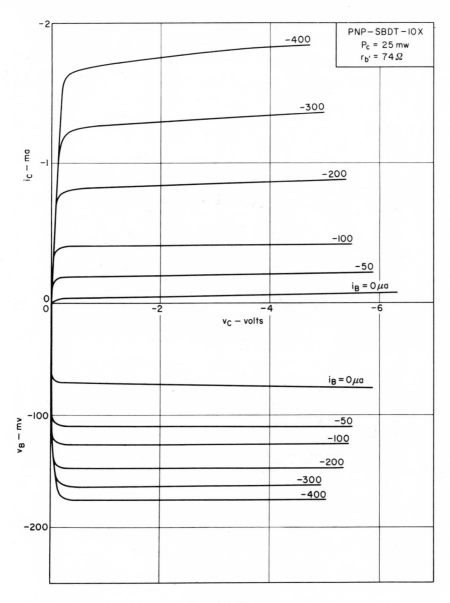

Fig. A-VII-87

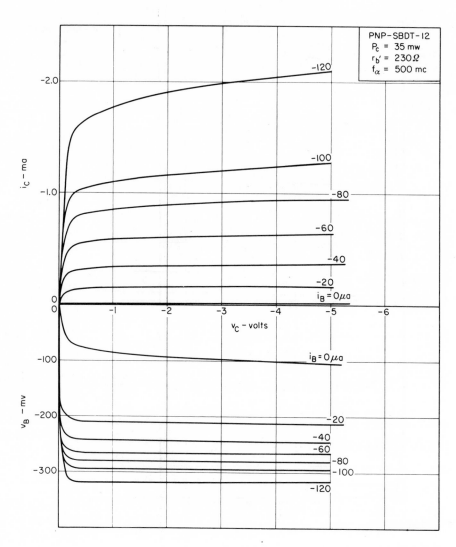

Fig. A-VII-88

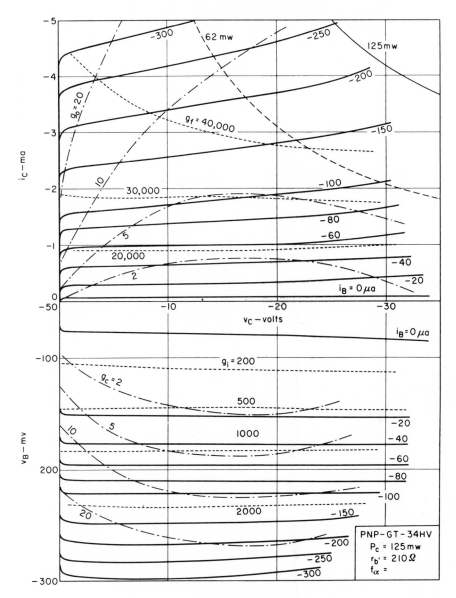

Fig. A-VII-89

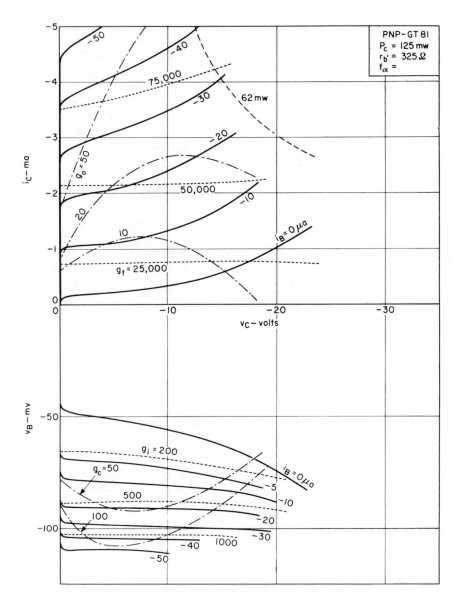

Fig. A-VII-90

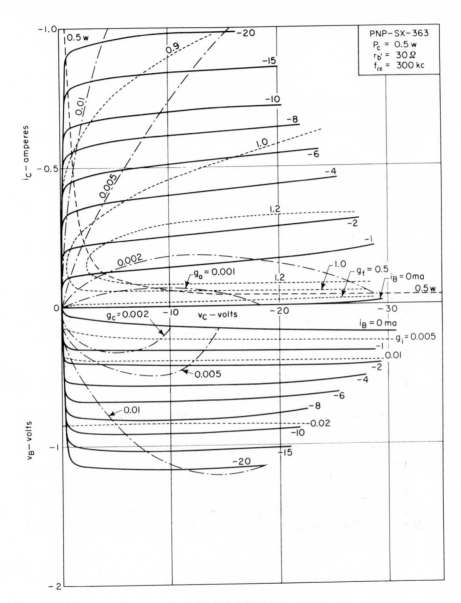

Fig. A-VII-91

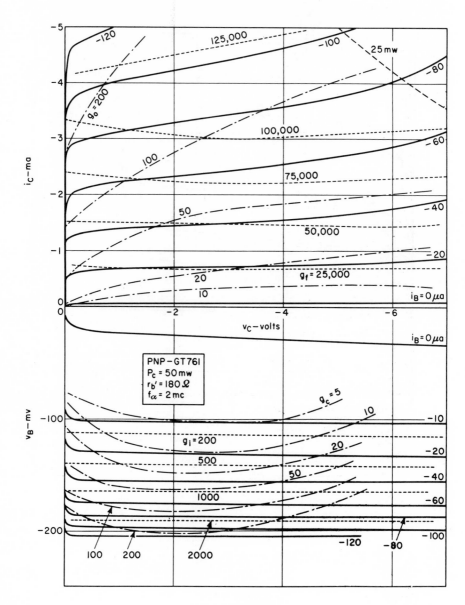

Fig. A-VII-92

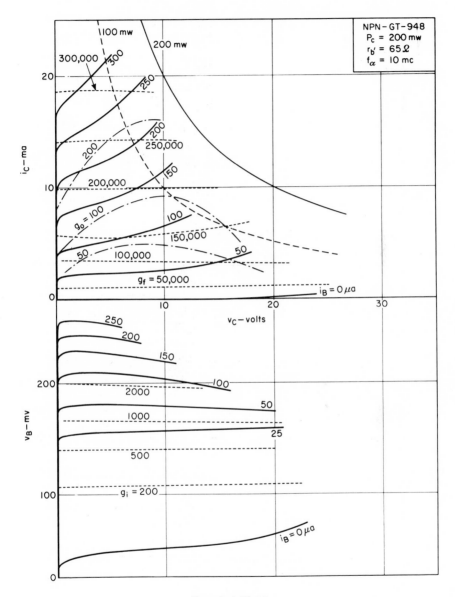

Fig. A-VII-93

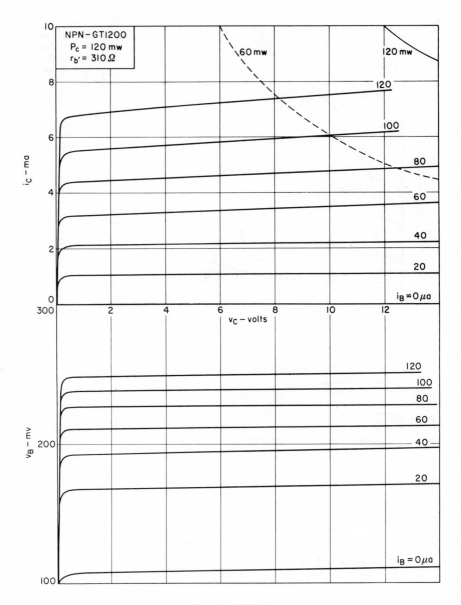

Fig. A-VII-94

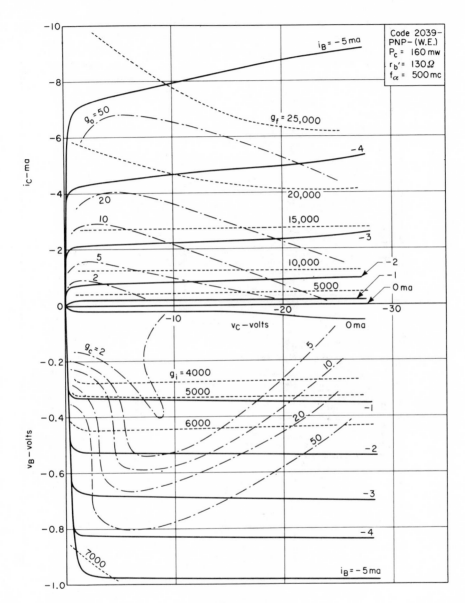

Fig. A-VII-95

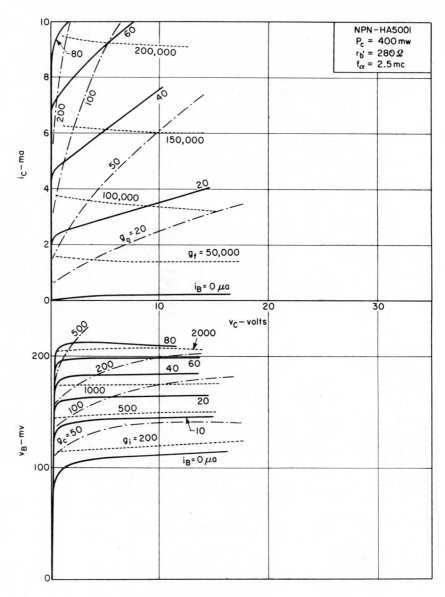

Fig. A-VII-96

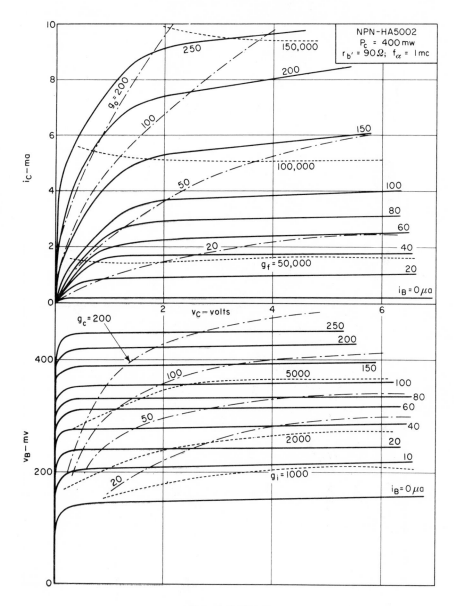

Fig. A-VII-97

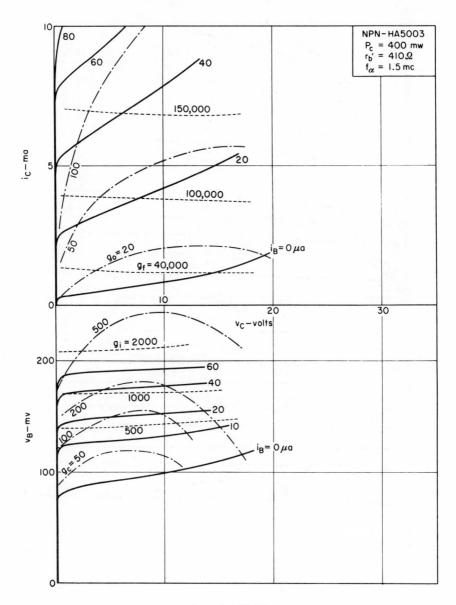

Fig. A-VII-98

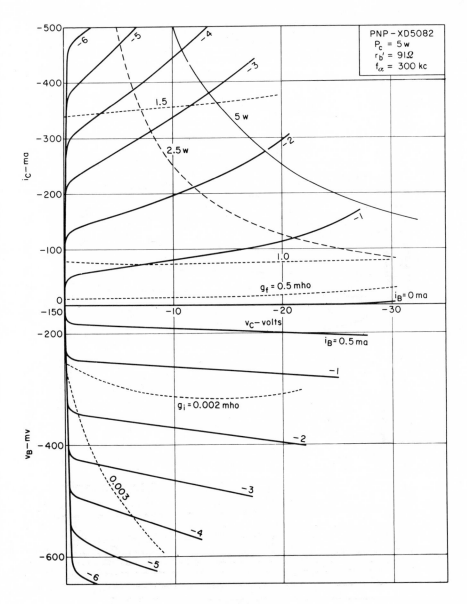

Fig. A-VII-99

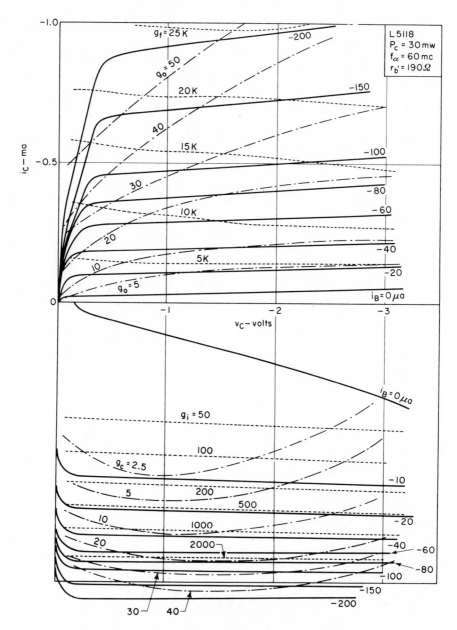

Fig. A-VII-100

APPENDIX EIGHT

A Calculation Nomograph for Transistor Circuits.

The attached nomograph for calculation of admittances for transistor circuits is based on the use of a series of "Z" nomographs.[1] These nomographs have linear calibrations, yet they can be used to calculate products.

The calculation of the forward admittance of the common-emitter amplifier includes six steps:

(1) Calculation of the product of g_c and R_L

(2) Calculation of the product of $(1 + g_c R_L)$ and g_i

(3) Calculation of the product of R_s and g_i $(1 + g_c R_L)$

(4) Calculation of the product of g_o and R_L

(5) Addition of $(1 + g_o R_L)$ and $g_i R_s$ $(1 + g_c R_L)$ to give D

(6) Division of g_f by D to give Y_f

To obtain product one, locate the value of R_L on line (1) and the value of g_c on line (2). When R_L is given in ohms, then the value of g_c must be given in mhos. Similarly, with R_L in kilohms or megohms, the value of g_c should be expressed in millimhos or micromhos, respectively. The positions of the g_i and R_s scales in respect to lines (1) and (2) add the unity to the value of the product scaled along line (3).

Now, if the value obtained on line (3) is connected by a straight line with the value of g_i on line (4), the product is indicated by the intersection with the transfer line. A second product can be obtained by passing a line from the applicable value of R_s on line (5) from the intersection point on the transfer line on to line (6).

Next, the value of $g_o R_L$ must be found and summed into the total, and unity added to give the value of the denominator, D, on line (10).

[1] Levens, A. S.: *Nomography*, 2nd ed. New York: John Wiley & Sons, Inc.

The value of R_L in ohms, kilohms, or megohms, is located on line (7), and a line drawn through the value of g_o in mhos, millimhos, or micromhos, respectively, on line (8). The product appears on line (9), and plotting a straight line through the appropriate points on lines (6) and (9) and extending to line (10) gives the required value of D. Introduction of the value of g_f in mhos, millimhos, or micromhos on line (11) and plotting the line from this point to the appropriate point on line (10) gives an intersection on line (12) corresponding to the transfer admittance in the same respective units.

The values of 10^j, 10^k or 10^{-k}, 10^m or 10^{-m}, and 10^n or 10^{-n} can be used to change the scales consistently to handle values which might be inconvenient in terms of ohms, kilohms, or megohms. If $R_L = 5000$ ohms on line (1), for example, taking the value of $n = 2$ places the datum point at midscale instead of at one end. The range of g_c calibrated on line (2) then is from 50 micromhos to 10 millimhos. Similar conversions may be used on all of the scales.

Although the nomograph has apparently been developed for the circuit in which r_b is neglected, it can be converted to make it useful with intrinsic data including r_b by making the substitutions:

g_i is replaced by g_i'

g_f is replaced by g_f'

R_s is replaced by $(r_b + R_s)$

Then the calculation procedure is as before.

This nomograph may be used for the calculation of the admittances for common-base and common-collector circuits by taking account of the following changes:

Common base

g_i is replaced by the sum $(g_f + g_o)$

The product $(g_f + g_i + g_o)R_s \doteq g_f R_s$ is determined on lines (7), (8), and (9) and added to the value of $g_o R_L$ on line (9)

Common collector

g_f is replaced by $(g_i + g_f)$

The product $\sigma(g)R_e$ is calculated on lines (7), (8), and (9) and added to the value of $g_o R_L$ on line (9)

Otherwise, the calculations are identical with those for the common-emitter circuit. The conversion to intrinsic parameters is accomplished in a similar manner to that described above.

If the input admittance is required, lines (1) through (6) may be used for the calculation of the value of the numerator, taking R_s as 100 units and $m = 2$ on line (5). If a value of $m = 0$ cannot be used on line (4), then the value used on line (4) should be included in a multiplying exponential 10^m for line (6). Lines (7) through (10) are used for the calculation of the denominator for the internal admittance for the circuit and lines (1) through (10) for the denominator for the generalized input admittance. The final quotient may be obtained by introducing the value obtained for the numerator on line (11) and the denominator on line (10). The answer appears on line (12).

Calculation of the output admittance uses the scales on lines (1) through (10) for the denominator unless the value of R_L is zero. The numerator values may be obtained by calculation of $g_c R_s$ on lines (1), (2), and (3) and the use of line (4) for g_i. Once again the value for line (5) is taken unity (nominally 100 with $m = 2$) to give $g_i g_c R_s$ on line (6). The value of g_o may be added to this and the result inserted on line (11). Again, the final value may be read on line (12).

Correction to intrinsic parameters for this equation, and calculation of the input and output admittances for common-base and common-collector configurations follow the patterns already described. They are left as exercises for the reader.

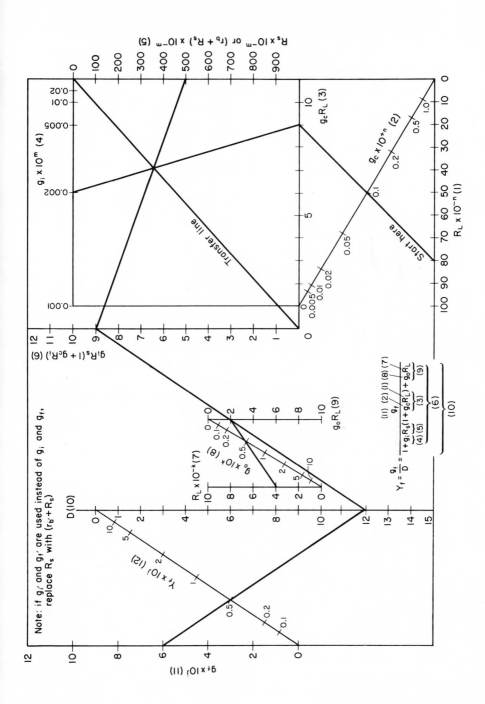

Problems

Problems

Chapter One

1. Calculate the value of energy for the ten and ninety percentile points for the Fermi function, $F(E)$. Take Boltzmann's constant as 8.3×10^{-6} volt per degree and use room temperature for the calculation.

2. Plot the slope of the Fermi function $F(E)$ as a function of the absolute temperature at the 10%, 50%, and 90% points. Discuss briefly the significance of the slope.

3. Look up the values for the constants in Eq. 1–5 for both germanium and for silicon, and calculate the resulting values of n_e to be expected, and their rate of change with temperature.

4. Calculate the data which are missing in the following table:

n_i	n_n	n_p	p_n	p_p	polarity
For germanium:					
2.5×10^{13}	10^{16}				
2.5×10^{13}			10^8		
2.5×10^{13}				5×10^{18}	
For silicon:					
1.5×10^{10}	2×10^{12}				
1.5×10^{10}		10^8			
Unknown:					
10^{12}			10^9		

5. If the gap energies of germanium and silicon are 0.78 and 1.2 volts respectively, what are the maximum values of base-to-emitter bias required to offset the gap bias and cause a start of conduction? Discuss the reason why this barrier potential may be as small as 0.1 volts with a germanium device.

6. If the minority-carrier transit time for a particle across the base region of a given transistor is 0.1 microsecond, and the ratio of the base-width to the mean-free-path is 0.10, what is the effective diffusion time across the base region? What is the approximate radian frequency for the upper noise corner (ω_{n2})? What is the minimum value of beta for the transistor, and what is its probable value?

7. Estimate the value of the collector-series resistance for the L5118 transistor, based on the slope of the collector characteristic curves in the saturation region, Appendix Eight. Repeat for the 2N1613 and the 903/2N1149 transistors.

Chapter Two

1. Convert sets of static contours such as those provided on the 2N456 transistor into a coordinated set similar to those presented in Appendix Seven. Calculate the approximate value of $r_{c'}$ from the low-voltage curves. (These data have been reproduced from the RCA data sheets for the 2N456 transistor.) For the plotting, assume that the input contours for values of collector voltage greater in magnitude that 1.5 volts coincide with the values for 1.5 volts.

2. Convert the static curves on the 2N1090 transistor into a coordinated set. Determine the approximate value of $r_{c'}$ for this transistor. (Attached data have been reproduced from the RCA data sheet for the 2N1090 transistor.)

3. Derive the relations between the H, Y, and Z parameters.

4. Derive the configuration relations between common-emitter, common-base, and common-collector hybrid parameters.

5. Derive the configuration relations for the admittance parameters.

6. Derive the configuration relations for the impedance parameters.

7. Derive the values of the common-emitter conductances from Eqs. 16 and 17, giving the values of g_{11}, g_{12}, g_{21}, and g_{22} in terms of these equations.

8. Fill in the appropriate vacancies in the table:

f_{max}	f_t	f_β	f_α	$r_{b'}$	C_c	$r_{b'}C_c$	α	β
100 mc					5 pf	0.1 ns		100
			50 mc	100 ohm	2 pf		0.90	
	90 mc			50 ohm		0.1 ns	0.90	

where pf $= 10^{-12}$ farads and ns $= 10^{-9}$ seconds.

9. Derive Eqs. 29 through 31.

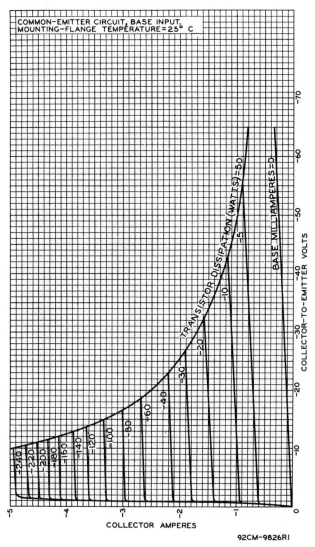

Problem 2-1. Fig. 1

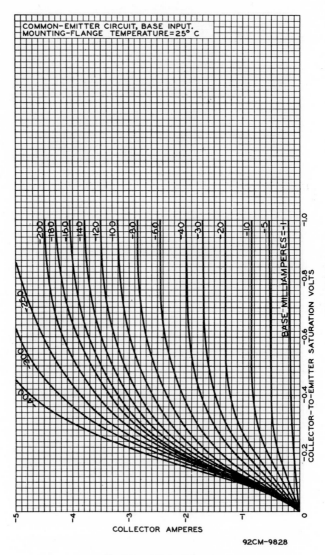

Problem 2-1. Fig. 2

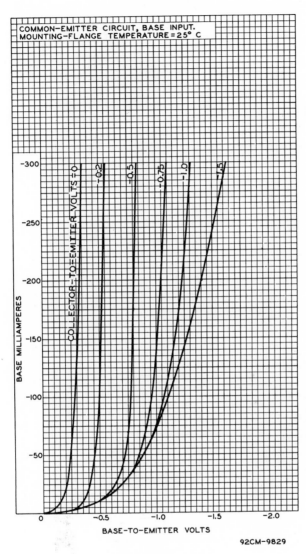

COMMON—EMITTER CIRCUIT, BASE INPUT.
MOUNTING—FLANGE TEMPERATURE = 25° C

COLLECTOR—TO—EMITTER VOLTS = 0

-0.2

-0.5

-0.75

-1.0

-1.5

BASE MILLIAMPERES

-300

-250

-200

-150

-100

-50

0   -0.5   -1.0   -1.5   -2.0

BASE-TO-EMITTER VOLTS

92CM-9829

Problem 2-1. Fig. 3

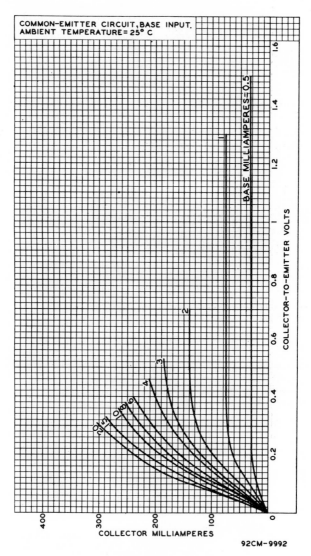

Problem 2-1. Fig. 4

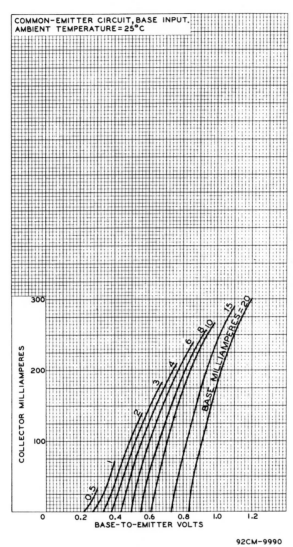

COMMON-EMITTER CIRCUIT, BASE INPUT.
AMBIENT TEMPERATURE = 25°C

92CM-9990

Problem 2-1. Fig. 5

Chapter Three

1. Derive Eq. 3–9.

2. Derive Eq. 3–10.

3. Derive Eq. 3–11.

4. Based on the curves for the tunnel diode T-D-2, plot the effect of adding series resistance to a circuit containing this device. Include sufficient resistance to cancel the negative resistance in the device.

5. Repeat Problem 4 using a shunt resistance.

6. Discuss the significance of the corners noted in Problem 4 and their absence on the curves of Problem 5.

Chapter Four

1. Derive Eqs. 4–3 and 4–5 by Kirchhoff's laws.

2. Repeat Problem 1 using the topological method of Appendix Three.

3. Derive Eqs. 4–7 and 4–8, and the corresponding equations in terms of impedance parameters, and tabulate the substitutions required to convert one to the other. What conclusions can you draw from these relations?

4. Derive Eqs. 4–9, 4–13, 4–14, and 4–19.

5. Derive Eqs. 4–10, 4–15, 4–16, and 4–20.

6. Derive Eqs. 4–22 and 4–23.

7. Derive Eqs. 4–21 and 4–24.

8. Derive Eqs. 4–25 and 4–28 by Kirchhoff's laws.

9. Derive Eqs. 4–26 and 4–27 by Kirchhoff's laws.

10. Repeat Problem 8 using topological methods.

11. Repeat Problem 9 using topological methods.

12. Derive Eqs. 4–32 through 4–34.

13. Derive Eqs. 4–37 through 4–40.

14. Derive Eq. 4–46.

Chapter Five

1. Design an amplifier similar to that in Example 1, using a 2N247 transistor, a supply voltage of five volts, and a load resistance of 1000 ohms. Select the optimum base bias resistance.

2. Repeat the distortion calculations of Problem 1 above, using the static data only in conjunction with the orthogonal polynomial techniques described in Appendix Four. Again determine the optimum operating conditions.

3. Design an amplifier using the 2N270 transistor with a supply voltage of five volts and a load resistance of 100 ohms. Use orthogonal methods to obtain the small-signal input admittance and the forward admittance, and select a suitable operating point.

4. If a transistor amplifier has a supply voltage of 10 volts, a static load resistance of 1000 ohms, and a dynamic load resistance of 500 ohms, select the optimum operating conditions assuming that the amplifier is linear. What is the maximum static and maximum dynamic dissipation for the transistor?

5. Design an amplifier using a GT761 transistor, first as a common-emitter amplifier, and then as a common-base amplifier. Tabulate their input admittances and gains with a supply voltage of five volts and a load resistance of 1000 ohms. Tabulate the power gains for both configurations.

6. Introduce 100 ohms as an emitter-degenerative resistor in the common-emitter amplifier in Problem 5. Determine the input admittance and the amplification and distortion for the resulting amplifier, and compare with the undegenerated amplifier.

7. Introduce a shunt feedback network across the amplifier of Problem 5. Take the source impedance of the signal source as 1000 ohms, and the feedback admittance as 100 micromhos. Calculate the input admittance, the current and voltage gains and distortion, and compare these results with the results of Problems 5 and 6.

8. Based on the data tabulated in Problems 5 and 6, discuss the behavior of cascaded R-C coupled amplifiers in the C-E and C-B configurations. Discuss the physical limitations which develop in the cascaded circuits, and determine how the difficulty can be corrected.

9. In cascading degenerative R-C amplifiers, which of the types discussed in this chapter should be used? Justify your selection.

Chapter Six

1. Determine the stability function per unit of gain for an emitter-degenerative amplifier as a function of base-spreading resistance. The output admittances may be considered negligible if desired. Take $R_{c2} = 0$.

2. Determine the maximum or minimum value of the function of Problem 1. Take $r_{b'}$ as the maximizing parameter. Discuss the significance of the result. Would you expect this?

3. What values of C_t in Eq. 6–32 should be made available to designers for use in instrument design? Discuss in detail the reasons for your choices.

4. Derive a stability equation for the amplifier of Fig. 6–4.

5. Modify the design of the amplifier in Exercise 1, Chapter Five, to introduce a factor-of-five improvement in the current stabilization. Complete the resulting design.

6. Modify Exercise 2, Chapter Five, to increase the current stability by a factor of ten. Complete the corresponding design.

Chapter Seven

1. Derive Eq. 7–1.

2. Derive Eq. 7–4.

3. Verify the limit-frequency conditions in Eqs. 7–5 through 7–8.

4. Verify Eq. 7–9.

5. Repeat Example 7–1 using the 2N301A transistor. Select your own operating conditions.

6. Repeat Example 7–2 using an 2N270 transistor as a driver and a 2N459 for the output. Use orthogonal methods.

7. Repeat Example 7–4 using a pair of 2N268 transistors.

8. Repeat Example 7–4 using orthogonal methods on a pair of 2N459 transistors.

Chapter Eight

1. Derive the equation for amplification of a common-emitter amplifier using a non-zero value for $r_{c'}$. Compare with previous results. Include a separate collector-base capacitance (to the intrinsic base, not the base terminal).

2. Repeat Problem 1 for the common-base amplifier.

3. What effect might the presence of $r_{c'}$ have on the apparent value of f_t for a transistor? Derive and discuss the results.

4. Select a transistor having an f_{n2} greater than 50 mc., and design an amplifier using it for operation at 50 mc. Let the design parallel that for Example 8–2. Use orthogonal methods for obtaining small-signal data.

5. Design unilateralization networks for the amplifier of Problem 4 and for that of Example 8–2.

6. Plot the variation of K with bias current for the amplifiers of Example 8–2 and Problem 4, both with and without a shunt input loading impedance of 30 ohms. Take the source impedance as 20 ohms. Design a differential amplifier for providing constant input load, and calculate the effect of the input loading.

7. Select a tunnel diode for use with 50 ohm coaxial cable, and design the components required for using it at 100 mc.

Chapter Nine

1. Derive Eqs. 9–7 and 9–10.

2. Verify Eq. 9–14.

3. Derive Eqs. 9–15 and 9–16.

4. Derive Eq. 9–18.

5. Derive Eq. 9–20.

6. Solve Example 9–1 completely, including Fourier, Legendre, and orthogonal solutions. With the latter, solve for the conditions $(2n + 1) = 11$, 15, and 19. Make trapezoidal corrections.

7. Repeat Problem 6 for $y = x^3$ as the basic device relation.

Chapter Ten

1. Derive Eqs. 10–1 through 10–3 and Eqs. 10–5 through 10–8.

2. Derive Eqs. 10–10, 10–11, 10–11a, and 10–12.

3. Derive Eqs. 10–14, 10–15, 10–18, 10–18a, 10–18b, and 10–19.

4. Assume that a transistor matching the curves for the 2N247 has a value of $f_{n2} = 100$ mc, and design a Colpitts oscillator for use at 75 mc based on it. Determine limit contours and oscillation amplitude.

5. Repeat Problem 4 using a Hartley circuit.

6. Design a Colpitts oscillator based on the 2N502 transistor operating at 100 mc. Use orthogonal techniques.

7. Design a series-mode crystal oscillator for use with a 25 mc crystal and a 2N1613 transistor. Take the series-resonant resistance of the crystal as 10 ohms, and its Q-factor as 10^6.

8. Calculate the frequency stability of the oscillator for Problem 7 in terms of its probable RMS value for $\overline{\Delta K_\sigma}$.

Chapter Eleven

1. Derive Eqs. 11–1 through 11–3.

2. Derive Eqs. 11–4 and 11–5.

3. Derive Eqs. 11–11 through 11–13.

4. Derive Eq. 11–17.

5. Derive Eqs. 11–24 through 11–29.

6. Design the amplifiers and impedance converters required for a forward-transmission, three-stage, phase-shift oscillator. Verify the adequacy of the terminating impedance levels.

7. Repeat Problem 6 using a reverse-transmission network.

8. Design the amplifiers required for use with a transistor zero-phase-shift oscillator, and verify the adequacy of the terminating impedance levels.

Chapter Twelve

1. Derive the values of conversion gain listed in Table 12–I.

2. Derive Eqs. 12–16 and 12–16a from 12–15.

3. Repeat Example 12–1 using the 2N1613 transistor and orthogonal techniques.

4. Verify the topological derivation of Eqs. 12–17 through 12–20.

5. Establish Eq. 12–32 topologically.

6. Determine the circuit characteristics required of the tunnel diode that it be usable as an oscillating modulator having reasonably linear behavior. The objective is to obtain an amplified signal by detection of the modulation envelope. Assume a square-law variation of conductance with bias.

7. Discuss the behavior of the circuit of Problem 6 with a cube-law variation for the diode conductance. Can a tunnel diode have such a conductance?

8. Establish the limiting conditions which must be applied to Problem 6 above, and see if you can find a way to generalize the above procedures.

Chapter Thirteen

1. Repeat the design of Example 13–1, using the 2N697 transistor and orthogonal methods of determining the small-signal properties. Take $V_{cc} = 10$ volts, and select your own load resistance.

2. Repeat the Problem 1, using the 2N1613 transistor.

3. Repeat Example 13–2 using the 2N1220 transistor as the active device and calculate small-signal values by orthogonal methods. Take $V_{cc} = -12$ volts.

4. Repeat Problem 3 using the SBDT-10X transistor with a supply of five volts.

Chapter Fourteen

1. Repeat Example 14–1 for conditions applying to a silicon transistor, i.e., $| V_{bz} | = 400$ mv.

2. Derive Eq. 14–1.

3. Repeat Example 14–2 using the 2N1613 transistor and $| V_{CC} | = | V_{BB} | = 10$ volts.

4. Repeat Example 14–3 using the 2N697 transistor with a supply voltage of 8 volts. Discuss ways in which the design can be improved.

5. Determine the number of diodes which may be used in a matrix consisting of 1N873A Fairchild diodes. Test conditions for the diodes are:

> Maximum forward voltage = 1 volt at 150 ma.
>
> Maximum reverse current = 15 microamperes at minus 75 volts.
>
> Reverse recovery time = 0.3 microsecond at 30 ma.
>
> Capacitance = 3.5 pf.

Take the barrier potential as 0.4 volts, and take the reverse current to be ohmic current.

6. Design a control circuit for a bi-directional binary counter such as is described in this chapter.

7. Design a reset circuit for a decade bi-directional counter based on the described configuration. Include all the sensor and the switching circuits.

Index

Index

A

Accelerating field, 31
Acceptor, 15 ff
Accuracies of parameters, 60 ff
Admittance:
  input, 229, 376
  limit of forward, 60
  parameters, 37 ff, 86 ff
  relations, 54
  symbols, 115
AGC, 205
Alloy junction transistors, 23
Alpha cutoff frequency, 63 ff, 94 ff, 116, 129, 145, 319
Alpha, 29, 43
Alpha tin, 11
Aluminum antimonide, 12 ff
American Institute of Electrical Engineers, 36
Amperex Electronics Corp., 41, 46, 423
Amplification:
  averaging, 221 ff
  control of, 204 ff
  loop, 213 ff, 298 ff
Amplifier:
  class A, 173
  class B, 177
  differential, 209
Amplitudes, harmonic, 113, 374 ff
Annular transistor, 29

Anthracene, 13
Armstrong, H. L., 47
Avalanche:
  breakdown, 11, 285
  multiplication, 43
Averaging, 221 ff

B

Back-diffusing, 32
Bandwidth, 205
Barrier potential, 22, 76
Base, 22 ff, 28
Base spreading resistance, 56 ff, 90 ff, 108 ff, 120 ff, 144, 192 ff, 213 ff, 232 ff, 248
Basic gain form, 375
Basic output function form, 374
Bell Laboratories, 37, 102
Bessel polynomials, 371
Beta, 43
Beta cutoff frequency, 50 ff, 56, 116, 129
Bibliography, 391
Bidirectional counters, 335 ff
Bistable multivibrators, 317
Black box, 48
  modified, 108 ff
Blocking potential, 22
Boltzmann's constant, 6
Boothroyd, A. R., 97
Bridge balance measurement, 83 ff
Bridging shorts, 333